Basic Electronics

Bernard Grob

INSTRUCTOR, RCA INSTITUTES, INC.

Author of *Basic Television*

Coauthor of *Applications of Electronics*

Basic Electronics

McGRAW-HILL BOOK COMPANY

New York

St. Louis

San Francisco

London

Toronto

Sydney

Basic Electronics

In memory of my father and mother

Preface

This basic text is for beginning students without any previous experience in electricity or electronics. It presents the necessary information for introductory technical training in electrical principles, vacuum tubes, and transistors needed for all electronic circuits. Starting with electrons and the atom, the topics progress to d-c circuits, magnetism, a-c circuits, vacuum tubes, and transistors. These fundamentals form the basis for the study of advanced applications, including communications electronics such as radio and television, industrial electronics, and computers.

The order of topics is based on the author's experience in teaching the technician's course in Electronics Fundamentals at RCA Institutes. For each subject, the basic principles are explained first, followed by typical applications and common troubles. This presentation has proved effective in helping students learn the fundamentals of electronics with a practical approach that is both interesting and useful for technicians and servicemen.

Summary of contents. As in the first edition, the book is organized into twenty-five chapters. This step-by-step development and thorough analysis of main subjects is very effective in helping the students to learn. For example, separate chapters on series circuits and parallel circuits build up to more advanced series-parallel circuits and networks. Similarly, there are separate chapters on inductance and inductive reactance before combining these fundamentals for inductive circuits. The same sequential development is used for capacitive circuits. Then all the principles are combined for a-c circuits and resonance. The same approach is used within the chapters. The sequential method, similar to programmed learning, is particularly helpful in Chapter 21, Complex Numbers, where the operations are developed in small steps, with a problem to illustrate each point. The mathematics needed for the problems illustrating the theoretical principles is explained in Appendix E, which includes simple trigonometry and powers of ten.

Each chapter has a section at the end to explain common troubles in components or practical applications of theory. To give some examples, the effects of an open circuit and a short circuit are explained in the first five chapters on d-c circuits. Typical troubles in resistors, coils, capacitors, tubes, and transistors are described in their respective chapters. As examples of theoretical principles explained in the context of practical applications, choke coils are described as an application of inductive reactance; also coupling and bypass capacitors as examples of capacitive reactance are described in detail. Such applications are explained with simple circuits in order to keep the principles clear, but the examples are basic to all types of electronic circuits.

Reorganization. In addition to being updated, this edition is more thorough in the analysis of fundamentals. There is greater use of graphs and sample problems in the text and more student problems at the end of each chapter. Such quantitative work makes the explanations and testing of the principles more definite and specific. As an example, there is increased emphasis on the concept of the general nature of current being the time rate of change of electric charge. This concept helps in understanding the modern techniques of producing current in solid semiconductors and in gases. Specifically, the quantitative relation is explained as $I = Q/T$. Another example of the more generalized treatment is the discussion of nonsinusoidal waveforms, including square waves, pulses, and sawtooth waves. Graphs are used to show the quantitative relations for induced voltage $e_L = L\, di/dt$ and capacitor current $i_c = C\, de/dt$. In addition, experimental work has been added to the discussion on resonance to create a more concrete understanding of the quantitative relations of Q and bandwidth.

The material on magnetism has been combined with magnetic units for an expanded discussion on units including the metric cgs, practical mks, and English fps systems. Also, the chapter on r-f losses has been deleted, but the most useful topics have been added to their appropriate subjects throughout the book.

New Chapters. Chapter 21, Complex Numbers, has been added in order to provide a more rigorous method of analyzing advanced a-c circuits. This technique is actually the quickest way to solve a circuit with complex series-parallel impedances. Also, any phase angle in the circuit can be determined easily with complex numbers. This powerful tool is explained in a logical step-by-step procedure to help the student learn to apply complex numbers to all types of a-c circuits, including low-Q parallel resonance.

Chapter 6, Network Theorems, has been added to provide a method of analyzing advanced circuits having one source or more, voltage or current sources, bridge circuits, and delta or wye networks. Specifically, the student is shown the practical procedures in using the Thévenin or Norton theorem to simplify circuits and how to make delta-wye conversions. These methods have been simplified so that the average technician can use the theorems for circuit analysis. The sample problems show how one circuit can be solved by the different theorems.

Teaching Aids. In addition to many photographs and drawings to illustrate components and circuits, the book emphasizes several teaching aids for effective study. Each chapter starts with an introduction that states the objective, followed by a listing of topics. At the end of the chapter, a summary lists the main points to remember. There are many tables for concise summaries and comparisons of similar or opposite characteristics. The short-answer questions for self-examination are based on the summary. Periodic summaries for groups of chapters are also included together with additional self-examination questions. Answers to all short-answer questions are given at the back of the book.

In this revised edition, there are more numerical problems at the end of each chapter, and they are separate from the essay questions. The numerical problems are graded in difficulty, progressing from round numbers to fractions and powers of ten. Also, the formulas are tested first in their usual form and then in transposed versions. Many essay questions test the student's ability to transpose or to derive equations. Practice in constructing graphs is also emphasized. Answers to selected problems are given at the back of the book. Bibliographies are included with each review summary and at the end of the book.

Appendix D, Physics Units, and Appendix E, Mathematics, are included as aids to solving numerical problems. For laboratory work, Appendix I describes soldering and tools. Abbreviations and schematic symbols are summarized in Appendix H, and Appendix G lists resistor and capacitor color codes.

Credits. The photographs of components and equipment have been made available through the cooperation of many manufacturers, as noted in each legend. My colleague Harry G. Rice of the RCA Institutes Home Study School has been especially helpful in the work on Network Theorems, Magnetic Units, and Transistors. Finally, it is a pleasure to thank my wife, Ruth, for her excellent work in typing the manuscript.

Bernard Grob

Contents

SURVEY OF ELECTRONICS   1

CHAPTER 1   ELECTRICITY   9

1·1   Negative and positive polarities
1·2   Electrons and protons in the atom
1·3   Structure of the atom
1·4   The coulomb unit of charge
1·5   The volt unit of potential difference
1·6   Charge in motion is current
1·7   Resistance is opposition to current
1·8   The closed circuit
1·9   Direct current (d-c) and alternating current (a-c)
1·10 Sources of electricity

CHAPTER 2   OHM'S LAW   31

2·1   The linear proportion between E and I
2·2 $I = E/R$
2·3 $E = IR$
2·4 $R = E/I$
2·5   The inverse relation between I and R
2·6   Definition of the practical units
2·7   Multiple and submultiple units
2·8   Power

CHAPTER 3   SERIES CIRCUITS   46

    3·1   Why the current is the same in all parts of a series
           circuit
    3·2   Total series resistance equals the sum of individual
           resistances
    3·3   Series *IR* voltage drops
    3·4   The sum of series *IR* voltage drops equals the applied
           voltage
    3·5   *IR* voltage drops are proportional to the series
           resistances
    3·6   Polarity of *IR* voltage drops
    3·7   Total power in a series circuit
    3·8   Analyzing a series circuit
    3·9   Effect of an open in a series circuit

CHAPTER 4   PARALLEL CIRCUITS   59

    4·1   The voltage is the same across parallel branches
    4·2   Each branch current equals E/R
    4·3   The main-line current equals the sum of the branch
           currents
    4·4   Resistances in parallel
    4·5   Conductances in parallel
    4·6   Total power in parallel circuits
    4·7   Analyzing parallel circuits
    4·8   Effect of an open in parallel circuits

CHAPTER 5   SERIES-PARALLEL CIRCUITS   74

    5·1   Resistance strings in parallel
    5·2   Resistance banks in series
    5·3   Resistance banks and strings in series-parallel
    5·4   Analyzing series-parallel circuits
    5·5   Series voltage divider with parallel branch currents
    5·6   Kirchhoff's laws
    5·7   Wheatstone bridge
    5·8   Effect of a short circuit

CHAPTER 6   NETWORK THEOREMS   88

    6·1   Applications of Kirchhoff's laws
    6·2   Thévenin's theorem
    6·3   Norton's theorem
    6·4   Thévenin-Norton conversions
    6·5   Millman's theorem
    6·6   The superposition theorem
    6·7   Delta-wye transformations

    REVIEW OF CHAPTERS 1 TO 6   114

CHAPTER 7   DIRECT-CURRENT METERS   116

    7·1   Moving-coil meter
    7·2   Measuring current
    7·3   Meter shunts
    7·4   Voltmeters
    7·5   Loading effect of voltmeter
    7·6   Ohmmeters
    7·7   Multimeters
    7·8   Meter applications
    7·9   Checking continuity with the ohmmeter

CHAPTER 8   CONDUCTORS AND INSULATORS   142

    8·1   Function of the conductor
    8·2   Standard wire gage sizes
    8·3   Types of wire conductors
    8·4   Switches
    8·5   Fuses
    8·6   Pilot lamps
    8·7   Wire resistance
    8·8   Ion current in liquids and gases
    8·9   Electrons and hole charges in semiconductors
    8·10   Insulators

CHAPTER 9   RESISTORS   161

    9·1   Resistor types
    9·2   Variable resistors
    9·3   Resistor color coding
    9·4   Power rating of resistors
    9·5   Choosing the resistor for a circuit
    9·6   Series and parallel combinations of resistors
    9·7   Resistors for specialized applications
    9·8   Resistor troubles

CHAPTER 10   BATTERIES   175

    10·1   Functions of batteries
    10·2   The voltaic cell
    10·3   The dry cell
    10·4   Series and parallel cells
    10·5   Lead-acid batteries
    10·6   Types of electromotive cells
    10·7   Internal resistance of a generator
    10·8   Matching a load resistance to a generator

REVIEW OF CHAPTERS 7 TO 10   196

CHAPTER 11   MAGNETISM   198

        11·1   The magnetic field
        11·2   Induction by the magnetic field
        11·3   Air gap of a magnet
        11·4   Types of magnets
        11·5   Ampere-turns of magnetizing force
        11·6   Field intensity *H*
        11·7   *B-H* magnetization curve
        11·8   Magnetic hysteresis
        11·9   Ohm's law for magnetic circuits
        11·10   Magnetic shielding

CHAPTER 12   ELECTROMAGNETIC INDUCTION   221

        12·1   Magnetic field around an electrical current
        12·2   Magnetic polarity of a coil
        12·3   Motor action between two magnetic fields
        12·4   Induced current
        12·5   Lenz's law
        12·6   Generating an induced voltage
        12·7   Faraday's law of induced voltage

CHAPTER 13   ALTERNATING VOLTAGE AND CURRENT   237

        13·1   Alternating-voltage generator
        13·2   The sine wave
        13·3   Alternating current
        13·4   Voltage and current values for a sine wave
        13·5   Frequency
        13·6   Period
        13·7   Wavelength
        13·8   Phase angle
        13·9   The time factor in frequency and phase
        13·10   A-c circuits with resistance
        13·11   The 60-cps a-c power line
        13·12   Motors and generators
        13·13   Nonsinusoidal a-c waveforms

        REVIEW OF CHAPTERS 11 TO 13   264

CHAPTER 14   INDUCTANCE   266

        14·1   Induction by alternating current
        14·2   Self-inductance

14·3   Self-induced voltage
14·4   Mutual inductance
14·5   Transformers
14·6   Core losses
14·7   Types of cores
14·8   Variable inductance
14·9   Inductances in series or parallel
14·10 Stray inductances
14·11 Troubles in coils

CHAPTER 15   INDUCTIVE REACTANCE   290

15·1   How X_L reduces the amount of alternating current
15·2 $X_L = 2\pi fL$
15·3   Series or parallel inductive reactances
15·4   Ohm's law applied to X_L
15·5   Applications of inductive reactance
15·6   Waveshape of e_L induced by sine-wave current

CHAPTER 16   INDUCTIVE CIRCUITS   303

16·1   Sine-wave i_L lags e_L by 90°
16·2   Inductive reactance and resistance in series
16·3   Inductive reactance and resistance in parallel
16·4 Q of a coil
16·5 L/R time constant
16·6   High voltage produced by opening RL circuit
16·7   The general case of voltage across L
16·8   Energy in magnetic field of inductance
16·9   A-f and r-f chokes

REVIEW OF CHAPTERS 14 TO 16   325

CHAPTER 17   CAPACITANCE   327

17·1   How charge is stored in the dielectric
17·2   Electric field between charges
17·3   Charging and discharging a capacitor
17·4   The farad unit of capacitance
17·5   Typical capacitors
17·6   Capacitor color coding
17·7   Parallel capacitances
17·8   Series capacitances
17·9   Stray capacitive and inductive effects
17·10 Troubles in capacitors

CHAPTER 18   CAPACITIVE REACTANCE   349

18·1   How alternating voltage produces alternating current in a capacitive circuit
18·2 $X_c = 1/(2\pi fC)$
18·3   Series or parallel capacitive reactances
18·4   Ohm's law for capacitive reactance
18·5   Applications of capacitive reactance
18·6   Charge and discharge current produced by sine-wave voltage

CHAPTER 19   CAPACITIVE CIRCUITS   363

19·1   Sine-wave e_c lags i_c by 90°
19·2   Capacitive reactance and resistance in series
19·3   Capacitive reactance and resistance in parallel
19·4   Capacitive voltage dividers
19·5 RC time constant
19·6   Energy in electrostatic field of capacitance
19·7   R-f and a-f coupling capacitors
19·8   Comparison of reactance and time constant

REVIEW OF CHAPTERS 17 TO 19   381

CHAPTER 20   ALTERNATING-CURRENT CIRCUITS   383

20·1   A-c circuits with resistance but no reactance
20·2   Circuits with inductance reactance alone
20·3   Circuits with capacitive reactance alone
20·4   Opposite reactances cancel
20·5   Series reactance and resistance
20·6   Parallel reactance and resistance
20·7   Series-parallel reactance and resistance
20·8   Real power
20·9   A-c meters
20·10 Wattmeters
20·11 Summary of types of ohms in a-c circuits
20·12 Summary of types of vectors in a-c circuits

CHAPTER 21   COMPLEX NUMBERS   401

21·1   Positive and negative numbers
21·2   The j operator
21·3   Definition of a complex number
21·4   How complex numbers are applied to a-c circuits
21·5   Impedance in complex form
21·6   Operations with complex numbers
21·7   Magnitude and angle of a complex number
21·8   Polar form of complex numbers
21·9   Converting polar to rectangular form
21·10 Complex numbers in series a-c circuits

21·11 Complex numbers in parallel a-c circuits
21·12 Complex numbers in series-parallel circuits

CHAPTER 22   RESONANCE   420

22·1   The resonance effect
22·2   Series resonance
22·3   Parallel resonance
22·4   Calculating the resonant frequency
22·5 Q magnification factor of resonant circuit
22·6   Bandwidth of resonant circuit
22·7   Tuning
22·8   Mistuning
22·9   Analysis of parallel-resonant circuits
22·10 Choosing L and C for a resonant circuit

CHAPTER 23   FILTERS   447

23·1   Examples of filtering
23·2   Direct current combined with alternating current
23·3   Transformer coupling
23·4   Capacitive coupling
23·5   Bypass capacitors
23·6   Filter circuits
23·7   Low-pass filters
23·8   High-pass filters
23·9   Resonant filters
23·10 Interference filters

REVIEW OF CHAPTERS 20 TO 23   467

CHAPTER 24   ELECTRON TUBES   470

24·1   Construction of tubes
24·2   Diodes
24·3   Plate current
24·4   Diode rectifier circuits
24·5   Triodes
24·6   How a triode amplifies the control-grid voltage
24·7   Triode characteristics
24·8   Tube constants
24·9   Tetrodes
24·10 Pentodes
24·11 Tube ratings
24·12 Tube types
24·13 Cathode-ray tubes
24·14 Phototubes
24·15 Gas tubes
24·16 Troubles in vacuum tubes

CHAPTER 25   TRANSISTORS   504

25·1   Advantages of transistors
25·2   Semiconductors
25·3   Atomic structure of germanium
25·4   N-type germanium
25·5   P-type germanium
25·6   The PN junction
25·7   Forward bias
25·8   Reverse bias
25·9   Transistor action
25·10   Transistor circuit arrangements
25·11   Transistor amplifier circuit
25·12   Collector characteristic curves
25·13   Transistor types
25·14   Semiconductor diodes
25·15   Troubles in transistors

REVIEW OF CHAPTERS 24 AND 25   536

APPENDIXES

A   Electronic frequency spectrum   539
B   FCC frequency allocations from 30 kc to 300,000 Mc   540
C   Alphabetical listing of the chemical elements   542
D   Physics units   544
E   Mathematics   547
F   Universal time-constant graph for *RC* or *RL* circuits   555
G   Color codes   557
H   Abbreviations and schematic symbols   561
I   Soldering and tools   565

BIBLIOGRAPHY   567

ANSWERS TO SELF-EXAMINATIONS   569

ANSWERS TO SELECTED PROBLEMS   572

INDEX   577

Basic Electronics

Survey of electronics

Electronics and radio communications are two practical applications of the general principles of electricity. The same electricity produced by a battery for a flashlight can be modified to do a limitless number of jobs, from running a motor or producing heat and light to the wireless application of radio broadcasting.

The word *radio* is an abbreviated form of *radiotelegraph* or *radiotelephone*. In its first form, wireless communication was by radiotelegraph, using short dots and longer dashes as symbols for letters in the Morse code. Now radiotelephone is used more, providing wireless voice communications or broadcasting voice and music programs for entertainment. In general, then, radio is the art of wireless communications.

The word *electronics* derives from the electron, which is a tiny, invisible quantity of electricity present in all materials. In terms of its many uses, electronics can be defined to include all applications of electricity flowing in a vacuum, as in vacuum tubes, in gas or vapor, and in certain solid materials such as transistors. More generally, electronics includes all effects of electricity where the action of individual electrons determines the application.

Radio and electronics are closely related. Sometimes they are even joined in their use. For example, an electronic heating unit generates radio waves that go through the work to produce heat. The heat bonds the solid materials together. Even if the applications are not so close, the principles of radio and electronics are essentially the same.

Development of electronics

Wireless transmission can be taken as starting with the work of Heinrich Hertz, a German physicist, who in 1887 was the first to demonstrate by experiment the process of electromagnetic radiation through space. The distance of transmission was only a few feet, but it demonstrated radio waves traveling from one place to another without the need for any connecting wires between the transmitting and receiving equipment. Hertz proved that radio waves, although invisible, travel with the same velocity as light waves. In fact, radio waves and light waves are just two examples of electromagnetic waves, a form of energy that combines the effects of electricity and magnetism. Additional examples of electromagnetic waves include heat radiation, X rays, and cosmic rays, among others, all of which can transmit energy through space without the need for any connecting wires.

The work of Hertz followed earlier experiments on electricity and magnetism. In 1820, a Danish physicist, H. C. Oersted, showed that an electrical current produces magnetic effects. Then in 1831 a British physicist, Michael Faraday, discovered that a magnet in motion can produce electricity. In 1864, the British physicist James Clerk Maxwell, on the basis of work in electricity and magnetism, predicted the electromagnetic waves demonstrated later by Hertz.

In 1895, Guglielmo Marconi used a long wire antenna and developed a practical radio system for long-distance communication. He succeeded in producing wireless communication across the Atlantic Ocean in 1901. The rapid advances after that are due largely to the introduction and progress of the vacuum tube. Dr. Lee De Forest, with his audion tube in 1906 that could amplify electric signals, was a leader in this field. As the design of vacuum tubes advanced, radio broadcasting progressed rapidly. Regularly scheduled programs were broadcast in 1920 by station KDKA in Pittsburgh, Pennsylvania. The commercial FM (frequency modulation) broadcast service for sound programs was started in 1941. With regard to television, after discarding previous mechanical systems that used rotating drums or disks, commercial television broadcasting was adopted officially in July, 1941, although its popular use did not begin until 1945.

With the development of vacuum tubes, or, more generally, electron tubes, their uses were extended to electronics in many applications of con-

Fig. 1 Components for electrical control or amplification. (a) Vacuum tube. (b) Transistor.

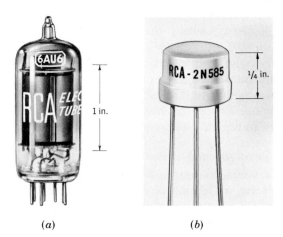

(a)   (b)

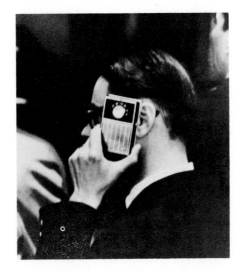

Fig. 2   The old and the new in radio. (RCA.)

trolling industrial equipment. The two advantages of the vacuum tube here are its speed, allowing practically instantaneous control, and the fact that the control can be made automatic. Some of these applications are in timing, heating, or counting. In addition to such industrial applications, electronics includes equipment for fire control of military equipment, for computers, guided missiles, medical applications, and many others.

Now with the invention of transistors in 1948 at Bell Telephone Laboratories, there are new applications in electronics and radio. The transistor is an application of controlled electron flow in solids such as germanium and silicon. Tubes and transistors both have similar applications for amplification or control purposes, but the transistor is smaller, more efficient, because there is no heater, and more rugged because of its simple construction.

Radio broadcast services

Broadcasting means to send out in all directions. As illustrated in Fig. 3, the transmitter radiates electromagnetic radio waves in all directions by means of its antenna. Receivers can pick up the transmitted radio waves by means of a receiving antenna or aerial. The transmission distance may be 10 or 5,000 miles, depending on the type of radio service. There are many services for different uses, including broadcast radio and television for home entertainment, radio navigation, maritime radio, police radio, amateur radio broadcasting, government radio services, and many others. These are all regulated by the Federal Communications Commission (FCC) in the United States. The FCC assigns the carrier wave to be used by the broadcast station. The carrier is the electromagnetic radio wave that

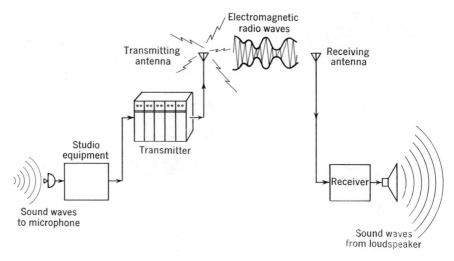

Fig. 3   *Radio broadcasting to provide wireless communication between the transmitter and receiver. An AM carrier wave is illustrated.*

conveys the desired information. A few of the more important radio services are listed here, but a more complete list is in Appendix B, with assigned channels.

Standard broadcast band. This band is the original system of broadcasting for what we generally call radio, using amplitude modulation (AM) in the transmission of the station's assigned carrier wave. Modulation is necessary so that the radio carrier wave can contain the desired voice or music.

FM broadcast band. The larger AM broadcast stations generally also have an FM station, broadcasting the same programs by frequency modulation. In addition, there are many stations for FM broadcast alone. This system reduces static and interference.

Television broadcasting. Television is just another application of radio, two separate carrier waves being broadcast by the station in its assigned channel. One is an AM carrier wave that has the information required for the picture; the other is an FM carrier wave for the sound.

Marine radio. This use is important for ship navigation and safety. In addition to ship-to-ship and ship-to-shore communications, radio is the basis of radar navigation systems.

Aeronautical radio. In addition to communications, radio is an important part of air navigation. It includes radar, radio compass, radio range, and automatic landing equipment.

Government radio. There are many radio stations operated by the Federal government for civilian and military requirements.

Citizens band (CB). This is used for mobile or fixed radio telephone equipment operated by any citizen. FCC license not needed with low-power units. Commonly used with small "walkie-talkie" combining transmitter and receiver in one.

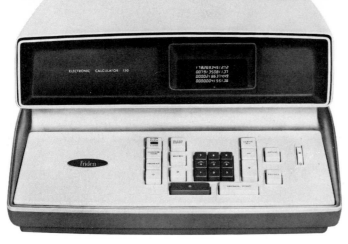

Fig. 4   Desk-size electronic calculating machine. (Friden Inc.)

Industrial radio. Radio waves are used for industrial, medical, and scientific equipment. Examples are the diathermy machines used by doctors and industrial heating equipment.

Amateur radio. This is perhaps the largest noncommercial radio broadcast service. These self-styled "hams" usually build and operate their own transmitters and receivers to call each other in one of the assigned amateur radio bands. The largest organization in this field is the American Radio Relay League, Newington, Connecticut.

Electronic applications

Electronics has its uses in almost all industries for quality control and automation, including printing, glass, oil, and paper production. Just a few examples are given here to indicate the wide scope. Additional applications are listed in Appendix A.

Office equipment. Computers and automatic equipment to replace manual office routines in filing, sorting, billing, and mailing. Very common in banks, insurance companies, government agencies and wherever voluminous records are kept. This application is generally called *electronic data processing* (EDP).

Nucleonics. Research and applications related to atomic energy and its uses require electronic control equipment.

Medical. Research in schools and laboratories, diagnosis, treatment, and surgery all use electronic equipment. Examples are the electron microscope, diathermy equipment, and the cardiograph machine.

Supersonics and ultrasonics. The applications of sound waves above the range of human hearing make use of electronic equipment. Examples are sonar equipment for marine ranging and depth finders, ultrasonic cleaning machines, and remote control for tuning television receivers.

Some additional types of electronic equipment include welding control, smoke detector, metal detector, moisture control, automatic door opener, and many types of remote-control units.

The field is so wide that it is generally considered in these broad categories:

1. Radio communications. This includes AM radio, FM radio, including stereo multiplex, and television broadcasting, including color television. The type of work can further be subdivided between receiver equipment and broadcast equipment, either at the transmitter or at the studio. High-fidelity audio equipment can be considered a specialized aspect of receivers.
2. Electronics. Some of the main subdivisions are computers, industrial control, servomechanisms, testing and recording instruments, and medical electronics.
3. Electrical power. Generation, distribution, and uses, including d-c and a-c machinery.

Specific branches in radio electronics are indicated by the following specialized titles for engineers: aeronautical, audio, antennas, communications, computer, engineering management, engineering sales, geophysical, illumination, information theory and coding, magnetics, medical electronics, microwaves, military including guided missiles, nuclear power, radio astronomy, tubes, solid state, space flight including satellites, and finally, ultrasonics.

The types of jobs in each of these fields include management, engineer for research, development, or production, teacher, technician, sales, technical writer, draftsman, serviceman, inspector, tester, and wirer. Technicians can work with engineers or with scientists in the fields of physics, chemistry, or biology. Both technicians and servicemen are needed for maintenance and repair on all the types of electronic equipment.

Electronic components

Considering so many different applications of electronics and radio, we can be a little surprised that there are only five basic types of components

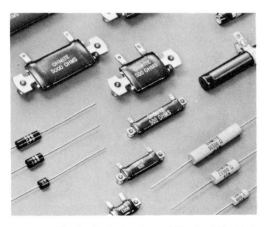

Fig. 5   *Typical resistors.* (Ohmite Mfg. Co.)

Fig. 6   *Typical capacitors.* (Cornell-Dubilier Electric Corp.)

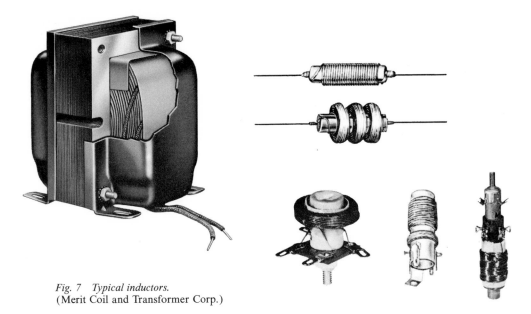

Fig. 7   Typical inductors.
(Merit Coil and Transformer Corp.)

for all the different kinds of equipment. Of course, each type has many variations for specific uses. Still, the following is a short list:

1. Electron tubes. Includes vacuum tubes and gas-filled tubes.
2. Transistors. This application is probably the most important use of solid-state semiconductors.
3. Resistors. (Fig. 5)
4. Capacitors, or condensers. (Fig. 6)
5. Inductors, or coils. (Fig. 7)

Types of tubes include the two-electrode tube, or *diode,* generally used as a rectifier to change alternating current to direct current, plus triodes, tetrodes, and pentodes for amplifier circuits. Similarly, semiconductor diodes are commonly used as rectifiers while transistors are generally amplifiers. Both tubes and transistors are used in circuits with resistors, inductors, and capacitors. Resistors can be the carbon-composition or wirewound type, with the function of limiting the amount of current, for either d-c or a-c circuits. A capacitor is constructed as an insulator between two conductors. Very often the purpose of capacitors in a circuit is to block direct current but pass alternating current. Finally, an inductor is just a coil of wire. Because of the coiled construction, an inductor can pass direct current better than alternating current. However, the transformer, which consists of two or more coils in the same magnetic field, can operate only with alternating current because of its alternating magnetic field.

In conclusion, it should be noted that whether we consider radio communications, electronics, or power machinery, all these applications are based on the fundamental principles of electricity and magnetism.

Chapter **1** *Electricity*

Electricity is an invisible force that can produce heat, light, motion by attraction or repulsion, and many other physical effects. More specifically, electricity can be explained in terms of electric charge, current, voltage, and resistance. The corresponding electrical units are the coulomb for measuring charge, ampere for current, volt for potential difference, and ohm for resistance. These characteristics can then be applied to electric circuits. The topics explained here are:

1·1   Negative and positive polarities
1·2   Electrons and protons in the atom
1·3   Structure of the atom
1·4   The coulomb unit of charge
1·5   The volt unit of potential difference
1·6   Charge in motion is current
1·7   Resistance is opposition to current
1·8   The closed circuit
1·9   Direct current (d-c) and alternating current (a-c)
1·10   Sources of electricity

1·1 Negative and positive polarities

We see the effects of electricity in a battery, static charge, lightning, radio, television, and many other applications. What do they all have in common that is electrical in nature? The answer is basic particles of electric charge with opposite polarities. All the materials we know, including solids, liquids, and gases, contain these two basic particles of electric charge: the *electron* and the *proton*. An electron is the smallest amount of electrical charge having the characteristic called *negative polarity*. The proton is a basic particle with *positive polarity*. Actually, the negative and positive polarities indicate two opposite characteristics that seem to be fundamental in all physical applications. Just as magnets have a north and south pole, electric charges have the opposite polarities labeled negative and positive. The opposing characteristics provide a method of balancing one against the other to explain different physical effects.

It is the arrangement of electrons and protons as basic particles of electricity that determines the electrical characteristics of all substances. As an example, this paper has electrons and protons in it. There is no evidence of electricity, though, because the number of electrons equals the number or protons. Then the opposite electrical forces cancel, making the paper electrically neutral. The neutral condition means that opposing forces are exactly balanced, without any net effect either way.

When we want to use the electrical forces associated with the negative and positive charges in all matter, work must be done to separate the electrons and protons. Changing the balance of forces thereby produces evidence of electricity. A battery, for instance, can do electrical work because its chemical energy separates electric charges to produce an excess of electrons at its negative terminal and an excess of protons at its positive terminal. With separate and opposite charges at the two terminals, electrical energy can be supplied to a circuit connected to the battery. Figure 1·1 shows a battery with its negative and positive terminals labeled in order to emphasize the two opposite polarities.

1·2　*Electrons and protons in the atom*

Although there are any number of possible methods by which electrons and protons might be grouped, they assemble in specific combinations that

Fig. 1·1　Negative and positive polarities on 1.5-volt dry cell.

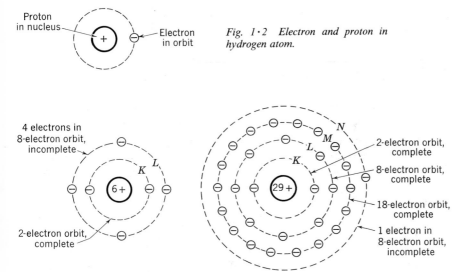

Proton in nucleus

Electron in orbit

Fig. 1·2   Electron and proton in hydrogen atom.

4 electrons in 8-electron orbit, incomplete

2-electron orbit, complete

2-electron orbit, complete

8-electron orbit, complete

18-electron orbit, complete

1 electron in 8-electron orbit, incomplete

(a)

(b)

Fig. 1·3   Atoms with more than one orbital ring. (a) Carbon atom with 6 protons in nucleus and 6 orbital electrons. (b) Copper atom with 29 protons in nucleus and 29 orbital electrons.

result in a stable arrangement. Each stable combination of electrons and protons makes one particular type of atom. For example, Fig. 1·2 illustrates the electron and proton structure of one atom of the gas hydrogen. This atom consists of a central mass called the *nucleus* and one electron outside. The proton in the nucleus makes it the massive and stable part of the atom because a proton is 1,840 times heavier than an electron.

In Fig. 1·2, the one electron in the hydrogen atom is shown in an orbital ring around the nucleus. In order to account for the electrical stability of the atom, we can consider the electron as spinning around the nucleus, as planets revolve around the sun. As a result, the electrical force attracting the electrons in toward the nucleus is balanced by the mechanical force outward on the rotating electron, maintaining the electron in its orbit around the nucleus.

In an atom that has more electrons and protons than hydrogen, all the protons are in the nucleus, while all the electrons are in one or more outside rings. For example, the carbon atom illustrated in Fig. 1·3a has 6 protons in the nucleus and 6 electrons in two outside rings. The total number of electrons in the outside rings must equal the number of protons in the nucleus in a neutral atom.

The distribution of electrons in the orbital rings determines the atom's electrical stability. Especially important is the number of electrons in the ring farthest from the nucleus. This outermost ring requires 8 electrons for stability, except when there is only one ring, which has a maximum of 2 electrons. In the carbon atom in Fig. 1·3a, with 6 electrons, there are just 2 electrons in the first ring because 2 is its maximum number. The remaining 4 electrons are in the second ring, which can have a maximum of 8 electrons. As another example, the copper atom in Fig. 1·3*b* has only 1 electron in the last ring, which can include 8 electrons. Therefore, the outside ring in the copper atom is less stable than the outside ring of the carbon atom.

When there are many atoms close together in a copper wire, the outermost orbital electrons are not sure which atoms they belong to and can migrate easily from one atom to another at random. Such electrons that can move freely from one atom to the next are often called *free electrons.* This freedom accounts for the ability of copper to conduct electricity very easily. It is the movement of free electrons that provides electrical current in a metal conductor.

Conductors, insulators, and semiconductors. When electrons can move easily from atom to atom in a material, it is a *conductor.* In general, all the metals are good conductors, with silver the best and copper second, because their atomic structure allows free movement of the outermost orbital electrons. Copper wire is generally used for practical conductors because it costs much less than silver. The purpose of using conductors is to allow electrical current to flow with minimum opposition.

A material with atoms in which the electrons tend to stay in their own orbits is an *insulator* because it cannot conduct electricity very easily. However, the insulators are able to hold or store electricity better than the conductors. An insulating material, such as glass, plastic, rubber, paper, air, or mica, is also called a *dielectric,* meaning it can store electric charge. It should be noted that insulators can be useful when it is necessary to prevent current flow. In addition, for applications requiring the storage of electric charge, as in capacitors, a dielectric material must be used because a good conductor cannot store any charge.

Carbon can be considered a semiconductor, conducting less than the

Table 1·1   *Examples of the chemical elements*

Group	*Examples*	*Symbol*	*Atomic number*	*Electron valence*
Metal conductors, in order of conductance	Silver	Ag	47	+1
	Copper	Cu	29	+1 or +2
	Gold	Au	79	+1 or +3
	Aluminum	Al	13	+3
Semiconductors	Carbon	C	6	±4
	Silicon	Si	14	±4
	Germanium	Ge	32	±4
Active gases	Hydrogen	H	1	+1
	Oxygen	O	8	−2
Inert gases	Helium	He	2	0
	Neon	Ne	10	0

metal conductors but more than the insulators. In the same group are germanium and silicon, which are commonly used for transistors and other semiconductor components.

Elements. The combinations of electrons and protons forming stable atomic structures result in different kinds of elementary substances having specific characteristics. A few familiar examples are the elements hydrogen, oxygen, carbon, copper, and iron. An *element* is defined as a substance that cannot be decomposed any further by chemical action. The atom is the smallest particle of an element that still has the same characteristics as the element. *Atom* itself is a Greek word meaning a particle too small to be subdivided. As an example of the fact that atoms are too small to be visible, a particle of carbon the size of a pinpoint contains many billions of atoms. The electrons and protons within the atom are even smaller.

Table 1·1 lists some more examples of elements. These are just a few out of a total of approximately 100.[1] Notice how the elements are grouped. Across the top row the common metals listed are all good conductors of electricity because each has an atomic structure with an unstable outside ring that allows many free electrons. The semiconductors have 4 electrons in the outermost ring. This means they can easily either gain or lose electrons. Among the gases, those which are active chemically and electrically have an atomic structure with an incomplete outside ring. The inert gases have a complete outside ring of 8 electrons, which makes them chemically inactive.

Molecules and compounds. A group of two or more atoms forms a molecule. For instance, two atoms of hydrogen (H) form a hydrogen molecule (H_2). When hydrogen unites chemically with oxygen, the result is water (H_2O), which is a compound. A compound, then, consists of two or more elements. The molecule is the smallest unit of a compound, with the same chemical characteristics. We can have molecules for either elements or compounds. However, atoms exist only for the elements.

1·3 Structure of the atom

Although nobody has even seen an atom, its hypothetical structure fits experimental evidence that has been measured very exactly. The size and electric charge of the invisible particles in the atom are indicated by how much they are deflected by known forces. Our present planetary model of the atom was proposed by Niels Bohr in 1913. His contribution was joining the new ideas of a nuclear atom developed by Lord Rutherford (1871–1937) with the quantum theory of radiation developed by Max Planck (1858–1947) and Albert Einstein (1879–1955).

As illustrated in Figs. 1·2 and 1·3, the nucleus contains protons for all the positive charge in the atom. The number of protons in the nucleus is equal to the number of planetary electrons. Thus, the positive and nega-

---

[1] A more complete listing of the elements, in alphabetical order, is given in Appendix C at the back of the book.

Table 1·2   Shells of orbital electrons in the atom

Shell	Maximum electrons	Inert gas
K	2	Helium
L	8	Neon
M	8 (up to calcium) Or 18	Argon
N	8, 18, or 32	Krypton
O	8 or 18	Xenon
P	8 or 18	Radon
Q	8	

tive charges are balanced, as the proton and electron have equal and opposite charges. The orbits for the planetary electrons are also called *shells* or *energy levels.*

The number of protons or electrons required in the atom is specified by the *atomic number* for each element. For the hydrogen atom in Fig. 1·1, its atomic number is 1, which means the nucleus has 1 proton balanced by 1 orbital electron. Similarly, the carbon atom in Fig. 1·2 with atomic number 6 has 6 protons in the nucleus and 6 orbital electrons, while the copper atom has 29 protons and 29 electrons because its atomic number is 29. The atomic number is listed for each of the elements in Table 1·1 to indicate the atomic structure.

The planetary electrons are in successive shells called K, L, M, N, O, P, and Q at increasing distances outward from the nucleus, Each shell has a maximum number of electrons for stability. As indicated in Table 1·2, these stable shells correspond to the inert gases, like helium and neon. The K shell, closest to the nucleus, is stable with 2 electrons, corresponding to the atomic structure for helium. Once the stable number of electrons has filled a shell, it cannot take any more electrons. The atomic structure with all its shells filled with the maximum number for stability corresponds to an inert gas.

For elements with higher atomic number, requiring more planetary electrons, these are in successive shells, tending to form the structure of the next inert gas in the periodic table.[2] After the K shell has been filled with 2 electrons, the L shell can take up to 8 electrons. The maximum number of electrons in the remaining shells can be 8 or 18 for different elements, usually, depending on the place in the periodic table. The maximum for an outermost shell, though, is always 8 rather than 18.

To illustrate these rules, we can use the copper atom in Fig. 1·3b as an example. The atomic number of 29 means there are 29 protons in the nucleus balanced by 29 planetary electrons. This number of electrons fills the K shell with 2 electrons, corresponding to the helium atom, and the L shell with 8 electrons. The 10 electrons in these two shells correspond to

[2] For more details of the periodic table of the elements, developed in 1869 by Dmitri Mendelyeev, refer to a textbook on chemistry or physics, or see "Periodic Chart of the Atoms," W. M. Welch Scientific Co., Chicago 10, Illinois.

the neon atom, which has an atomic number of 10. The remaining 19 electrons for the copper atom then fill the M shell with 18 electrons and the net result is 1 electron in the outermost N shell. It should be noted, however, that for atomic numbers 11 to 20, inclusive, the M shell can be filled with 8 electrons. The copper atom is considered to have 18 electrons in the M shell in order to allow 1 electron in the outermost shell, which is the most common structure.

Electron valence. This value is the number of electrons in an incomplete outermost shell. Copper, for instance, has a valence of 1 because there is 1 electron in the last shell, after the inner shells have been completed with their stable number. Similarly, hydrogen has a valence of 1 and carbon has a valence of 4. The number of outer electrons is considered positive valence, as these electrons are in addition to the stable shells.

Except for H and He, the goal of valence is 8 for all the atoms, as each tends to form the stable structure of 8 electrons in the outside ring. For this reason, valence can also be considered as the number of electrons in the outside ring needed for 8. This value is the negative valence. As examples, the valence of copper can be considered $+1$ or -7; carbon has the valence of ±4. The inert gases have a valence of 0, as they all have a complete, stable, outer shell of 8 electrons.

The valence indicates how easily the atom can gain or lose electrons. For instance, atoms with a valence of $+1$ can lose this 1 outside electron, especially to atoms with a valence of $+7$ or -1, which need 1 electron to complete the outside shell with 8 electrons.

Subshells. Although not shown in the drawing here, all the shells except K are divided into subshells. This subdivision accounts for different types of orbits in the same shell. For instance, electrons in one subshell may have elliptical orbits, while other electrons in the same main shell have circular orbits. The subshells indicate magnetic properties of the atom.

Particles in the nucleus. In a stable nucleus, which is not radioactive, the nucleus contains protons and neutrons. A neutron has no electrical charge. Its mass is slightly greater than a proton. The proton has the positive charge of a hydrogen nucleus. This charge is the same amount as a planetary electron, but of opposite polarity. There are no electrons in the nucleus. The main facts about these three basic particles are listed in Table 1·3. The number of protons in the nucleus is equal to the atomic number, to balance the charge of the orbital electrons.

In an unstable nucleus, each proton can be split into a neutron, which

Table 1·3 *Stable particles in the atom*

Particle	Charge	Mass
Electron, in orbital shells	0.16×10^{-18} coulomb, negative	9.108×10^{-28} gram
Proton, in nucleus	0.16×10^{-18} coulomb, positive	1.672×10^{-24} gram
Neutron, in nucleus	None	1.675×10^{-24} gram

remains in the nucleus, plus other particles expelled as emission. These particles include positrons, which have the same mass as electrons, but positive charge, and neutrinos. The neutrino, conceived in 1936 by Enrico Fermi, has no charge and very little mass.

Very large amounts of energy are needed for such transformations in the nucleus, however. In any case, the nucleus is stable for ordinary chemical and electrical effects. In electronics, therefore, we can consider the nucleus as simply a stable center of neutrons and protons, providing positive charge equal to the negative charge of the electrons in the orbital shells.

1·4   The coulomb unit of charge

If you rub a hard rubber pen or comb on a sheet of paper, the rubber will attract a corner of the paper if it is free to move easily. The paper and rubber then give evidence of a static electric charge. The work of rubbing resulted in separating electrons and protons to produce a charge of excess electrons on the surface of the rubber and a charge of excess protons on the paper.

Because paper and rubber are dielectric materials, they hold their extra electrons or protons. As a result, the paper and rubber are no longer neutral, but each has an electric charge. The resultant electric charges provide the force of attraction between the rubber and the paper. This mechanical force of attraction or repulsion between charges is the fundamental method by which electricity makes itself evident.

The charge is *static electricity* because the electrons or protons are not in motion. There are many examples of static electricity produced by the mechanical work of rubbing against friction. When you walk across a wool rug, your body becomes charged with an excess of electrons. Similarly, silk, fur, and glass can be rubbed to produce a static charge. This effect is more evident in dry weather, as a moist dielectric does not hold its charge so well.

The charge of many billions of electrons or protons is necessary for common applications of electricity. Therefore, it is convenient to define a practical unit called the *coulomb* (coul),[3] equal to the charge of 6.25×10^{18} electrons or protons stored in a dielectric. See Fig. 1·4. The symbol for electric charge is Q or q, for quantity. For instance, a charge of 6.25×10^{18} electrons[4] is stated $Q = 1$ coulomb.

Negative and positive polarities. Historically, the negative polarity has been assigned to the static charge produced on rubber, amber, and resinous materials in general. Positive polarity refers to the static charge produced on glass and other vitreous materials. On this basis, the electrons in all atoms are basic particles of negative charge because their polarity is the same as the charge on rubber. Protons have positive charge because the polarity is the same as the charge on glass.

[3] Named after Charles A. Coulomb (1736–1806), a French physicist.
[4] See Appendix E for an explanation of how to use powers of 10.

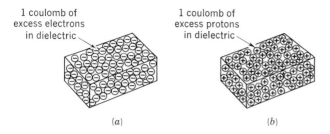

1 coulomb of
excess electrons
in dielectric

1 coulomb of
excess protons
in dielectric

(a)   (b)

*Fig. 1·4   The coulomb unit of charge. (a) 6.25 × 10¹⁸ excess electrons
stored in dielectric equals 1 coul of negative charge. (b) Same number of
protons equals 1 coul of positive charge.*

Charges of opposite polarity attract. If two small charged bodies of light
weight are mounted so that they are free to move easily and are placed
close to each other, one can be attracted to the other when the two charges
have opposite polarity (Fig. 1·5a). In terms of electrons and protons,
they tend to be attracted to each other by the force of attraction between
opposite charges. Furthermore, the weight of an electron is only about
$\frac{1}{1,840}$ the weight of a proton. As a result, the force of attraction tends to
make electrons move to protons.

Charges of the same polarity repel. In Fig. 1·5b and c, it is shown that,
when the two bodies have an equal amount of charge with the same
polarity, they repel each other. The two positive charges repel in Fig. 1·5b,
while two negative charges of the same value repel each other in Fig. 1·5c.

Polarity of a charge. An electric charge must have either negative or
positive polarity, labeled $-Q$ or $+Q$, with an excess of either electrons or
protons. A neutral condition is considered zero charge. On this basis, consider the following examples, remembering that the electron is the basic
particle of charge and the proton has exactly the same amount, although
of opposite polarity.

Example 1. A neutral dielectric has added to it 12.5 × 10¹⁸ electrons. What is
its charge in coulombs?

Answer. Since this number of electrons is double the charge of 1 coul,
$-Q = 2$ coul.

Example 2. A dielectric has a positive charge of 12.5 × 10¹⁸ protons. What is
its charge in coulombs?

Fig. 1·5   Force between charges.

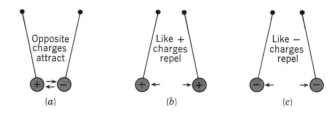

Opposite
charges
attract

Like +
charges
repel

Like −
charges
repel

(a)   (b)   (c)

Answer. This is the same amount of charge as in Example 1 but positive. Therefore **+Q = 2 coul.**

Example 3. A dielectric with $+Q$ of 2 coul has 12.5×10^{18} electrons added. What is its charge then?

Answer. The 2 coul of negative charge added by the electrons cancels the 2 coul of positive charge, making the dielectric neutral, with **zero charge.**

Example 4. A neutral dielectric has 12.5×10^{18} electrons removed. What is its charge?

Answer. The 2 coul of electron charge removed allows an excess of 12.5×10^{18} protons. Since the proton and electron have exactly the same amount of charge, now the dielectric has a positive charge of **+Q = 2 coul.**

Note that we generally consider the electrons moving, rather than the heavier protons. However, a loss of a given number of electrons is equivalent to a gain of the same number of protons.

1·5   The volt unit of potential difference

Potential refers to the possibility of doing work. Any charge has the potential to do the work of moving another charge, by either attraction or repulsion. This ability of a charge to do work is its potential. When we consider two unlike charges, they have a difference of potential.

A charge is the result of work done in separating electrons and protons. Because of the separation, there is stress and strain associated with opposite charges, since normally they would be balancing each other to produce a neutral condition. We could consider that the accumulated electrons are drawn tight and are straining themselves to be attracted toward protons in order to return to the neutral condition. Similarly, the work of producing the charge causes a condition of stress in the protons, which are trying to attract electrons and return to the neutral condition. Because of these forces, the charge of electrons or protons has potential, as it is ready to give back the work put into producing the charge.

Potential between different charges. When one charge is different from the other, there must be a difference of potential between them. For instance, consider a positive charge of 3 coul shown at the right in Fig. 1·6a. The charge has a certain amount of potential, corresponding to the amount of work this much charge can do. The work to be done is moving some

Fig. 1·6   *The work done in moving electrons between two charges depends on their difference in potential. Potential difference is equivalent to work for 2-coul charge in a, b, and c.*

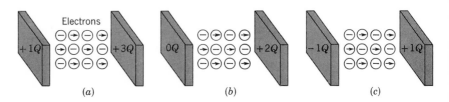

(a)	(b)	(c)

(a)

$E = 2.2 \text{ v}$

(b)

Fig. 1·7   Chemical cell as voltage source. (a) Voltage output is potential difference between the two terminals. (b) Schematic symbol, with longer line for positive terminal. (Welch Scientific Co.)

electrons, as illustrated. Assume a charge of $1Q$ can move 3 electrons. Then the charge of $+3Q$ can attract 9 electrons toward the right. However, the charge of $+1Q$ at the opposite side can attract 3 electrons toward the left. The net result, then, is that 6 electrons can be moved toward the right to the more positive charge.

Note that this number of electrons moved in a is the same as in b, where one charge is $+2Q$ compared with zero charge for the opposite end. Similarly, 6 electrons are moved to the right in c, where the charge of $+1Q$ attracts 3 electrons and the charge of $-1Q$ repels 3 electrons. Therefore, the net number of electrons moved in the direction of the more positive charge depends on the difference of potential between the two charges. This difference corresponds to $2Q$ for all three cases in Fig. 1·6.

The only case without any potential difference between charges is where they both have the same polarity and are equal in amount. Then the repelling and attracting forces cancel and no work can be done in moving electrons between the two identical charges.

The volt. The practical unit of potential difference is the *volt*,[5] which is a measure of the amount of work required for moving 1 coul of charge. When 0.7376 ft-lb (foot-pound) of work is necessary to move 6.25×10^{18} electrons between two points, each having its own charge, the potential difference between these two points is 1 volt.

The symbol for potential difference is E, for *electromotive force*, indicating the ability to do the work of forcing electrons to move. Because the volt unit is used so often, potential difference is often called *voltage*. However, voltage is fundamentally the difference in potential between two points. Consider the 2.2-volt lead-acid cell in Fig. 1·7. Its output of 2.2 volts means that this is the amount of potential difference between the two terminals. The term *emf* as an abbreviation of electromotive force is sometimes used for a voltage source.

[5] Named after Alessandro Volta (1745–1827).

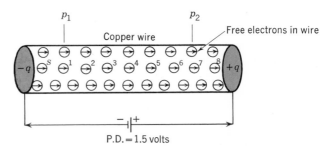

Fig. 1·8   *Potential difference across two ends of wire conductor causes drift of free electrons through the wire, producing electric current.*

1·6   *Charge in motion is current*

When the potential difference between two charges forces a third charge to move, the charge in motion is an *electrical current*. To produce current, therefore, charge must be moved by a potential difference. In solid materials, such as copper wire, the free electrons are charges that can be forced to move with relative ease by a potential difference, since they require relatively little work to be moved. As illustrated in Fig. 1·8, if a potential difference is connected across two ends of a copper wire, the applied voltage forces the free electrons to move. This current is a drift of electrons, from the point of negative charge at one end, moving through the wire, and returning to the positive charge at the other end.

To illustrate the drift of free electrons through the wire shown in Fig. 1·8, each electron in the middle row is numbered, corresponding to a copper atom to which the free electron belongs. The electron at the left is labeled s to indicate that it comes from the negative charge of the source of potential difference. This one electron s is repelled from the negative charge $-q$ at the left and is attracted by the positive charge $+q$ at the right. Therefore, the potential difference of the voltage source can make electron s move toward atom 1. Now atom 1 has an extra electron. As a result, the free electron of atom 1 can then move to atom 2. In this way, there is a drift of free electrons from atom to atom. The final result is that the one free electron labeled 8 at the extreme right in Fig. 1·8 moves out from the wire to return to the positive charge of the voltage source.

Considering this case of just one electron moving, note that the electron returning to the positive side of the voltage source is not the electron labeled s that left the negative side. All electrons are the same, however, and have the same charge. Therefore, the drift of free electrons resulted in the charge of one electron moving through the wire. This charge in motion is the current. With more electrons drifting through the wire, the charge of many electrons moves, resulting in more current.

The current is a continuous flow of electrons. Only the electrons move, not the potential difference. For ordinary applications, where the wires are not long lines, the potential difference produces current instantaneously through the entire length of wire. Furthermore, the current must be the same at all points of the wire at any time. Although a point nearer to the negative terminal of the voltage source has a greater repelling force on the free electrons, at this point the free electrons are farther from the positive terminal and have less attracting force. At the middle of the wire, the free electrons have equal forces of attraction and repulsion. Near the positive terminal, there is a greater attracting force on the free electrons but less repelling force from the negative terminal of the voltage source. In all cases, the total force causing motion of the free electrons is the same at any point of the wire, therefore resulting in the same current through all parts of the wire.

Potential difference is necessary to produce current. The number of free electrons that can be forced to drift through the wire to produce the moving charge depends upon the amount of potential difference across the wire. With more applied voltage, the forces of attraction and repulsion can make more free electrons drift, producing more charge in motion. A larger amount of charge moving with the same speed means a higher value of current. Less applied voltage across the same wire results in a smaller amount of charge in motion, which is a smaller value of current. With zero potential difference across the wire, there is no current.

Two cases of zero potential difference and no current can be considered in order to emphasize the important fact that potential difference is needed to produce current. Assume the copper wire to be by itself, not connected to any voltage source, so that there is no potential difference across the wire. The free electrons in the wire can move from atom to atom, but this motion is random, without any organized drift through the wire. If the wire is considered as a whole, from one end to the other, the current is zero. As another example, suppose that the two ends of the wire have the same potential. Then free electrons cannot move to either end, because both ends have the same force, and there is no current through the wire. A practical example of this case of zero potential difference would be connecting both ends of the wire to just one terminal of a battery. Each end of the wire would have the same potential and there would be no current. The conclusion, therefore, is that two connections are needed to two points at different potentials in order to produce current.

The ampere of current. Since current is the movement of charge, the unit for stating the amount of current is defined in rate of flow of charge. When the charge moves at the rate of 6.25×10^{18} electrons flowing past a given point per second, the value of the current is one *ampere* (amp).[6] This is the same as one coulomb of charge per second. Referring back to Fig. 1·8, note that if 6.25×10^{18} free electrons move past p_1 in a second, the current is one ampere. Similarly, the current is one ampere at p_2 because the electron drift is the same throughout the wire. If twice as many electrons moved past either point in one second, the current would be two amperes.

[6] Named after André M. Ampère (1775–1836).

The symbol for current is I or i for intensity, since the current is a measure of how intense or concentrated the electron flow is. Two amperes of current in a copper wire is a higher intensity than 1 amp; then a greater concentration of moving electrons results because of more electrons in motion, although all the electrons move with the same speed. Sometimes current is called *amperage*.

How current differs from charge. Charge is a quantity of electricity accumulated in a dielectric. The charge is static electricity, at rest, without any motion. When the charge moves, usually in a conductor, the current I indicates the intensity of the electricity in motion. This characteristic is a fundamental definition of current:

$$I = \frac{Q}{T} \qquad (1 \cdot 1)$$

where I is the current in amperes, Q is in coulombs, and the time T is in seconds. It does not matter whether the moving charge is positive or negative. The only question is how much charge moves and what is its rate of motion.

Example 5. The charge of 12 coul moves past a given point every second. How much is the intensity of charge flow?

$$I = \frac{12 \text{ coul}}{1 \text{ sec}} = \textbf{12 amp}$$

Example 6. The charge of 5 coul moves past a given point in 0.1 sec. How much is the current?

$$I = \frac{Q}{T} = \frac{5}{0.1} = \textbf{50 amp}$$

This fundamental definition of current can also be used to consider the charge as equal to the product of the current multiplied by the time. Or,

$$Q = I \times T \qquad (1 \cdot 2)$$

For instance, we can have a dielectric connected to conductors with a current of 5 amp. If the current can deposit electrons for the time of 2 sec, the accumulated charge in the dielectric will be

$$\begin{aligned} Q &= I \times T \\ &= 5 \text{ amp} \times 2 \text{ sec} \\ Q &= 10 \text{ coul} \end{aligned}$$

The formulas $Q = IT$ for charge and $I = Q/T$ for current illustrate the fundamental nature of Q as an accumulation of charge, while I measures the intensity of moving charges.

The general nature of current. The moving charges that provide current in metal conductors like a copper wire are the free electrons of the copper atoms. In this case, the moving charges have negative polarity. The direction of motion between two terminals for this *electron current,* therefore, is toward the more positive end. It is important to note, however, that there are examples of positive charges in motion. Common applications include current in liquids, gases, and semiconductors. Whether negative or positive charges move, though, the current is still defined fundamentally as Q/T. For the case of current resulting from the motion of positive charges, its direction is opposite from the direction of electron flow. Then the direction of current between two terminals is toward the more negative end. This direction of moving positive charges is called *conventional current* to distinguish it from the opposite direction of electron flow.

1·7   Resistance is opposition to current

The fact that a wire conducting current can become hot is evidence of the fact that the work done by the applied voltage in producing current must be accomplished against some form of opposition. This opposition, which limits the amount of current that can be produced by the applied voltage, is called *resistance.* Conductors have very little resistance; insulators have a large amount of resistance.

The atoms of a copper wire have a large number of free electrons, which can be moved easily by a potential difference. Therefore, the copper wire has little opposition to the flow of free electrons when voltage is applied, corresponding to a low value of resistance. Carbon, however, has fewer free electrons than copper. When the same amount of voltage is applied to the carbon as to the copper, fewer electrons will flow. It should be noted that just as much current can be produced in the carbon by applying more voltage. For the same current, though, the higher applied voltage means that more work is necessary, causing more heat. Carbon opposes the current more than copper, therefore, and has a higher value of resistance.

The ohm. The practical unit of resistance is the ohm. A resistance that develops 0.24 calorie[7] of heat when one ampere of current flows through it for one second has one ohm of opposition. As an example of a low resistance, a good conductor like copper wire can have a resistance of 0.01 ohm for a 1-ft length. The resistance-wire heating element in a 600-watt toaster has a resistance of 24 ohms, and the tungsten filament in a 100-watt light bulb has a resistance of 144 ohms.

Figure 1·9 shows a carbon-composition resistor. This type of resistance can be manufactured with a value from a few hundred ohms to millions of ohms. The abbreviation for resistance is R or r. The symbol used for the ohm is the Greek letter *omega,* written as Ω. In diagrams, resistance is indicated by a zigzag line as shown by R in Fig. 1·9.

---

[7] One calorie is the quantity of heat that will raise the temperature of one gram of water by one degree centigrade. See Appendix D on Physics Units.

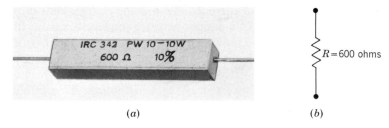

(a)   (b)

Fig. 1·9   (a) Wirewound resistor with cement coating. (b) Schematic symbol for any type of resistance. (International Resistance Co.)

Conductance. The opposite of resistance is conductance. The less the resistance, the higher is the conductance. Its symbol is G or g and the unit is the *mho,* which is "ohm" spelled backward. G is the reciprocal of R, or $G = 1/R$. For example, 10 ohms of resistance is equal to $\frac{1}{10}$ mho of conductance. Whether to use R or G for components is usually a matter of convenience. In general, R is easier to use when considering voltages in a series circuit; G may be convenient when considering different currents in parallel circuits. (Series and parallel circuits are explained in Chaps. 3 and 4.)

1·8   The closed circuit

In electrical applications requiring the use of current, the components are arranged in the form of a circuit, as shown in Fig. 1·10. A circuit can be defined as a path for current flow. The purpose of this circuit is to light the incandescent bulb. The bulb lights when the tungsten-filament wire inside is white hot, producing an incandescent glow. By itself the tungsten filament cannot produce current. A source of potential difference is necessary. Since the battery produces a potential difference of 1.5 volts across its two output terminals, this voltage is connected across the filament of the bulb by means of the two wires so that the applied voltage can produce current through the filament.

Fig. 1·10   An electric circuit, consisting of voltage source connected to a resistance load. (a) Photograph of circuit. (b) Wiring diagram. (c) Schematic diagram.

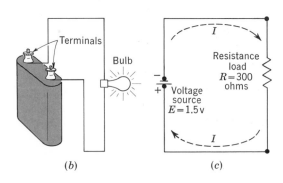

(a)   (b)   (c)

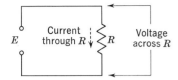

Fig. 1·11
Difference between voltage and current.

In Fig. 1·10c the schematic diagram of the circuit is shown. Here the components are represented by shorthand symbols. Note the symbols for the battery and resistance. The connecting wires are shown simply as straight lines because their resistance is small enough to be neglected. A resistance of less than 0.01 ohm for the wire is practically zero compared with the 300-ohm resistance of the bulb. If the resistance of the wire must be considered, the schematic diagram includes it as additional resistance in the same current path. It should be noted that the schematic diagram need not look like the physical layout of the circuit. The schematic shows only the symbols for the components and their electrical connections.

Any electric circuit has three important characteristics:

1. There must be a source of potential difference. Without the applied voltage, current cannot flow.
2. There must be a complete path for current flow, from one side of the applied voltage source, through the external circuit, and returning to the other side of the voltage source.
3. The current path normally has resistance. The resistance is in the circuit for the purpose of either generating heat or limiting the amount of current.

Note that it is the current that moves through the circuit. The potential difference does not move. The voltage across the filament resistance makes electrons flow from one side to the other, but the potential difference remains across the filament to do the work of moving electrons through the resistance of the filament. As illustrated in Fig. 1·11, the voltage is the potential difference across the two ends of the resistance, while the current is the intensity of the electron flow past any one point in the circuit.

The voltage source maintains the current. As current flows in the circuit, electrons leave the negative terminal of the cell, and the same number of free electrons in the conductor are returned to the positive terminal. With electrons lost from the negative charge and gained by the positive charge, the two charges would tend to neutralize each other. The chemical action inside the dry cell, however, continuously separates electrons and protons to maintain the negative and positive charges on the outside terminals that provide the potential difference. Otherwise, the current would neutralize the charges, resulting in no potential difference, and the current would stop. Therefore, the dry cell keeps the current flowing by maintaining the potential difference across the circuit. Thus the cell is the generator, or voltage source, for the circuit.

The circuit is a load on the voltage source. We can consider the circuit as a means whereby the energy of the voltage source is carried by means of the current through the filament of the bulb, where the electrical energy is used in producing heat energy. On this basis, the battery is the *source* in the circuit, since its voltage output represents the potential energy to be used. The part of the circuit connected to the voltage source is the *load resistance,* since it determines how much work the source will supply. In this case, the bulb's filament is the load resistance for the battery.

The resistance of the filament determines how much current the 6-volt source will produce. Specifically, the current here is 0.005 amp, equal to 1.5 volts divided by 300 ohms. With more opposition, the same voltage will produce less current; less opposition allows more current. The current that flows through the load resistance is the *load current.* Note that a lower value of ohms for the load resistance corresponds to a higher load current. Unless noted otherwise, the term *load* by itself can be assumed generally to mean the load current. Therefore, a heavy or big load electrically means a high value of load current, corresponding to a large amount of work supplied by the source.

Direction of the current. As shown in Fig. 1·10c, the direction of the electron drift is from the negative side of the battery, through the load resistance R, and back to the positive terminal of the voltage source. Note that this is the direction in the external circuit connected across the output terminals of the voltage source. Inside the battery, the electrons move to the negative terminal because this is how the voltage source produces its potential difference. The battery is doing the work of separating charges, accumulating electrons at the negative terminal and protons at the positive terminal, so that the potential difference across the two output terminals can do the work of moving electrons around the external circuit. In the circuit outside the voltage source, then, the direction of the electron flow is from a point of negative potential to a point of positive potential.

1·9   Direct current (d-c) and alternating current (a-c)

The electron flow illustrated in the circuit of Fig. 1·10c is direct current because it has just one direction. The reason for the unidirectional current is that the battery maintains the same polarity of output voltage. We can say that the battery is a steady d-c voltage source, therefore, as it has a fixed polarity of output voltage that produces direct current in the circuit.

It is the flow of charges in just one direction, with a fixed polarity of applied voltage, that are the characteristics of a d-c circuit. Actually, the current can be a motion of positive charges, rather than electrons, but the conventional direction of current does not change the fact that direct current has just one direction. Furthermore, the d-c voltage source can change the amount of its output voltage, but if the same polarity is maintained, direct current will flow in just one direction, meeting the requirements of a d-c circuit. A battery is a steady d-c voltage source because it has fixed polarity and its output voltage is a steady value.

An alternating voltage source periodically reverses or alternates in

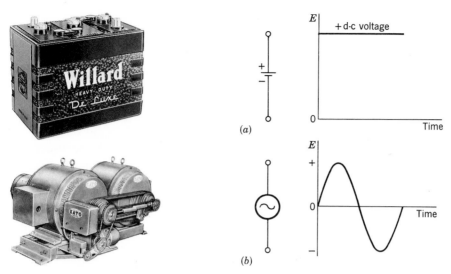

Fig. 1·12 (a) Steady d-c voltage from battery. (b) Sine-wave a-c voltage from rotary generator.

polarity. The resulting alternating current, therefore, periodically reverses in direction. In terms of electron flow, the current always flows from the negative terminal of the voltage source, through the circuit, and back to the positive terminal, but when the generator alternates in polarity, the current must reverse its direction. The 60-cycle a-c power line used in most homes is a common example. The frequency of 60 cycles per second (cps) means the voltage polarity and current direction reverse 60 times per second.

The details of a-c circuits are explained in Chap. 13 and the remainder of the book. D-c circuits are analyzed first because they usually are simpler. However, the principles of d-c circuits also apply to a-c circuits. Both types are important, as most electronic circuits include a-c voltages and d-c voltages. The waveforms for these two types of voltages are illustrated in Fig. 1·12. Their uses are compared in Table 1·4.

Table 1·4 Comparison of d-c voltage and a-c voltage

D-C VOLTAGE	A-C VOLTAGE
Fixed polarity	Reverses in polarity
Can be steady or vary in magnitude	Varies in magnitude between reversals in polarity
Steady value cannot be stepped up or down by a transformer	Used for electrical power distribution to homes and factories
Electrode voltages for vacuum tubes and transistor amplifiers	Signal input and output for vacuum tubes and transistor amplifiers
Easier to measure	Easier to amplify
Heating effect the same for direct or alternating current	

1·10 Sources of electricity

There are electrons and protons in the atoms of all materials, but to do useful work, the charges must be separated to produce a potential difference that can make current flow. Some of the more common methods of providing electrical effects are listed here.

1. **Static electricity by friction.** In this method, electrons and protons in an insulator can be separated by the work of rubbing to produce opposite charges that remain in the dielectric.

2. **Conversion of chemical energy.** Wet or dry cells and batteries are the applications. Here a chemical reaction produces opposite charges on two dissimilar metals, which serve as the negative and positive terminals. In the common zinc-carbon dry cell, the zinc container is the negative electrode and the carbon electrode in the center is the positive electrode. In the lead-acid wet cell, sulfuric acid diluted with water is the liquid electrolyte, while the negative terminal is lead and the positive terminal is lead peroxide.

3. **Conversion of magnetic energy.** Electricity and magnetism are closely related. A motor is an example of how current can react with a magnetic field to produce motion; a generator produces voltage by means of a conductor rotating in a magnetic field.

4. **Photoelectricity.** Some materials are photoelectric, meaning they can emit electrons when light strikes the surface. The element cesium is often used as a source of *photoelectrons.* In another effect, the resistance of the element selenium changes with light. Combined with a fixed voltage source, then, wide variations between dark current and light current can be produced. Such characteristics are the basis of many photoelectric devices, including television camera tubes, photoelectric cells, and phototransistors, where variations in light intensity can be translated into electrical effects.

5. **Thermal emission.** Some materials when heated can "boil off" electrons from the surface. Then these emitted electrons can be controlled to provide useful applications of electrical current. The emitting electrode is called a *cathode,* while an *anode* is used to collect the emitted electrons. A common material for thermionic cathodes is barium oxide, heated to a dull-red temperature. The vacuum tubes in radio and television receivers operate on this principle. The details of electron tubes are explained in Chap. 24.

6. **Doping of semiconductors.** Because of a valence of ± 4, combined with a crystalline molecular structure, semiconductors such as germanium and silicon can be changed from the neutral condition by adding small amounts of an appropriate impurity element. This technique of adding charges to a semiconductor is called *doping.* When electrons are added, the result is negative or N-type material; a deficiency of electrons makes the material positive or P-type. With one type between two opposite types, the result is a PNP or NPN transistor. The details of transistors are explained in Chap. 25.

Although there are so many different applications, remember that all electrons are the same, with identical charge and mass. Whether the electron flow results from a battery, rotary generator, or photoelectric device and is controlled by a vacuum tube or transistor, the analysis of voltage, current, and resistance in the different types of circuits must follow the basic principles described here.

SUMMARY

1. Electricity is present in all matter in the form of electrons and protons.
2. The electron is the basic quantity of negative electricity, the proton of positive electricity. Both have the same amount of charge but opposite polarities. The charge of 6.25×10^{18} electrons or protons equals 1 coulomb.
3. Charges of the same polarity tend to repel each other; charges of opposite polarities attract. There must be a difference of charges for any force of attraction or repulsion.
4. Electrons tend to move toward protons because an electron has $\frac{1}{1,840}$ the weight of a proton. Electrons in motion provide an electron current.
5. The atomic number of an element gives the number of protons in the nucleus of its atom, balanced by an equal number of orbital electrons. The number of electrons in the outermost orbit is the valence of the element.
6. Table 1·5 summarizes the main features of electric circuits.
7. An electric circuit is a closed path for electron flow. Potential difference must be connected across the circuit to produce current. In the external circuit outside the voltage source, electrons flow from the negative terminal toward the positive terminal.
8. Direct current has just one direction, as the d-c voltage source has a fixed polarity. Alternating current periodically reverses in direction as the a-c voltage source reverses its polarity.

SELF-EXAMINATION (*Answers at back of book.*)

Here's a chance to see how well you have learned the material in this chapter. These exercises are for your self-testing only.
Answer true or false.
1. All matter has electricity in the form of electrons and protons in the atom.
2. The electron is the basic unit of negative charge.
3. A proton has the same amount of charge as the electron but opposite polarity.
4. Electrons are repelled from other electrons but are attracted to protons.
5. An electron moves to a proton because a proton is 1,840 times heavier.
6. The nucleus is the massive stable part of an atom, with positive charge.

Table 1·5   Electrical characteristics

Characteristic	Symbol*	Unit	Description
Charge	Q or q	Coulomb	Quantity of stored electrons or protons; $Q = I \times T$
Voltage	E or e	Volt	Potential difference between two unlike charges; makes electrons move to produce current
Current	I or i	Ampere	Electrons in motion; $I = Q/T$
Resistance	R or r	Ohm	Opposition that reduces amount of current
Conductance	G or g	Mho	Reciprocal of resistance, $G = 1/R$

*The small letters q, e, and i are used when the quantity varies with respect to time; r and g indicate internal characteristics of a source.

7. Neutrons add to the weight of the atom's nucleus but not to its electrical charge.
8. An element with atomic number 12 has 12 orbital electrons.
9. This element has an electron valence of $+2$.
10. To produce current in a circuit, potential difference is connected across a closed path.
11. D-c voltage has fixed polarity while a-c voltage periodically reverses its polarity.
12. The coulomb is a measure of the quantity of stored charge.
13. If a dielectric has 2 coul of excess electrons, removing 3 coul of electrons will leave the dielectric with the positive charge of 1 coul.
14. A charge of 5 coul flowing past a point each second is a current of 5 amp.
15. A current of 7 amp charging a dielectric will accumulate a charge of 14 coul after 2 sec.
16. A voltage source has two terminals with different charges.
17. The voltage between two equal and opposite charges is zero.
18. The resistance of a few feet of copper wire is practically zero.
19. The resistance of the rubber or plastic insulation on this wire is also practically zero.
20. A resistance of 600 ohms has a conductance of 6 mhos.

ESSAY QUESTIONS

1. Define each of the following briefly, with its unit and symbol: charge, potential difference, current, resistance, and conductance.
2. Name two good conductors, two good insulators, and two semiconductors.
3. Explain briefly why there is no current in a light bulb unless it is connected across a source of applied voltage.
4. What is the difference between voltage and current?
5. In any circuit: (*a*) state two requirements for producing current; (*b*) give the direction of electron flow.
6. Show the atomic structure of the element sodium (Na) with atomic number 11. What is its electron valence?
7. What is meant by direct current, as compared with alternating current?
8. State the formulas for each of the following two statements: (*a*) Current is the time rate of change of charge. (*b*) Charge is current accumulated over a period of time.
9. State two laws of the force between charges.

PROBLEMS (*Answers to selected problems at back of book.*)

1. A charged insulator has an excess of 25×10^{18} electrons. Give its charge in coulombs, with polarity.
2. Another insulator has a deficiency of 50×10^{18} electrons. Give its charge in coulombs, with polarity.
3. The charge of 8 coulombs flows past a given point every 2 sec. How much is the current in amperes?
4. The current of 4 amp charges an insulator for 2 sec. How much charge is accumulated?
5. Convert the following to mhos of conductance: (*a*) 0.04 ohm, (*b*) 0.5 ohm, (*c*) 1,000 ohms.
6. Convert the following to ohms of resistance: (*a*) 0.001 mho, (*b*) 2 mhos, (*c*) 100 mhos.
7. If 1.25×10^{18} electrons per second flow through a bulb's filament, how much is the current?
8. A material with a deficiency of 25×10^{18} electrons then gains 31.25×10^{18} electrons. The excess electrons are then made to flow past a given point in 1 sec. How much current is produced by the resultant electron flow?

Chapter 2 — Ohm's law

This unit explains how the amount of current I in a circuit depends on its resistance R and the applied voltage E. Specifically $I = E/R$, determined in 1828 by the experiments of George Simon Ohm. If you know any two of the factors E, I, and R, you can calculate the third. Ohm's law also determines the amount of electrical power in the circuit.

If we keep the same resistance in a circuit but vary the voltage, the current will vary. The circuit in Fig. 2·1 demonstrates this idea. The applied voltage E can be varied from zero to 12 volts, as an example. The bulb has a 12-volt filament, which requires this much voltage for its normal current to light with normal intensity. The meter I indicates the amount of current in the circuit for the bulb. With 12 volts applied, the bulb lights, indicating normal current. When E is reduced to 10 volts, there is less light because of less I. As E decreases, the bulb becomes dimmer. For zero volts applied there is no current and the bulb cannot light. In summary, the changing brilliance of the bulb shows that the current is varying with the changes in applied voltage. More details of E, I, and R are explained in the following topics:

2·1 The linear proportion between E and I
2·2 $I = E/R$
2·3 $E = IR$
2·4 $R = E/I$
2·5 The inverse relation between I and R
2·6 Definition of the practical units
2·7 Multiple and submultiple units
2·8 Power
2·9 Power dissipation in resistance
2·10 Electric shock

2·1   The linear proportion between E and I

The relation between E and I can be analyzed more exactly by using a fixed resistance of 2 ohms for R_L, as in Fig. 2·2a. Then when E is varied the meter shows I values directly proportional to E. For instance, when E is 12 volts, I equals 6 amp; for 10-volt E, the current is 5 amp; 8-volt E produces 4 amp. All the values of E and I are listed in the table and plotted in the graph shown in Fig. 1·2b. Except for zero volts applied, all the I values are one-half the E values because R is 2 ohms.

The reason a fixed resistor is used instead of the light bulb is that we want the resistance to remain constant as E is varied to measure the effect on I. With a light bulb, its resistance depends on the amount of current.

In the graph, voltage values E are marked on the horizontal axis, called the *x axis* or *abscissa*. The current values are on the vertical axis, called the *y axis* or *ordinate*. Because the values for E and I depend on each other, they are variable factors. E is the independent variable here because we assign values of voltage and note the resulting current. Generally, the independent variable is plotted on the x axis, which is why the E values are shown here horizontally while the I values are on the ordinate. The two scales need not be the same. The only requirement is that equal distances on either scale represent equal changes in magnitude. On the x axis here 2-volt steps are chosen, while the y axis has 1-amp scale divisions. The zero point at the origin is the reference.

The plotted points in the graph show the values in the table. For instance,

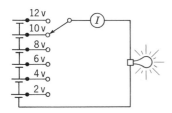

Fig. 2·1   *Increasing the applied voltage E produces more current I to light the bulb with greater intensity.*

Fig. 2·2   *The current I is directly proportional to applied voltage E. (a) Circuit with variable E but constant R. (b) Table and graph showing linear increase in I as E increases.*

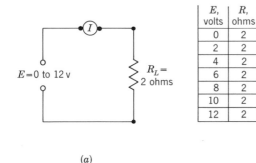

E, volts	R, ohms	I, amps
0	2	0
2	2	1
4	2	2
6	2	3
8	2	4
10	2	5
12	2	6

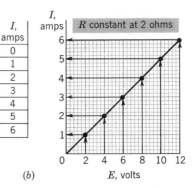

(a)   (b)

the lowest point is 2 volts horizontally from the origin, and 1 amp up. Similarly, the next point is at the intersection of the 4-volt mark and the 2-amp mark. A line joining these two plotted points includes all values of *I*, for any value of *E*, with *R* constant at 2 ohms. This also applies to values not listed in the table. For instance, if we take the value of 7 volts for *E*, up to the straight-line graph and over to the *I* axis, the graph shows 3.5 amp for *I*.

The linear graph shows a direct proportion between *E* and *I*. Doubling the value of *E* from 4 to 8 volts results in twice the current, from 2 to 4 amp. This linear relation results because *R* is constant. In effect the graph is a plot of *I* values for *E/2*, as *R* is constant at 2 ohms for this example.

2·2 $I = E/R$

For the general case, where *R* can be any value, Ohm's law is stated specifically as

$$I = \frac{E}{R} \tag{2·1}$$

where *I* is the amount of current through the resistance *R* connected across the source of potential difference *E*. With volts as the practical unit for *E* and ohms for *R*, the amount of current *I* is in amperes. Therefore,

$$\text{Amperes} = \frac{\text{volts}}{\text{ohms}}$$

This formula says simply divide the voltage across *R* by the ohms of resistance between the two points of potential difference to calculate the amperes of current through *R*. In Fig. 2·3, for instance, with 6 volts applied across a 3-ohm resistance, by Ohm's law the current equals ⅔ or 2 amp.

(a)

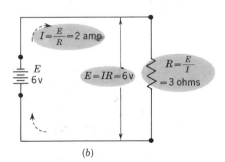

(b)

Fig. 2·3   *Applying Ohm's law to a circuit. (a) Voltage source E applied across R. (b) Schematic diagram with values calculated by Ohm's law.*

It is important to realize that with high voltage, the current can have a low value when there is a very large amount of resistance in the circuit. For example, 1,000 volts applied across 1,000,000 ohms results in a current of only ¹⁄₁,₀₀₀ amp. By Ohm's law

$$I = \frac{E}{R} = \frac{1{,}000 \text{ volts}}{1{,}000{,}000 \text{ ohms}} = \frac{1}{1{,}000} = \textbf{0.001 amp}$$

At the opposite extreme, a low value of voltage in a very low resistance circuit can produce a very large amount of current. A 6-volt battery connected across a resistance of 0.01 ohm produces 600 amp of current:

$$I = \frac{E}{R} = \frac{6 \text{ volts}}{0.01 \text{ ohm}} = \textbf{600 amp}$$

Consider the following two examples also.

Example 1. A heater with a resistance of 8 ohms is connected across the 120-volt power line. How much is the current I?

Answer. $\qquad I = \dfrac{E}{R} = \dfrac{120 \text{ volts}}{8 \text{ ohms}} = \textbf{15 amp}$

Example 2. A small light bulb with a resistance of 2,400 ohms is connected across the same 120-volt power line. How much is the current I?

Answer. $\qquad I = \dfrac{E}{R} = \dfrac{120 \text{ volts}}{2{,}400 \text{ ohms}} = \textbf{0.05 amp}$

Although both cases have the same applied E of 120 volts, note that the current is much less in Example 2 because of the higher resistance.

2·3 $E = IR$

Referring to Fig. 2·3, the amount of voltage across R must be the same as E because the resistance is connected directly across the battery. The numerical value of this voltage E is equal to the product $I \times R$.[1] For instance, the IR voltage in Fig. 2·3 is 2 amp × 3 ohms, which equals the 6 volts of the applied voltage E. The formula is

$$E = IR \qquad\qquad (2·2)$$

With I in ampere units and R in ohms, their product E is in volts. Actually, this must be so because the I value equal to E/R is the amount that allows the IR product to be the same as the voltage across R.

Besides the numerical calculations possible with the IR formula, it is

---

[1] Appendix E, Mathematics, explains how to transpose equations.

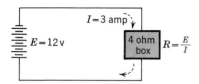

Fig. 2·4   *The resistance of any part of a circuit is its E/I ratio.*

useful to consider that the *IR* product means voltage. Whenever there is current through a resistance, it must have a potential difference across its two ends equal to the *IR* product. If there were no potential difference, no electrons could flow to produce the current.

2·4   R = E/I

As the third and final version of Ohm's law, the three factors *E*, *I*, and *R* are related by the formula

$$R = \frac{E}{I} \tag{2·3}$$

In Fig. 2·3, *R* is 3 ohms because 6 volts applied across the resistance produces 2 amp through it. Whenever *E* and *I* are known, the resistance can be calculated as the voltage across *R* divided by the current through it.

Physically, a resistance can be considered as some material with elements having an atomic structure that allows free electrons to drift through it with more or less force applied. Electrically, though, a more practical way of considering resistance is simply as an *E/I* ratio. Anything that allows 1 amp of current with 10 volts applied has a resistance of 10 ohms. This *E/I* ratio of 10 ohms is its characteristic. If the voltage is doubled to 20 volts, the current will also double to 2 amp, providing the same *E/I* ratio of a 10-ohm resistance.

Furthermore, we do not need to know the physical construction of a resistance to analyze its effect in a circuit, so long as we know its *E/I* ratio. This idea is illustrated in Fig. 2·4. Here, a box with some unknown material in it is connected into a circuit where we can measure the 12 volts applied across the box and the 3 amp of current through it. The resistance is 12 volts/3 amp, or 4 ohms. There may be liquid, gas, metal, powder, or any other material in the box, but electrically it is just a 4-ohm resistance because its *E/I* ratio is 4 ohms.

The *E/I* ratio as a definition of *R* is useful for the case of a resistance that is not constant. In general, the ohms of opposition for liquids, gases, heater wire, and semiconductor materials depend on the operating conditions, especially with wide variations in temperature. Still, for any one combination of applied voltage and current, the resistance is equal to the *E/I* ratio. When we consider wire conductors and resistor components, however, the resistance can generally be considered constant for typical values of voltage and current.

2·5   The inverse relation between I and R

The formula $I = E/R$ means that the current I decreases when the resistance increases, with the applied voltage E constant. This inverse relation is illustrated in Fig. 2·5. The circuit in a has the constant E of 6 volts applied. R_1 is a variable resistor that can be set to any value between 1 and 6 ohms. The resulting values of current are in the table. For the case in the top row, R_L is 1 ohm. Then $I = E/R$ or $^6\!/_1$, which equals 6 amp. For the case of R_L equal to 2 ohms, I is $^6\!/_2$ or 3 amp. All the values of I in the table are calculated the same way.

When I is plotted against R, the decreasing curve in Fig. 2·5b results. I starts at its highest value of 6 amp for 1-ohm R. Then I decreases for more R in the circuit. The relation is not linear. Note that the I values drop sharply at first and then decrease more gradually. These values result because the variable R is in the denominator of the fraction E/R. Actually, the graph is a plot of the values for $I = 6/R$, as E is constant at 6 volts. This type of curve is called a *hyperbola*, corresponding to the reciprocal relation $y = 1/x$ when the numerator is constant.

2·6   Definition of the Practical Units

The International Electrical Congress in 1881 set up a commission to standardize electrical units in more practical terms than the absolute basis of a charge of electrons so that the units of one volt, one ampere, and one ohm could be duplicated more easily in standardizing electrical measuring instruments such as voltmeters and ammeters. We can consider the ampere first. In absolute units, the intensity of electron flow that is the current equals one ampere when the rate of flow of the moving charge is one coulomb, or 6.25×10^{18} electrons passing any one point each second. It was determined experimentally that the amount of direct current through a nitrate of silver solution, made to standard specifications, also is 1 amp when silver is deposited at the rate of 0.001118 gram per sec. One volt is then defined practically as the potential difference that produces this one ampere of current through a resistance of one ohm.

Fig. 2·5   The current I is inversely proportional to R. (a) Circuit with variable R but constant E. (b) Table and graph showing how I decreases as R increases.

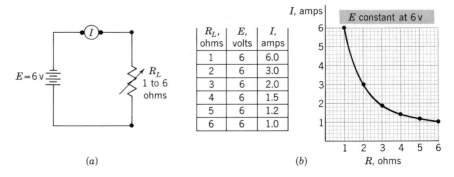

R_L, ohms	E, volts	I, amps
1	6	6.0
2	6	3.0
3	6	2.0
4	6	1.5
5	6	1.2
6	6	1.0

(a)

(b)

Table 2·1   Conversion factors

Prefix	Symbol	Relation to basic unit	Examples
Mega	M	1,000,000 or 1×10^6	5 megohms = 5,000,000 ohms = 5×10^6 ohms
Kilo	k or K	1,000 or 1×10^3	18 kilovolts = 18,000 volts = 18×10^3 volts
Milli	m	0.001 or 1×10^{-3}	48 ma = 48×10^{-3} amp = 0.048 amp
Micro	μ	0.000001 or 1×10^{-6}	15 μv = 15×10^{-6} volt = 0.000015 volt

The value of one ohm is standardized as the resistance of a column of mercury liquid, at the temperature of 0° centigrade, with its height and width specified. This actually is the value of resistance that allows one ampere of current with a potential difference of one volt. For this reason, the units used in applying Ohm's law must be volts for potential difference and ohms for resistance in order for the current to be in amperes.

The practical units can be defined more simply in terms of Ohm's law, therefore, as follows:

$$1 \text{ amp} = \frac{1 \text{ volt}}{1 \text{ ohm}} \qquad 1 \text{ volt} = 1 \text{ amp} \times 1 \text{ ohm} \qquad 1 \text{ ohm} = \frac{1 \text{ volt}}{1 \text{ amp}}$$

One ampere is the amount of current through a one-ohm resistance that has one volt of potential difference applied across it; one volt is the potential difference across a one-ohm resistance that has one ampere of current through it; one ohm is the amount of opposition in a resistance that has an E/I ratio of 1, allowing one ampere of current with one volt applied.

2·7   Multiple and submultiple units

The basic units—ampere, volt, and ohm—are practical values in most electrical power circuits, but in many electronics applications these units are either too small or too big. As examples, resistances can be a few million ohms, the output of a high-voltage supply in a television receiver is about 20,000 volts, and current through tubes and transistors is generally thousandths or millionths of an ampere. In such cases, it is helpful to use multiples and submultiples of the basic units. As shown in Table 2·1, these units are based on the decimal system of tens, hundreds, thousands, etc. The common conversions for E, I, and R are given here, but a complete listing of all the prefixes is in Appendix H. Note that capital M is used for 10^6 to distinguish from small m for 10^{-3}.

The examples of megohms (abbreviated M) and microvolts (μv) indicate how much more convenient the calculations can be when powers of 10 are used, as explained in Appendix E. Note the use of powers of 10 in the following examples.

Example 3. If 8-ma I flows through a 5-kilohm R, how much is the IR voltage drop?

Answer. $E = IR = 8 \times 10^{-3} \times 5 \times 10^3 = 8 \times 5 = $ **40 volts**

In general, ma multiplied by kilohms (abbreviated K) results in volts for the answer, as 10^{-3} and 10^3 cancel.

Example 4. How much current is produced by 60 volts across 12 K?

Answer. $I = \dfrac{E}{R} = \dfrac{60}{12 \times 10^3} = 5 \times 10^{-3} = $ **5 ma**

Note that volts across kilohms produces ma of current. Similarly, volts across megohms produces μa.

2·8   Power

The unit of electrical power is the *watt,* named after James Watt (1736–1819). One watt of power equals the work done in one second by one volt of potential difference in moving one coulomb of charge. Since one coulomb per second is an ampere, power in watts equals the product of amperes times volts:

$$\text{Power in watts} = \text{volts} \times \text{amperes}$$
$$P = E \times I \tag{2·4}$$

When a 6-volt battery produces 2 amp in a circuit, for example, the battery is generating 12 watts of power. Note the following additional examples:

Example 5. A toaster takes 10 amp from the 120-volt power line. How much power is used?

Answer. $P = E \times I = 120 \text{ volts} \times 10 \text{ amp}$
$P = $ **1,200 watts**

Example 6. How much current flows in the filament of a 300-watt bulb connected to the 120-volt power line?
Answer. $P = E \times I$ or $I = P/E$.

Then, $I = \dfrac{300 \text{ watts}}{120 \text{ volts}} = $ **2.5 amp**

Example 7. How much current flows in a 60-watt bulb connected to the 120-volt power line?

Answer. $P = E \times I$ or $I = P/E$.

$$\text{Then } I = \frac{60 \text{ watts}}{120 \text{ volts}} = \textbf{0.5 amp}$$

Note that the lower-wattage bulb uses less current.

Work and power. Work and energy are essentially the same with identical units. Power is different, however, because it is the time rate of doing work. For instance, if you move 100 lb a distance of 10 ft, the work is 100 lb $\times$ 10 ft or 1,000 ft-lb regardless of how fast or how slowly the work is done. Note that the unit of work is foot-pounds, without any reference to time. However, power equals the work divided by the time it takes to do the work. If it takes 1 sec, the power in this example is 1,000 ft-lb per sec; if the work takes 2 sec, the power is 1,000 ft-lb in 2 sec, or 500 ft-lb per sec.

Similarly, electrical power is the time rate at which charge is forced to move by voltage. This is why the power in watts is the product of volts and amperes. The voltage states the amount of work per unit of charge; the current value includes the time rate at which the charge is moved.

A further example of how electrical power corresponds to mechanical power is the fact that

$$746 \text{ watts} = 1 \text{ horsepower} = 550 \text{ ft-lb/sec}$$

This relation can be remembered more easily as 1 hp equals approximately ¾ kilowatt (kw). One kw = 1,000 watts.

Practical units of power and work. Starting with the watt, we can develop several other important units. The fundamental principle to remember is that power is the time rate of doing work, while work is power used during a period of time. The formulas are

$$P = \frac{W}{T} \tag{2·5}$$

and
$$W = P \times T \tag{2·6}$$

With the watt unit for power, one watt used during one second equals the work of one joule. Or one watt is one joule per second. The "per" means "divided by." Therefore, 1 watt = 1 joule/sec.

The joule is a basic practical unit of work or energy. In mechanics, one joule is the work done when a force of one newton[2] acts through the distance of one meter. Electrically, the joule is one watt-second (watt-sec). In more specific units, one joule is the work done by one volt in moving one coulomb of charge; one watt of power results from one volt producing one ampere of current.

[2] See Appendix D on Physics Units.

A unit of work that can be used with individual electrons is the electron-volt (ev), which equals the amount of work required to move an electron between two points having a potential difference of one volt. Since 6.25×10^{18} electrons equal 1 coul and a joule is a volt-coulomb, there are 6.25×10^{18} ev in one joule. Note that the electron-volt or the joule unit of work is the product of charge times voltage, but the watt unit of power is the product of voltage times current. The time division to convert work to power corresponds to the time division that converts charge to current.

Example 8. How much power in watts corresponds to 800 joules used in 2 sec?

Answer.
$$P = \frac{W}{T} = \frac{800 \text{ joules}}{2 \text{ sec}} = \textbf{400 watts}$$

Example 9. How much energy is required for a 300-watt bulb that is on for 1 min (60 sec)?

Answer.
$$W = P \times T = 300 \text{ watts} \times 60 \text{ sec}$$
$$W = 18{,}000 \text{ watt} \times \text{sec} = \textbf{18,000 joules}$$

Example 10. How much energy is used in moving 12.5×10^{18} electrons between two points with a potential difference of 100 volts?
Answer. Since 12.5×10^{18} electrons equals 2 coul,

$$W = 2 \text{ coul} \times 100 \text{ volts}$$
$$W = \textbf{200 joules}$$

Kilowatthours. This is a unit commonly used for large amounts of electrical work or energy. The amount is calculated simply as the product of the power in kilowatts multiplied by the time during which the power is used, in hours. As an example, if a light bulb uses 300 watts or 0.3 kw for 4 hr, the amount of energy is 0.3×4, which equals 1.2 kwhr. The cost of electricity is about 4 cents per kwhr. It may be of interest to note that 1 kwhr equals 3.6×10^6 joules, both being units of energy.

2·9   *Power dissipation in resistance*

When current flows in a resistance, heat is produced because friction between the moving free electrons and the atoms obstructs the path of electron flow. The heat is evidence that power is used in producing current. This is how a fuse opens, as heat resulting from excessive current melts the metal link in the fuse.

The power is generated by the source of applied voltage and consumed in the resistance in the form of heat. As much power as the resistance dissipates in heat must be supplied by the voltage source; otherwise, it cannot maintain the potential difference required to produce the current. The correspondence between electrical power and heat is indicated by the fact that 1 watt used during the time of 1 sec is equivalent to 0.24 calorie of heat energy. The electrical energy converted to heat is considered to be dissipated or used up because the calories of heat cannot be returned to the circuit as electrical energy.

Since power is dissipated in the resistance of a circuit, it is convenient to express the power in terms of the resistance R. The $E \times I$ formula can be rearranged as follows:

Substituting IR for E,

$$P = E \times I = IR \times I$$
$$P = I^2R \tag{2·7}$$

Substituting E/R for I,

$$P = E \times I = E \times \frac{E}{R}$$
$$= \frac{E^2}{R} \tag{2·8}$$

In all the formulas, E is the voltage across R, in ohms, producing the current I in amperes.

Any one of the three formulas can be used to calculate the power dissipated in a resistance. The one to be used is just a matter of convenience, depending on which factors are known. In Fig. 2·6, for example, the power dissipated with 2 amp through the resistance and 6 volts across it is $2 \times 6 = 12$ watts. Or, calculating in terms of just the current and resistance, the power is the product of 2 squared, or 4, times 3, which equals 12 watts. Using the voltage and resistance, the power can be calculated as 6 squared, or 36, divided by 3, which also equals 12 watts.

No matter which formula is used, 12 watts of power is dissipated, in the form of heat. This amount of power must be generated continuously by the battery in order to maintain the potential difference of 6 volts that produces the 2-amp current against the opposition of 3 ohms.

In some applications the electrical power dissipation is desirable because the component must produce heat in order to do its job. For instance, a 600-watt toaster must dissipate this amount of power to produce the necessary amount of heat. Similarly, a 300-watt light bulb must dissipate this power to make the filament white-hot so that it will have the incandescent glow that furnishes the light. In other applications, however, the heat may be just an undesirable by-product of the need for providing current through the resistance in a circuit. In any case, though, whenever there is current in a resistance, it dissipates power equal to I^2R.

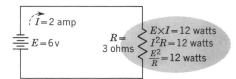

Fig. 2·6 Calculating the electrical power in a circuit.

Example 11. Calculate the power in a circuit where the source of 100 volts produces 2 amp in a 50-ohm R.

Answer.
$$P = I^2R = 4 \times 50$$
$$P = \textbf{200 watts}$$

This means the source generates 200 watts of power while the resistance dissipates 200 watts in the form of heat.

Example 12. Calculate the power in a circuit where the same source of 100 volts produces 4 amp in a 25-ohm R.

Answer.
$$P = I^2R = 16 \times 25$$
$$P = \textbf{400 watts}$$

Note the higher power because of more I, even though R is less. For the same applied voltage, the power equal to EI is doubled because the 4-amp I is twice the 2-amp I value in Example 11.

Components that utilize the power dissipated in their resistance, such as light bulbs and toasters, are generally rated in terms of power. The power rating is at normal applied voltage, which is usually the 120 volts of the power line. For instance, a 600-watt 120-volt toaster has this rating because it dissipates 600 watts in the resistance of the heating element when connected across 120 volts.

In order to calculate I or R for components rated in terms of power at a specified voltage, it may be convenient to use the power formulas in the following transposed forms: $I = P/E$, or $R = E^2/P$, or $I = \sqrt{P/R}$.

Example 13. How much current is needed for a 600-watt 120-volt toaster?

Answer.
$$I = \frac{P}{E} = \frac{600}{120} = \textbf{5 amp}$$

Example 14. How much is the resistance of a 600-watt 120-volt toaster?

Answer.
$$R = \frac{E^2}{P} = \frac{14,400}{600} = \textbf{24 ohms}$$

Example 15. How much current is needed for a 24-ohm R that dissipates 600 watts?

Answer.
$$I = \sqrt{\frac{P}{R}} = \sqrt{\frac{600}{24}} = \sqrt{25} = \textbf{5 amp}$$

Note that all these formulas are just different forms of Ohm's law. The following example with a 300-watt bulb illustrates this idea. Connected across the 120-volt line, the 300-watt filament requires 2.5 amp, equal to P/E or $^{300}/_{120}$. The proof is that the EI product then is 120×2.5, which is

300 watts. Therefore, the resistance of the filament, equal to E/I, is $^{120}\!/_{2.5}$, or 48 ohms. If we use the formula $R = E^2/P$, or $14,400/300$, the answer is the same 48 ohms. In any case, when this bulb is connected across the 120-volt line so that it can dissipate its rated power, it draws 2.5 amp from the power line and the resistance of its white-hot filament is 48 ohms.

2·10   *Electric shock*

While you are working on electric circuits, there is often the possibility of receiving an electric shock by touching the "live" conductors when the power is on. The shock is a sudden involuntary contraction of the muscles, with a feeling of pain, caused by current through the body. If severe enough, the shock can be fatal. Safety first, therefore, should always be the rule.

The greatest shock hazard is from high-voltage circuits that can supply appreciable amounts of power. The resistance of the human body is also an important factor. If you hold a conducting wire in each hand, the resistance of the body across the conductors is about 10,000 to 50,000 ohms. Holding the conductors tighter lowers the resistance. If you hold only one conductor, your resistance is much higher. It follows that the higher the body resistance, the smaller is the current that can flow through you.

A safety rule, therefore, is to work with only one hand if the power is on. Also, keep yourself insulated from earth ground when working on power-line circuits, since one side of the line is usually connected to earth. In addition, the metal chassis of radio and television receivers is often connected to the power-line ground. The final and best safety rule is to work on the circuits with the power disconnected if at all possible.

Note that it is current through the body, not through the circuit, which causes the electric shock. This is why high-voltage circuits are most important, since sufficient potential difference can produce a dangerous amount of current through the relatively high resistance of the body. For instance, 300 volts across a body resistance of 30,000 ohms produces 0.01 amp, which can be fatal. As little as 1 ma through the body can cause a definite electric shock.

In addition to high voltage, the other important consideration in how dangerous the shock can be is the amount of power the source can supply. The current of 0.01 amp through 30,000 ohms means the body resistance dissipates 3 watts. If the source cannot supply 3 watts, its output voltage drops with the excessive current load. Then the current is reduced to the amount corresponding to how much power the source can produce.

In summary, then, the greatest danger is from a source having output more than about 30 volts with enough power to maintain the load current through the body when it is connected across the applied voltage. In general, components that can supply high power are physically big because of the need for dissipating heat.

SUMMARY

1. The three forms of Ohm's law are $I = E/R$, $E = IR$, and $R = E/I$. The basic practical units are volts for E, amperes for I, and ohms for R.
2. One ampere is the amount of current produced by one volt of potential difference across one ohm of resistance. This current of 1 amp is the same as 1 coul per sec.
3. With constant R, the amount of current I increases in direct proportion as the voltage E increases. This linear relation between E and I is shown by the graph in Fig. 2·2.
4. With constant E, the current I decreases as R increases. This inverse relation between R and I is shown by the graph in Fig. 2·5.
5. Power is the time rate of doing work or using energy. The unit is the watt. One watt equals one volt × one ampere. Also, watts = joules/sec.
6. The unit of work or energy is the joule. One joule equals 1 watt × 1 sec. One joule also equals 1 volt × 1 coul, as 1 coul is 1 amp × 1 sec.
7. The most common multiples and submultiples of the practical units are listed in Table 2·1.
8. Voltage applied across your body can produce a dangerous electric shock. Whenever possible, shut off the power when working a circuit. If the power must be on, use only one hand. Do not let the other hand rest on a conductor.

SELF-EXAMINATION (*Answers at back of book.*)

Here's a chance to see how well you have learned the material in this chapter. These exercises are for your self-testing only.

Fill in the blank space in the following statements.

1. With 10 volts E across 5 ohm R, the current I is _____ amp.
2. When 10 volts E produces 2.5 amp, R is _____ ohms.
3. With 8 amp I through a 2-ohm R, the IR voltage is _____ volts.
4. The resistance of 500,000 ohms is _____ megohms.
5. With 10 volts E across 5,000 R, the current I is _____ ma.
6. The power of 50 watts = 2 amp × _____ volts.
7. The energy of 50 joules = 2 coul × _____ volts.
8. The current drawn from the 120-volt power line by a 1,200-watt toaster = _____ amp.
9. The current of 400 μa = _____ ma.
10. With 12 volts E across 2 ohms R, its power dissipation = _____ watts.
11. A circuit has 4-amp I. If E is doubled and R is the same, I = _____ amp.
12. A circuit has 4-amp I. If R is doubled and E is the same, I = _____ amp.
13. A television receiver using 240 watts from the 120-volt power line draws current I = _____ amp.
14. The rated current for a 500-watt 120-volt bulb = _____ amp.
15. The resistance of the bulb in question 14 is _____ ohms.
16. The energy of 12.5×10^{18} ev = _____ joules.
17. In the cathode circuit of a vacuum-tube amplifier, the cathode resistor R_k has 3 volts potential difference with 6 ma through it. Then R_k = _____ ohms.
18. In a vacuum-tube amplifier circuit, the plate load resistor R_L of 50 K has 150 volts across it. Through R_L, then, the current = _____ ma.
19. In a transistor circuit, a 1-K resistor R_1 has 200 μa through it. Across R_1, then its voltage = _____ volts.
20. In a transistor circuit a 50-K resistor R_2 has 6 volts across it. Through R_2, then, its current = _____ ma.

ESSAY QUESTIONS

1. State the three forms of Ohm's law relating E, I, and R.
2. (*a*) Why does higher applied voltage with the same resistance result in more current? Draw a graph showing the direct proportion between E and I. (*b*) Why does more resistance with

the same applied voltage result in less current? Draw a graph showing the inverse relation between R and I.

3. Calculate the resistance of a 300-watt bulb connected across the 120-volt power line, using two different methods to arrive at the same answer.
4. State which unit in each of the following pairs is larger: (*a*) volt or kilovolt; (*b*) ampere or milliampere; (*c*) ohm or megohm; (*d*) volt or microvolt; (*e*) mho or micromho; (*f*) electron-volt or joule; (*g*) watt or kilowatt; (*h*) kilowatthour or joule; (*i*) volt or millivolt; (*j*) megohm or kilohm.
5. State two safety precautions to follow when working on electric circuits.
6. Referring back to the resistor shown in Fig. 1·9, suppose that it is not marked. How could you determine its resistance by Ohm's law? Show your calculations that result in the E/I ratio of 600 ohms. However, do not exceed the power rating of 10 watts.
7. What is the difference between work and power? Give two units for each.
8. Referring to the two resistors in series with each other in Fig. 3·1, if the current through R_1 is 2 amp, how much would you guess is the current through R_2?
9. Prove that 1 kwhr is equal to 3.6×10^6 joules.
10. (*a*) How many electron-volts equal 1 coul-volt? (*b*) How many joules equal 1 coul-volt? (*c*) How many joules equal 1 watt-sec?
11. A circuit has a constant R of 5,000 ohms, while E is varied from 0 to 50 volts in 10-volt steps. Make a table listing the values of I for each value of E. Then draw a graph plotting these values of ma vs. volts.
12. A circuit has a constant applied E of 100 volts, while R is varied from 100 to 200 ohms, 1,000 ohms, 2,000 ohms, 10,000 ohms, and 20,000 ohms. Make a table listing the values of I for each value of R. Then draw a graph plotting these values of I vs. R.

PROBLEMS (*Answers to selected problems at back of book.*)

1. A 90-volt source is connected across a 30-K resistance. (*a*) Draw the schematic diagram. (*b*) How much current flows through the resistance? (*c*) How much current flows through the voltage source? (*d*) If the resistance is tripled, how much is the current in the circuit?
2. A 6-volt battery is connected across a 2-ohm resistance. (*a*) Draw the schematic diagram. (*b*) Calculate the power dissipated in the resistance. (*c*) How much power is supplied by the battery? (*d*) If the resistance is doubled, how much is the power?
3. Convert the following units using powers of 10 where necessary: (*a*) 12 ma to amp; (*b*) 5,000 volts to kv; (*c*) ½ M to ohms; (*d*) 100,000 ohms to M; (*e*) ½ amp to ma; (*f*) 9,000 μmhos to mho; (*g*) 1,000 μa to ma; (*h*) 5 K to ohms; (*i*) 8 nanosec to sec.
4. A vacuum-tube heater has 0.3 amp of current with 6.3 volts applied. (*a*) Draw the schematic diagram, showing the heater as a resistance. (*b*) How much is the resistance of the heater?
5. The current of 2 amp flows through a 6-ohm resistance connected across a battery. (*a*) How much is the applied voltage of the battery? (*b*) How much power is dissipated in the resistance? (*c*) How much power is supplied by the battery?
6. A source of applied voltage produces 1 ma through a 10-M resistance. How much is the applied voltage?
7. (*a*) How much resistance allows 30-amp current with 6 volts applied? (*b*) How much resistance allows 1-ma current with 10 kv applied? Why is it possible to have less current in (*b*) with the higher applied voltage?
8. Calculate the current I, in ampere units, for the following examples: (*a*) 45 volts E applied across 68-K R; (*b*) 250 volts E across 1.2-M R; (*c*) 1,200 watts dissipated in 600 ohms.
9. Calculate the voltage E for the following examples: (*a*) 68-μa I through 47-K R; (*b*) 2.3-ma I through 22-M R; (*c*) 237 amp through 0.012-ohm R.
10. Calculate the resistance R, in ohms, for the following examples: (*a*) 134-ma I produced by 220 volts; (*b*) 800 watts dissipated with 120 volts applied; (*c*) a conductance of 9,000 μmhos.

Chapter **3** *Series circuits*

When the components in a circuit are connected in successive order with an end of each joined to an end of the next, as shown in Fig. 3·1, they form a series circuit. The result, then, is only one path for electron flow. Therefore, the current is the same in all parts of a series circuit. This and other important characteristics are analyzed in the following sections:

3·1 Why the current is the same in all parts of a series circuit
3·2 Total series resistance equals the sum of individual resistances
3·3 Series *IR* voltage drops
3·4 The sum of series *IR* voltage drops equals the applied voltage
3·5 *IR* voltage drops are proportional to the series resistances
3·6 Polarity of *IR* voltage drops
3·7 Total power in a series circuit
3·8 Analyzing a series circuit
3·9 Effect of an open in a series circuit

3·1 Why the current is the same in all parts of a series circuit

An electric current is a movement of charges between two points, produced by the potential difference of the applied voltage. In Fig. 3·2, the battery supplies the potential difference that forces electrons to drift from the negative terminal at A, toward B, through the connecting wires and resistances R_1, R_2, and R_3, back to the positive battery terminal at J.

At the negative battery terminal its negative charge repels electrons. Therefore, free electrons in the atoms of the wire at this terminal are repelled from A toward B. Similarly, free electrons at point B can then repel adjacent electrons, producing an electron drift toward C in the direction away from the negative battery terminal. At the same time, the positive charge of the positive battery terminal attracts free electrons, causing electrons to drift toward *I* and *J*. As a result, the free electrons in the resistances R_1, R_2, and R_3 are forced to drift in the direction away from the negative terminal of the battery toward the positive terminal.

The positive terminal of the battery attracts electrons just as much as the negative side of the battery repels electrons. Therefore, the motion of free electrons in the circuit starts at the same time at the same speed in all parts of the circuit.

The electrons returning to the positive battery terminal are not the same electrons as those leaving the negative terminal but are free electrons forced to move from the wire to the positive terminal because of the potential difference of the battery. The free electrons moving away from one point are continuously replaced by free electrons flowing from an adjacent point in the series circuit. All electrons have the same speed as those leaving the battery. In all parts of the circuit, therefore, the electron drift is the same, with an equal number of electrons moving at one time with the

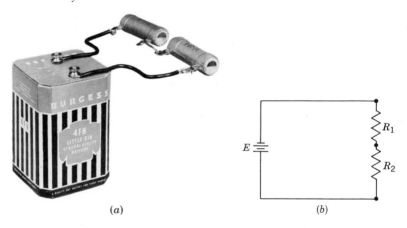

Fig. 3·1 A series circuit. (a) Photograph of circuit wiring. (b) Schematic diagram. Components R_1 and R_2 are in series with each other and the battery E.

(a)   (b)

Fig. 3·2 (a) Electron drift is the same at all points in series circuit. (b) Current is the same at all points in series circuit.

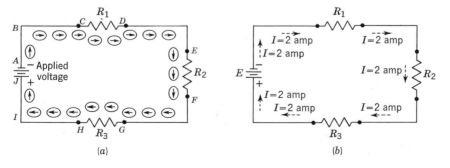

(a)   (b)

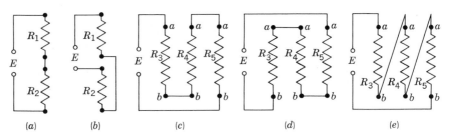

Fig. 3·3   *Series connections. R_1 and R_2 are in series in both a and b.
R_3, R_4, and R_5 are in series in c, d, and e.*

same speed. That is why the current is the same in all parts of the series circuit.

In Fig. 3·2b, when the current is 2 amp, for example, this is the value of the current through R_1, R_2, R_3, and the battery. Not only is the amount of current the same throughout, but in all parts of a series circuit the current cannot differ in any way because there is just one current path for the entire circuit.

The order in which components are connected in series does not affect the current. In Fig. 3·3a, resistances R_1 and R_2 are connected in reverse order compared with Fig. 3·3b, but in both cases they are in series and the current through each is the same because there is only one path for the electron flow. Similarly, R_3, R_4, and R_5 are in series and have the same current for the connections shown in Fig. 3·3c, d, and e. Furthermore, the resistances need not be equal. The question of whether a component is first, second, or last in a series circuit has no meaning in terms of current, since the current is the same amount at the same time in all the components of a series circuit.

3·2   Total series resistance equals the sum of individual resistances

When a series circuit is connected across a voltage source, as shown in Fig. 3·3, the free electrons forming the current must drift through all the series resistances. This path is the only way the electrons can return to the battery. With two or more resistances in the same current path, therefore, the total resistance across the voltage source is the opposition of all the resistances. Specifically, the total resistance of a series string is equal to the sum of the individual resistances. This rule is illustrated in Fig. 3·4. In b, 2 ohms is added in series with the 3 ohms of a, producing the total resistance of 5 ohms. The total opposition of R_1 and R_2 limiting the amount of current is the same as though a 5-ohm resistance were used, as shown in the equivalent circuit in c.

A combination of series resistances is often called a *string*. The string resistance equals the sum of the individual resistances. For instance, R_1 and R_2 in Fig. 3·4 form a series string having the total resistance of 5 ohms.

By Ohm's law, the amount of current between two points in a circuit

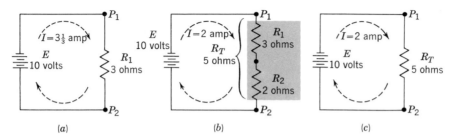

Fig. 3·4 Series resistances add. (a) R_1 alone is 3 ohms. (b) R_1 and R_2 in series total 5 ohms. (c) Total is equivalent to one resistance of 5 ohms between P_1 and P_2.

equals the potential difference divided by the resistance between these points. As the entire series string is connected across the voltage source, the current equals the voltage applied across the entire string divided by the total series resistance of the string. Between points P_1 and P_2 in Fig. 3·4, for example, 10 volts is applied across 5 ohms in *b* and *c* to produce 2 amp. This current flows through R_1 and R_2.

In summary, the total resistance of a series string equals the sum of the individual resistances. The formula is

$$R_T = R_1 + R_2 + R_3 + \cdots + \text{etc.} \qquad (3 \cdot 1)$$

where R_T is the total resistance and R_1, R_2, and R_3 are individual series resistances. This formula applies to any number of resistances, whether equal or not, as long as they are in the same series string.

By Ohm's law, the current in the series string is

$$I = \frac{E_T}{R_T} \qquad (3 \cdot 2)$$

where R_T is the sum of all the resistances, E_T is the voltage applied across the total resistance, and I is the current in all parts of the string.

Example 1. Two resistances R_1 and R_2 of 5 ohms each and R_3 of 10 ohms are in series. How much is R_T?

Answer. $R_T = R_1 + R_2 + R_3 = 5 + 5 + 10$
                     $R_T = \textbf{20 ohms}$

Example 2. With 40 volts E applied across the series string of Example 1, how much is the current in R_3?

Answer. $I = \dfrac{E_T}{R_T} = \dfrac{40 \text{ volts}}{20 \text{ ohms}}$
                 $I = \textbf{2 amp}$

This 2-amp current is the same in R_3, R_2, R_1, or any part of the series circuit.

3·3   *Series IR voltage drops*

With current through a resistance, there is a voltage across it equal to $I \times R$, by Ohm's law. This rule is illustrated in Fig. 3·5. Here the current equals 1 amp through the 4-ohm R_1 and 6-ohm R_2 in series, as the total R_T of 10 ohms is across the applied E of 10 volts. The result is an IR voltage of 4 volts across R_1 and 6 volts across R_2. The IR voltage across each resistance is called an *IR drop,* or a *voltage drop,* because it reduces the potential difference available for the remaining resistance in the series circuit. Note that the symbols V_1 and V_2 are used for the voltage drops across each resistor to distinguish them from the applied voltage source E.

In Fig. 3·5, note that 10 volts is applied across the total series resistance of R_1 and R_2, but because of the IR voltage drop of 4 volts across R_1, the potential difference across R_2 is 6 volts. The potential drops from 10 volts at point *a*, with respect to the common reference point at *c*, down to 6 volts at point *b*. This potential results from the IR drop of 4 volts across R_1. Similarly, there is an IR voltage drop of 6 volts across R_2. The potential drops from 6 volts at point *b* with respect to point *c*, down to 0 volts at point *c* with respect to itself. The potential difference between any two points on the return line to the battery must be zero because the wire has practically zero resistance and therefore no IR drop.

It should be noted that voltage must be applied by a source of potential difference such as the battery in order to produce current and have an IR voltage drop across resistance. With no current through a resistor, it has resistance only, but there is no potential difference across the two ends. The IR drop of 4 volts across R_1 in Fig. 3·5 represents that part of

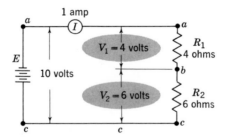

Fig. 3·5   *IR voltage drops in a series circuit.*

Fig. 3·6   *IR drops across resistances in series heater string of typical a-c/d-c radio.*

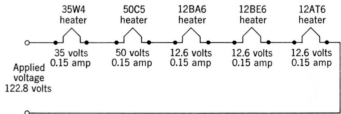

the applied voltage used for producing the current of 1 amp through the 4-ohm resistance. Across R_2 the IR drop is 6 volts because more potential difference is necessary to produce the same current in the higher resistance.

3·4 The sum of series IR voltage drops equals the applied voltage

The whole applied voltage is equal to the sum of its parts. For example, in Fig. 3·5, the individual voltage drops of 4 volts and 6 volts total the same 10 volts produced by the battery. This relation for series circuits can be stated

$$E_T = V_1 + V_2 + V_3 + \cdots + \text{etc.} \qquad (3·3)$$

where E_T is the applied voltage equal to the total of the individual IR drops.

Example 3. A voltage source produces an IR drop of 40 volts across a 20-ohm R_1, 60 volts across a 30-ohm R_2, and 180 volts across a 90-ohm R_3, all in series. How much is the applied voltage?

Answer. $\qquad E_T = 40 + 60 + 180 = \textbf{280 volts}$

Note that the IR drop across each R results from the same current of 2 amp, produced by 280 volts across the total R_T of 140 ohms.

Example 4. An applied voltage E_T of 120 volts produces IR drops across two series resistors R_1 and R_2. If the drop across R_1 is 40 volts, how much is the voltage across R_2?

Answer. 80 volts. Since V_1 and V_2 must total 120 volts, and one is 40 volts, the other must be the difference between 120 volts and 40 volts. Or $V_2 = E - V_1$, which equals 120–40, or **80 volts.**

A very common practical application of series circuits is shown in Fig. 3·6. This is a typical circuit for the series heaters in a five-tube a-c/d-c table model radio. The first group of digits in the tube-type number is the required heater voltage for the rated amount of heater current. Each heater needs less than the 120 volts provided by the power line, but all require the same current for normal operation. Therefore, the heaters are connected in a series string across the available voltage source so that the total of the IR voltage drops equals the power-line voltage, approximately. Each heater has its proportionate part equal to the required heater voltage, as determined by the heater resistance, while the series circuit results in the same current for all the heaters. The reason there can be different voltages in the series string with the same current is that the heaters with higher resistance have more IR voltage drop.

This circuit illustrates how series circuits are used. Components that require the same current but less voltage than the source are connected in series. Then the applied voltage E must be high enough to produce the required current I for the total resistance R_T.

3·5   IR voltage drops are proportional to the series resistances

The current is the same in all the resistances in a series circuit. Also the voltage drops equal the product of I times R. Therefore, the IR voltages are proportional to the value of the series resistances. A higher resistance has a greater IR voltage than a smaller resistance in the same series circuit; equal resistances have the same amount of IR drop.

The series string can be considered as a *voltage divider*. Each resistance provides an IR drop V equal to its proportional part of the applied voltage. Stated as a formula,

$$V = \frac{R}{R_T} \times E_T \tag{3·4}$$

Example 5. Three 50-K resistors R_1, R_2, and R_3 are in series across an applied voltage of 180 volts. How much is the IR voltage drop across each resistor?

Answer. 60 volts. Since R_1, R_2, and R_3 are equal, each has one-third the total resistance of the circuit and one-third the total applied voltage. Using the formula,

$$V = \frac{R}{R_T} \times E_T = \frac{50 \text{ K}}{150 \text{ K}} \times 180$$

$$V = \frac{1}{3} \times 180 = \textbf{60 volts}$$

The circuit in Fig. 3·7 illustrates another example of a proportional voltage divider. Let the problem be to find the voltage across R_3. We can either calculate this voltage as IR_3 or determine its proportional part of E, and arrive at the same answer both ways. In the proportional method, V_3 is $^{20}/_{100}$ of the applied voltage, as R_3 is 20 K and R_T is 100 K. Therefore, V_3 is $^{20}/_{100} \times 200$, which is equal to 40 volts.

If we want to solve for the current, $I = E/R_T$ or $^{200}/_{100,000}$, which is equal to 2 ma or 0.002 amp for I. To calculate the IR drop V_3 across R_3, then, it equals 0.002×20 K, which is 40 volts. Similarly, V_2 is 60 volts and V_1 is 100 volts. Note that the largest series resistance has the largest voltage drop.

3·6   Polarity of IR voltage drops

When there is an IR voltage drop across a resistance, one end must be more positive or more negative than the other end; otherwise, without a potential difference, there could be no current through the resistance. The polarity of this potential difference can be associated with the direction of electron flow in a circuit from a negative to a more positive potential. In Fig. 3·8, the electrons move through R_1 from point c to d. Therefore the end of R_1 connected to point c has a more negative potential than point d. The polarity of the potential difference or voltage across R_1 is

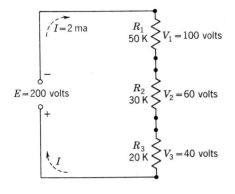

Fig. 3·7   Series string as a proportional voltage divider, where each V is R/R_T of E.

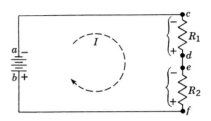

Fig. 3·8   Polarity of IR voltage drops corresponds to direction of electron flow from negative to positive potential.

such that point c is the negative side and point d the positive side. Similarly the voltage polarity across R_2 is negative at point e compared with the other end of the resistance connected to point f.

A more fundamental way to consider the polarity of the *IR* voltage drops in a circuit is the fact that between any two points the one nearer to the positive terminal of the voltage source is more positive; also, the point nearer to the negative terminal of the applied voltage is more negative. A point nearer to the terminal means there is less resistance in its path. Point c in Fig. 3·8 is nearer to the negative battery terminal than point d, since c has no resistance to a, while the path from d to a includes the resistance of R_1. Similarly, point f is nearer to the positive battery terminal than point e, which makes f more positive than e.

Notice that points d and e in Fig. 3·8 are marked with both plus and minus polarities. The plus polarity at d indicates it is more positive than c. This polarity, however, is shown just for the voltage across R_1. Point d cannot be more positive than points f and b. The positive terminal of the applied voltage must be the most positive point because the battery is generating the positive potential for the entire circuit. Similarly, points a and c must have the most negative potential in the entire string, since this point is the negative terminal of the applied voltage. Therefore, the minus polarity at point e means only that it is the more negative side of the voltage across R_2.

Consider the potential difference between e and d in Fig. 3·8: it is zero because there is no resistance between these two points. Without any resistance here, the current cannot produce the *IR* drop necessary for a difference in potential. Points e and d are the same electrically, therefore, since they have the same potential. This potential is positive with respect to the negative battery terminal, or less negative, because of the *IR* drop across R_1; this point is also negative compared with the positive battery terminal, or less positive, because of the IR drop across R_2.

3·7 Total power in a series circuit

The power used in producing current in each series resistor is used up in the form of heat. Therefore, the total power used is the sum of the individual values of power dissipated in each part of the circuit.

$$P_T = P_1 + P_2 + P_3 + \cdots + \text{etc.} \qquad (3 \cdot 5)$$

In Fig. 3·9, R_1 dissipates 40 watts, equal to 4×10 for I^2R, 20×2 for VI, or $^{400}\!/_{10}$ for V^2/R. Similarly, the power dissipated in R_2 equals 80 watts. The total power dissipated by R_1 and R_2, then, is $40 + 80$, which equals 120 watts. This power is generated by the source of applied voltage.

The total power can also be calculated as $I \times E$, since the applied voltage E is the total of the individual voltages. In this case, $P_T = 2 \times 60$ for $I \times E$ or 120 watts. Thus the total power here is 120 watts, calculated either way, as this is the amount of power produced by the battery. The voltage source produces the power, equal to the amount used by the load.

3·8 Analyzing a series circuit

Refer to Fig. 3·10. Suppose that the source E of 50 volts is known, with the 14-ohm R_1 and 6-ohm R_2. The problem is to find R_T, I, the individual voltage drops V_1 and V_2 across each resistor, and the power dissipated.

We must know the total resistance R_T to calculate I because the total applied voltage E is given. In this example, R_T is $14 + 6 = 20$ ohms. Now I can be calculated as E/R_T, or $^{50}\!/_{20}$, which equals 2.5 amp. This 2.5-amp I flows through R_1 and R_2.

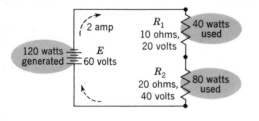

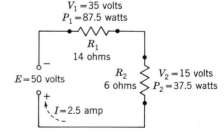

Fig. 3·9 *The sum of the individual values of power used in each resistance equals the total power produced by the source.*

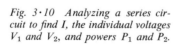

Fig. 3·10 *Analyzing a series circuit to find I, the individual voltages V_1 and V_2, and powers P_1 and P_2.*

The individual voltage drops are

$$V_1 = IR_1 = 2.5 \times 14 = 35 \text{ volts}$$
$$V_2 = IR_2 = 2.5 \times 6 = 15 \text{ volts}$$

Note that V_1 and V_2 total 50 volts, equal to the applied E.
To find the power dissipated in each resistor,

$$P_1 = V_1 \times I = 35 \times 2.5 = 87.5 \text{ watts}$$
$$P_2 = V_2 \times I = 15 \times 2.5 = 37.5 \text{ watts}$$

These two values of dissipated power total 125 watts. The power generated by the source equals $E \times I$ or 50×2.5, which is also 125 watts.

For other types of problems with series circuits it is useful to remember the following:

1. When you know the I for one component, use this for I in all the components, as the current is the same in all parts of a series circuit.
2. To calculate I, the total E can be divided by the total R_T, or an individual IR drop can be divided by its R. For instance, the current in Fig. 3·10 could be calculated as V_2/R_2 or $^{15}\!/_6$, which equals the same 2.5 amp for I. However, do not mix a total value for the entire circuit with an individual value for only part of the circuit.
3. When you know the individual voltage drops around the circuit, these can be added to equal the applied voltage E. This also means a known voltage drop can be subtracted from the total E to find the remaining voltage drop.

These principles are illustrated by the problem in Fig. 3·11. In this circuit R_1 and R_2 are known but not R_3. However, the current through R_3 is given as 3 ma.

With just this information, all values in this circuit can be calculated. The I of 3 ma is the same in all three series resistances. Therefore, $V_1 = 3 \text{ ma} \times 10 \text{ K}$, which is 30 volts; $V_2 = 3 \text{ ma} \times 30 \text{ K}$, which is 90 volts.

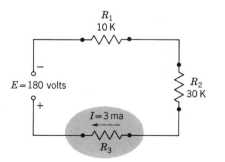

Fig. 3·11 *Find the resistance of R_3. See text for analysis of this series circuit.*

The sum of V_1 and V_2 is 120 volts. This plus V_3 must total 180 volts. Therefore, V_3 is $180 - 120$, or 60 volts.

With 60 volts for V_3, equal to IR_3, then R_3 must be $60/0.003$, equal to 20,000 ohms or 20 K. The total circuit resistance is 60 K, which results in the current of 3 ma with 180 volts applied.

The power dissipated in each resistance is 90 mw in R_1, 270 mw in R_2, and 180 mw in R_3. The total power is 540 mw.

3·9 *Effect of an open in a series circuit*

An open is a break in the current path. The resistance of the open is very high, as an insulator like air takes the place of a conducting part of the circuit. Because the current is the same in all parts of a series circuit, an open in any part of the circuit results in no current for the entire circuit. As illustrated in Fig. $3 \cdot 12$, the circuit is normal in *a*, but in *b* there is no current in R_1, R_2, or R_3, because of the open in the series path.

The open between P_1 and P_2, or at any other point in the circuit, has practically infinite resistance because its opposition to electron flow is so great compared with the resistance of R_1, R_2, and R_3. Therefore, the value of current is practically zero, even though the battery produces its normal applied voltage of 40 volts. To take an example, suppose that the open between P_1 and P_2 has a resistance of 40 billion ohms. The resistance of the entire circuit is essentially 40 billion ohms, since the resistance of R_1, R_2, and R_3 can then be neglected compared with the resistance of the open. By Ohm's law, the current that results from 40 volts applied across 40 billion ohms is one-billionth of an ampere, which is practically zero. This is the value of current in all parts of the series circuit. With practically no current, the IR voltage drop is practically zero across the 25 ohms of R_1, the 10 ohms of R_2, and the 5 ohms of R_3. In summary, then, with an open in any part of a series circuit the current is essentially zero in the entire circuit and there is practically no IR voltage drop across any of the series resistances, although the generator still maintains its output voltage.

Fig. $3 \cdot 12$ *Effect of an open in a series circuit. (a) Normal closed circuit. (b) Open in any part of series circuit results in no current in the entire circuit.*

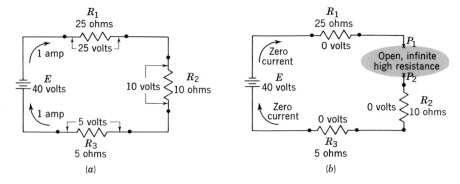

It is useful to note that the entire applied voltage is present across the open circuit. Between P_1 and P_2 in Fig. 3·12, there is 40 volts. The reason is that essentially all of the resistance of the series circuit is between P_1 and P_2. Therefore, the resistance of the open circuit develops all of the IR voltage drop. The extremely small current of one-billionth of an ampere is not enough to develop any appreciable IR drop across R_1, R_2, and R_3. However, across the open the resistance is 40 billion ohms. Therefore, the IR voltage across the open here is one-billionth of an ampere multiplied by 40 billion ohms, which equals 40 volts.

As another example, refer to the series heaters in Fig. 3·6. If one opens, the entire string is open and none of the tubes can light. This idea also applies to television receivers if the tubes are in a series string. With the heater string open, the radio or television receiver does not operate at all. You can tell if series heaters are used by the tube numbers. If 6-volt tubes are not used, generally this indicates a series-heater string. The first numbers in the tube type generally give the heater voltage. Some examples of tubes for series heaters are 3CB6, 10DE7, 17DQ6, and 35Z5, in addition to those in Fig. 3·6.

SUMMARY

1. There is only one current I in a series circuit. $I = E/R_T$, where E is the voltage applied across the total series resistance R_T. This I is the same in all the series components.
2. The total resistance R_T of a series string is the sum of the individual resistances.
3. The applied voltage E equals the sum of the series IR voltage drops.
4. The sum of the individual values of power used in the individual resistances equals the total power supplied by the source.
5. An open results in no current in all parts of the series circuit.

SELF-EXAMINATION (*Answers at back of book.*)

Here's a chance to find out how well you have learned the material in this chapter. These exercises are for your self-testing only.

1. When two resistances are connected in series (*a*) they must both have the same resistance value; (*b*) the voltage across each must be the same; (*c*) they must have different resistance values; (*d*) there is only one path for current through both resistances.
2. In Fig. 3·3c, if the current through R_5 is 1 amp, then the current through R_3 must be (*a*) ⅓ amp; (*b*) ½ amp; (*c*) 1 amp; (*d*) 3 amp.
3. With a 10-K resistance in series with a 2-K resistance, the total R_T equals (*a*) 2 K; (*b*) 8 K; (*c*) 10 K; (*d*) 12 K.
4. With two equal resistances in series across a 90-volt battery, the voltage across each resistance equals (*a*) 30 volts; (*b*) 45 volts; (*c*) 90 volts; (*d*) 180 volts.
5. The sum of series IR voltage drops (*a*) is less than the smallest voltage drop; (*b*) equals the average value of all the voltage drops; (*c*) equals the applied voltage; (*d*) is usually more than the applied voltage.
6. R_1 and R_2 are in series with an applied E of 90 volts. If V_1 is 30 volts then V_2 must be (*a*) 30 volts; (*b*) 90 volts; (*c*) 45 volts; (*d*) 60 volts.
7. With a 4-ohm resistance and a 2-ohm resistance in series across a 6-volt battery, the current in (*a*) the larger resistance is 1½ amp; (*b*) the smaller resistance is 3 amp; (*c*) both resistances is 1 amp; (*d*) both resistances is 2 amp.

8. When one resistance in a series string is open, the (a) current is maximum in the normal resistances; (b) current is zero in all the resistances; (c) voltage is zero across the open resistance; (d) current increases in the voltage source.

9. The resistance of an open series string is (a) zero; (b) infinite; (c) equal to the normal resistance of the string; (d) about double the normal resistance of the string.

10. E of 100 volts is applied across a 20-ohm R_1 and 30-ohm R_2 in series. V_1 is 40 volts. The current through R_2 is (a) 5 amp; (b) 3⅓ amp; (c) 1⅓ amp; (d) 2 amp.

ESSAY QUESTIONS

1. Show how to connect two resistances in series with each other across a voltage source.
2. State three rules for the current, voltage, and resistance in a series circuit.
3. For a given amount of current, why does more resistance have a bigger voltage drop across it?
4. Two 300-watt 120-volt light bulbs are connected in series across a 240-volt line. If the filament of one bulb burns open, will the other bulb light? Why? With the open, how much is the voltage across the source and across each bulb?
5. Prove that if $E = V_1 + V_2 + V_3$, then $R_T = R_1 + R_2 + R_3$.
6. State briefly a rule for determining polarity of the voltage drop across each resistor in a series circuit.
7. Redraw the circuit in Fig. 3·7, marking the polarity of V_1, V_2, and V_3.
8. Derive the formula $P_T = P_1 + P_2 + P_3$ from the fact that $E = V_1 + V_2 + V_3$.

PROBLEMS (Answers to selected problems at back of book.)

1. Draw the schematic diagram of 20-, 30-, and 40-ohm resistances in series. (a) How much is the total resistance of the entire series string? (b) How much current flows in each resistance, with a voltage of 180 volts applied across the series string? (c) Find the voltage drop across each resistance. (d) Find the power dissipated in each resistance.
2. A circuit has 10 volts applied across a 10-ohm resistance R_1. How much is the current in the circuit? How much resistance R_2 must be added in series with R_1 to reduce the current one-half? Show the schematic diagram of the circuit with R_1 and R_2.
3. Make a schematic diagram showing two resistances R_1 and R_2 in series across a 100-volt source. (a) If the IR voltage drop across R_1 is 60 volts, how much is the IR voltage drop across R_2? (b) Label the polarity of the voltage drops across R_1 and R_2. (c) If the current is 1 amp through R_1, how much is the current through R_2? (d) How much is the resistance of R_1 and R_2? How much is the total resistance across the voltage source? (e) If the voltage source is disconnected how much is the voltage across R_1 and across R_2?
4. R_1 of 90 K and R_2 of 10 K are in series across a 3-volt source. (a) Draw the schematic diagram. (b) How much is V_2?
5. How much resistance R_1 must be added in series with 100 ohms R_2 to limit the current to 0.3 amp with 120 volts applied? Show the schematic diagram. How much power is dissipated in each resistance?
6. Three 10-ohm resistances are in series across a voltage source. Show the schematic diagram. If the voltage across each resistor is 10 volts, how much is the applied voltage? How much is the current in each resistance?
7. Referring to Fig. 3·6, calculate the resistance of each heater with its normal load current. How much is the total resistance of the heater string?
8. Find the total R_T of the following resistances in series: 2 M, 0.5 M, 47 K, 5 K, and 470 ohms.
9. Draw the circuit with values for three equal series resistances across a 90-volt source, where each R has one-third the applied voltage and the current in the circuit is 2 ma.
10. A 100-watt bulb normally takes 0.833 amp and a 200-watt bulb takes 1.666 amp from the 120-volt power line. If these two bulbs were connected in series across a 240-volt power line, prove that the current would be 1.111 amp in both bulbs, assuming the resistances were constant.

4

When two or more components are connected across one voltage source, as shown in Fig. 4·1, they form a parallel circuit. Each parallel path is then a branch, with its own individual current. Parallel circuits, therefore, have one common voltage across all the branches but individual branch currents that can be different, compared with series circuits that have one common current but individual voltage drops that can be different. The characteristics of parallel circuits are explained as follows:

4·1   The voltage is the same across parallel branches
4·2   Each branch current equals E/R
4·3   The main-line current equals the sum of the branch currents
4·4   Resistances in parallel
4·5   Conductances in parallel
4·6   Total power in parallel circuits
4·7   Analyzing parallel circuits
4·8   Effect of an open in parallel circuits

4·1   *The voltage is the same across parallel branches*

In Fig. 4·1b, the points a, b, c, and e are really equivalent to a direct connection at the negative terminal of the battery because the connecting wires have practically no resistance. Similarly, points h, g, d, and f are the same as a direct connection at the positive battery terminal. Since R_1 and R_2 are directly connected across the two terminals of the battery, both resistances must have the same potential difference as the battery. It follows that the voltage is the same across components connected in parallel. The parallel circuit arrangement is used, therefore, to connect components that require the same voltage.

A common application of parallel circuits is typical house wiring to the

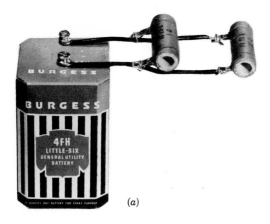

(a)

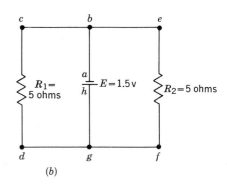

(b)

Fig. 4·1 *A parallel circuit. (a) Photograph of wiring. (b) Schematic diagram. R_1 and R_2 are in parallel with each other and the voltage source.*

power line, with many lights and appliances connected across the 120-volt source (Fig. 4·2). The wall receptacle has the potential difference of 120 volts across each pair of terminals. Therefore, any resistance connected to an outlet has the applied voltage of 120 volts. The light bulb is connected to one outlet and the toaster to another outlet, but both have the same applied voltage of 120 volts. Therefore, each operates independently of any other appliance, with all the individual branch circuits connected across the 120-volt line.

4·2 Each branch current equals E/R

In applying Ohm's law, it is important to note that the current equals the voltage applied across the circuit divided by the resistance between the two points where that voltage is applied. In Fig. 4·3, 10 volts is applied across the 5 ohms of R_2, resulting in the current of 2 amp between points e and f through R_2. The battery voltage is also applied across the parallel resistance of R_1, applying 10 volts across 10 ohms. Through R_1, therefore,

Fig. 4·2 *Light bulb and toaster connected in parallel to the 120-volt line. (a) Wiring diagram. (b) Schematic diagram.*

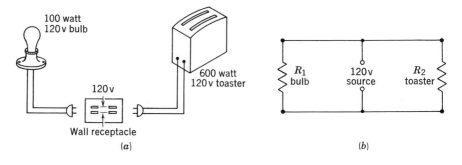

(a)

(b)

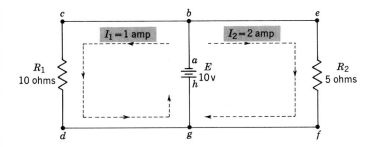

Fig. 4·3 *The current in each parallel branch equals the applied voltage divided by the branch resistance.*

the current is 1 amp between points *c* and *d*. The current has a different value through R_1, with the same applied voltage, because the resistance is different. These values are calculated as follows:

$$I_1 = \frac{E}{R_1} = \frac{10}{10} = 1 \text{ amp}$$

$$I_2 = \frac{E}{R_2} = \frac{10}{5} = 2 \text{ amp}$$

If R_1 had as much resistance as R_2, the two branch currents would have the same value. In Fig. 4·1*b*, for instance, each branch has current equal to 1.5 volts/5 ohms, or 0.3 amp.

The current can be different in parallel circuits having different resistances because the applied voltage is the same across the branches. The function of the voltage source is to generate a potential difference across its two terminals. This voltage does not move but is available across the source to make electrons move around any closed circuit connected to the generator terminals. Assuming the generator is not overloaded, its two terminals supply the same potential difference across all circuits connected in parallel. Each parallel branch current equals this value of applied voltage divided by the branch resistance. Just as in a circuit with one resistance, any branch that has less resistance allows more current than a higher-resistance branch, with the same applied voltage.

4·3 The main-line current equals the sum of the branch currents

Components to be connected in parallel are usually wired directly across each other, with the entire parallel combination connected to the voltage source, as illustrated in Fig. 4·4. This circuit is equivalent to wiring each parallel branch directly to the voltage source, as shown in Fig. 4·1, when the connecting wires have essentially zero resistance. The advantage of having only one pair of connecting leads to the source for all the parallel branches is that usually less wire is necessary. The pair of leads connecting all the branches to the terminals of the voltage source is the

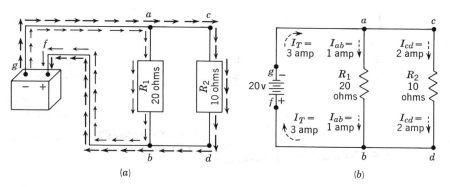

Fig. 4·4 *The main-line current equals the sum of the branch currents. From g to a is the negative side and from b to f is the positive side of the main line. (a) Wiring diagram. Arrows inside lines indicate current for R_1; arrows outside lines indicate current for R_2. (b) Schematic diagram. I_T is total line current.*

main line. In Fig. 4·4, the wires from *g* to *a* on the negative side and from *b* to *f* in the return path form the main line.

In Fig. 4·4*b*, with 20 ohms of resistance for R_1 connected across the 20-volt battery, the current through R_1 must be 1 amp. This current is electron flow from the negative terminal of the source, through R_1, and back to the positive battery terminal. Similarly, the R_2 branch of 10 ohms across the battery has its own branch current of 2 amp from the negative terminal of the source, through R_2, and back to the positive terminal, since it is a separate path for electron flow. All the current in the circuit, however, must come from one side of the voltage source and return to the opposite side for a complete path. In the main line, therefore, the amount of current is equal to the total of the branch currents.

For example, in Fig. 4·4*b*, the total current in the line from point *g* to point *a* is 3 amp. The total current at branch point *a* subdivides into its component branch currents for each of the branch resistances. Through the path R_1 from *a* to *b* the current is 1 amp, equal to 20 volts/20 ohms. The other branch path *acdb* through R_2 has the current of 2 amp, equal to 20 volts/10 ohms. At the branch point *b*, the electron flow from both parallel branches combines, so that the current in the main-line return path from *b* to *f* has the same value of 3 amp as in the other side of the main line.

The formula for the total current I_T in the main line is

$$I_T = I_1 + I_2 + I_3 + \cdots + \text{etc.} \qquad (4 \cdot 1)$$

This rule applies for any number of parallel branches, whether the resistances are equal or unequal.

Example 1. R_1 of 20 ohms, R_2 of 40 ohms, and R_3 of 60 ohms are connected in parallel across the 120-volt power line. How much is the total line current I_T?

Answer. I_1 for the R_1 branch is $^{120}\!/_{20}$ or 6 amp. Similarly I_2 is $^{120}\!/_{40}$ or 3 amp and I_3 is $^{120}\!/_{60}$ or 2 amp. The total current in the main line is

$$I_T = I_1 + I_2 + I_3 = 6 + 3 + 2 = \textbf{11 amp}$$

Example 2. Two branches R_1 and R_2 across the 120-volt power line draw a total line current of 15 amp. The R_1 branch takes 10 amp. How much is the current I_2 in the R_2 branch?

Answer. $\qquad\qquad I_2 = I_T - I_1 = 15 - 10 = \textbf{5 amp}$

Notice that the total line current I_T must be more than any one branch current; or any branch current must be less than I_T.

4·4 Resistances in parallel

The total resistance across the main line in a parallel circuit can be found by Ohm's law: Divide the common voltage across the parallel resistances by the total current of all the branches. Referring to Fig. 4·5a, note that the parallel resistance of R_1 with R_2, indicated by the combined resistance R_T, is the opposition to the total current in the main line. Therefore, the total resistance is the applied voltage across the main line divided by the line current, which equals 60 volts/3 amp in this example, or 20 ohms.

The total load connected to the source voltage is the same as though one equivalent resistance of 20 ohms were connected across the main line, as illustrated by the equivalent circuit in Fig. 4·5b. For any number of parallel resistances of any value, therefore,

$$R_T = \frac{E}{I_T} \qquad\qquad (4\cdot2)$$

where I_T is the sum of all the branch currents and R_T is the equivalent resistance of all the parallel branches across the voltage source E.

Fig. 4·5   Resistances in parallel. (a) Combined parallel resistance of R_1 and R_2 is the total resistance in the main line. (b) Equivalent circuit showing R_T equal to the parallel combination of R_1 with R_2.

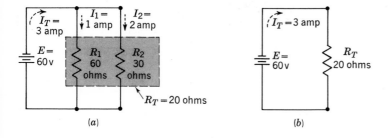

(a)   (b)

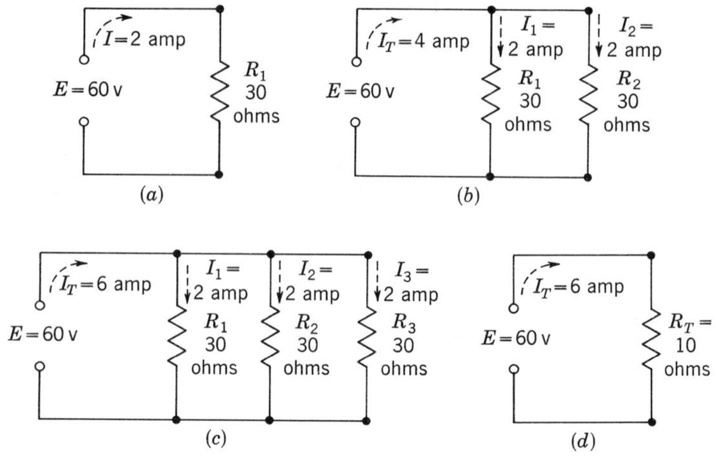

Fig. 4·6   *How adding parallel branches increases I_T and reduces R_T.*
(a) One branch. (b) Two branches. (c) Three branches. (d) Equivalent of c.

Example 3. Five branches, each with 2-amp current, are connected across a 90-volt source. How much is the equivalent total resistance?

Answer. The total line current I_T is 5×2 or 10 amp. Then

$$R_T = \frac{E}{I_T} = \frac{90}{10} = 9 \text{ ohms}$$

A combination of parallel branches is often called a *bank*. In Fig. 4·5 the bank consists of R_1 and R_2 in parallel. Their combined parallel resistance R_T is the bank resistance, equal to 20 ohms in this example.

When a circuit has more current with the same applied voltage, this greater value of I corresponds to less R because of their inverse relation. Therefore, the combination of parallel resistances R_T is always less than the smallest individual branch resistance, as I_T must be more than any one branch current.

It may seem unusual at first that putting more resistances into a circuit lowers the equivalent resistance. This feature of parallel circuits is illustrated in Fig. 4·6. Note that equal resistances of 30 ohms each are added across the source E, one branch at a time. The circuit in *a* has just R_1, which allows 2 amp with 60 volts applied. In *b* the R_2 branch is added across the same E. This branch also has 2 amp. Now the parallel circuit has 4 amp total line current because of $I_1 + I_2$. Then the third branch is added in *c*, which also takes 2 amp for I_3. The combined circuit with three branches therefore requires a total load current of 6 amp, which is supplied by the voltage source. The combined resistance across the source then is E/I_T, which is $^6\!\%$ or 10 ohms. This equivalent resistance R_T, representing the entire load on the voltage source, is shown in *d*. More resistance branches reduce the combined resistance of the parallel circuit, because more current is required from the same voltage source.

Reciprocal resistance formula. The total line current equals E/R_T. Each branch current is E/R. Since the line current equals the sum of the branch currents,

$$I_T = I_1 + I_2 + I_3 + \cdots \text{ etc.}$$

or,

$$\frac{E}{R_T} = \frac{E}{R_1} + \frac{E}{R_2} + \frac{E}{R_3} + \cdots + \text{ etc.}$$

Dividing by E because it is the same across all the resistances gives

$$\frac{1}{R_T} = \frac{1}{R_1} + \frac{1}{R_2} + \frac{1}{R_3} + \cdots + \text{ etc.} \qquad (4 \cdot 3)$$

This reciprocal formula applies to any number of parallel resistances of any value. Using the values in Fig. $4 \cdot 7a$ as an example,

$$\frac{1}{R_T} = \frac{1}{20} + \frac{1}{10} + \frac{1}{10} = \frac{1}{20} + \frac{2}{20} + \frac{2}{20} = \frac{5}{20}$$

$$R_T = \frac{20}{5} = \textbf{4 ohms}$$

Notice that the value for $1/R_T$ must be inverted to obtain R_T.

Total-current method. Figure $4 \cdot 7b$ shows how this same problem can be calculated in terms of total current instead of by the reciprocal formula, if it is easier to work without fractions. Although the applied voltage is not known always, any convenient value can be assumed because it cancels in the calculations. It is usually simplest to assume an applied voltage of the same numerical value as the highest resistance. Then one assumed branch current will automatically be 1 amp and the other branch currents will be more, eliminating fractions less than 1 in the calculations. With the highest resistance equal to 20 ohms and an applied voltage assumed of 20 volts, the branch currents are 1, 2, and 2 amp for R_1, R_2, and R_3, respectively. Then the total line current is 5 amp. The combined resist-

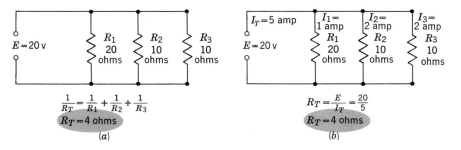

Fig. $4 \cdot 7$ *Calculating total parallel resistance. (a) Reciprocal resistance formula method. (b) Total line current method, using an assumed line voltage of 20 volts.*

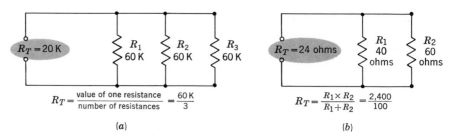

Fig. 4·8   (a) For any number of equal branch resistances, R divided by number of branches is R_T. Here R_T is 20 K. (b) For any two parallel resistances, R_T is their product divided by the sum. Here R_T is 24 ohms.

ance in the line is 20 volts/5 amp, therefore, which equals 4 ohms, the same value obtained by using the reciprocal resistance formula.

Short-cut calculations. Two common cases of parallel circuits can be calculated much more easily by two special rules. When all the parallel resistances are equal, the combined resistance equals the value of one branch resistance divided by the number of resistances. This rule is illustrated in Fig. 4·8a, where three 60-K resistances in parallel equal 20 K. The rule applies to any number of parallel resistances, but they must all be equal. As another example, five 60-ohm resistances in parallel have the combined resistance of $^{60}\!/_5$, or 12 ohms.

When there are just two parallel resistances and they are not equal, it is usually quicker to calculate the combined resistance by the method shown in Fig. 4·8b. This rule says that the combination of two parallel resistances is their product divided by the sum:

$$R_T = \frac{R_1 \times R_2}{R_1 + R_2} \tag{4·4}$$

where R_T is in the same units as all the individual resistances. For the example in Fig. 4·8b,

$$R_T = \frac{R_1 \times R_2}{R_1 + R_2} = \frac{40 \times 60}{40 + 60} = \frac{2,400}{100}$$

$$R_T = \textbf{24 ohms}$$

The resistances can have any values but there must be only two. Note that this method gives R_T directly, not its reciprocal. If you use the reciprocal formula for this example, the answer will be $1/R_T = \frac{1}{24}$, which is the same as R_T equal to 24.

Figure 4·9 shows how these short-cut calculations can help in reducing parallel branches to a simpler equivalent circuit. In a, the 10-ohm R_1 and R_4 are equal and in parallel. Therefore, they are equivalent to the 5-ohm R_{14} in b. Similarly, the 20-ohm R_2 and R_3 are equivalent to the 10 ohms of R_{23}. The circuit in a is equivalent to the simpler circuit in b with just

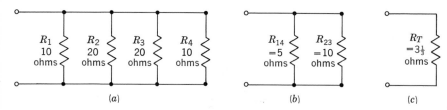

Fig. 4·9 *Example of reducing parallel-resistance calculations. (a) Circuit with four parallel resistances. (b) Four
branches combined into two branches. (c) Equivalent circuit
reduced to the one combined resistance R_T.*

the two parallel resistances of 5 and 10 ohms. Finally, the combined resistance for these two equals their product divided by the sum, which is $^{50}/_{15}$,
or $3\frac{1}{3}$ ohms, as shown in c. This value of R_T in c is equivalent to the combination of the four branches in a. If you connect a voltage source across
either circuit, the generator current in the main line will be the same for
both cases.

The order of connections for parallel resistances does not matter in determining R_T. There is no question as to which is first or last because they
are all across the same voltage source.

In some cases with two parallel resistors it is useful to be able to determine what size R to connect in parallel with a known R in order to obtain
a required value of R_T. Then the factors can be transposed as follows:

$$R_x = \frac{R \times R_T}{R - R_T} \qquad (4 \cdot 5)$$

Example 4. What R in parallel with 40 ohms will provide R_T of 24 ohms?

Answer. $$R_x = \frac{R \times R_T}{R - R_T} = \frac{40 \times 24}{40 - 24} = \frac{960}{16}$$

$$R_x = \textbf{60 ohms}$$

This problem corresponds to the circuit in Fig. 4·8b.

Example 5. What R in parallel with 50 K will provide R_T of 25 K?

Answer. $$R = \textbf{50 kilohms}$$

4·5 Conductances in parallel

Since conductance G is equal to $1/R$, the reciprocal resistance formula
(4·3) can be stated for conductance as

$$G_T = G_1 + G_2 + G_3 + \cdots + \text{etc.} \qquad (4 \cdot 6)$$

With R in ohms, G is in mhos. An example is illustrated in Fig. 4·10.
Notice that adding the conductances does not require reciprocals.
Actually, each value of G is the reciprocal of R.

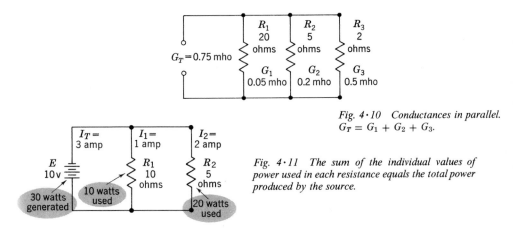

Fig. 4·10   Conductances in parallel. $G_T = G_1 + G_2 + G_3$.

Fig. 4·11   The sum of the individual values of power used in each resistance equals the total power produced by the source.

Working with conductances may be more convenient than working with resistances in some parallel circuits, in order to avoid using the reciprocal formula. The reason why parallel conductances are added directly can be illustrated by assuming a 1-volt source. Then calculating the values of $1/R$ for the conductances corresponds to the branch currents, which are added for the total current of the line.

4·6   Total power in parallel circuits

Since the power dissipated in the branch resistances must come from the voltage source, the total power equals the sum of the individual values of power in each branch. This rule is illustrated in Fig. 4·11. We can also use this circuit as an example of how to apply the rules of current, voltage, and resistance for a parallel circuit.

The applied E of 10 volts is across the 10-ohm R_1 and the 5-ohm R_2 in Fig. 4·11. The branch current I_1 then is E/R_1 or $^{10}\!/_{10}$, which equals 1 amp. Similarly I_2 is $^{10}\!/_5$, or 2 amp. The total I_T is $1 + 2 = 3$ amp. If we want to find R_T, it equals E/I_T or $^{10}\!/_3$, which is 3⅓ ohms.

The power dissipated in each branch is EI. In the R_1 branch, I_1 is 1 amp and P_1 equals 10×1 or 10 watts. For the R_2 branch, I_2 is 2 amp. P_2 then is $2 \times 10 = 20$ watts. Adding P_1 and P_2, the answer is $10 + 20 = 30$ watts for P_T, which is the total power dissipated in all the branches. This must be equal to the total power supplied by the voltage source by means of its total line current I_T. Multiplying $E \times I_T$, or $10 \times 3 = 30$ watts for P_T, equal to $P_1 + P_2$. The 30 watts of power supplied by the source is dissipated in the branch resistances.

Note that in both parallel and series arrangements the sum of the individual values of power dissipated in the circuit equals the total power generated by the source. The series or parallel circuit arrangement can alter the distribution of voltage or current, but power is the rate at which energy is supplied and the circuit arrangement cannot change the fact that all the energy in the circuit comes from the source.

4·7   Analyzing parallel circuits

For many types of problems with parallel circuits it is useful to remember the following points:

1. When you know the voltage across one branch, this voltage is across all the branches.
2. If you know I_T and one of the branch currents I_1 you can find I_2 by subtracting from I_T. Since $I_T = I_1 + I_2$, it is also true that $I_2 = I_T - I_1$ or $I_1 = I_T - I_2$.

The circuit in Fig. 4·12 illustrates these points. The problem is to find the applied voltage E and the value of R_3. Of the three branch resistances, only R_1 and R_2 are known. However, since I_2 is given at 2 amp, the I_2R_2 voltage must be 2×60 or 120 volts.

The applied voltage E is not given, but this must also be 120 volts as the voltage across all the parallel branches is the same. Therefore, I_1 can be calculated as E/R_1 or $120/30$, which equals 4 amp.

Since I_T is given as 7 amp and two branches take $2 + 4$ or 6 amp, the third branch current through R_3 must be $7 - 6$ or 1 amp. Now R_3 can be calculated as E/I_3, which is $120/1$ or 120 ohms.

Parallel heater circuits. In equipment with tubes that all have 6.3-volt heaters they are generally wired in parallel (Fig. 4·13). Note that for a circuit like this all the tubes have the same voltage rating, as the voltage must be the same across parallel branches. The individual heater currents can be different, however. The source E must be able to supply the total line current I_T, equal to the sum of the individual values of heater current.

Current-divider circuits. In some circuits it may be necessary to find the individual branch currents in a bank from the resistances and total line current, but without knowing the voltage across the bank. This problem can be solved by using the fact that the currents divide inversely as the branch resistances. A higher branch resistance takes less current while the lower branch resistance requires more. The formulas for I are in Fig. 4·14.

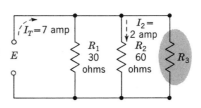

Fig. 4·12   Analyzing a parallel circuit. What are the values for E and R₃?

Fig. 4·13   Parallel heater circuit for 6.3-volt tubes.

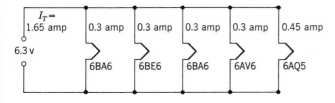

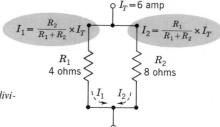

Fig. 4·14 How to find the current division in two parallel branches.

For the example illustrated in Fig. 4·14, notice that the formula for each branch I has the opposite branch R in the numerator. To solve this example,

$$I_1 = \frac{R_2}{R_1 + R_2} \times I_T = \frac{8}{4 + 8} \times 6$$

$$I_1 = \frac{48}{12} = \textbf{4 amp}$$

For the other branch current,

$$I_2 = \frac{R_1}{R_1 + R_2} \times I_T = \frac{4}{4 + 8} \times 6$$

$$I_2 = \frac{24}{12} = \textbf{2 amp}$$

Remember that the branch currents must add up to equal I_T. Here the 4-amp I_1 plus the 2-amp I_2 total 6 amp for I_T.

Notice that the division of branch currents in a parallel bank is opposite from the voltage division of resistances in a series string. With series resistances, a higher resistance develops a larger IR voltage proportional to its R; with parallel branches a lower resistance takes more branch current equal to E/R.

Fig. 4·15 Open in parallel circuits. (a) Open in main line—no current and no light in all bulbs. (b) Open in one branch—bulb 1 dark, but two other bulbs operate normally.

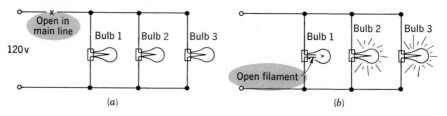

4·8   *Effect of an open in parallel circuits*

An open in any circuit is an infinite resistance that results in no current. However, in parallel circuits there is a difference between an open in the main line and an open in a parallel branch. These two cases are illustrated in Fig. 4·15. In *a* the open in the main line prevents any electron flow in the line to all the branches. The current is zero in every branch, therefore, and none of the bulbs can light. In *b*, though, the open is in the branch circuit for bulb 1. The open branch circuit has no current, then, and this bulb cannot light. The current in all the other parallel branches is normal, however, because each is connected to the voltage source. Therefore, the other bulbs light. This circuit shows the advantage of wiring components in parallel, since an open in one component just opens one branch, while the other parallel branches can operate normally.

SUMMARY

In parallel circuits:
1. The voltage is the same across all components connected in parallel.
2. The current in each parallel branch equals the voltage across the branch divided by the branch resistance.
3. The total line current equals the sum of all the branch currents.
4. The equivalent resistance of parallel branches is less than the smallest branch resistance. For two parallel branches, the equivalent value equals the product of the two resistances divided by their sum. For any number of equal parallel resistances, the equivalent value equals the resistance of one branch divided by the number of branches. For the general case of any number of branches having any values of resistance, calculate R_T as E/I_T, or use the reciprocal resistance formula (4·3).
5. The sum of the individual values of power dissipated in the resistances equals the total power produced by the source.
6. An open in one branch results in no current in that branch, but the other branches can have their normal value of current. An open in the main line, however, results in no current in all the branches.

SELF-EXAMINATION (*Answers at back of book.*)

Here's a chance to find out how well you have learned the material in this chapter. These exercises are for your self-testing only.
1. With two resistances connected in parallel, (*a*) the current through each must be the same; (*b*) the voltage across each must be the same; (*c*) their combined resistance equals the sum of the individual values; (*d*) each must have the same resistance value.
2. With 100 volts applied across ten 50-ohm resistances in parallel, the current through each resistance equals (*a*) 2 amp; (*b*) 10 amp; (*c*) 50 amp; (*d*) 100 amp.
3. With three 1-K resistances connected in parallel, their combined equivalent resistance equals (*a*) ⅓ K; (*b*) 1 K; (*c*) 2 K; (*d*) 3 K.
4. A 1-ohm resistance in parallel with a 2-ohm resistance provides a combined equivalent resistance of (*a*) 3 ohms; (*b*) 1 ohm; (*c*) 2 ohms; (*d*) 2/3 ohm.
5. With resistances of 100, 200, 300, 400, and 500 ohms in parallel, R_T is (*a*) less than 100 ohms; (*b*) more than 1 M; (*c*) about 500 ohms; (*d*) about 1 K.
6. With two resistances connected in parallel, if each dissipates 10 watts, the total power supplied by the voltage source equals (*a*) 5 watts; (*b*) 10 watts; (*c*) 20 watts; (*d*) 100 watts.
7. With eight 10-M resistances connected in parallel across a 10-volt source, the main line current equals (*a*) 0.1 μa; (*b*) ⅛ μa; (*c*) 8 μa; (*d*) 10 μa.

8. A parallel circuit with 20 volts applied across two branches has a total line current of 5 amp. One branch resistance equals 5 ohms. The other branch resistance equals (*a*) 5 ohms; (*b*) 20 ohms; (*c*) 25 ohms; (*d*) 100 ohms.

9. Three 100-watt light bulbs are connected in parallel across the 120-volt power line. If one bulb opens, how many bulbs can light? (*a*) none; (*b*) one; (*c*) two; (*d*) all.

10. If a parallel circuit is open in the main line, the current (*a*) increases in each branch; (*b*) is zero in all the branches; (*c*) is zero only in the branch that has highest resistance; (*d*) increases in the branch that has lowest resistance.

ESSAY QUESTIONS

1. Draw a wiring diagram showing three resistances connected in parallel across a battery. Indicate each branch line and the main line.

2. State two rules for the voltage and current values in a parallel circuit.

3. Explain briefly why the current is the same in both sides of the main line that connects the voltage source to the parallel branches.

4. (*a*) Show how to connect three equal resistances for a combined equivalent resistance one-third the value of one resistance. (*b*) Show how to connect three equal resistances for a combined equivalent resistance three times the value of one resistance.

5. Why can the current in parallel branches be different when they all have the same applied voltage?

6. Why does the current increase in the voltage source as more parallel branches are added to the circuit?

7. Derive the formula $R_T = R_1R_2/(R_1 + R_2)$ from the reciprocal formula for two resistances.

8. Give two differences between a voltage divider in a series circuit and a current divider in a parallel circuit.

9. State briefly why the total power equals the sum of the individual values of power, whether a series circuit or parallel circuit is used.

10. State briefly why the total conductance in a parallel circuit is calculated as the sum of the individual values of conductances, rather than using the reciprocal formula.

11. Explain why an open in the main line disables all the branches, but an open in one branch affects only that branch current.

12. List as many differences as you can, in comparing series circuits with parallel circuits.

PROBLEMS (*Answers to selected problems at back of book.*)

1. A 15-ohm R_1 and a 45-ohm R_2 are connected in parallel across a 45-volt battery. (*a*) Draw the schematic diagram. (*b*) How much is the voltage across R_1 and R_2? (*c*) How much is the current in R_1 and R_2? (*d*) How much is the main-line current? (*e*) How much is the combined equivalent resistance?

2. For the circuit in question 1, how much is the total power supplied by the battery?

3. (*a*) Draw the schematic diagram of a parallel circuit with three branch resistances, each having 10 volts applied and 2-amp branch current. (*b*) How much is the total line current? (*c*) How much is the combined equivalent resistance of all the branches?

4. A parallel circuit has three branch resistances of 20, 10, and 5 ohms each. The current through the 20-ohm branch is 1 amp. (*a*) Draw the schematic diagram. (*b*) How much is the voltage applied across all the branches? (*c*) Find the current through the 10-ohm branch and the 5-ohm branch.

5. Referring to Fig. 4·11, assume that R_2 opens. (*a*) How much is the current in the R_2 branch? (*b*) How much is the current in the R_1 branch? (*c*) How much is the line current? (*d*) How much is the total resistance of the circuit? (*e*) How much power is generated by the battery?

6. Find the combined parallel resistance for the following groups of branch resistances: (*a*) 10 ohms and 25 ohms; (*b*) five 10-kilohm resistances; (*c*) two 500-ohm resistances;

(*d*) 100 ohms, 200 ohms, and 300 ohms; (*e*) two 5-K and two 2-K resistances; (*f*) four 40-K and two 20-K resistances.

7. Two resistances R_1 and R_2 are in parallel across a 100-volt source. The total line current is 10 amp. The current I_1 through R_1 is 4 amp. Make a schematic diagram of the circuit, giving the values of currents I_1 and I_2 and resistances R_1 and R_2 in both branches. How much is the combined equivalent resistance of both branches across the voltage source?

8. How much parallel R must be connected across a 100-K resistance to reduce R_T to (*a*) 50 K; (*b*) 25 K; (*c*) 10 K?

9. (*a*) How much is the current in a 9-volt battery with 47-K R across it? (*b*) Then another 47-K resistor is connected in parallel. Now how much is the current in the battery?

10. Find the total conductance in mhos, for the following branches: $G_1 = 9,000$ μmhos, $G_2 = 7,000$ μmhos, $G_3 = 22,000$ μmhos.

11. I_T is 7 ma for two branch resistances. R_1 is 20 K and R_2 is 56 K. Find I_1 and I_2 in this parallel current-divider circuit.

12. Referring to Fig. 4·13, calculate the resistance of each of the five branches and the combined R_T across the 6.3-volt source.

Chapter 5 Series-parallel circuits

In many circuits, some components are connected in series to have the same current, while others are in parallel for the same voltage. Figure 5·1 shows an example. Such a circuit is used where it is necessary to provide different amounts of current and voltage with one source of applied voltage. The main features of series-parallel circuits are explained in the following topics.

5·1   Resistance strings in parallel
5·2   Resistance banks in series
5·3   Resistance banks and strings in series-parallel
5·4   Analyzing series-parallel circuits
5·5   Series voltage divider with parallel branch currents
5·6   Kirchhoff's laws
5·7   Wheatstone bridge
5·8   Effect of a short circuit

5·1   Resistance strings in parallel

In Fig. 5·2 there are four 120-volt 100-watt light bulbs to be wired, with a voltage source that produces 240 volts. Each bulb needs 120 volts across the filament to produce approximately 0.9-amp current for normal brilliance. If the bulbs were connected across the source, each would have the applied voltage of 240 volts, causing excessive current in all the bulbs, which could result in burned-out filaments. If the four bulbs were connected in series, each would have a potential difference of 60 volts, equal to one-fourth the applied voltage. With too low a voltage, there would be insufficient current for normal operation and the bulbs would not operate at normal brilliance. However, two bulbs in series across the 240-volt line provide 120 volts for each filament, which is the normal operating voltage.

Therefore, the four bulbs are wired in strings of two in series, with the two strings in parallel across the 240-volt source. Both strings have 240 volts applied. In each string two series bulbs divide the applied voltage equally to provide the required 120 volts for the filaments.

Another example is illustrated in Fig. 5·3. This circuit has just two parallel branches where one branch includes R_1 in series with R_2. The other branch has just the one resistance R_3. Ohm's law can be applied as follows:

1. Each branch current equals the voltage applied across the branch divided by the total series resistance in the branch. In branch 1, R_1 and R_2 total 12 ohms. With 12 volts applied, this branch current I_1 equals 1 amp. In the R_3 branch I_2 is 2 amp because this branch resistance is 6 ohms.
2. For any one resistance in a string, the current in the string multiplied by the resistance equals the *IR* voltage drop across that particular resistance. Also, the sum of the series *IR* drops in the string equals the voltage applied across the entire string. In string 1 the I_1R_1 drop equals 8 volts, while the I_1R_2 drop is 4 volts. These drops add to equal the 12 volts applied. The voltage across the R_3 branch is also 12 volts.

Fig. 5·1 Series-parallel circuit. (a) Photograph of circuit. (b) Schematic diagram.

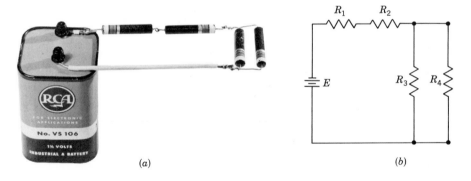

(a) (b)

Fig. 5·2 Two identical series strings in parallel. All bulbs have 120-volt 100-watt rating. (a) Wiring diagram. (b) Schematic diagram.

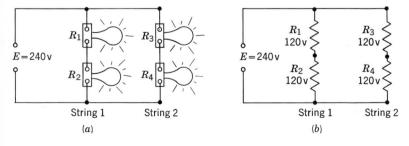

(a) (b)

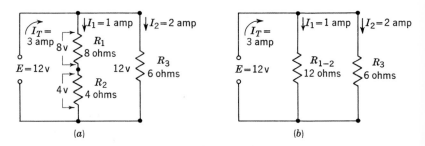

Fig. 5·3 *Series string in parallel with another branch. (a) Schematic
diagram. (b) Equivalent circuit.*

3. The total line current equals the sum of the branch currents for all the parallel strings. Here I_T is 3 amp, equal to the sum of 1 amp in branch 1, and 2 amp in branch 2.
4. The resistance of the total series-parallel circuit across the voltage source equals the applied voltage divided by the total line current. In Fig. 5·3, R_T equals 12 volts/3 amp, or 4 ohms. This resistance can also be calculated as 12 ohms in parallel with 6 ohms, equivalent to one combined resistance of 4 ohms.

There can be any number of parallel strings and more than two series resistances in a string. Still, Ohm's law can be applied the same way to the series and parallel parts of the circuit.

5·2 Resistance banks in series

In Fig. 5·4a, the group of parallel resistances R_1 and R_2 is called a *bank*. The bank is in series with R_1 because the total current of the bank must go through R_1. This circuit provides an arrangement for connecting R_2 and R_3 in parallel in one bank so that these two resistances will have the same potential difference of 20 volts across them. The source applies

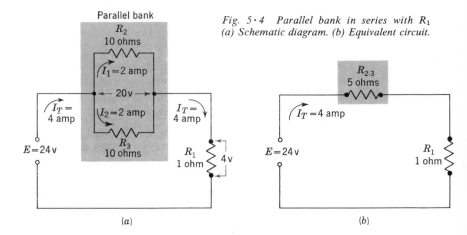

Fig. 5·4 *Parallel bank in series with R_1
(a) Schematic diagram. (b) Equivalent circuit.*

24 volts, but there is a 4-volt drop across R_1. The two series voltage drops of 4 volts across R_1 and 20 volts across the bank add to equal the applied voltage of 24 volts. The purpose of a circuit like this is to provide the same voltage for two or more resistances in a bank where the bank voltage must be less than the applied voltage by the amount of IR drop across any series resistance.

To find the resistance of the entire circuit, combine the parallel resistances in each bank and add the series resistance. As shown in *b*, the two 10-ohm resistances R_2 and R_3 in parallel are equivalent to 5 ohms. Since the bank resistance of 5 ohms is in series with 1 ohm for R_1, the total resistance is 6 ohms across the 24-volt source. Therefore, the main-line current is 24 volts/6 ohms, which equals 4 amp.

The total line current of 4 amp divides into two parts of 2 amp each in the parallel resistances R_2 and R_3. Note that each branch current equals the bank voltage divided by the branch resistance. The branch currents are combined in the line to provide the total 4 amp in R_1. This is the same total current flowing in the main line, in the source, into the bank, and out of the bank.

There can be more than two parallel resistances in a bank and any number of banks in series. Still, Ohm's law can be applied the same way to the series and parallel parts of the circuit. The general procedure for circuits of this type is to find the equivalent resistance of each bank and then add all the equivalent series resistances.

5·3 *Resistance banks and strings in series-parallel*

In the solution of such circuits, the most important fact is to know which components are in series with each other and what parts of the circuit are parallel branches. The series components must be in one current path without any branch points. A branch point such as point A or B in Fig. 5·5 is common to two or more current paths. For instance, R_1 and R_6 are *not* in series with each other. They do not have the same current, because the current in R_1 divides at point A into its two component branch currents. Similarly, R_5 is not in series with R_2, because of the branch point B.

To analyze a series-parallel circuit, start reducing the branch farthest from the source and work in toward the applied voltage. This way R_T can be found in order to calculate the main-line current as E/R_T. For the example in Fig. 5·5, the steps are as follows:

1. The bank of R_3 and R_4 in parallel in *a* is equal to R_7 in *b*.
2. R_7 and R_6 in series in the same current path equal R_{13} in *c*.
3. R_{13} and R_5 are in parallel across the branch points A and B. Their equivalent resistance then equals R_{18} in *d*.
4. Now the circuit in *d* has just the series resistances R_1, R_{18}, and R_2. These total 50 ohms, as shown in *e*.
5. With 50 ohms R_T across the source E of 100 volts, the line current is 2 amp.

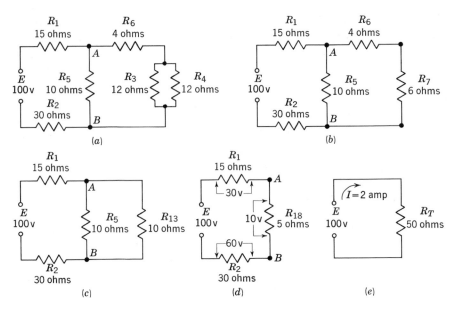

Fig. 5·5   *Reducing series-parallel circuit to equivalent series circuit. (a) Circuit diagram. (b) R_3 and R_4 in parallel equal R_7. (c) R_7 in series with R_6 equals R_{13}. (d) R_{13} in parallel with R_5 equals R_{18}. (e) R_{18} in series with R_1 and R_2 equals the total circuit resistance R_T of 50 ohms.*

To see the individual voltages and currents, we can proceed from the equivalent circuit in *d*. The *IR* drops are 30 volts across the 15 ohms of R_1, 60 volts across the 30 ohms of R_2, and 10 volts across R_{18}. The 10-volt *IR* drop across R_{18} means this is the potential difference between branch points *A* and *B*. This means 10 volts across both R_5 and R_{13}. The 10 volts produces 1 amp in the R_5 branch. The same 10 volts is also across the R_{13} branch.

Remember that the R_{13} branch is actually the string of R_6 in series with the R_3R_4 bank. Since this branch resistance is 10 ohms, with 10 volts across it the branch current here is 1 amp. The 1 amp through the 4 ohms of R_6 produces a voltage drop of 4 volts. The remaining 6-volt *IR* drop is across the R_3R_4 bank. With 6 volts across the 12-ohm R_3, its current is ½ amp; the current is also ½ amp in R_4.

Tracing all the current paths from the source, the main-line current through R_1 is 2 amp. At the branch point *A*, this current divides into 1 amp for R_5 and 1 amp for the string with R_6. There is 1-amp branch current in R_6, but it subdivides in the bank with ½ amp in R_3 and ½ amp in R_4. At the branch point *B*, the total bank current of 1 amp combines with the 1 amp through the R_5 branch, resulting in 2-amp total line current through R_2, the same as through R_1 in the opposite side of the line.

5·4   *Analyzing series-parallel circuits*

The circuits in Figs. 5·6 to 5·8 illustrate how to apply the rules for series and parallel circuits. In Fig. 5·6, the I_1 branch current is given.

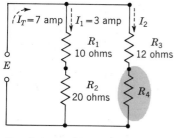

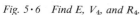

Fig. 5·6 *Find E, V₄, and R₄.*

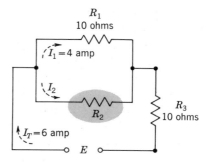

Fig. 5·7 *Find R₂.*

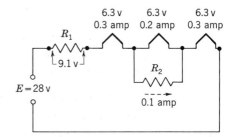

Fig. 5·8 *Filament circuit requiring series voltage-dropping resistor R_1 and parallel shunt R_2 across middle filament.*

This 3-amp current through the 10-ohm R_1 produces a 30-volt drop V_1 across R_1. The same 3-amp current through the 20-ohm R_2 produces 60 volts for V_2 across R_2. The 30-volt V_1 and 60-volt V_2 are in series with each other across the applied voltage E. Therefore, E equals the sum of 30 + 60 or 90 volts. This 90 volts is also across the other branch combining R_3 and R_4 in series.

The other branch current I_2 in Fig. 5·6 must be 4 amp, equal to the 7-amp I_T minus the 3-amp I_1. With 4 amp for I_2, the voltage drop across the 12-ohm R_3 equals 48 volts for V_3. Then the voltage across R_4 is 90 − 48, or 42 volts for V_4, as the sum of V_3 and V_4 must equal the applied 90 volts. Finally, with 42 volts across R_4 and 4 amp through it, this resistance equals ⁴²⁄₄, or 10.5 ohms. Note that 10.5 ohms for R_4 added to 12 ohms of R_3 equals 22.5 ohms, which allows ⁹⁰⁄₂₂.₅ or 4 amp branch current for I_2.

The division of branch currents also applies to Fig. 5·7, but the main principle here is that the voltage must be the same across R_1 and R_2 in parallel. For the branch currents, I_2 is 2 amp, equal to the 6-amp I_T minus the 4-amp I_1. The voltage across 10-ohm R_1 is 4 × 10 or 40 volts. This same voltage is also across R_2. With 40 volts across R_2 and 2 amp through it, R_2 equals ⁴⁰⁄₂ or 20 ohms. Notice that I_2 is one-half I_1 because R_2 is double R_1.

If we want to find E in Fig. 5·7, it can be calculated as 100 volts. The 6-amp I_T through R_3 produces a voltage drop of 60 volts for V_3. Also, the voltage across the parallel bank with R_1 and R_2 has been calculated as 40 volts. This 40 volts across the bank in series with 60 volts across R_3 totals 100 volts for the total applied voltage E.

The circuit in Fig. 5·8 illustrates a parallel filament circuit that must be designed for the correct operating voltages and currents. The values next to each filament give the rated voltage and current for normal operation. With three 6.3-volt IR drops in series, they total 6.3 × 3 or 18.9 volts. However, the available applied E is 28 volts. Therefore, R_1 must provide an IR drop of 9.1 volts, or the difference between 28 volts applied and 18.9 volts across the three series filaments. The current through R_1 is 0.3 amp. Its resistance, then, is 9.1/0.3, which equals 30.3 ohms.

R_2 in Fig. 5·8 has the function of allowing 0.1 amp branch current around the middle filament. This parallel path is necessary to provide a bank that has the same 0.3 amp I as the other series components. The resistance of R_2 is 6.3/0.1, which equals 63 ohms.

In all these examples notice that the source voltage E is applied only across the total circuit. Any individual series resistance has its own IR voltage that must be less than the total E. Similarly, the total line current I_T is used only for the main-line current. Any individual current in a parallel branch must be less than I_T.

5·5   Series voltage divider with parallel branch currents

The circuit in Fig. 5·9 illustrates how the voltage division is affected by a parallel branch across a series resistance in the divider. We can start with the series divider in *a*, where there is no branch current. Then R_1 and R_2 simply form a proportional series divider across E. V_1 across the 40-K R_1 is 40 volts, equal to ⅔ of the 60 volts for E, because R_1 is ⅔ of the total 60-K R_T. Similarly V_2 is ⅓ of 60 volts, or ⁶⁰⁄₃, which equals 20 volts.

However, in *b* the 20-K R_3 branch across R_2 changes the equivalent resistance, which changes the voltage division. Now the resistance across points B and C is reduced to 10 K, equal to R_2 and R_3 in parallel. This bank resistance is shown as R_{2-3} in *c*. As a result, the resistance of 10 K from B to C is only one-fifth the total E. This value equals ⁶⁰⁄₅ or 12 volts. Note that the 40 K of R_1 stays the same because it has no parallel branch. Therefore, the voltage across R_2 and across R_3 is reduced to 12 volts, from 20 volts, because of the reduced resistance from B to C when R_3 is connected across R_2. The voltage across R_1 increases to 48 volts, as its 40 K is now ⅘ R_T, making V_1 equal to ⅘ of the 60-volt E.

It is useful to trace the current paths in the voltage divider because of the added branch current for the load R_3. All the current in the circuit must come from the source. Tracing electron current for R_3, it starts from the − side of E, goes through R_3, and returns through R_1 to the + side of E. Note that this current I_3 goes through R_1 but not through R_2.

However, both R_1 and R_2 have their own current from the source. This current through the divider is called *bleeder current*. In summary, then, the R_3 branch has just its load current; R_2 has only the bleeder current; R_1 has both the load current and the bleeder current.

These factors can be applied to the design of a practical voltage divider often used to provide the voltages and currents needed for different load requirement. See Fig. 5·10. Note the load specifications. Load C requires

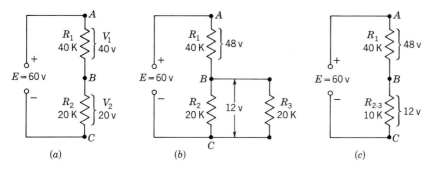

Fig. 5·9 *Effect of a parallel load on part of a series voltage divider. (a) R_1 and R_2 in series without any branch current. (b) Reduced voltage across R_2 with the parallel R_3. (c) Equivalent circuit of the loaded voltage divider.*

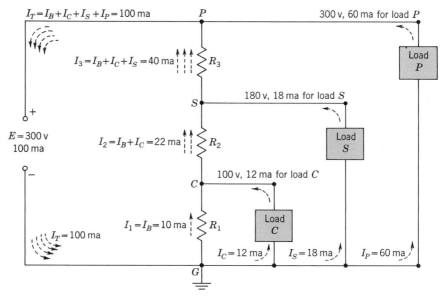

Fig. 5·10 *Voltage divider for different voltages and load currents from the voltage source E. See text for design calculations to find R_1, R_2, and R_3.*

100 volts from point C to chassis ground at point G. When the 100 volts is supplied by this part of the divider, 12 ma branch current I_c will flow through this load. Similarly, 180 volts is required at point S for 18 ma I_s in load S, and 300 volts at 60 ma for load P. The total load current here is $60 + 18 + 12$ or 90 ma. In addition, the bleeder current I_B through the entire divider is generally specified at about 10 per cent of the load current. For the example here I_B is taken as 10 ma to make the total line current I_T equal 100 ma.

The problem in Fig. 5·10 is to find the values for R_1, R_2, and R_3 needed to provide the specified voltages. Each value of R is calculated as its ratio of V/I, but the question is to use the correct V and I for each part of the divider. We start with R_1 because its current is only the 10 ma for I_B. The voltage across R_1 is specified at 100 volts. Therefore,

$$R_1 = \frac{V_1}{I_1} = \frac{100}{0.01} = 10,000 \text{ ohms}$$

The potential difference across R_2 is 80 volts. This value results from the fact that point S is at 180 volts with respect to G, while point C is at 100 volts with respect to G. Then the voltage between points S and C, which is V_2, must be the 80-volt difference between 180 and 100. The current through R_2 equals 22 ma. This value equals the 10 ma for I_B, which goes through all the resistors, plus the 12 ma for I_c, adding up to 22 ma. Therefore,

$$R_2 = \frac{V_2}{I_2} = \frac{80}{0.022} = 3,636 \text{ ohms}$$

The potential difference across R_3 is 120 volts, equal to $300 - 180$. The current I_3 through R_3 is 40 ma, equal to the sum of the 10 ma for I_B, 12 ma for I_c, and 18 ma for I_s. Note that the current I_P for load P does not go through R_3. Therefore,

$$R_3 = \frac{V_3}{I_3} = \frac{120}{0.040} = 3,000 \text{ ohms}$$

When these values are used for R_1, R_2, and R_3 connected in a voltage divider across the source of 300 volts, as in Fig. $5 \cdot 10$, each load will have the specified voltage at its rated current.

5·6   Kirchhoff's laws

In all the circuits considered so far, there was only one voltage source. For many applications, though, the circuit can have two or more applied voltages. Then each voltage source produces its own current in all parts of the circuit. To analyze such a circuit, two rules stated by G. R. Kirchhoff in 1847 can be applied. These laws allow a more general method of circuit analysis:

1. Around any closed circuit, the algebraic sum of the voltage sources (E) and the IR drops (V) must total zero. For circuits with one voltage source, this statement reduces to the practical rule that the sum of the series IR drops must be equal to the applied voltage.
2. At any junction of two or more conductors in a circuit, the algebraic sum of the currents into a junction must equal the current out of the junction. For circuits with one voltage source, this statement reduces to the practical rule that the sum of parallel branch currents must equal the total line current.

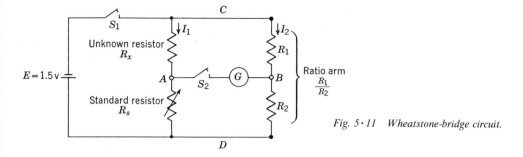

Fig. 5·11   *Wheatstone-bridge circuit.*

The method of using Kirchhoff's laws to solve more complicated circuits is explained in Chap. 6 on Network Theorems.

5·7   Wheatstone[1] bridge

A bridge circuit has four terminals, two for input voltage and two for output. The purpose is to have a circuit where the voltage drops can be balanced to provide zero voltage across the output terminals, with voltage applied across the input. In Fig. 5·11 the input terminals are C and D, while the output terminals are A and B. This circuit has many applications for comparison measurements. In the Wheatstone bridge, an unknown resistance R_x is balanced against a standard accurate resistor R_s for precise measurement of resistance.

In Fig. 5·11, S_1 applies battery voltage to the four resistors in the bridge. S_2 protects the sensitive meter against excessive current when the bridge is unbalanced. To balance the bridge, the value of R_s is varied. Balance is indicated by zero current in the galvanometer.

The reason for zero current in the galvanometer can be seen by analysis of the voltage drops across the resistors. R_s in series with R_x forms a voltage divider across E; the parallel string of R_1 in series with R_2 is also a voltage divider across the same source. When the voltage division is in the same ratio for both strings, the voltage drop across R_s equals the voltage across R_2. Also, the voltage across R_x then equals the voltage across R_1. In this case, points A and B must be at the same potential. The difference of potential across the meter then must be zero and there is no deflection.

At balance, the equal voltage ratios in the two arms of the Wheatstone bridge can be stated as

$$\frac{I_1 R_x}{I_1 R_s} = \frac{I_2 R_1}{I_2 R_2} \qquad \text{or} \qquad \frac{R_x}{R_s} = \frac{R_1}{R_2}$$

Transposing,
$$R_x = R_s \times \frac{R_1}{R_2}$$

[1] Sir Charles Wheatstone (1802–1875), English physicist and inventor.

Usually, the total resistance of R_1 and R_2 is fixed but any desired ratio can be chosen by moving point B on the ratio arm. The bridge is balanced by varying R_s for zero current in the meter. At balance, then, the value of R_x can be determined by multiplying R_s by the ratio of R_1/R_2. As an example, if the ratio is $\frac{1}{100}$ and R_s is 248 ohms the value of R_x equals 248×0.01 or 2.48 ohms.

The balanced bridge circuit can be analyzed as simply two series resistance strings in parallel when the current is zero through the meter. Without any current between A and B, this path is effectively open. When current flows through the meter path, however, the bridge circuit must be analyzed by network analysis, as explained in Chap. 6.

5·8   Effect of a short circuit

A short circuit has practically zero resistance. Its effect, therefore, is to allow excessive current. Two examples are illustrated in Fig. 5·12. Considering the parallel circuit in a, suppose that the conducting wire at point a should accidentally contact the wire at b. Since the wire is an excellent conductor, the short circuit results in practically zero resistance from a to b. These two points are connected directly across the voltage source. With no opposition, the applied voltage could produce an infinitely high value of current through this current path. Practically, though, the current is limited by the small resistance of the wires and the fact that the source usually cannot maintain its output voltage while providing excessive current. Still the amount of current can be dangerously high. For instance, the short-circuit current might be several hundred amperes instead of the normal line current of 1 amp illustrated here. This excessive current is present in the voltage source, the line to the short circuit at point a, in the short, and the line returning from point b. Because of the large amount of current, these parts of the circuit can become hot enough to ignite and burn.

There is no current in R_1 and R_2. Since the short circuit offers a parallel path with practically zero resistance, all the current flows in this path, bypassing the resistances. R_1 and R_2 are short-circuited or shorted-out, therefore, and cannot function without their normal current. If they were filament resistances of light bulbs, for instance, the bulbs would not light, because there is no current through the filaments. The short-circuited components are not damaged, however; they can operate again when the circuit is restored to normal by removal of the short.

If there were only one resistance in Fig. 5·12a or any number of additional parallel resistances, they would all be shorted by the short circuit from a to b. Therefore, a short circuit across one branch in a parallel circuit shorts out all the parallel branches. Also, a short circuit across the voltage source in any circuit shorts out the entire circuit.

In Fig. 5·12b the short circuit between c and d shorts out R_4 and R_5, and there is no voltage across these shorted resistances, but R_3 is in series with this short-circuited path. The result is excessive current through R_3,

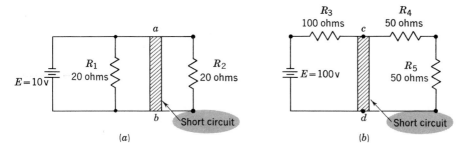

Fig. 5·12   *Examples of a short circuit. (a) Across parallel branches. (b) In a series circuit.*

since the entire source voltage is applied across the resistance. In this example, the current through R_3 is 1 amp, compared with the normal value of ½ amp in the series circuit without a short. If there is a short in a series circuit, therefore, the part of the circuit bypassed by the short has no current, but there is excessive current in the components connected between the short and the voltage source.

SUMMARY

Table 5·1 summarizes the main characteristics of series and parallel circuits. In circuits combining series and parallel connections, the components in one current path without any branch points are in series; the parts of the circuit connected across the same two branch points are in parallel.

Table 5·1   Comparison of series and parallel circuits

SERIES CIRCUIT	PARALLEL CIRCUIT
Current the same in all series components	Voltage the same across all branches
V across each resistance is $I \times R$	Current in each branch is E/R
Applied voltage equals sum of series IR drops: $E_T = V_1 + V_2 + V_3 + \cdots + $ etc.	Total line current equals sum of branch currents: $I_T = I_1 + I_2 + I_3 + \cdots + $ etc.
$R_T = R_1 + R_2 + R_3 + \cdots + $ etc.	$\dfrac{1}{R_T} = \dfrac{1}{R_1} + \dfrac{1}{R_2} + \dfrac{1}{R_3} + \cdots + $ etc.
R_T must be more than the largest individual resistance	R_T must be less than the smallest branch resistance
Open in one component causes entire circuit to be open	Open in one branch does not prevent current in other branches
Used for dividing series voltages, where $V_1 = E \times R_1/R_T$	Used for dividing two parallel branch currents, where $I_1 = I_T \times R_2/(R_1 + R_2)$
Total power $P_T = P_1 + P_2 + P_3 + \cdots + $ etc.	Total power $P_T = P_1 + P_2 + P_3 + \cdots + $ etc.

SELF-EXAMINATION (*Answers at back of book.*)

Here's a chance to find out how well you have learned the material in this chapter. These exercises are for your self-testing only.

1. In the series-parallel circuit in Fig. $5 \cdot 1b$, (*a*) R_1 is in series with R_3; (*b*) R_2 is in series with R_3; (*c*) R_4 is in parallel with R_3; (*d*) R_1 is in parallel with R_3.
2. In the series-parallel circuit in Fig. $5 \cdot 2b$, (*a*) R_1 is in parallel with R_3; (*b*) R_2 is in parallel with R_4; (*c*) R_1 is in series with R_2; (*d*) R_2 is in series with R_4.
3. In the series-parallel circuit in Fig. $5 \cdot 5$, the total of all the branch currents into branch point *A* and out of branch point *B* equals (*a*) ½ amp; (*b*) 1 amp; (*c*) 2 amp; (*d*) 4 amp.
4. In the circuit in Fig. $5 \cdot 2$ with four 120-volt 100-watt light bulbs, the resistance of one bulb equals (*a*) 72 ohms; (*b*) 100 ohms; (*c*) 144 ohms; (*d*) 120 ohms.
5. In the series-parallel circuit in Fig. $5 \cdot 4a$, (*a*) R_2 is in series with R_3; (*b*) R_1 is in series with R_3; (*c*) the equivalent resistance of the R_1R_2 bank is in parallel with R_3; (*d*) the equivalent resistance of the R_2R_3 bank is in series with R_1.
6. In the short circuit in Fig. $5 \cdot 12b$, the (*a*) voltage across R_4 is higher than normal; (*b*) current through R_4 is very high; (*c*) voltage across R_3 is more than normal; (*d*) current through R_5 is very high.
7. In a series voltage divider, the (*a*) lowest *R* has the highest *V*; (*b*) highest *R* has the highest *V*; (*c*) lowest *R* has the most *I*; (*d*) highest *R* has the most *I*.
8. In parallel bank with three unequal branch resistances, the (*a*) current is highest in the highest *R*; (*b*) current is equal in all the branches; (*c*) voltage is highest across the lowest *R*; (*d*) current is highest in the lowest *R*.
9. In the series-parallel filament circuit in Fig. $5 \cdot 8$, the (*a*) current through R_1 is 0.1 amp; (*b*) voltage across R_2 is 28 volts; (*c*) resistance is the same for all three filaments; (*d*) voltage across R_2 is 6.3 volts.
10. In the voltage divider in Fig. $5 \cdot 10$, the total load and bleeder current flows through (*a*) R_1; (*b*) R_2; (*c*) R_3; (*d*) the source *E*.

ESSAY QUESTIONS

1. In a series-parallel circuit, how can you tell which resistances are in series with each other and which are in parallel?
2. State the two rules of Kirchhoff's laws.
3. Draw a schematic diagram showing two resistances in a bank that is in series with one resistance.
4. Draw a diagram showing how to connect three resistances of equal value so that the combined resistance will be 1½ times the resistance of one unit.
5. Draw a diagram showing two strings in parallel across a voltage source, where each string has three series resistances.
6. Explain why components are connected in series-parallel, showing a circuit as an example of your explanation.
7. Give two differences between a short circuit and an open circuit.
8. Give two differences between a voltage divider and a current divider.

PROBLEMS (*Answers to selected problems at back of book.*)

1. Refer to Fig. $5 \cdot 1$. (*a*) Calculate the total resistance of the circuit if all resistances are 10 ohms. (*b*) How much is the main-line current if *E* equals 100 volts?
2. In Fig. $5 \cdot 2$, calculate the total power supplied by the source for the four 100-watt bulbs.
3. Refer to the diagram in Fig. $5 \cdot 13$. (*a*) Why is R_1 in series with R_3 but not with R_2? (*b*) Find the total circuit resistance across the battery.
4. Refer to the diagram in Fig. $5 \cdot 14$. (*a*) Calculate *R* across points *AD*. (*b*) How much is *R* across points *AD* with R_4 open?
5. Two 60-ohm resistances R_1 and R_2 in parallel require 60 volts across the bank with 1 amp

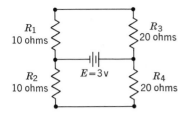

Fig. 5·13   *Circuit for Prob. 3.*

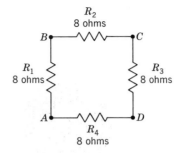

Fig. 5·14   *Circuit for Prob. 4.*

through each branch. Show how to connect a series resistance R_3 in the main line to drop an applied voltage of 100 volts to 60 volts across the bank. (*a*) How much is the required voltage across R_3? (*b*) How much is the required current through R_3? (*c*) How much is the required resistance of R_3? (*d*) If R_3 opens, how much is the voltage across R_1 and R_2? (*e*) If R_1 opens what are the voltages across R_2 and R_3?

6. Show how to connect four 100-ohm resistances in a series-parallel circuit with a combined resistance equal to 100 ohms. (*a*) If the combination is connected across a 100-volt source, how much power is supplied by the source? (*b*) How much power is dissipated in each resistance?

7. The following four resistors are in series with a 32-volt source: R_1 is 24 ohms, R_2 is 8 ohms, R_3 is 72 ohms, and R_4 is 240 ohms. (*a*) Find the voltage drop across each resistor. (*b*) Calculate the power dissipated in each resistor. (*c*) Which resistor has the most voltage drop? (*d*) Which resistor dissipates the most power?

8. The same four resistors are in parallel with the 32-volt source. (*a*) Find the branch current in each resistor. (*b*) Calculate the power dissipated in each resistor. (*c*) Which resistor has the most branch current? (*d*) Which resistor dissipates the most power?

9. Find R_1 and R_2 for a voltage divider that takes 10 ma from a 200-volt source, with 50 volts across R_2. There are no load-current branches.

10. Referring to the voltage divider in Fig. 5·10: (*a*) Calculate the power dissipated in R_1, R_2, and R_3. (*b*) How much is the resistance of load C, load S, and load P?

11. Design a voltage divider similar to Fig. 5·10 with values of R_1, R_2, and R_3 across a 450-volt source and the following loads: 450 volts at 80 ma, 200 volts at 40 ma, and 50 volts at 30 ma. Make the bleeder current I_B 10 per cent of the total load.

12. In the Wheatstone-bridge circuit in Fig. 5·11, let R_1 be 5 K, R_2 10 K, and R_s 1.2 K. Find (*a*) resistance of R_x required for balance; (*b*) voltage across each of the four resistances.

A network is just a combination of elements such as resistances. A four-terminal network has two connections for input and two for output. Analysis of the network between the input and output terminals is called network analysis. In advanced applications, practical circuits often include networks of series-parallel connections with many branches and more than one voltage source. In addition, there can be bridge circuits with unbalanced branch currents. As examples that may require network analysis, computer circuits usually have many branches, while in transistor circuits it may be necessary to consider the effect of the output voltage on the input voltage. In such applications, the analysis of the circuit is made much shorter by using one or more of the network theorems. Some types of circuits can be solved only by network analysis. Although resistance networks with batteries are shown here to demonstrate the theorems, they apply to a-c circuits and d-c circuits with resistance, capacitance, and inductance. The topics are:

6·1   Applications of Kirchhoff's laws
6·2   Thévenin's theorem
6·3   Norton's theorem
6·4   Thévenin-Norton conversions
6·5   Millman's theorem
6·6   The superposition theorem
6·7   Delta-wye transformations

6·1   Applications of Kirchhoff's laws

Although the theorems given later allow some "short cuts," they are not always applicable. However, any circuit can always be solved by the use of Kirchhoff's laws. This is why they are explained first here, as the basic tool for network analysis, although the application of Thévenin's theorem or Norton's theorem is usually shorter and easier in solving most practical circuits.

Kirchhoff's voltage law. The algebraic sum of the voltages around any closed loop is zero. Or stated in another important way: around any closed circuit, the algebraic sum of the applied voltages must equal the algebraic sum of the voltage drops.

Kirchhoff's current law. The algebraic sum of the currents entering and leaving any point in a circuit is equal to zero. Or stated another important way: the algebraic sum of the currents entering a point in the circuit must equal the algebraic sum of the currents leaving that point.

Algebraic signs for the directions of current. In using Kirchhoff's laws to solve circuits it is necessary to adopt conventions to establish the proper algebraic signs for current and voltage terms. A convenient system for currents is: *Consider all currents flowing into a branch point as positive, and all currents flowing away from that same point as negative.*

For example, in Fig. 6·1, Kirchhoff's current law allows us to write

$$5a + 3a - I_3 = 0$$

This equation says that the sum of the currents entering and leaving a point equals zero. The $5a$ and $3a$ terms are positive because they flow toward A. This equation may be transposed to the form

$$5a + 3a = I_3 = 8a$$

In this form the equation says that the currents entering A must be equal to the currents leaving A.

In Fig. 6·1 we can see that, with 5 amp and 3 amp flowing in, there must be 8 amp flowing out. But suppose we arbitrarily label the diagram opposite to the true situation. See Fig. 6·2. Then we must write

$$5a + 3a + I_3 = 0$$

and solving we get $I_3 = -8a$. Thus, the minus sign tells us that the actual current direction is opposite to the original label on our diagram. This example shows that, when a circuit is solved and the current value is nega-

Fig. 6·1 *Current I_3 out of point A equals $5a + 3a$ into A.*

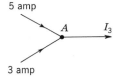

5 amp

3 amp

Fig. 6·2 *Same as Fig. 6·1 but wrong direction for I_3.*

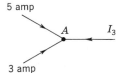

5 amp

3 amp

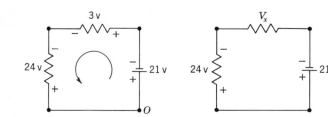
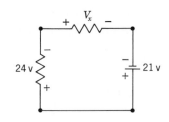

Fig. 6·3 Adding voltages around a loop. Starting from point O, $+21 + 3 - 24 = 0$.

Fig. 6·4 Same as Fig. 6·3 but V_x is unknown.

Fig. 6·5 Same as Fig. 6·4 but V_x marked with wrong polarity.

tive, it means the actual direction is opposite from the assumed direction.

Voltage-sign conventions. In a similar way, a convenient system for adding the voltages is as follows: *Go around a closed circuit loop in any convenient direction, and take any voltage source or voltage drop whose plus terminal is reached first as positive, and vice versa.*

As an example, Fig. 6·3 shows a portion of a circuit that will be completely solved later. Suppose you decide to sum voltages in a counter-clockwise travel around the loop, starting at point O. Then in accordance with the rule just given you write

$$+21 + 3 - 24 = 0$$

If you decide to travel clockwise around the loop, then you write, starting from point O

$$+24 - 3 - 21 = 0$$

which amounts to the same thing.

Now suppose the 3-volt drop is unknown, as in Fig. 6·4, where it is labeled V_x. If it is unknown, both its magnitude and polarity are unknown. In order to write a Kirchhoff's law equation around the loop, you must assign polarity marks to V_x. This you do arbitrarily. We can deliberately

Fig. 6·6 Application of Kirchhoff's laws. (a) Circuit. (b) Two loops used for two equations.

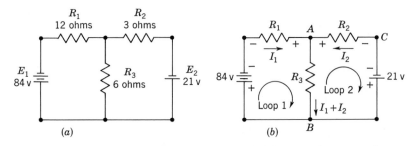

(a)

(b)

mark it wrong, as in Fig. 6·5, to see what happens. Going counterclockwise around the loop of Fig. 6·5:

$$+21 - V_x - 24 = 0$$

Solving,

$$V_x = -3 \text{ volts}$$

Just as in the case of a negative current, a negative solution for the voltage tells us that the actual polarity is opposite from the originally assumed polarity. We merely reverse the marks on the diagram, and the solution is complete: V_x is 3 volts, with polarity as originally shown in Fig. 6·3.

Method of analysis. Now we can solve a complete problem of a network containing two voltage sources, as shown in Fig. 6·6a. The problem is to find the currents and voltages for the three resistors. In analyzing this network, the procedure is as follows:

First, label all parts of the diagram with any convenient current direction, and put polarity marks across all resistors consistent with the assumed current direction. Remember that electron current in a resistor produces negative polarity where it enters and positive polarity where it leaves. The assumed current arrows and resultant polarity marks are shown in Fig. 6·6b.

With regard to the currents, we could label the three current arrows I_1, I_2, and I_3, but this gives three unknowns. From Kirchhoff's current law, we know that, for the circuit in Fig. 6·6b,

$$I_3 = I_1 + I_2$$

which we can use immediately to eliminate I_3, and the diagram is so labeled.

There are now two unknowns I_1 and I_2, and we must have two independent equations. These are obtained by writing two Kirchhoff's voltage-law equations around two closed loops in the circuit. Although any direction can be used, it is conventional to work in a clockwise direction as shown by the curved arrows for loop 1 and loop 2. The loop is just a complete closed path. We can start at any point in a loop, as long as we return to the same point. We shall use V_1 for the voltage drop across R_1, V_2 across R_2, etc.

Starting from point B around loop 1,

$$84 - V_1 - V_3 = 0$$

Starting from point C around loop 2,

$$-21 + V_3 + V_2 = 0$$

Notice that we have $-V_3$ going with the electron current around loop 1, but $+V_3$ in loop 2, going against the assumed current in R_3. Substituting the known values of R_1, R_2, and R_3,

$$V_1 = I_1 R_1 = 12I_1$$
$$V_2 = I_2 R_2 = 3I_2$$
$$V_3 = (I_1 + I_2)R_3 = 6(I_1 + I_2)$$

Substituting these values in loop 1,

$$84 - 12I_1 - 6(I_1 + I_2) = 0$$

Also, in loop 2,

$$-21 + 6(I_1 + I_2) + 3I_2 = 0$$

Combining and transposing,

$$-18I_1 - 6I_2 = -84$$
$$6I_1 + 9I_2 = 21$$

These two equations in the two unknowns I_1 and I_2 contain the solution of the network. They may be solved by any of the methods for the solution of simultaneous equations. Using the method of "elimination," multiply the bottom equation by 3, which gives

$$-18I_1 - 6I_2 = -84$$
$$18I_1 + 27I_2 = 63$$

Adding both equations, term by term, eliminates I_1 and gives

$$21I_2 = -21$$
$$I_2 = -1 \text{ amp}$$

The negative sign, as shown earlier, means only that the actual direction of electron current flow is opposite to the direction assumed at the start. Just reverse the direction of the arrow on the diagram, and the solution for I_2 is complete.

Now substitute -1 for I_2 in either of the two equations, and solve for I_1. Notice that the original algebraic sign from the solution must be used for the substitution. Using the first equation,

$$-18I_1 - 6(-1) = -84$$
or
$$-18I_1 + 6 = -84$$
$$-18I_1 = -90$$
$$I_1 = +5 \text{ amp}$$

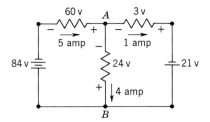

Fig. 6·7 Solution of Fig. 6·6 with all currents and voltages.

Since this result is positive, the assumed direction of I_1 is unchanged. The current through R_3 is $I_3 = I_1 + I_2$. Therefore,

$$I_3 = I_1 + I_2$$
$$= 5 + (-1) = 4 \text{ amp}$$

With all the currents known, now the voltages across the individual resistors can be calculated. Then

$$V_1 = I_1R_1 = 5 \times 12 = 60 \text{ volts}$$
$$V_2 = I_2R_2 = 1 \times 3 = 3 \text{ volts}$$
$$V_3 = I_3R_3 = 4 \times 6 = 24 \text{ volts}$$

As a summary of all the answers for this problem, Fig. 6·7 shows the network with all the currents and voltages labeled. The polarity marks for V_1, V_2, V_3 are determined from the known current directions. Remember that electron flow enters the negative side of R and leaves at the positive side.

As a check on the work, we can see whether Kirchhoff's current and voltage laws are satisfied:

At junction A, $5a = 4a + 1a$
At junction B, $4a + 1a = 5a$
Around loop 1, $84 - 60 - 24 = 0$
Around loop 2, $-21 + 24 - 3 = 0$

Mesh-current analysis. At the start of the solution of this network, three currents I_1, I_2, and I_3 were assumed. These are branch currents because they are the currents in each branch of the network. There were three unknowns, therefore. In order to eliminate one unknown, the Kirchhoff's current-law relation $I_3 = I_1 + I_2$ was used. A slightly different method of analysis, using *mesh currents,* performs the above step automatically and makes it possible to write the loop equations more conveniently.

Figure 6·8a shows again the problem of Fig. 6·6, but with mesh currents I_A and I_B. A *mesh* is the simplest possible loop in a circuit. This circuit contains two meshes, *abed* and *bcfe*. The path *acfd* is a loop but not a mesh because it contains two smaller loops.

A mesh current is a current that is assumed to flow in a mesh. Any convenient direction can be assumed; often, a clockwise direction is assumed as shown in Fig. 6·8b, in order to have a consistent procedure. A mesh current does not split up when it comes to a junction but is assumed to continue around its mesh unchanged. This is the difference between mesh currents and branch currents. Thus in this figure there are two independent mesh currents I_A and I_B.

After the mesh currents are drawn on the diagram, polarity marks are placed on each resistor, according to the assumed direction of the mesh currents, as shown in Fig. 6·8b. Notice that two sets of marks are placed across R_3. One set corresponds to the voltage drop produced by I_A, which is used when writing the equation for mesh A; the other set corresponds to the voltage drop produced by I_B and is used when writing the equation for mesh B.

Once this is done, the voltage equations can be immediately written. Note that the total voltage drop across R_3 is now due to two components—one caused by mesh current I_A and another caused by mesh current I_B flowing in the opposite direction. When writing the voltage equations, it is most convenient to go around the mesh in the same direction as the assumed mesh current. However, for a circuit with only two meshes, it may be preferable to take mesh currents in opposite directions in order to have the same voltage polarity across a common resistor like R_3. Either way, if you solve the circuit in Fig. 6·8 by mesh currents, you should get the same answers as in Fig. 6·7 for all the voltages and branch currents.

6·2   Thévenin's theorem

This is a very important and powerful theorem that is very useful in simplifying networks. It allows a complicated circuit containing many sources and many resistors, no matter how interconnected, to be represented by a single voltage source and a single resistor.

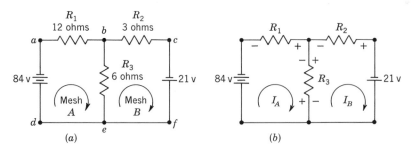

(a)   (b)

Fig. 6·8   Analysis by mesh currents for same circuit as Fig. 6·6. (a) Circuit considered in two parts, mesh A and mesh B. (b) Mesh currents I_A and I_B.

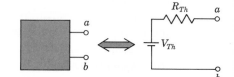

Fig. 6·9   Thévenin equivalent voltage source V_{Th} and series resistance R_{Th}.

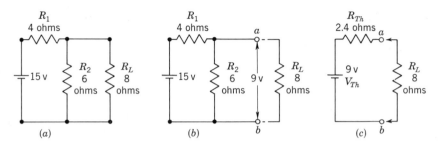

Fig. 6·10 Application of Thévenin's theorem. (a) Circuit. (b) Locating the output terminals a and b. (c) Thévenin equivalent circuit across terminals a and b.

Imagine that the block of Fig. 6·9 contains a circuit with many sources and many resistors. Terminals *a* and *b* are any two terminals of the circuit. Thévenin's theorem states that *the entire network of sources and resistors connected to terminals a and b may be replaced by a single voltage source* V_{Th} *and a single series resistance* R_{Th}, as shown in Fig. 6·9. V_{Th} is equal to the open-circuit voltage at the two terminals; R_{Th} is equal to the resistance seen looking back into the network with all voltage sources shorted.

As an example, consider the circuit of Fig. 6·10a, in which we wish to find the current in the 8-ohm resistor. A quick way to solve this problem is to use Thévenin's theorem.

Mentally disconnect the 8-ohm resistor from the circuit, as in *b* of the figure. Now we find the "Thévenin equivalent" of the circuit to the left of terminals *a* and *b*. This Thévenin equivalent always consists of a single voltage source in series with a single resistor, as shown in Fig. 6·10c. Our problem is only to find the size of the equivalent voltage source, generally designated V_{Th} because it is not actually a generated emf, and the equivalent resistance R_{Th}.

V_{Th} is the open-circuit voltage at the two Thévenin terminals of the network. That is, it equals the voltage across terminals *a* and *b* with nothing connected to those terminals except the circuit we are going to thevenize. In Fig. 6·10, we have taken care of this requirement by disconnecting the 8-ohm resistor. Notice that R_1 and R_2 then form a series voltage divider across the 15-volt battery. Also, the open-circuit voltage between terminals *a* and *b* is the same as the voltage across R_2. As a result, the open-circuit voltage V_{Th} is given by

$$V_{Th} = \frac{6}{10} \times 15 \text{ volts} = 9 \text{ volts}$$

R_{Th} is the resistance seen looking back into the circuit from terminals *a* and *b*, with all voltage sources shorted out. With the 15-volt battery mentally shorted out, then looking back into the network we see 6 ohms and 4 ohms in parallel, or 2.4 ohms. Thus the Thévenin equivalent of the circuit to the left of terminals *a* and *b* in Fig. 6·10c consists of a 9-volt source in series with a 2.4-ohm resistor.

To find the current I_L through the 8-ohm R_L,

$$I_L = \frac{V_{Th}}{R_{Th} + R_L} = \frac{9}{2.4 + 8} = \frac{9}{10.4} = 0.865 \text{ amp}$$

R_{Th} and R_L are added because they are in series with the equivalent voltage source V_{Th}.

The advantage of thevenizing a circuit like this is that the effect of changing the 8-ohm resistor can be calculated easily for different values of R_L. In the original circuit, a complete new solution of the series-parallel combination would be required each time the load resistor was changed.

As another example of the use of Thévenin's theorem, let us solve for the current in R_3 of Fig. 6·6. This circuit has already been solved by Kirchhoff's laws but is repeated in Fig. 6·11 to show how it can be simplified by Thévenin's theorem. First mark terminals *a* and *b* across R_3. Then calculate the open-circuit voltage from *a* to *b*—that is, the voltage at these terminals with R_3 disconnected. This voltage is V_{Th}. Also, we must find the resistance looking back into the circuit from terminals *a* and *b*.

With R_3 removed in Fig. 6·11b, we are left with a simple series circuit in which the current is

$$I = \frac{84 \text{ volts} - 21 \text{ volts}}{15 \text{ ohms}} = \frac{63 \text{ volts}}{15 \text{ ohms}} = 4.2 \text{ amp}$$

The net voltage here is the difference between the two opposing voltages, while the total resistance of 15 ohms is the sum of R_1 and R_2.

This 4.2-amp through the 12-ohm R_1 produces 50.4 volts for V_1. Simi-

Fig. 6·11   *Solving the same circuit as Fig. 6·6 by using Thévenin's theorem. (a) Circuit. (b) Disconnect R_3 to find the open-circuit voltage V_{Th} between terminals a and b across R_3. (c) Calculating R_{Th}. (d) Thévenin equivalent circuit.*

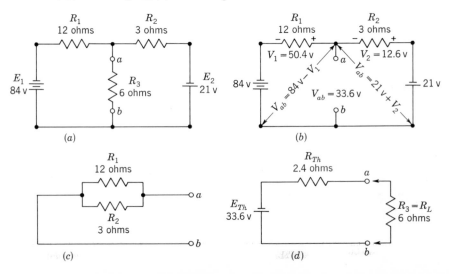

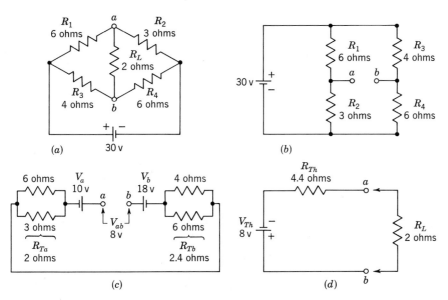

Fig. 6·12 *Solving an unbalanced bridge circuit by using Thévenin's theorem.*
(a) Circuit. (b) Disconnect R_L to find V_{Th} between terminals a and b. (c) Calculating R_{Th}. (d) Thévenin equivalent circuit.

larly, V_2 is 12.6 volts. As a result, the open-circuit voltage from a to b is

$$V_{Th} = V_{ab} = 84 \text{ volts} - V_1 = 84 \text{ volts} - 50.4 \text{ volts} = 33.6 \text{ volts}$$

or $\quad V_{Th} = V_{ab} = 21 \text{ volts} + V_2 = 21 \text{ volts} + 12.6 \text{ volts} = 33.6 \text{ volts}$

Notice that V_2 adds to the 21-volt E_2 because their polarities are series-aiding, while V_1 and E_1 are series-opposing. In either case, the voltage across terminals a and b equals 33.6 volts, for the value of the Thévenin equivalent voltage source.

The resistance looking back from terminals a and b is shown in c of Fig. 6·11. Now R_1 and R_2 are in parallel, with the voltage sources E_1 and E_2 shorted. As a result,

$$R_{Th} = \frac{3 \times 12}{3 + 12} = \frac{36}{15} = 2.4 \text{ ohms}$$

The final result is the Thévenin equivalent in d with V_{Th} of 33.6 volts and R_{Th} of 2.4 ohms.

In order to find the current through R_3, it is reconnected as a load resistance across terminals a and b of the Thévenin equivalent circuit. Then

$$I_3 = \frac{V_{Th}}{R_{Th} + R_3} = \frac{33.6}{2.4 + 6} = \frac{33.6}{8.4} = 4 \text{ amp}$$

This is the same answer calculated for I_3 by Kirchhoff's laws in Fig. 6·7.

As another example, let us solve the unbalanced bridge circuit shown in Fig. 6·12. How much is the current through the 2-ohm R_L at the center of the bridge?

The first step is to remove the 2-ohm resistor, in order to find the open-circuit voltages. Then the remainder of the circuit can be redrawn as in Fig. 6·12b. Now, each of the branches has two resistors in a series voltage divider. As a result, the open-circuit voltage V_a at terminal a with respect to the negative return line is:

$$V_a = \frac{3}{6+3} \times 30 = 10 \text{ volts}$$

and

$$V_b = \frac{6}{6+4} \times 30 = 18 \text{ volts}$$

These voltages are shown in Fig. 6·12c. The total open-circuit voltage across terminals a and b is the difference between V_a and V_b. Then V_{ab} is 18 volts − 10 volts, which equals 8 volts. This value of 8 volts is V_{Th}.

To find the value of R_{Th} in Fig. 6·12c, short out the voltages V_a and V_b and look back into the circuit from terminals a and b. In this case it is easiest to consider one terminal at a time. Looking into terminal a we see 6 ohms and 3 ohms in parallel for an R_{T_a} of 2 ohms. Looking into terminal b, we see 4 ohms and 6 ohms in parallel for an R_{T_b} of 2.4 ohms. Also, R_{T_a} and R_{T_b} are in series for a total of 4.4 ohms. The final Thévenin equivalent, therefore, is an 8-volt source V_{Th} in series with a 4.4-ohm resistance R_{Th}, as shown in d.

Now we can reconnect the 2-ohm resistor R_L to the Thévenin equivalent across terminals a and b. The current through R_L is

$$I_L = \frac{V_{Th}}{R_{Th} + R_L} = \frac{8}{4.4 + 2} = \frac{8}{6.4} = 1.25 \text{ amp}$$

This value is the current through the 2-ohm R_L in the unbalanced bridge circuit in Fig. 6·12a. Furthermore, the amount of I_L for any value of R_L in the bridge circuit in a can be calculated from the Thévenin equivalent in d.

6·3   Norton's theorem

A source of electrical energy is often shown as a voltage source in series with a resistance, which symbolizes the internal resistance of the source. This representation is shown in Fig. 6·13a. However, a source may be represented equally well by a *current* source *shunted* by a resistance, as in Fig. 6·13b. Just as a voltage source is rated at, say, 10 volts, a current source is rated at, for example, 1 amp. Similarly, when we say that the voltage source delivers 10 volts across its terminals regardless of the current, an ideal current source delivers its rated current regardless of the voltage across its terminals.

If the current source I in Fig. 6·13b is a 2-amp source, it supplies 2 amp no matter what is connected across terminals a and b. If nothing is connected across the terminals then all of the 2 amp flows through R. If a load

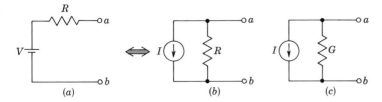

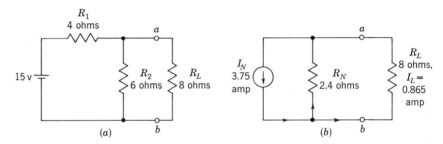

Fig. 6·13   *General forms for a source of power to be connected to a load across terminals a and b. (a) Voltage source with series R. (b) Current source with parallel R. (c) Current source with shunt conductance G.*

Fig. 6·14   *Same circuit as Fig. 6·10, solved by Norton's theorem. (a) Original circuit. (b) Norton equivalent to find* I_L.

is connected across *a* and *b* then the 2 amp divides according to the current-division principles of parallel branches. Remember that parallel currents divide inversely as the branch resistances but directly with conductance. For this reason, it may be more convenient sometimes to consider the current source *I* shunted by a conductance *G*, as in *c*, where $1/R$ ohms is equal to *G* in mhos.

The symbol for a current source is a circle with an arrow inside, as shown in Fig. 6·13*b*. The arrow indicates the direction of the current output of the source. In this book it is used to indicate the direction of electron flow.

Norton's theorem is very useful in the simplification of the *currents* in a network. This theorem states that *any two-terminal network containing voltage and current sources and resistors, no matter how interconnected, may be represented by a single current source shunted by a single resistance. The size of the current source is equal to the current that flows through the terminals of the network when they are short-circuited; the size of the shunting resistor is equal to the resistance seen from the terminals looking back into the network.*

Actually, the single resistor in both the Norton and Thévenin equivalent circuits is the same. In the Norton case it is shunted across the current source; in the Thévenin case it is in series with the voltage source.

As an example of calculations using Norton's theorem, let us recalculate the current in the circuit of Fig. 6·10, which was solved before by Thévenin's theorem. This circuit is repeated in Fig. 6·14, as a Norton equivalent to find the current through R_L.

The first step is to imagine a short circuit across the terminals *ab*. How much current is flowing in the short circuit? Note that a short across *ab* also shorts out the 6-ohm R_2. The short-circuit current is

$$I_N = \frac{15 \text{ volts}}{4 \text{ ohms}} = 3.75 \text{ amp}$$

This amount is the total current available from the current source, to be divided between the R_N and R_L branches in Fig. 6·14b.

To find the equivalent resistance R_N, remove the short across *a* and *b* and consider the terminals open, without R_L. Now the source voltage is considered to be shorted. Then the resistance seen looking back from terminals *ab* is 4 ohms in parallel with 6 ohms, which equals 2.4 ohms for R_N. Thus the Norton equivalent is as shown in Fig. 6·14b. It consists of a 3.75-amp current source I_N shunted by the 2.4-ohm R_N. The arrow is placed on the current source so that current flows from *b* up to *a*, as in the original circuit.

Now replace the 8-ohm resistor R_L. The current source still delivers 3.75 amp, but now that current divides according to the principles of current dividers for parallel circuits. Then the current through R_L is

$$I_L = \frac{R_N}{R_N + R_L} \times I_N = \frac{2.4}{2.4 + 8} \times 3.75a = 0.865 \text{ amp}$$

This value is the same as calculated before by Thévenin's theorem in Fig. 6·10.

As another example of the use of Norton's theorem, let us solve again

Fig. 6·15   *Same circuit as Fig. 6·6, solved by Norton's theorem. (a) Original circuit. (b) Shorting R_3 to determine I_N. (c) Norton equivalent to find I_3.*

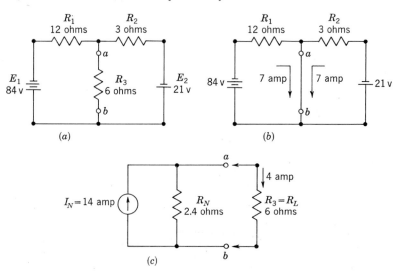

the circuit of Fig. 6·6, which was solved before by Kirchhoff's laws but is repeated in Fig. 6·15 as a Norton equivalent. How much is the current through the 6-ohm R_3?

As the first step to find I_N, solve for the current that flows in a short placed across terminals *ab*. The short separates this circuit into two isolated parts, as shown in Fig. 6·15*b*. Each is solved separately for its own current contribution to I_N. Because of the 84-volt battery, there is a current

$$I_{s_1} = \frac{84 \text{ volts}}{12 \text{ ohms}} = 7 \text{ amp}$$

flowing in the short circuit. Because of the 21-volt battery there is a current

$$I_{s_2} = \frac{21 \text{ volts}}{3 \text{ ohms}} = 7 \text{ amp}$$

also flowing in the short circuit. Since both these currents flow in the same direction, the total short-circuit current I_N is 14 amp.

The resistance looking back from *ab* with both voltage sources shorted consists of R_1 and R_2 in parallel. Then

$$R_N = \frac{3 \times 12}{3 + 12} = \frac{36}{15} = 2.4 \text{ ohms}$$

Therefore, the Norton equivalent circuit, as shown in Fig. 6·15*c*, consists of a 14-amp current source shunted by a 2.4-ohm resistance. The current-source direction is taken such that the terminal current flows through the terminals in the same direction as in the original circuit.

Now we replace the 6-ohm R_3 as the load resistance and the current through it is

$$I_3 = \frac{R_N}{R_N + R_3} \times I_N = \frac{2.4}{2.4 + 6} \times 14 = 4 \text{ amp}$$

This answer for I_3 is the same value calculated before by using Kirchhoff's laws and by Thévenin's theorem. Any one of the methods could be used for solving this problem. If the value of the load resistance is to be varied, though, it will be much faster to use a Thévenin or Norton equivalent circuit to solve for the different values of load voltage or current.

6·4 Thévenin-Norton conversions

Thévenin's theorem says that any network can be represented by a voltage source and series resistance, while Norton's theorem says that the same network can be represented by a current source and shunt resistance. It must therefore be possible to convert directly from a Thévenin form to a Norton form and vice versa. Such conversions often prove helpful in circuit analysis.

Consider the Thévenin equivalent circuit in Fig. 6·16a. What is its Norton equivalent? To find it, we apply Norton's theorem to this circuit, just as we would to any other network. The short-circuit current is

$$I_N = \frac{V_{Th}}{R_{Th}} = \frac{6 \text{ volts}}{3 \text{ ohms}} = 2 \text{ amp}$$

The resistance looking backward from the terminals, with the voltage source considered a short circuit, is 3 ohms. Hence the Norton equivalent consists of a current source that delivers the short-circuit current of 2 amp shunted by the same resistance that appears in the Thévenin circuit. The results are shown in Fig. 6·16b.

For the opposite conversion, we can start with the Norton circuit of Fig. 6·16b and get back to the original Thévenin circuit in a. To do this, apply Thévenin's theorem just as you would for any other network. Find the Thévenin resistance by looking back from the terminals. But, whereas a voltage source is a short circuit for this purpose, a *current source is an open circuit.* Thus, looking back from terminals a and b we see the 3-ohm R_N in parallel with the infinite resistance of the open current-source. The

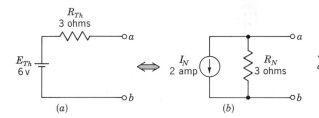

Fig. 6·16 The Thévenin equivalent in a corresponds to the Norton equivalent in b.

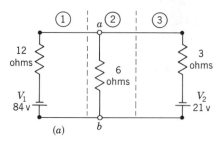

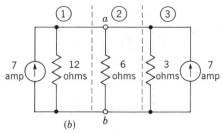

Fig. 6·17 Application of Millman's theorem by considering circuit in three parts or segments. See text for analysis. (a) Original circuit. (b) Norton equivalent of each segment. (c) Norton equivalent of entire circuit.

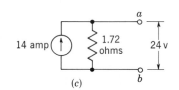

total resistance then is 3 ohms. In other words, the resistance R_N is the same as R_{Th}. It just moves from shunt to series connections.

So, all that is required is to calculate the open-circuit voltage. With terminals a and b open in Fig. 6·16b, note that all the current of the current source flows through the 3-ohm R_N. Then the open-circuit voltage is simply

$$V_{Th} = I_N R_N = 2 \text{ amp} \times 3 \text{ ohms} = 6 \text{ volts}$$

As a result, we have the original Thévenin circuit in a, consisting of the 6-volt source V_{Th} in series with the 3-ohm R_{Th}.

In summary, the following formulas can be used for these conversions:

Thévenin from Norton	*Norton from Thévenin*
$R_{Th} = R_N$	$R_N = R_{Th}$
$V_{Th} = I_N \times R_N$	$I_N = V_{Th} \div R_{Th}$

6·5 Millman's theorem

The application of Norton's theorem to a certain type of circuit gives another useful relationship known as Millman's theorem. Let us consider again the network of Fig. 6·6, which has been redrawn in slightly different form in Fig. 6·17. The voltage across terminals a and b is what we are interested in finding. We can solve this problem by nortonizing separately each of the three segments into which the circuit has been divided. Consider the first segment separately. This short-circuit current is

$$I_s = \frac{84 \text{ volts}}{12 \text{ ohms}} = 7 \text{ amp}$$

Therefore, this segment can be replaced by a 7-amp current source shunted by a 12-ohm resistor, as shown in Fig. 6·17b. Segment 2 contains only a resistor; so this resistor is just retained in its position. However, segment 3 is replaced by a 7-amp current source shunted by a 3-ohm resistor, similar to segment 1.

Since the two resulting current sources are in parallel, they may be combined into a single 14-amp current source. Also, the three resistors are in parallel and may be combined into a single 1.72-ohm resistor. The final circuit is shown in c, with a 14-amp current source shunted by 1.72 ohms.

In Fig. 6·17c, the entire 14 amp of the equivalent current source can flow through the 1.72-ohm resistance. Then the voltage across ab is given by Ohm's law as

$$V_{ab} = IR = 14 \text{ amp} \times 1.72 \text{ ohms} = 24 \text{ volts}$$

This voltage across terminals a and b is the voltage across the 6-ohm R in the original circuit in Fig. 6·17a.

Let us retrace our steps, using the letter notation for the segments 1, 2, and 3 in Fig. 6·17a. First we converted each branch containing a voltage source to the current-source form and added all the current sources:

$$I_{total} = \frac{V_1}{R_1} + \frac{V_2}{R_2} + \frac{V_3}{R_3} + \cdots + \text{etc.}$$

In this case V_2 happened to be zero, but in general it can have any value. The three dots mean that similar terms are included for each additional branch the circuit may contain. Then we found the equivalent resistance of all the parallel resistors:

$$R_T = \frac{1}{1/R_1 + 1/R_2 + 1/R_3 + \cdots}$$

Using Ohm's law we then multiplied I_{total} by R_T to give

$$V_{ab} = \frac{V_1/R_1 + V_2/R_2 + V_3/R_3 + \cdots}{1/R_1 + 1/R_2 + 1/R_3 + \cdots}$$

This formula, obtained by using Norton's theorem on a network of the form in Fig. 6·17a, is known as Millman's theorem. Such networks occur frequently in the analysis of electronic circuits. Using Millman's theorem, the voltage across the network may be readily obtained by direct substitution in the formula. For this example, with V_2 zero, the substitution results in:

$$V_{ab} = \frac{7 + 0 + 7}{\frac{1}{12} + \frac{1}{6} + \frac{1}{3}} = \frac{14}{\frac{7}{12}} = 24 \text{ volts}$$

6·6   The superposition theorem

The superposition principle is a very simple idea, yet it provides a powerful and often used method for the analysis of networks. This theorem states that *in any network containing more than one voltage or current source, the current in any part of the network is the algebraic sum of the currents produced by each source acting separately.*

The superposition principle requires that all the circuit elements be *linear.* This means that the resistances in the network must be constant—their value must not depend on the amount of current flowing. Also, the network must be *bilateral*—it must conduct current equally well in either direction. It should be noted that networks containing diodes, vacuum tubes, or transistors are neither linear nor bilateral.

As an example of the use of the superposition principle, let us solve again the network of Fig. 6·6, which has been redrawn as Fig. 6·18a. Now the problem is to find the current in the 3-ohm R_2.

First consider only the I components produced by the 84-volt E_1. In

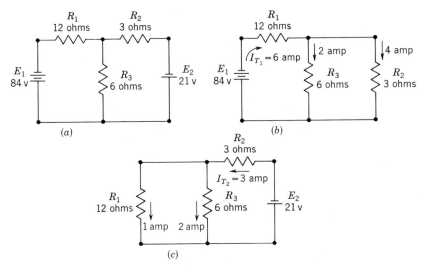

Fig. 6·18 *Application of the superposition theorem. (a) Circuit the same as Fig. 6·6. (b) Current produced by E_1 without E_2. (c) Current produced by E_2 without E_1.*

order to do this we short-circuit all other voltage sources in the network (and open-circuit any current sources in the network). With E_2 shorted, the circuit appears as in Fig. 6·18b. Now R_1 is in series with the parallel bank of R_2 and R_3. Then the total resistance seen by the 84-volt E_1 is

$$R_{T_1} = 12 + \frac{3 \times 6}{3 + 6} = 12 + 2 = 14 \text{ ohms}$$

And the total current drawn from the 84-volt battery is

$$I_{T_1} = \frac{84 \text{ volts}}{14 \text{ ohms}} = 6 \text{ amp}$$

In Fig. 6·18b, therefore, the 6-amp I_{T_1} leaves the battery, flows through the 12-ohm R_1, and divides at the junction of the 3-ohm R_2 and 6-ohm R_3. Using the rule for current division between the two parallel branches of R_2 and R_3, the current through the 3-ohm R_2 is

$$I_2 = \frac{R_3}{R_3 + R_2} \times I_T = \frac{6}{6 + 3} \times 6 = 4 \text{ amp}$$

Thus the current in the 3-ohm R_2 due to the 84-volt battery is 4 amp. The remainder of 2 amp flows through R_3, but we are interested now in the current I_2 in R_2.

Next we short out the 84-volt E_1 and consider the component of current produced by the 21-volt E_2. The resulting circuit is in Fig. 6·18c. The total resistance seen by the 21-volt battery is

$$R_{T_2} = 3 + \frac{6 \times 12}{6 + 12} = 3 + 4 = 7 \text{ ohms}$$

And the total current drawn from the 21-volt battery is

$$I_{T_2} = \frac{21 \text{ volts}}{7 \text{ ohms}} = 3 \text{ amp}$$

This current flows from right to left, as shown in c. Note that here the current in R_2 is the total line current of 3 amp produced by E_2.

Thus there are two components of current in R_2: 4 amp to the right produced by E_1 and 3 amp to the left produced by E_2. The result is a net actual current of 1 amp to the right. This answer is the same as obtained before by using Kirchhoff's laws in Fig. 6·7.

As another example of the use of the superposition principle, what is the voltage between point b and ground in Fig. 6·19? Using the superposition principle we determine the voltage produced at point b by each source separately and then add the results algebraically. All the voltages marked on the diagram give the potential at each point with respect to the common chassis ground.

First, we find the contribution by the +240 volts of E_1 by temporarily grounding point c. Then R_1 and R_2 form a series voltage divider. As a result,

$$V_{b_1} = \frac{R_1}{R_1 + R_2} \times E_1 = \frac{60}{60 + 30} \times 240 \text{ volts} = 160 \text{ volts}$$

Next, to find the contribution of the -90-volt source, we ground point a. Again we have a series voltage divider, but this time for negative voltage. Then

$$V_{b_2} = \frac{R_2}{R_2 + R_1} \times E_2 = \frac{30}{30 + 60} \times -90 \text{ volts} = -30 \text{ volts}$$

Fig. 6·19 Using the superposition theorem to find the net voltage at point b to ground.

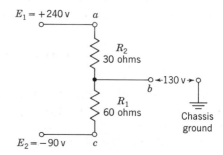

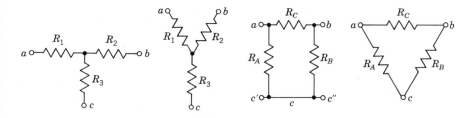

Fig. 6·20   The form of a T or Y network.   Fig. 6·21   The form of a π or Δ network.

The total voltage at point b, therefore, is

$$V_b = V_{b_1} + V_{b_2} = +160 - 30 = +130 \text{ volts}$$

Notice that, by means of superposition, the problem was reduced to two simple series voltage dividers.

6·7   Delta-wye transformations

In the solution of electrical networks, it is often very helpful to convert a circuit of the form in Fig. 6·20 to a circuit of the form in Fig. 6·21, or vice versa. Without the conversion, it may be impossible to solve the circuit, or the conversion makes the solution shorter.

The network in Fig. 6·20 is known as a T (tee) or Y (wye). These names are suggested by the shape of the configuration. The T and Y are different names for the identical circuit, the only difference being that the R_1 and R_2 arms are drawn horizontally in the case of the T, or inclined upward in the case of the Y.

The network in Fig. 6·21 is known as a π (pi) or Δ (delta), these names being suggested by the resemblance to these Greek letters. The π and Δ are different names for the same configuration, the only difference being that the single point c of the Δ is separated into the two points c' and c'' for the π. People in electronics generally speak of T and π circuits, whereas in the electrical power industry they are generally called Y and Δ.

The formulas for T and π transformation are given here. The proof of these conversions can be found in most books on electrical engineering. All these formulas and the network theorems are derived from Kirchhoff's laws.

Converting T to π, or Y to Δ

$$R_A = \frac{R_1R_2 + R_1R_3 + R_2R_3}{R_2}$$

$$R_B = \frac{R_1R_2 + R_1R_3 + R_2R_3}{R_1}$$

$$R_C = \frac{R_1R_2 + R_1R_3 + R_2R_3}{R_3}$$

Converting π to T, or Δ to Y

$$R_1 = \frac{R_AR_C}{R_A + R_B + R_C}$$

$$R_2 = \frac{R_BR_C}{R_A + R_B + R_C}$$

$$R_3 = \frac{R_AR_B}{R_A + R_B + R_C}$$

As an aid to remembering these formulas, the following scheme is useful. Place the Y inside the Δ, as shown in Fig. 6·22. Notice that the Δ has three closed sides, while the Y has three open arms. Also note how resistors can be considered opposite each other in the two networks. For instance, the open arm R_2 is opposite the closed side R_A, while R_1 is opposite R_B and R_3 opposite R_C. Furthermore, each resistor in an open arm has two adjacent resistors in the closed sides. For R_1, its adjacent resistors are R_A and R_C; R_C and R_B are adjacent to R_2 while R_B and R_A are adjacent to R_3.

In the formulas for Y to Δ conversion, each side of the delta is found by first taking all possible cross products of the arms of the Y, using two arms at a time. There are three such cross products. The sum of the three cross products is then divided by the opposite arm to find the value of each side in the delta. Notice that the numerator remains the same for the sum of the three cross products. However, each side of the delta is calculated by dividing this sum by the opposite arm.

For the case of Δ to Y conversion, each arm of the wye is found by taking the product of the two adjacent sides in the delta, and dividing each product by the sum of the three sides of the delta. Notice that the denominator for the sum of the three sides remains the same in the three formulas. However, each arm is calculated by dividing this sum into each cross product.

The values shown for the equivalent Y and Δ in Fig. 6·22 are calculated as follows: Starting with 4, 6, and 10 ohms for sides R_A, R_B, and R_C, respectively, in the delta, the corresponding arms in the Y are

$$R_1 = \frac{R_A R_C}{R_A + R_B + R_C} = \frac{4 \times 10}{4 + 6 + 10} = \frac{40}{20} = 2 \text{ ohms}$$

$$R_2 = \frac{R_B R_C}{20} = \frac{10 \times 6}{20} = \frac{60}{20} = 3 \text{ ohms}$$

$$R_3 = \frac{R_A R_B}{20} = \frac{6 \times 4}{20} = \frac{24}{20} = 1.2 \text{ ohms}$$

As a check on these values, we can calculate the equivalent delta for this wye. Starting with values of 2, 3, and 1.2 ohms for R_1, R_2, and R_3, respectively, in the wye, the corresponding values in the delta are

Fig. 6·22   Converting between Y and Δ networks. See text for conversion formulas.

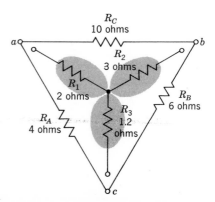

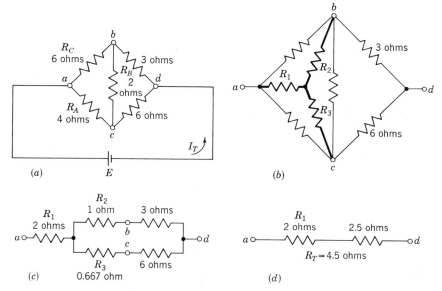

Fig. 6·23 Solving a bridge circuit by delta-to-wye conversion. (a) Original circuit. (b) How $R_1R_2R_3$ wye in heavy lines corresponds to $R_AR_BR_C$ delta. (c) The wye substituted for the delta. (d) Total resistance of bridge circuit across points a and d equals 4.5 ohms for R_T.

$$R_A = \frac{R_1R_2 + R_1R_3 + R_2R_3}{R_2} = \frac{6 + 2.4 + 3.6}{3} = \frac{12}{3} = 4 \text{ ohms}$$

$$R_B = \frac{12}{R_1} = \frac{12}{2} = 6 \text{ ohms}$$

$$R_C = \frac{12}{R_3} = \frac{12}{1.2} = 10 \text{ ohms}$$

These results show that the Y and Δ networks in Fig. 6·22 are equivalent to each other when they have the values obtained with the conversion formulas.

As an example of the use of such transformations, consider the bridge circuit of Fig. 6·23. The total current I_T from the battery is desired. There are two possible approaches to the solution of this problem by transformations, and both will be shown. In either case we must first find the total resistance R_T.

One approach is to note that the bridge consists of two deltas, and that one of them can be replaced by an equivalent Y. We can replace the delta $R_AR_BR_C$ by an equivalent Y, as shown in b. Using the conversion formulas,

$$R_1 = \frac{R_AR_C}{R_A + R_B + R_C} = \frac{24}{12} = 2 \text{ ohms}$$

$$R_2 = \frac{R_BR_C}{12} = \frac{12}{12} = 1 \text{ ohm}$$

$$R_3 = \frac{R_AR_B}{12} = \frac{8}{12} = 0.667 \text{ ohm}$$

These values for R_1, R_2, and R_3 are labeled in c.

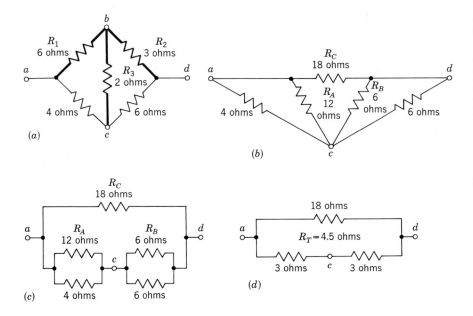

Fig. 6·24   Solving the same bridge circuit as Fig. 6·23 but with wye-to-delta conversion. (a) Circuit with $R_1R_2R_3$ in heavy lines to show wye. (b) This wye converted to $R_AR_BR_C$ delta. (c) Series-parallel circuit. (d) Total resistance of bridge circuit across points a and d equals 4.5 ohms for R_T.

When this equivalent Y replaces the original delta, the resistances can be combined as ordinary parallel and series circuits. The result is a total resistance R_T of 4.5 ohms for the entire bridge, as shown in *d*. The current drawn from the battery can then be readily found from Ohm's law, as equal to E/R_T.

Another approach is to recognize that the 6-ohm, 3-ohm, and 2-ohm resistors of the bridge are also connected in a Y configuration, as shown by the heavy lines of Fig. 6·24a. These can be replaced by an equivalent delta, as shown in *b*, with values determined as follows:

$$R_A = \frac{R_1R_2 + R_1R_3 + R_2R_3}{R_2} = \frac{36}{3} = 12 \text{ ohms}$$

$$R_B = \frac{36}{R_1} = \frac{36}{6} = 6 \text{ ohms}$$

$$R_C = \frac{36}{R_3} = \frac{36}{2} = 18 \text{ ohms}$$

When this equivalent delta replaces the original Y, we have the parallel and series combinations in *c*. Combining these resistances in *d* results in a total resistance of 4.5 ohms for the bridge.

SUMMARY

1. *Kirchhoff's voltage law.* The algebraic sum of the voltages around any closed loop in a circuit is equal to zero.
2. *Kirchhoff's current law.* The algebraic sum of all the currents entering any point in a circuit is equal to the algebraic sum of the currents leaving that same point.
3. *Thévenin's theorem.* Any two-terminal network can be replaced by a single voltage source and a single series resistance.
4. *Norton's theorem.* Any two-terminal network can be replaced by a single current source and a single shunt resistance.
5. *Superposition theorem.* In a network containing more than one source, the current in any part of the network can be found by adding algebraically the effect of each source separately, with all other sources shorted out if they are voltage sources, or open-circuited if they are current sources.
6. The comparison between delta and wye networks is illustrated in Fig. 6·22.

SELF-EXAMINATION (*Answers at back of book.*)

Here's a chance to see how well you have learned the material in this chapter. These exercises are for your self-testing only.

1. According to Kirchhoff's laws, the algebraic sum of the voltages around any closed loop is equal to (*a*) the highest voltage; (*b*) zero; (*c*) the magnitude of the constant-current source; (*d*) the Thévenin voltage source.
2. According to Kirchhoff's laws, the sum of the currents entering a point in the circuit is equal to the (*a*) sum of the currents leaving that point; (*b*) constant-current source in the circuit; (*c*) sum of the voltages around the loop; (*d*) sum of the applied voltages.
3. The magnitude of the voltage source in a Thévenin equivalent circuit is equal to the (*a*) closed-circuit terminal voltage; (*b*) short-circuit terminal current; (*c*) open-circuit terminal voltage; (*d*) open-circuit terminal current.
4. The series resistance in a Thévenin equivalent circuit is equal to the resistance seen looking backward from the terminals with the (*a*) load resistance connected; (*b*) load resistance disconnected; (*c*) internal voltage sources open-circuited; (*d*) internal current sources short-circuited.
5. The magnitude of the current source in a Norton equivalent circuit is equal to the (*a*) closed-circuit terminal voltage; (*b*) short-circuit terminal current; (*c*) open-circuit terminal voltage; (*d*) open-circuit terminal current.
6. The shunt resistance in a Norton equivalent circuit is equal to the resistance seen looking backward from the terminals with the (*a*) load resistance connected; (*b*) load resistance disconnected; (*c*) internal voltage sources open-circuited; (*d*) internal current sources short-circuited.
7. In a Thévenin equivalent circuit, the single resistor R_{Th} is in (*a*) shunt with the current source; (*b*) series with the voltage source; (*c*) shunt with the voltage source; (*d*) series with the current source.
8. In a Norton equivalent circuit, the single resistor R_N is in (*a*) shunt with the current source; (*b*) series with the voltage source; (*c*) shunt with the voltage source; (*d*) series with the current source.
9. A Δ network is the same as a (*a*) T; (*b*) Y; (*c*) π; (*d*) Ω.
10. In determining the size of the resistance in both Thévenin and Norton equivalent circuits: (*a*) voltage sources are short-circuited and current sources are open-circuited; (*b*) current sources are short-circuited and voltage sources are open-circuited; (*c*) only voltage sources are open-circuited; (*d*) only current sources are short-circuited.
11. Referring to the Norton equivalent circuit in Fig. 6·14*b*, the branch current through R_N equals (*a*) 0.865 amp; (*b*) 2.4 amp; (*c*) 2.885 amp; (*d*) 3.75 amp.
12. Refer to the equivalent of the bridge circuit with R_T of 4.5 ohms in Fig. 6·23*d*. If *E* is 9 volts, then I_T is (*a*) 1.5 amp; (*b*) 2 amp; (*c*) 4.5 amp; (*d*) 9 amp.

ESSAY QUESTIONS

1. In applying Kirchhoff's current law, give the rule for the algebraic sign of currents.
2. In applying Kirchhoff's voltage law, give the rule for the algebraic sign of voltages.
3. State the rules for determining V_{Th} and R_{Th} for a Thévenin equivalent circuit.
4. State the rules for determining I_N and R_N for a Norton equivalent circuit.
5. State the superposition theorem.
6. What is the difference between a mesh and a loop?
7. What is the difference between a mesh current and a branch current?
8. Draw a delta network and a wye network, and give the six formulas needed to convert from one to the other.

PROBLEMS (*Answers to selected problems at back of book.*)

1. Find the Thévenin equivalent for the network between terminals *a* and *b* across R_L in Fig. 6·25.
2. Find the Norton equivalent circuit for Fig. 6·25.
3. Find the voltage E_0 with respect to chassis ground in Fig. 6·26.
4. Find the voltage across R_L in Fig. 6·27.
5. Find the current in R_L in Fig. 6·27.
6. Find the Thévenin equivalent circuit seen by R_L in Fig. 6·28.
7. Convert the Thévenin circuit found in Prob. 6 to a Norton circuit.
8. Solve for all the currents and voltages in Fig. 6·28.
9. Solve for all the currents in Fig. 6·29.
10. Convert the T in Fig. 6·30 to an equivalent π network.
11. Convert the π network in Fig. 6·31 to an equivalent T.
12. Solve for the current in R_1 at the center of the bridge in Fig. 6·32.

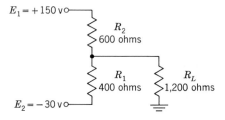

Fig. 6·25   For Probs. 1 and 2.

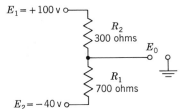

Fig. 6·26   For Prob. 3.

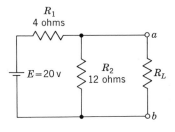

Fig. 6·27   For Probs. 4 and 5.

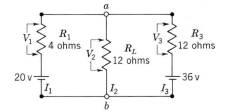

Fig. 6·28   For Probs. 6, 7, and 8.

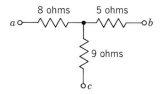

Fig. 6·29   For Prob. 9.

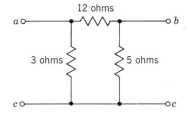

Fig. 6·30   For Prob. 10.

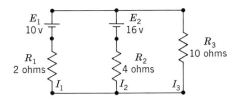

Fig. 6·31   For Prob. 11.

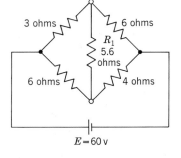

Fig. 6·32   For Prob. 12.

Review of chapters ① to ⑥

SUMMARY

1. The electron is the basic quantity of negative electricity; the proton of positive electricity. Both have the same charge but opposite polarities.

2. A quantity of electrons is a negative charge; a deficiency of electrons is a positive charge. Like charges repel each other; unlike charges attract.

3. Charge is measured in coulombs; 6.25×10^{18} electrons equals one coulomb. Charge in motion is current. One coulomb per second equals one ampere of current.

4. Potential difference is measured in volts. One volt produces one ampere of current against the opposition of one ohm of resistance.

5. The three forms of Ohm's law are $I = E/R$, $E = IR$, and $R = E/I$.

6. Power in watts equals EI, I^2R, or E^2/R, with E, I, and R in volts, amperes, and ohms, respectively.

7. The most common multiples and submultiples of the practical units are *meg* or M for 10^6, *micro* or μ for 10^{-6}, *kilo* or K for 10^3, and *milli* or m for 10^{-3}.

8. For series resistances: (*a*) the current is the same in all resistances; (*b*) the *IR* drops can be different with unequal resistances; (*c*) the applied voltage equals the sum of the series *IR* drops; (*d*) the total resistance equals the sum of the individual resistances; (*e*) an open in one resistance results in no current through the entire series circuit.

9. For parallel resistances: (*a*) the voltage is the same across all resistances; (*b*) the branch currents can be different with unequal resistances; (*c*) the total line current equals the sum of the parallel branch currents; (*d*) the combined resistance of parallel branches is less than the smallest resistance, as determined by the reciprocal formula $(4 \cdot 1)$; (*e*) an open in one branch does not open the other branches; (*f*) a short across one branch shorts all the branches.

10. In series-parallel circuits, the resistances in one current path without any branch points are in series; all the rules of series resistances apply. The resistances across the same two branch points are in parallel; all the rules of parallel resistances apply.

11. Advanced circuits can be solved by network analysis, including Kirchhoff's laws, Thévenin's theorem, Norton's theorem, superposition, and delta-wye conversions, as explained in Chap. 6.

REFERENCES (*Additional references at back of book.*)

Cooke, N. M., *Basic Mathematics for Electronics*, McGraw-Hill Book Company, New York.

Croft, T., *Practical Electricity*, 4th ed., McGraw-Hill Book Company, New York.

De France, J. J., *Direct Current Fundamentals*, Prentice-Hall, Inc., Englewood Cliffs, N.J.

Maedel, G. F., *Basic Mathematics for Radio and Television*, Prentice-Hall, Inc., Englewood Cliffs, N.J.

Mueller, G. V., Introduction to Electrical Engineering, McGraw-Hill Book Company, New York.

Oppenheimer, S. L., and J. P. Borchers, *Direct and Alternating Currents*, McGraw-Hill Book Company, New York.

Suffern, M. G., *Basic Electrical and Electronic Principles*, McGraw-Hill Book Company, New York.

Timbie, W. H., *Basic Electricity for Communications*, John Wiley & Sons, Inc., New York.

Watson, H. M., H. E. Welch, and G. S. Eby, *Understanding Radio*, 3d ed., McGraw-Hill Book Company, New York.

Welch Scientific Co., *Periodic Chart of the Atoms*.

REVIEW SELF-EXAMINATION (*Answers at back of book.*)

Here's another chance to check your progress. Work the exercises just as you did those at the end of each chapter.

1. In which of the following circuits will the voltage source produce the most current? (*a*) 10 volts across a 10-ohm resistance; (*b*) 10 volts across two 10-ohm resistances in series; (*c*) 10 volts across two 10-ohm resistances in parallel; (*d*) 1,000 volts across a 1-M resistance.

2. Three 120-volt 100-watt bulbs are in parallel across the 120-volt power line. If one bulb burns open, (*a*) the other two bulbs cannot light; (*b*) all three bulbs light; (*c*) the other two bulbs can light; (*d*) there is excessive current in the main line.

3. A circuit allows 1 ma of current to flow with 1 volt applied. The conductance of the circuit equals (*a*) 0.001 ohm; (*b*) 0.001 μmho; (*c*) 1,000 μmhos; (*d*) 1 mho.

4. If 2 amp of current is allowed to accumulate charge for 5 sec, the resultant charge equals (*a*) 2 coul; (*b*) 10 coul; (*c*) 5 amp; (*d*) 10 amp.

5. A potential difference applied across a 1-M resistor produces 1 ma of current. The applied voltage equals (*a*) 1 μv; (*b*) 1 mv; (*c*) 1 kv; (*d*) 1,000,000 volts.

6. A string of two 1,000-ohm resistances is in series with a parallel bank of two 1,000-ohm resistances. The total resistance of the series-parallel circuit equals (*a*) 250 ohms; (*b*) 2,500 ohms; (*c*) 3,000 ohms; (*d*) 4,000 ohms.

7. In the circuit of question 6, one of the resistances in the series string opens. Then the current in the parallel bank (*a*) increases slightly in both branches; (*b*) equals zero in one branch but is maximum in the other branch; (*c*) is maximum in both branches; (*d*) equals zero in both branches.

8. With 100 volts applied across a 10,000-ohm resistance, the power dissipation equals (*a*) 1 mw; (*b*) 1 watt; (*c*) 100 watts; (*d*) 1 kw.

9. Ten volts is applied across R_1, R_2, and R_3 in series, producing 1 amp in the series circuit. R_1 equals 6 ohms and R_2 equals 2 ohms. Therefore, R_3 equals (*a*) 2 ohms; (*b*) 4 ohms; (*c*) 10 ohms; (*d*) 12 ohms.

10. Ten volts is applied across R_1 and R_2 in parallel. The current in the R_1 branch is 1 amp. The total line current is 3 amp. The resistance of R_2 equals (*a*) 1 ohm; (*b*) 5 ohms; (*c*) 7 ohms; (*d*) 10 ohms.

11. For an equivalent voltage source with series R, use (*a*) Norton's theorem; (*b*) Kirchhoff's voltage law; (*c*) Thévenin's theorem; (*d*) Millman's theorem.

12. For an equivalent current source with shunt R, use (*a*) Norton's theorem; (*b*) Kirchhoff's voltage law; (*c*) Thévenin's theorem; (*d*) Millman's theorem.

Chapter **7** Direct-current meters

Voltage, current, and resistance measurements are generally made with a combination voltmeter-ohmmeter-milliammeter (VOM) like the one in Fig. 7·1. To measure voltage, connect the meter test leads across the two points of potential difference, as in *a*. Similarly, when using the ohmmeter, connect the two leads across the resistance to be measured, but the power must be off. To measure current, the meter is connected as a series component in the circuit. The details of these meter measurements are explained in the following topics:

7·1   Moving-coil meter
7·2   Measuring current
7·3   Meter shunts
7·4   Voltmeters
7·5   Loading effect of voltmeter
7·6   Ohmmeters
7·7   Multimeters
7·8   Meter applications
7·9   Checking continuity with the ohmmeter

7·1   Moving-coil meter

This type of meter movement, illustrated in Figs. 7·2 and 7·3, is generally used in a VOM. Direct current in the coil of wire forces the drum to turn with its pointer. The amount of deflection indicates the amount of current in the coil. Correct polarity allows the pointer to read up-scale, to the right; the opposite polarity makes the pointer move off-scale to the left.

The amount of pointer deflection is directly proportional to the amount of current in the coil. In Fig. 7·3, 100 μa is the current for full-scale de-

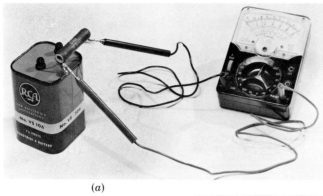

(a)

Fig. 7·1 (a) To read voltage, connect the voltmeter leads across the
potential difference being measured.
(b) To read resistance, connect the
ohmmeter leads across R, but with
power off.

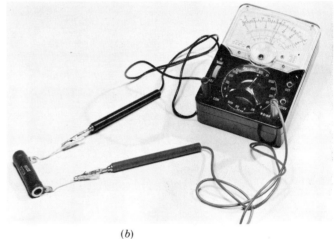

(b)

flection. Therefore, 50 μa will produce half-scale deflection. With 80 μa
in the coil, the deflection is 8/10 of full scale, resulting in the 80-μa reading
on the 100-μa scale. The accuracy of the moving-coil meter mechanism
is 0.1 to 2 per cent.

The moving-coil principle is applied in several meter types which have
different names. A *galvanometer* is an extremely sensitive instrument for
measuring very small values of current. Laboratory-type galvanometers,
which include a suspended moving-coil with an optical system to magnify
small deflection, can measure a small fraction of one microampere. A
ballistic galvanometer is used for reading the value of a small momentary
current. The suspended moving-coil arrangement of a galvanometer is
often called a *D'Arsonval movement,* after its inventor, who patented this
meter movement in 1881. The practical, commercial moving-coil instrument illustrated in Figs. 7·2 and 7·3 is a *Weston movement.*

7·2   Measuring current

Meters of the moving-coil type are available to measure current values
from a few microamperes to many amperes. A microammeter for measur-

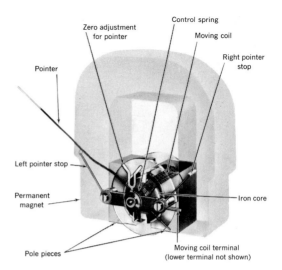

Fig. 7·2 Details of moving-coil
meter. (Weston Electrical Instrument Corp.)

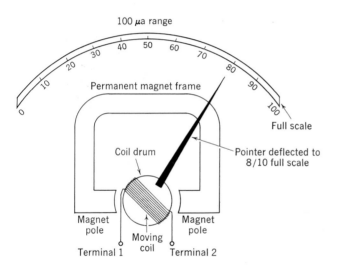

Fig. 7· 3 Pointer deflection is proportional to current in the moving coil.

ing small values of direct current accurately is shown in Fig. 7·4. Notice
the mirror along the scale. The deflection is read on the scale when the
pointer and its mirror reflection are one. This eliminates the optical error
of parallax when you look at the meter from the side. The schematic symbol
for a current meter is a circle with the current range, as in *b*.

When a meter is used to measure current, two important facts to
remember are:

1. The current meter must be in series in the circuit where the current is to
   be measured. The amount of deflection depends on the current through
   the meter. In a series circuit, the current is the same through all series
   components. Therefore, the current to be measured must be made to
   flow through the meter as a series component in the circuit.
2. A d-c meter must be connected in the correct polarity for the meter to

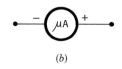

(b)

Fig. 7·4 (a) Microammeter with mirror on scale to minimize parallax error. (Weston Electrical Instrument Corp.) (b) Schematic symbol for meter.

read up-scale. Reversed polarity makes the meter read down-scale, forcing the pointer against the stop at the left, which can bend the pointer.

How to connect a current meter in series. As illustrated in Fig. 7·5, the circuit must be opened at one point in order to insert the current meter in series in the circuit. Since R_1, R_2, R_3, and the meter are all in series, the current is the same in each and the meter reads the current in any part of the series circuit. If E is 150 volts with a total series resistance of 1,500 ohms, the current is 0.1 amp, or 100 ma. This value is the current in R_1, R_2, R_3, and the battery, as shown in a. Note that in b, the circuit is opened at the junction of R_1 and R_2 for insertion of the meter. In c, the meter completes the series circuit to read the current of 100 ma. The meter inserted in series at any point in the circuit would read the same current. The resistance of the milliammeter is so low that the current in the circuit is the same with or without the meter.

Fig. 7·5 Inserting a current meter in series. (a) Circuit without meter. (b) Circuit opened between points b and c for meter. (c) Meter connected between R_1 and R_2 in series with the circuit.

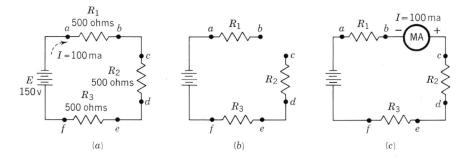

(a)   (b)   (c)

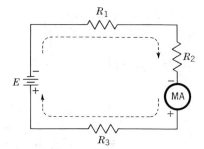

Fig. 7·6   *Correct polarity for a d-c meter.*

How to connect a d-c meter in the correct polarity. A d-c meter has its terminals marked for polarity, either with + and − signs or red for plus and black for minus. Electrons must flow into the negative side through the movement and out from the positive side for the meter to read up-scale. To have the meter polarity correct, always connect its negative terminal to the point in the circuit that has a path back to the negative side of the voltage source, *without going through the meter.* Similarly, the positive terminal of the meter returns to the positive terminal of the voltage source (Fig. 7·6). Here the negative terminal of the meter is joined to R_2 because this path with R_1 connects to the negative terminal of the battery. The positive meter terminal is connected to R_3. Electrons in the circuit will flow through R_1 and R_2 into the negative side of the meter, through the movement, and out from the meter and return through R_3 to the positive battery terminal.

A current meter has low resistance. A current meter is a low-resistance instrument, many of them having an internal resistance less than 1 ohm.

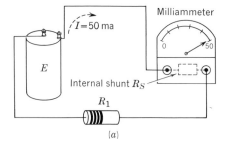

Fig. 7·7   *Effect of shunt in bypassing current around movement to extend its range. (a) Wiring arrangement. (b) Schematic diagram showing effect of shunt. With R_S equal to R_M, range is doubled. (c) Circuit schematic.*

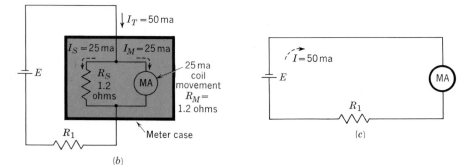

If the meter resistance were high, the added resistance of the meter could reduce the current; then the meter would read less than the actual current in the circuit without the meter. Therefore, a current meter should have a resistance much smaller than the total resistance of the series circuit being measured. This requirement is usually satisfied in typical circuits. For example, with a 1-ma meter having an internal resistance of 50 ohms in a circuit with 5,000-ohm resistance, there is practically no error due to the resistance of the meter. In general, the higher the current range of the meter, the smaller is its resistance.

7·3   Meter shunts

A meter shunt is a precision resistor connected in parallel across the meter movement for the purpose of shunting, or bypassing, a specific fraction of the circuit's current around the meter movement. The combination then provides a current meter with an extended range. Compared with the maximum deflection current of about 30 ma for the moving coil alone, a d-c meter with a shunt is commonly used for current ranges of 50 ma, 100 ma, 250 ma, 1 amp, and 10 amp. The shunt is usually mounted inside the meter case.

In current measurements, the combination of the movement with its shunt is still connected as a low-resistance current meter in series in the circuit (Fig. 7·7). A meter with an internal shunt has the scale calibrated to take into account the current through the shunt. Therefore, the scale reads total circuit current. The meter resistance is actually lower with the shunt, reducing the effect of the meter in the circuit. The shunt usually is not shown in the schematic symbol for a current meter.

Resistance of the meter shunt. In Fig. 7·7b, the 25-ma movement has a resistance of 1.2 ohms, which is the resistance of the moving coil R_M. To double the range, the shunt's resistance R_s is made equal to the 1.2 ohms of the movement. When the meter is connected in series in a circuit where the current is 50 ma, this total current into one terminal of the meter divides equally between the shunt and the meter movement. At the opposite meter terminal, these two branch currents combine to provide the 50 ma equal to the circuit current. Inside the meter, the current is 25 ma through the shunt and 25 ma through the moving coil. Since it is a 25-ma movement, this current produces full-scale deflection. The scale is doubled, however, reading 50 ma, to account for the additional 25 ma through the shunt. Therefore, the scale reading indicates total current at the meter terminals, not just coil current. The movement with its shunt, then, is a 50-ma meter having an internal resistance of 0.6 ohm.

Another example is shown in Fig. 7·8. In general, the shunt resistance for any range can be calculated with Ohm's law from the formula

$$R_s = \frac{V_M}{I_s} \qquad\qquad (7·1)$$

R_s is the resistance of the shunt and I_s is the current through it, while V_M is the voltage across both the shunt and the meter movement, which are in parallel. The procedure can be as follows:

1. Find V_M. Calculate this for full-scale deflection, as the full-scale current is usually given. In Fig. 7·8, with 10 ma full-scale current through the 8-ohm movement, V_M is $0.01 \times 8 = 0.08$ volt.
2. Find I_s. This current through the shunt alone is the difference between the total meter current and the current through the movement. Or,

$$I_s = I_T - I_M$$

In Fig. 7·8, $I_s = 50 - 10 = 40$ ma $= 0.04$ amp.
3. Divide V_M by I_s to find R_s. Here, $R_s = 0.08/0.04 = 2$ ohms.

This shunt enables the 10-ma movement to be used for the extended range of 0 to 50 ma. Note that R_s and R_M are inversely proportional to their full-scale currents. The 2 ohms for R_s equals one-fourth the 8 ohms of R_M because the shunt current of 40 ma is four times the 10 ma through the movement for full-scale deflection. The same proportion applies for less than full-scale current. As an example, when reading the half-scale current of 25 ma, 5 ma goes through the movement and 20 ma through the shunt.

Example. A 50-μa meter movement has 1,000 ohms R_M. What R_s is needed to extend the range to 500 μa?
Answer. The shunt current I_s is $500 - 50$, or 450 μa. Then

$$R_s = \frac{V_M}{I_s} = \frac{50 \times 10^{-6} \times 10^3}{450 \times 10^{-6}} = \frac{50,000}{450} = \frac{1,000}{9} = \textbf{111.1 ohms}$$

The shunts usually are precision wirewound bobbin-type resistors. For very low values, a short piece of wire can be used.

Universal shunt. In Fig. 7·9, R_1, R_2, and R_3 are used in series-parallel combinations with the meter movement for different current ranges. The

Fig. 7·8   The shunt resistance R_s equals the voltage across the meter divided by the current through the shunt.

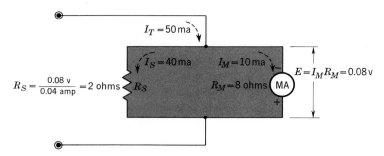

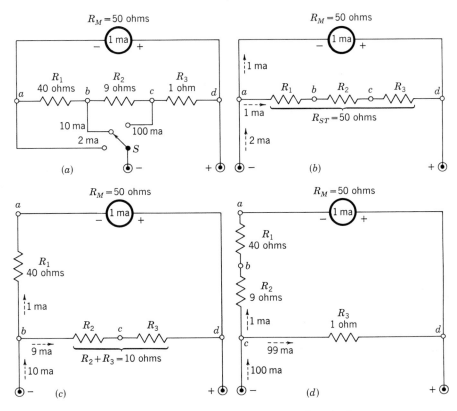

Fig. 7·9   Universal or Ayrton shunt for three current ranges. I values indicated for full-scale deflection. (a) Actual circuit with switch. (b) 0- to 2-ma range. (c) 0- to 10-ma range (d) 0- to 100-ma range.

circuit is called an *Ayrton shunt* or *universal shunt*. This method is generally used for multiple current ranges in a VOM because the series-parallel circuit provides a safe method of switching between current ranges without danger of excessive current through the meter movement. The universal shunt consists of R_1, R_2, and R_3 in Fig. 7·9. How they are connected as a shunt is determined by the switch S for the different current ranges. Their total resistance (R_{ST}) of 50 ohms is used as a shunt in parallel with R_M for the 2-ma range in *b*. For the higher current ranges in *c* and *d* part of R_{ST} is connected in series with R_M while the remainder of R_{ST} is in parallel as a shunt path.

The values in Fig. 7·9 are calculated as follows: Since the 2-ma range in *b* is double the 1-ma current rating of the meter movement, the shunt resistance must equal the R_M of 50 ohms so that 1 ma can flow in each of the two parallel paths. Therefore, R_{ST} is equal to the 50 ohms of R_M.

For the 10-ma range in *c*, 9 ma must flow through the shunt path and 1 ma through the meter path. R_M now has R_1 in series with it, in the path *bad*. The shunt now includes R_2 in series with R_3, in the path *bcd*. Remember that the voltage is the same across the two parallel paths *bad* and *bcd*. The current is 1 ma in one path and 9 ma in the other path. To calculate R_1 we can equate the voltage across the two paths:

$$1 \text{ ma} \times (R_1 + R_M) = 9 \text{ ma} (R_2 + R_3)$$

We know R_M is 50 ohms. We also know R_{ST} is 50 ohms. We do not know R_1, R_2, or R_3 but $(R_2 + R_3)$ must be 50 ohms minus R_1. Therefore,

$$1 \text{ ma} (R_1 + 50) = 9 \text{ ma} (50 - R_1)$$

Solving for R_1,

$$R_1 + 50 = 450 - 9R_1$$
$$10R_1 = 400$$
$$R_1 = \textbf{40 ohms}$$

Not only do we know now that R_1 is 40 ohms but $(R_2 + R_3)$ must be 10 ohms, as they all must add up to 50 ohms. This value of 10 ohms for $(R_2 + R_3)$ is used for the next step in the calculations.

For the 100-ma range in *d*, 1 ma flows through R_1, R_2, and R_M in the path *cbad*, and 99 ma through R_3 in the path *cd*. The voltage is the same across both paths. To calculate R_2, therefore,

$$1 \text{ ma} (R_1 + R_2 + R_M) = 99 \text{ ma} (R_3)$$

We know R_1 is 40 ohms. Then

$$40 + R_2 + 50 = 99(R_3)$$

If $(R_2 + R_3)$ is 10 ohms, then R_3 must be $(10 - R_2)$. Substituting $(10 - R_2)$ for R_3,

$$40 + R_2 + 50 = 99(10 - R_2)$$
$$R_2 + 90 = 990 - 99R_2$$
$$100R_2 = 900$$
$$R_2 = \textbf{9 ohms}$$

Finally, R_3 must be 1 ohm. The total of $R_1 + R_2 + R_3$ equals $40 + 9 + 1$, which equals the 50 ohms of R_{ST}.

As a proof of the resistance values note that in *b*, 1 ma in each 50-ohm branch produces 50 mv across both parallel branches. In *c*, 1 ma in the 90-ohm branch with the meter produces 90 mv from *b* to *d*, while 9 ma through the 1 ohm of $R_1 + R_2$ produces the same 90 mv. In *d*, 99 ma through the 1-ohm R_3 produces 99 mv, while 1 ma through the 99 ohms in path *cbad* produces the same 99 mv.

7·4 Voltmeters

Although a meter movement responds only to current in the moving coil, it is commonly used for measuring voltage by the addition of a high resistance in series with the movement (Fig. 7·9). The series resistance must be much higher than the coil resistance in order to limit the current through the coil. The combination of the meter movement with its added series resistance then forms a voltmeter. The series resistor, called a *multiplier*, is usually connected inside the voltmeter case.

Since a voltmeter has high resistance, it must be connected in parallel to measure the potential difference across two points in a circuit. Otherwise, the high-resistance multiplier would add so much series resistance that the current in the circuit would be reduced to a very low value. Connected in parallel, though, the high resistance of the voltmeter is an advantage. The higher the voltmeter resistance, the smaller is the effect of its parallel connection on the circuit being tested.

The circuit is not opened to connect the voltmeter in parallel. Because of this convenience, it is common practice to make voltmeter tests in trouble shooting. The voltage measurements apply the same way to either an *IR* drop or a generated emf.

The correct polarity must be observed in using a d-c voltmeter. Connect the negative voltmeter lead to the negative side of the potential difference being measured and the positive lead to the positive side.

Multiplier resistance. Figure 7·10 illustrates how the meter movement and its multiplier R_1 form a voltmeter. With 10 volts applied by the

Fig. 7·10 A multiplier resistor added in series with the meter movement forms a voltmeter. (a) The multiplier R_1 provides full-scale meter deflection with 10 volts applied. (b) The voltmeter leads can be connected across a circuit to measure 0 to 10 volts. (c) 10-volt scale and corresponding 1-ma scale.

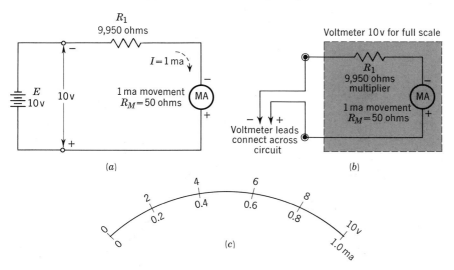

battery in *a*, there must be 10,000 ohms of resistance to limit the current to 1 ma for full-scale deflection of the meter movement. Since the movement has 50-ohm resistance, 9,950 ohms is added in series, resulting in 10,000-ohm total resistance. With 1 ma in the movement, the full-scale deflection can be calibrated as 10 volts on the meter scale, as long as the 9,950-ohm multiplier is included in series with the movement. The multiplier can be connected on either side of the movement.

If the battery is taken away, as in *b*, the movement with its multiplier forms a voltmeter that can indicate a potential difference of 0 to 10 volts applied across its terminals. When the voltmeter leads are connected across a potential difference of 10 volts in a d-c circuit, the resulting 1-ma current through the meter movement produces full-scale deflection and the reading is 10 volts. In *c* the 10-volt scale is shown corresponding to the 1-ma range of the movement.

If the voltmeter is connected across a 5-volt potential difference, the current in the movement is ½ ma, the deflection is one-half of full scale, and the reading is 5 volts. Zero voltage across the terminals means no current in the movement, and the voltmeter reads zero. In summary, then, any potential difference up to 10 volts, whether an *IR* voltage drop or generated emf, can be applied across the meter terminals, and it will indicate less than 10 volts in the same ratio that the meter current is less than 1 ma.

The resistance of a multiplier can be calculated from the formula

$$R_{mult} = \frac{\text{full-scale } E}{\text{full-scale } I} - R_M \qquad (7\cdot2)$$

Applying this formula to the example in Fig. 7·10 gives

$$R_{mult} = \frac{10 \text{ volts}}{0.001 \text{ amp}} - 50 \text{ ohms} = 10,000 - 50 = \textbf{9,950 ohms}$$

Fig. 7·11 *Voltmeter with range of either 10 or 25 volts. (a) Range switch selects scale by connecting either R_1 or R_2 as the multiplier in series with meter movement. (b) Dual scales on meter face.*

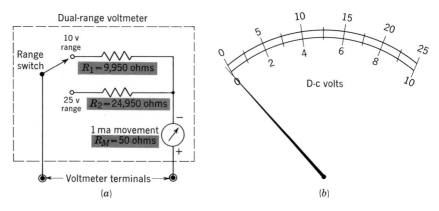

(a)

(b)

Table 7·1 Multiple voltage-scale readings for Fig. 7·11

| Applied voltage | 10-volt scale, R* = 10,000 ohms | | | 25-volt scale, R* = 25,000 ohms | | |
	Meter, ma	Deflection	Scale reading, volts	Meter, ma	Deflection	Scale reading, volts
0	0	0	0	0	0	0
5	0.5	½ scale	5	0.2	²/₁₀	5
10	1.0	Full scale	10	0.4	⁴/₁₀	10
12.5				0.5	½ scale	12.5
25				1.0	Full scale	25

* R is total resistance of multiplier and meter movement.

For the same 10-volt scale with a 50-μa meter movement, which is commonly used, the multiplier resistance is much higher. Taking the resistance of the 50-μa movement as 1,000 ohms gives

$$R_{mult} = \frac{10 \text{ volts}}{0.000050 \text{ amp}} - 1{,}000 \text{ ohms} = 200{,}000 - 1{,}000 = \textbf{199,000 ohms}$$

Multiple voltmeter ranges. Voltmeters often have several multipliers, used with one meter movement, where a range switch selects one multiplier for the required scale. The higher the voltage range, the higher the multiplier resistance, in essentially the same proportion as the ranges. Figure 7·11 illustrates two ranges. When the switch is on the 10-volt range, multiplier R_1 is connected in series with the 1-ma movement. Then you read the 10-volt scale on the meter face. With the range switch on 25 volts, R_2 is the multiplier and the measured voltage is read on the 25-volt scale. Several examples of using these two scales are listed in Table 7·1. Note that voltages less than 10 volts can be read on either scale. It is preferable, however, to have the pointer read on the middle third of the scale. That is why the scales are usually multiples of 10 and 2.5 or 3.

Range switch. With multiple ranges, the setting of the selector switch is the voltage that produces full-scale deflection (Fig. 7·12). One scale is generally used for ranges that are multiples of 10. If the range switch is set for 250 volts in Fig. 7·12, read the top scale as is. With the range switch at 25 volts, however, the readings on the 250-volt scale are divided by 10. Similarly, the 100-volt scale is used for the 100-volt range and the 10-volt range. In Fig. 7·12 the pointer indicates 30 volts when the switch is on the 100-volt range; this reading on the 10-volt range is 3 volts.

Typical multiple voltmeter circuit. Another example of multiple voltage ranges is shown in Fig. 7·13, with a typical switching arrangement. R_1 is the series multiplier for the lowest voltage range. When higher resistance is needed for the higher ranges, the switch adds the required series resistors.

The meter in Fig. 7·13 requires 50 μa for full-scale deflection. For the 2.5-volt range, a series resistance of 2.5/(50 × 10⁻⁶), or 50,000 ohms is

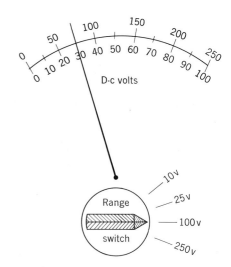

Fig. 7·12 The range switch selects
the voltage that can produce full-
scale deflection. The reading shown
here is 30 volts on the 100-volt range.

Fig. 7·13 Typical voltmeter circuit for multiple
ranges. (Simpson VOM Model 260.)

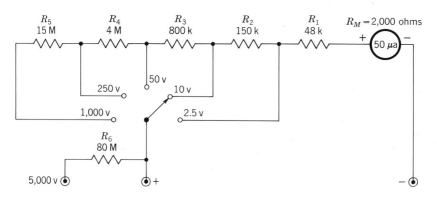

needed. Since R_M is 2,000 ohms, the value of R_1 is 50,000 − 2,000, which equals 48,000 ohms. This 2.5-volt range is convenient for measuring the small bias voltages used in transistor circuits.

For the 10-volt range, a series resistance of $10/(50 \times 10^{-6})$, or 200,000 ohms is needed. Since $R_1 + R_M$ provide 50,000 ohms, R_2 is made 150,000 ohms for a total of 200,000 ohms series resistance on the 10-volt range. Similarly, additional resistors are switched in to increase the multiplier resistance for the higher voltage ranges. Note the separate jack and extra multiplier R_6 on the highest range for 5,000 volts.

Ohms-per-volt rating. To indicate the loading effect of the voltmeter's resistance independently of the range, voltmeters are generally rated in the ohms of multiplier resistance needed for 1 volt of deflection. This is the *ohms-per-volt rating*, often called the voltmeter's *sensitivity*. To calculate the ohms-per-volt rating, take the reciprocal of the full-scale current value of the meter movement in ampere units. For example, a 1-ma movement results in 1/0.001, or 1,000 ohms per volt; a 50-μa movement allows 20,000 ohms per volt. These values are for d-c volts only. The sensitivity for a-c voltage is made lower, generally, to prevent erratic meter deflection produced by stray magnetic fields before the meter leads are connected into the circuit. Usually the ohms-per-volt rating of a voltmeter is printed on the meter face.

The sensitivity of 1,000 ohms/volt with a 1-ma movement used to be common for d-c voltmeters, but 20,000 ohms per volt with a 50-μa movement is generally used now. Higher sensitivity is an advantage, not only for less voltmeter loading, but lower voltage ranges and higher ohmmeter ranges can be obtained.

7·5 *Loading effect of voltmeter*

When the voltmeter resistance is not high enough, connecting it across a circuit can reduce the measured voltage, compared with the voltage present without the voltmeter. This effect is called *loading down* the circuit, since the measured voltage decreases because of the additional load current.

As shown in Fig. 7·14, the voltmeter loading effect can be appreciable in high-resistance circuits. In Fig. 7·14a, without the voltmeter, R_1 and R_2 form a voltage divider across the applied voltage of 100 volts, resulting in 50 volts across R_1 and R_2. When the voltmeter is connected across R_2 to measure its potential difference, however, the voltage division changes. Now the voltmeter in parallel with R_2 draws additional current, and the equivalent resistance between the measured points 1 and 2 is reduced from 100,000 to 50,000 ohms. This resistance is one-third the total circuit resistance, and the measured voltage across points 1 and 2 becomes 33⅓ volts, as shown in c. As additional current drawn by the voltmeter flows through the other series resistance R_1, this voltage goes up to 66⅔ volts. Similarly, if the voltmeter were connected across R_1, this voltage would go down to 33⅓ volts, with the voltage across R_2 rising to 66⅔ volts. When the voltmeter is disconnected, the circuit returns to the condition in *a*, with 50 volts across both R_1 and R_2.

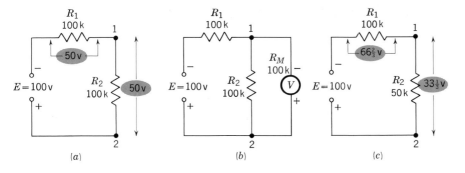

Fig. 7·14 *Loading effect of voltmeter. (a) High-resistance series circuit. (b) Voltmeter connected across one of the series resistances. (c) Reduced resistance and voltage between points 1 and 2 caused by the voltmeter resistance as a parallel branch.*

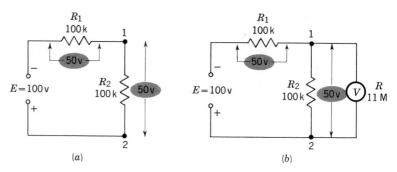

Fig. 7·15   Negligible loading with a high-resistance voltmeter. (a) High-resistance series circuit. (b) Same voltage in circuit with voltmeter connected.

The loading effect is minimized by using a voltmeter having a resistance much greater than the resistance across which the voltage is measured. As shown in Fig. 7·15, with a voltmeter resistance of 11 M, its loading effect is negligible. Because R_M is so high, it does not change the voltage division in the circuit. The 11 M of the meter in parallel with the 100,000 ohms for R_2 results in an equivalent resistance practically equal to 100,000 ohms.

With multiple ranges on a VOM, the voltmeter resistance changes with the range selected. Higher ranges require more multiplier resistance, increasing the voltmeter resistance for less loading. As examples, a 20,000 ohms per volt meter on the 250-volt range has an internal resistance of 20,000 × 250, or 5 M. On a 2.5-volt range, though, the same meter has an input resistance of 20,000 × 2.5, which is only 50,000 ohms. On any one range, however, it should be noted that the voltmeter resistance is constant whether you read full-scale or less than full-scale deflection, as the multiplier resistance is determined by the range switch.

7·6   Ohmmeters

Basically, an ohmmeter consists of an internal battery, the meter movement, and a current-limiting resistance, as illustrated in Fig. 7·16. When measuring resistance, the ohmmeter leads are connected across an external resistance to be measured, with power off in the circuit being tested, so that only the ohmmeter battery produces current for deflecting the meter movement. Since the amount of current through the meter depends on the external resistance, the scale can be calibrated in ohms. The amount of deflection on the ohms scale indicates directly the measured resistance. The ohmmeter reads up-scale regardless of the polarity of the leads because the polarity of the internal battery determines the direction of current through the meter movement.

Series-ohmmeter circuit. In Fig. 7·16a, the series circuit with 1,500-ohm resistance and the 1.5-volt dry cell produces 1 ma, deflecting the moving coil full-scale. When these components are enclosed in a case, as in b, the series circuit forms an ohmmeter. If the leads are shorted together, or con-

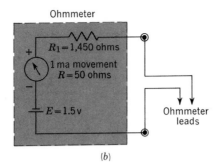

Ohmmeter

Fig. 7·16 *Ohmmeter circuit. (a) Equivalent closed circuit when ohmmeter leads are shorted by connecting across zero ohms of resistance. (b) Circuit with ohmmeter leads open.*

nected across a short circuit, 1 ma flows and the meter movement is deflected full-scale to the right. With the ohmmeter leads open, not touching each other, the current is zero and the ohmmeter indicates infinitely high resistance or an open circuit across its terminals. Therefore, the meter face can be marked zero ohms at the right for full-scale deflection and infinite ohms at the left for no deflection. In-between values of resistance result in less than 1 ma through the meter movement. The corresponding deflection on the ohms scale indicates how much resistance is across the ohmmeter terminals.

Back-off ohmmeter scale. Figure 7·17 illustrates the calibration of an ohmmeter scale in terms of meter current. The current equals E/R_T. E is the fixed applied voltage of 1.5 volts supplied by the internal battery. R_T is

Fig. 7·17 *Back-off ohmmeter. (a) Series ohmmeter circuit with external resistor R_x. (b) Table of decreasing deflection as measured resistance R_x increases. (c) Ohms scale reads higher resistances from right to left.*

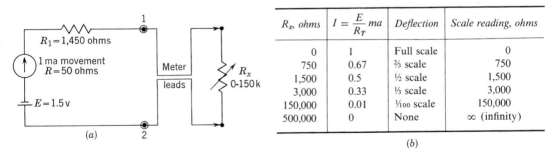

R_x, ohms	$I = \dfrac{E}{R_T}$ ma	Deflection	Scale reading, ohms
0	1	Full scale	0
750	0.67	⅔ scale	750
1,500	0.5	½ scale	1,500
3,000	0.33	⅓ scale	3,000
150,000	0.01	¹⁄₁₀₀ scale	150,000
500,000	0	None	∞ (infinity)

(b)

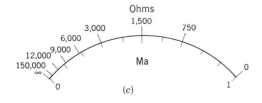

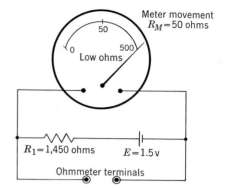

Meter movement
$R_M = 50$ ohms

50

0   500
Low ohms

Fig. 7·18   Shunt-ohmmeter circuit.

$R_1 = 1,450$ ohms $E = 1.5$ v

Ohmmeter terminals

the total resistance of R_x and the ohmmeter's internal resistance. Note that R_x is the external resistance to be measured. The ohmmeter's internal resistance is constant at $50 + 1,450$, or 1,500 ohms here. If R_x also equals 1,500 ohms, for example, R_T equals 3,000 ohms. The current then is 1.5 volts/3,000 ohms, or 0.5 ma, resulting in half-scale deflection for the 1-ma movement. Therefore, the center of the ohms scale is marked for 1,500 ohms. Similarly, the amount of current and meter deflection can be calculated for any value of R_x.

Note that the ohms scale increases from right to left. This arrangement is called a *back-off scale*, with ohms values increasing to the left as the current backs off from full-scale deflection. Also, the ohmmeter scale is expanded at the right near zero ohms and crowded at the left near infinite ohms. This nonlinear scale results from the reciprocal relation of $I = E/R$ with E constant at 1.5 volts.

The highest resistance that can be indicated by the ohmmeter is about 100 times its total internal resistance. Therefore, the infinity mark on the ohms scale, or the "lazy eight" symbol ∞ for infinity, is only relative, meaning just that the measured resistance is infinitely greater than the ohmmeter resistance. For instance, if a 500,000-ohm resistor in good condition were measured with the ohmmeter in Fig. 7·17, it would indicate infinite resistance because this ohmmeter cannot measure as high as 500,000 ohms. To read higher values of resistance, the battery voltage can be increased to provide more current, or a more sensitive meter movement is necessary to provide deflection with less current. At the low end of the resistance scale, to read values less than R_M, the meter movement can be shunted to allow more current in the circuit without exceeding full-scale deflection current through the meter.

Shunt-ohmmeter circuit. As shown in Fig. 7·18, the unknown R_x to be measured acts as a shunt across the meter movement. With the test leads shorted across the ohmmeter terminals, there is no current in the meter as all the battery current goes through the shorted shunt path. Zero ohms corresponds to zero current in the meter, therefore, at the left end of the scale. This ohms scale reads left to right, like current and voltage scales, but opposite from a series ohmmeter. The internal R_1 is the value needed for full-scale deflection with an open across the meter leads. It should be noted that the mistake of applying voltage to an ohmmeter will easily damage the meter movement in this circuit because the coil is directly across the terminals without any series resistance.

The shunt circuit expands the low ohms values. As an example, half-scale deflection is 50 ohms for the shunt ohmmeter in Fig. 7·18, compared with 1,500 ohms in the series ohmmeter of Fig. 7·17c, using the same 1-ma meter movement and 1.5-volt battery.

Multiple ohmmeter ranges. Commercial multimeters provide for resistance measurements of less than 1 ohm up to many megohms, in several ranges. The range switch in Fig. 7·19 shows the multiplying factors for the ohms scale. On the $R \times 1$ range, for low-resistance measurements, read the ohms scale directly. In the example here, the pointer indicates 12 ohms. When the range switch is on $R \times 100$, multiply the scale reading by 100; this reading would then be 12×100 or 1,200 ohms. On the $R \times 10,000$ range, the pointer would indicate 120,000 ohms.

A multiplying factor is given, instead of full-scale resistance, for each ohms range because the highest resistance is infinite on all the ohms ranges. This method for ohms should not be confused with the full-scale values for voltage ranges. For the ohmmeter ranges, always multiply the scale reading by the $R \times$ factor. On voltage ranges, you may have to multiply or divide the scale reading, to match the full-scale voltage with the value on the range switch.

Typical ohmmeter circuit. In order to provide for multiple ranges, the ohmmeter operation of a VOM generally uses the circuit in Fig. 7·20. This shows the $R \times 1$ range. Although a shunt is combined with series resistance, this circuit has a back-off ohms scale. Zero ohms corresponds to full-scale deflection with the meter leads shorted. Half-scale deflection is at 12 ohms, when the measured R_x equals the resistance of the meter shunt.

To analyze this ohmmeter circuit, Fig. 7·20 shows three conditions. In

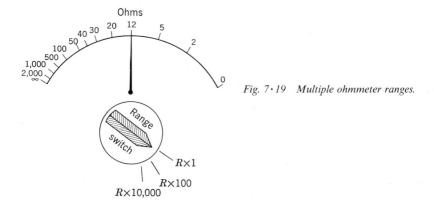

Fig. 7·19 Multiple ohmmeter ranges.

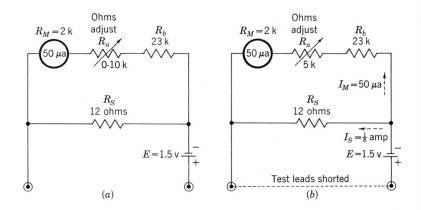

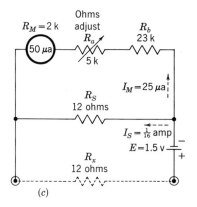

Fig. 7·20 *Typical ohmmeter circuit for R × 1 range. Half-scale deflection is 12 ohms. (a) Circuit before zero-ohms adjustment. (b) Test leads shorted to adjust for zero ohms. (c) Measuring external resistance R_x.*

a is the internal circuit, before the ohmmeter is adjusted for zero ohms. In *b* the test leads are shorted. Then there are two paths for branch current produced by the battery *E*. One branch is R_s. The other branch includes R_b, R_a, and the meter movement. The 1.5-volt *E* is across both branches. To allow 50 μa through the meter, R_a is adjusted to 5,000 ohms. Then the total resistance in this branch is 23 K + 5 K + 2 K, which equal 30 K. With 30 K across 1.5 volts. I_M equals 50 μa. Therefore, R_a is adjusted for full-scale deflection to read zero ohms with the test leads shorted.

In *c*, assume a resistance being measured is 12 ohms, equal to R_s. Then the meter current is practically 25 μa for half-scale deflection. The center ohms reading on the $R \times 1$ scale, therefore, is 12 ohms. For higher values of R_x, the meter current decreases to indicate higher resistances on the back-off ohms scale.

For higher ohms ranges, the resistance of the R_s branch is increased. The half-scale ohms reading on each range is equal to the total resistance of the R_s branch. A higher battery voltage can also be used for the highest ohms range. On any range, R_a is adjusted for full-scale deflection to read zero ohms with the test leads shorted. This variable resistor is the *ohms adjust* or *zero-ohms* adjustment.

Fig. 7·21 VOM with back cover off to show multipliers, shunts, and dry cell for ohmmeter. (Triplett Model 630.)

Fig. 7·22 Typical VOM. (Simpson Model 260.)

Zero-ohms adjustment. To compensate for lower voltage output as the internal battery ages, an ohmmeter includes a variable resistor such as R_a in Fig. 7·20, to calibrate the ohms scale. A back-off ohmmeter is always adjusted for zero ohms. With the test leads shorted, vary the ZERO OHMS control on the front panel of the meter until the pointer is exactly on zero at the right edge of the ohms scale. Then the ohms readings are correct for the entire scale. This type of ohmmeter must be zeroed again every time you change the range. When the adjustment cannot deflect the pointer all the way to zero at the right edge, it usually means the battery voltage is too low and the internal dry cells must be replaced. Usually, this trouble shows up first on the $R \times 1$ range, which takes the most current from the battery. The ohmmeter battery in a typical VOM can be seen in Fig. 7·21.

7·7 Multimeters

The two main types are the volt-ohm-milliammeter (VOM) in Fig. 7·22 and the vacuum-tube-voltmeter (VTVM) in Fig. 7·23. The VOM features compactness, simplicity, and portability. The VTVM must be plugged into the power line for operation. Its advantage, though, is a very high input resistance of 11 M or more as a d-c voltmeter, resulting in negligible loading. Usually, the VTVM has no provision for any current measurements.

With a VOM, the same two leads are used for all measurements. On d-c volts, the sensitivity with a 50-μa meter is 20,000 ohms per volt. Its input

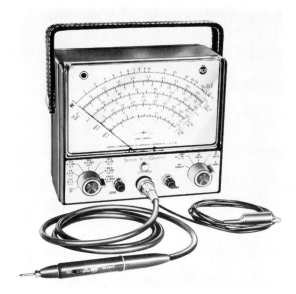

Fig. 7·23 Typical VTVM. (RCA Model WV-98 C.) *Range switch at left. Selector switch at right; transit position shorts meter movement to prevent damage in transportation.*

resistance depends on the voltage range, increasing with higher ranges. For a-c voltage, the input is rectified to provide direct current for the meter. The sensitivity for a-c voltage ranges is usually less than for d-c voltage. Direct current can be measured by the VOM, with ranges from milliamperes to amperes. Usually there is no provision for measuring alternating current. On ohms operation, the highest range is generally $R \times 10,000$ with a 50-μa meter, allowing measurements up to $2,000 \times 10,000$, or 20 M. It is important to zero the ohms adjustment each time the ohms range is changed.

The VTVM needs a power supply because the meter movement is in a bridge circuit with an amplifier. However, some transistorized units are battery-operated. The input resistance of 11 M or more on d-c volts is the same for all ranges because the VTVM has a constant-resistance voltage divider in the input circuit. Too high an input resistance, however, results in stray pickup by the test leads, which makes the voltmeter read erratic values when not connected across a closed circuit, especially on the a-c voltage ranges. The VTVM usually has ohms ranges up to $R \times 1$ M, which allows resistance measurements as high as 1,000 M. The ohms scale reads from left to right, like the volts scale. An internal battery is needed for the ohms ranges but the VTVM must be turned on because the ohms operation uses the voltmeter amplifier.

The test leads for the VTVM in Fig. 7·23 are used as follows: The black common lead is connected to chassis ground for all measurements. The probe is used with the switch on DC for d-c volts. Inside is a 1-M series resistor to isolate the probe from the capacitance of the shielded cable. The shield reduces stray pickup. For both ohms and a-c volts measurements, as determined by the selector switch, the probe switch shorts out the internal resistor.

The two adjustments on the front panel of the VTVM are adjusted as follows:

1. First, set the ZERO ADJUST control to line up the pointer at zero, with the selector switch on d-c volts. Allow a few minutes for the meter to warm up before making the adjustment. This adjustment calibrates the instrument as a d-c voltmeter.
2. Next, turn the selector switch to the ohms position and vary the OHMS ADJUST control to line up the pointer with the extreme right line in the ohms scale. The test leads must be open, not shorted, for this ohms adjustment, which is opposite from a VOM.

When the ZERO ADJUST and OHMS ADJUST controls have been set, usually they need not be changed for different ranges. The selector switch has + and − positions for d-c volts, so that the meter leads are not reversed for reading opposite polarities. In fact, for many measurements, the black lead must be on chassis ground for correct readings.

7·8 Meter applications

Table 7·2 summarizes the main points to remember when a voltmeter, ohmmeter, or milliammeter is used. These rules apply whether the meter is a single unit or one function either on a multimeter or on a VTVM. To avoid excessive current through the meter movement, it is good practice to start on a high range when measuring an unknown value of voltage or current. It is very important not to make the mistake of connecting a current meter in parallel, because usually this mistake ruins the meter. The mistake of a voltmeter in series does not damage the meter, but the reading is wrong. If the ohmmeter is connected to a circuit where power is on, the meter can be damaged, especially with a shunt-ohmmeter circuit.

Connecting current meter in circuit. In a series-parallel circuit, the current meter must be inserted in a branch to read branch current. In the main line, the meter reads the total current (Fig. 7·24). The meters are

Table 7·2   Direct-current meters

Voltmeter	Milliammeter or ammeter	Ohmmeter
Power on in circuit	Power on in circuit	Power off in circuit; has internal battery
Connect in parallel	Connect in series	Connect in parallel
Very high internal resistance	Very low internal resistance	Internal resistance varied for ohms adjustment
Has internal series multipliers for extended ranges	Has internal shunts for extended ranges	Range extended by higher battery voltage or by meter shunts

Fig. 7·24 Inserting current meter in series-parallel circuit. At a, b, or c, meter reads total line current; at d or e, R_2 branch current; at f or g, R_3 branch current.

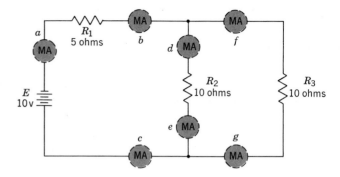

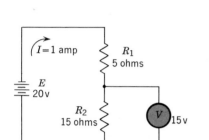

Fig. 7·25 With 15 volts measured across 15 ohms, the current is $E/R = 1$ amp.

shown dashed to illustrate where one could be connected to read the respective currents. If the circuit is opened at point *a* to insert the meter in series in the main line here, it will read total line current through R_1. A meter at *b* or *c* will read the same line current. In order to read the branch current through R_2, it must be disconnected from its junction with the main line at either end. A meter inserted at *d* or *e*, therefore, will read the R_2 branch current. Similarly, a meter at *f* or *g* will read the R_3 branch current.

Calculating I from measured voltage. The inconvenience of opening the circuit to measure current can often be eliminated by use of Ohm's law. The voltage and resistance can be measured without opening the circuit and the current calculated as E/R. In the example in Fig. 7·25, when the voltage across R_1 is 15 volts and its resistance is 15 ohms, the current through R_1 must be 1 amp. When values are checked for trouble shooting, if the voltage and resistance are normal, so is the current.

7·9 Checking continuity with the ohmmeter

A wire conductor that is continuous without a break has practically zero ohms of resistance. Therefore, the ohmmeter can be useful in testing for continuity. This test should be done on the lowest ohms range. There are many applications. A wire conductor can have an internal break, which is not visible because of the insulated cover, or the wire can have a bad connection at the terminal. Checking for zero ohms between any two points along the conductor tests continuity. A break in the conducting path is evident from a reading of infinite resistance, showing an open circuit.

As another application of checking continuity, suppose there is a cable of wires harnessed together as illustrated in Fig. 7·26, where the individual wires cannot be seen, but it is desired to find the conductor that connects

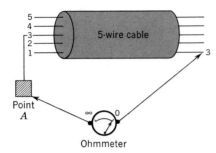

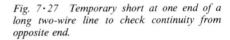

Fig. 7·26   Continuity from A to 3 shows this wire is connected to terminal A.

Fig. 7·27   Temporary short at one end of a long two-wire line to check continuity from opposite end.

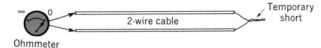

to terminal *A*. This is done by checking continuity for each conductor to point *A*. The wire that has zero ohms to *A* is the one connected to this terminal. Often the individual wires are color-coded, but it may be necessary to check the continuity of each lead.

An additional technique that can be helpful is illustrated in Fig. 7·27. Here it is desired to check the continuity of the two-wire line, but its ends are too far apart for the ohmmeter leads to reach. The two conductors are temporarily shorted at one end, however, so that the continuity of both wires can be checked at the other end.

In summary, then, the ohmmeter is helpful in checking the continuity of any wire conductor. This check includes resistance-wire heating elements, like the wires in a toaster or the filament of an incandescent bulb. Their cold resistance is normally just a few ohms. Infinite resistance means that the wire element is open. Similarly, a good fuse has practically zero resistance; a burned-out fuse has infinite resistance, meaning it is open.

SUMMARY

1. Direct current in a moving-coil meter deflects the coil in proportion to the amount of current.
2. A current meter is a low-resistance meter connected in series to read the amount of current in the circuit.
3. A meter shunt in parallel with the moving coil extends the range of a current meter.
4. A voltmeter consists of the meter movement in series with a high-resistance multiplier. The voltmeter with its multiplier is connected across two points to measure their potential difference in volts.
5. The ohms-per-volt rating of a voltmeter with series multipliers equals the reciprocal of the full-scale deflection current of the meter. A typical value is 20,000 ohms per volt for a voltmeter using a 50-μa movement. The higher the ohms-per-volt rating, the better, since it has less loading effect on the circuit being measured, allowing more accurate voltage readings.

6. An ohmmeter consists of an internal battery in series with the meter movement. Power must be off in a circuit being checked with an ohmmeter.

7. The VTVM is a multimeter having the high resistance of 11 M for all d-c voltage ranges, resulting in practically no loading effect. Also, its high resistance ranges allow readings up to 1,000 M.

8. In checking wire conductors, the ohmmeter reads 0 ohms or very low resistance for normal continuity, and infinite ohms for an open.

SELF-EXAMINATION (*Answers at back of book.*)

Here's a chance to find out how well you have learned the material in this chapter. These exercises are for your self-testing only.

1. To connect a current meter in series, (*a*) Open the circuit at one point and use the meter to complete the circuit. (*b*) Open the circuit at the positive and negative terminals of the voltage source. (*c*) Short the resistance to be checked and connect the meter across it. (*d*) Open the circuit at one point and connect the meter to one end.

2. To connect a voltmeter in parallel to read an *IR* drop, (*a*) Open the circuit at one end and use the meter to complete the circuit. (*b*) Open the circuit at two points and connect the meter across both points. (*c*) Allow the circuit to remain as is and connect the meter across the resistance. (*d*) Allow the circuit to remain closed but disconnect the voltage source.

3. A shunt for a milliammeter (*a*) extends the range and reduces the meter resistance; (*b*) extends the range and increases the meter resistance; (*c*) decreases the range and the meter resistance; (*d*) decreases the range but increases the meter resistance.

4. In a check of continuity, the best of the following ohms ranges to use is R × (*a*) 1; (*b*) 1,000; (*c*) 10,000; (*d*) 1,000,000.

5. A voltmeter using a 50-μa meter movement has a sensitivity of (*a*) 1,000 ohms per volt; (*b*) 5,000 ohms per volt; (*c*) 20,000 ohms per volt; (*d*) 11 M per volt.

6. When using an ohmmeter, disconnect the applied voltage from the circuit being checked because (*a*) the voltage source will increase the resistance; (*b*) the current will decrease the resistance; (*c*) the ohmmeter has its own internal battery; (*d*) no current is needed for the meter movement.

7. A multiplier for a voltmeter is (*a*) a high resistance in series with the meter movement; (*b*) a high resistance in parallel with the meter movement; (*c*) usually less than 1 ohm in series with the meter movement; (*d*) usually less than 1 ohm in parallel with the meter movement.

8. To double the current range of a 50-μa 2,000-ohm meter movement, the shunt resistance is (*a*) 40 ohms; (*b*) 50 ohms; (*c*) 2,000 ohms; (*d*) 18,000 ohms.

9. A VOM with a 50-μa movement has an input resistance of 6 M on the d-c voltage range of (*a*) 3; (*b*) 12; (*c*) 60; (*d*) 300.

10. For a 1-volt range, a 50-μa movement with internal R of 2,000 ohms needs a multiplier resistance of (*a*) 1 K; (*b*) 3 K; (*c*) 18 K; (*d*) 50 K.

ESSAY QUESTIONS

1. (*a*) Why is a milliammeter connected in series in a circuit? (*b*) Why should the milliammeter have low resistance?

2. (*a*) Why is a voltmeter connected in parallel in a circuit? (*b*) Why should the voltmeter have high resistance?

3. A circuit has a battery across two resistances in series. (*a*) Draw a diagram showing how to connect a milliammeter in the correct polarity to read current through the junction of the two resistances. (*b*) Draw a diagram showing how to connect a voltmeter in the correct polarity to read the voltage across one resistance.

4. Explain briefly why a meter shunt equal to the resistance of the moving coil doubles the current range.

5. Describe how to adjust the ZERO OHMS control on a back-off ohmmeter.

6. Describe how to set the ZERO VOLTS and OHMS ADJUST controls on a VTVM.
7. State two precautions to be observed when you use a milliammeter.
8. State two precautions to be observed when you use an ohmmeter.
9. Why is a voltmeter able to read either generator voltage from a source or an *IR* voltage drop?
10. Redraw the schematic diagram in Fig. 5·1b, showing a milliammeter to read line current through R_1 and R_2, a meter for R_3 branch current, and a meter for R_4 branch current. Label polarities on each meter.

PROBLEMS (*Answers to selected problems at back of book.*)

1. Calculate the shunt resistance needed to extend the range of a 50-ohm 1-ma movement to (*a*) 2 ma, (*b*) 10 ma, (*c*) 100 ma. In each case, how much current is indicated by half-scale deflection?
2. With a 50-ohm 1-ma movement, calculate the multiplier resistances needed for ranges of (*a*) 10 volts, (*b*) 30 volts, (*c*) 100 volts, (*d*) 300 volts. How much voltage is indicated by half-scale deflection for each range?
3. A voltmeter reads 30 volts across a 100-ohm resistance. How much is the current in the resistor? If the current through the same resistance were doubled, how much would its *IR* voltage be?
4. A voltmeter has a sensitivity of 10,000 ohms per volt on all ranges. How much is the total voltmeter resistance on the 5-volt range? On the 50-volt range? On the 500-volt range? How much is the voltmeter resistance for a reading of 225 volts on the 500-volt range?
5. A 50-μa meter movement has an internal resistance of 1,000 ohms. Calculate the multiplier resistance needed for voltmeter ranges of 10 volts, 30 volts, and 500 volts. How much is the ohms-per-volt sensitivity rating on all ranges? How much is the voltmeter resistance on the 500-volt range?
6. For the same meter movement as in Prob. 5, calculate the shunt resistances needed for current ranges of 10 ma, 30 ma, and 500 ma. How much is the resistance of the meter with its shunt on each range?
7. Referring to the universal shunt in Fig. 7·9, calculate the required values of R_1, R_2, and R_3 for a 50-μa, 2,000-ohm movement to provide current ranges of 1.2 ma, 12 ma, and 120 ma.
8. Referring to the voltmeter loading problem in Fig. 7·14, exactly how much voltage would be indicated by a 20,000 ohms-per-volt meter on its 100-volt range?
9. Refer to Fig. 7·13. (*a*) How much is the total voltmeter resistance using the 5,000-volt jack with the range switch on the 1,000-volt position? (*b*) How much is the ohms-per-volt sensitivity? (*c*) Why must the range switch be on the 1,000-volt position?

Chapter **8** *Conductors and insulators*

Conductors have very low resistance, less than 1 ohm for 10 ft of copper wire being a typical value. The function of the wire conductor is to connect a source of applied voltage to a load resistance with minimum IR voltage drop in the conductor, so that all the applied voltage can produce current in the load resistance. At the opposite extreme, materials having a very high resistance of many megohms are insulators. Some common examples are air, paper, mica, glass, plastics, rubber, cotton, and shellac or varnish. Between the extremes of conductors and insulators are semiconductor materials such as carbon, silicon, and germanium. Carbon is used in the manufacture of resistors. Silicon and germanium are used for transistors.

8·1 Function of the conductor
8·2 Standard wire gage sizes
8·3 Types of wire conductors
8·4 Switches
8·5 Fuses
8·6 Pilot lamps
8·7 Wire resistance
8·8 Ion current in liquids and gases
8·9 Electrons and hole charges in semiconductors
8·10 Insulators

8·1 Function of the conductor

In Fig. 8·1, the resistance of the two 10-ft lengths of copper-wire conductors is approximately 0.5 ohm, which is negligibly small compared with 144-ohm resistance for the tungsten filament in the bulb. When the current of approximately 0.9 amp flows in the bulb and the series conductors, the IR voltage drop across the conductors is 0.5 volt with 119.5 volts across

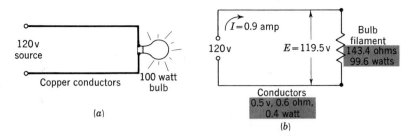

Fig. 8·1 *The conductors should have minimum resistance to light the bulb with full brilliance. (a) Wiring diagram. (b) Schematic diagram.*

the bulb. Practically all the applied voltage is across the filament of the bulb. Since the bulb then has its rated voltage of 120 volts, approximately, it will dissipate its rated power of 100 watts and light with full brilliance.

The current in the wire conductors and the bulb is the same, since they are in series, but because of its low resistance, the *IR* voltage drop in the conductor is practically zero. Also, the *I²R* power dissipated in the conductor is negligibly small, allowing the conductor to operate without becoming hot. Therefore, the conductor delivers energy from the source to the load with minimum loss, by means of electron flow in the copper wires.

Although the resistance of wire conductors is very small, for some cases of excessive current the resultant *IR* drop can be appreciable. The complaint that the size of a television picture shrinks at night is one example. With many lights on and possibly other appliances, the high value of current can produce too much voltage drop in the power line. A 30-volt *IR* drop results in only 90 volts at the load, which is low enough to reduce the picture size. As additional examples, excessive *IR* drop in the line and low voltage at the load can be the cause of a toaster that does not heat quickly or an electric motor that does not start properly.

8·2 Standard wire gage sizes

Table 8·1 lists the standard wire sizes in the system known as the American Wire Gage (AWG), or Brown and Sharpe (B&S) gage. The gage numbers specify the size of round wire in terms of its diameter and cross-sectional circular area. Note the following:

1. As the gage numbers increase from 1 to 40, the diameter and circular area decrease. Higher gage numbers indicate thinner wire sizes.
2. The circular area doubles for every three gage sizes. For example, No. 10 wire has approximately twice the area of No. 13 wire.
3. The higher the gage number and the thinner the wire, the greater the resistance of the wire for any given length.

In typical applications, hookup wire for radio receiver circuits with current in the order of milliamperes is generally about No. 22 gage. For this size, 0.5 to 1 amp is the maximum current the wire can carry without

Table 8·1   Copper Wire Table

Gage No.	Diam, mils	Circular-mil area	Ohms per 1,000 ft of copper wire at 25°C*	Gage No.	Diam, mils	Circular-mil area	Ohms per 1,000 ft of copper wire at 25°C
1	289.3	83,690	0.1264	21	28.46	810.1	13.05
2	257.6	66,370	0.1593	22	25.35	642.4	16.46
3	229.4	52,640	0.2009	23	22.57	509.5	20.76
4	204.3	41,740	0.2533	24	20.10	404.0	26.17
5	181.9	33,100	0.3195	25	17.90	320.4	33.00
6	162.0	26,250	0.4028	26	15.94	254.1	41.62
7	144.3	20,820	0.5080	27	14.20	201.5	52.48
8	128.5	16,510	0.6405	28	12.64	159.8	66.17
9	114.4	13,090	0.8077	29	11.26	126.7	83.44
10	101.9	10,380	1.018	30	10.03	100.5	105.2
11	90.74	8,234	1.284	31	8.928	79.70	132.7
12	80.81	6,530	1.619	32	7.950	63.21	167.3
13	71.96	5,178	2.042	33	7.080	50.13	211.0
14	64.08	4,107	2.575	34	6.305	39.75	266.0
15	57.07	3,257	3.247	35	5.615	31.52	335.0
16	50.82	2,583	4.094	36	5.000	25.00	423.0
17	45.26	2,048	5.163	37	4.453	19.83	533.4
18	40.30	1,624	6.510	38	3.965	15.72	672.6
19	35.89	1,288	8.210	39	3.531	12.47	848.1
20	31.96	1,022	10.35	40	3.145	9.88	1,069

*20 to 25°C or 68 to 77°F is considered average room temperature.

heating. House wiring for circuits where the current is 5 to 15 amp is about No. 12 gage. Minimum sizes for house wiring are set by Fire Underwriters requirements in most localities.

Circular-mil area. The cross-sectional area of round wire is measured in circular mils, abbreviated cir mils. A mil is one-thousandth of an inch, or 0.001 in. One circular mil is the cross-sectional area of a wire having a diameter of 1 mil. The number of circular mils in an area is equal to the square of the diameter in mils.

Example 1. What is the area in circular mils of a wire with a diameter of 0.005 in.?

Answer. Since 0.005 in. equals 5 mils,

$$\text{Area} = (5 \text{ mils})^2 = \textbf{25 cir mils}$$

Note that the circular mil is a unit of area, obtained by squaring the diameter, while the mil is a linear unit of length equal to thousandths of an inch. Therefore, the circular-mil area increases as the square of the diameter. As illustrated in Fig. 8·2, doubling the diameter quadruples the circular-mil area.

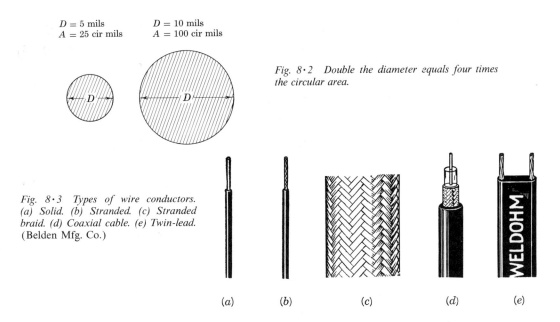

$D = 5$ mils
$A = 25$ cir mils

$D = 10$ mils
$A = 100$ cir mils

Fig. 8·2 Double the diameter equals four times the circular area.

Fig. 8·3 Types of wire conductors. (a) Solid. (b) Stranded. (c) Stranded braid. (d) Coaxial cable. (e) Twin-lead. (Belden Mfg. Co.)

(a)   (b)   (c)   (d)   (e)

8·3   *Types of wire conductors*

Most wire conductors are copper, although aluminum and silver are also used. Generally the copper is tinned with a thin coating of solder,[1] which gives it a silvery appearance. The wire can be solid or stranded, as shown in Fig. 8·3a and b. Stranded wire is flexible and less likely to break open. Sizes for stranded wire are equivalent to the sum of the areas for the individual strands. For instance, two strands of No. 30 wire are equivalent to solid No. 27 wire.

Two or more conductors in a common covering form a wire *cable*. The two-conductor line in Fig. 8·3d is called *coaxial cable*. The metallic braid is one conductor, which is connected to ground for shielding the inner conductor against external magnetic interference. Constant spacing between two conductors provides a *transmission line*. Coaxial cable is one type of transmission line. The twin-lead transmission line in Fig. 8·3e is commonly used in television for connecting the antenna to the receiver.

Types of wire insulation. To prevent the conductors from shorting to each other or to some other metal in the circuit, the wires are usually insulated. The insulation should have very high resistance, be tough, and age without becoming brittle. Very thin wire such as No. 30 often has an insulating coating of enamel or shellac. It may look like copper, but the coating must be scraped off at the ends to make a good connection to the wire. Heavier wires generally are in an insulating sleeve, which may be rubber, cotton, or one of many plastics. Hookup wire that is bare should be enclosed in a hollow insulating sleeve called *spaghetti*.

---

[1] See Appendix I for more information about solder.

Fig. 8·4   Printed wiring board with resistors, capacitors, and tube sockets. (RCA.)

Printed wiring. To eliminate the need for soldering wire connections to many components, electronic equipment often uses the relatively new technique of printed circuits. Each assembly has the electrical components bonded to a flat insulating plate. As shown in Fig. 8·4, conducting paths are printed with silver or copper. Carbon is used to provide resistance where required. Printed circuits have the advantage of compactness and good connections.

8·4   Switches

As shown in Fig. 8·5, switches are commonly used to open or close a circuit. Closed is the ON, or *make,* position; open is the OFF, or *break,* position. The switch is in series with the voltage source and its load. In the

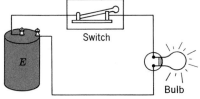

Fig. 8·5   Single-pole single-throw switch to open or close one circuit.

Fig. 8·6   Switch applications. (a) SPDT to make one connection to either of two circuits. (b) DPDT to make two connections to either of two circuits. (c) Construction of DPDT knife switch.

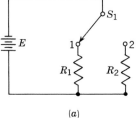

(a)

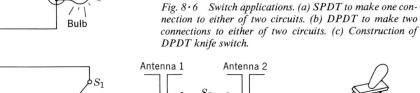

(b)

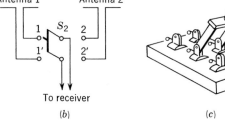

(c)

Fig. 8·7 (a) DPDT toggle switch. (J-B-T Instruments Inc.) (b) Rotary switch with three wafers or decks on common shaft. (Centralab Division of Globe-Union Inc.)

ON position, the closed switch has very little resistance, so that maximum current can flow in the load, with practically zero voltage drop across the switch. Open, the switch has infinite resistance and no current flows in the circuit. Note that the switch is in just one side of the line, but the entire series circuit is open when the switch is turned off. In the open position, the applied voltage is across the switch contacts. Therefore, the insulation must be good enough to withstand this amount of voltage without arcing.

Note that the switch in Fig. 8·5 is a single-pole single-throw (SPST) switch. It provides an ON or OFF position for one circuit. Two connections are necessary. Figure 8·6 shows double-throw switches for two circuits. S_1 in *a* is single-pole double-throw (SPDT) to switch one side of the circuit. This switching can be done because R_1 and R_2 both have a common line. Three connections are necessary, one for the common line and one for each of the circuits to be switched. In *b*, S_2 is a double-pole double-throw (DPDT) to switch both sides of two circuits. This switching is done because there is no common return line for the two separate antennas. Six connections are necessary here, two for each of the circuits to be switched and two for the center contacts.

Figure 8·7 illustrates a toggle switch and a rotary switch. Additional types of construction include the knife switch and the push-button switch. In general, larger switches are necessary for high-current circuits, where the contacts must be heavy for minimum resistance. In high-voltage circuits, wider spacing is needed for maximum insulation between contacts in the open position.

8·5 Fuses

Many circuits have a fuse in series as a protection against an overload resulting from a short circuit. Excessive current melts the fuse element, blowing the fuse and opening the series circuit. The purpose is to let the

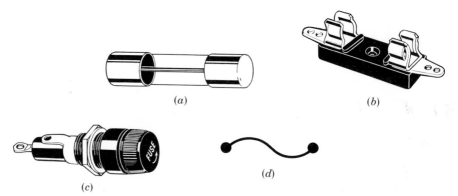

Fig. 8·8 Fuses. (a) Glass-cartridge type. (b) and (c) Fuse holders. (d) Schematic symbol.

fuse blow before the components are damaged. The blown fuse can easily be replaced by a new one, after the overload has been eliminated. A glass-cartridge fuse type is shown in Fig. 8·8. The metal fuse element may be made of aluminum, tin-coated copper, or nickel. Fuses are available in a current rating from $\frac{1}{500}$ amp to hundreds of amperes. The thinner the wire element in the fuse, the smaller is its current rating. As typical applications, the rating for plug fuses in each branch of house wiring is often 15 amp; the high-voltage circuit in a television receiver is usually protected by a glass-cartridge ¼-amp fuse. *Slow-blow* fuses are designed to open only on a continued overload such as a short circuit.

The resistance of a good fuse is very low. An open fuse has infinitely high resistance. When a fuse blows, the full applied voltage is across the terminals of the open fuse, as illustrated in Fig. 8·9. For this reason, fuses also have a voltage rating, which gives the maximum voltage without arcing in the open fuse.

Protection against excessive current without the inconvenience of changing fuses can be obtained by the use of a *circuit breaker* or *thermal cut-out*. The thermal element, generally in the form of a spring, expands with heat

Fig. 8·9 When a fuse opens, the applied voltage is across the fuse terminals. (a) Circuit closed with good fuse. (b) Fuse open.

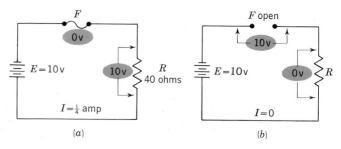

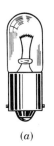

(a)   (b)

(c)   (d)

Fig. 8·10 Panel lamps and sockets. Diameter of base is ½ in.
(a) Bayonet base. (b) Screw base. (c) Bayonet socket. (d) Glass bezel
and screw socket.

and trips open the circuit. The thermal element can be reset for normal
operations, however, after the short circuit has been eliminated.

8·6 Pilot lamps

A small incandescent bulb is often used as a panel lamp to light a dial
or as a pilot lamp that lights to show that the equipment is on. Typical
lamps and sockets are shown in Fig. 8·10. The side wall of the socket is
one connection. In the bayonet socket, the center connection has a spring
that holds the bulb tight. To insert or remove the bulb, it is pressed down
and twisted slightly. The mounting for a pilot lamp usually has a red or
green glass cover, as shown in Fig. 8·10d, called a *bezel*.

The characteristics of several lamps are listed in Table 8·2. Lamps with
a voltage rating of 6 to 8 volts, such as No. 47, are generally operated at
6.3 volts, which is a common value of filament supply voltage in electronic
equipment. Note that pilot lamps with a 120-volt rating are available for
operation directly from the power line. The current rating is indicated by
the color of the bead that supports the wire filament inside the bulb. Pilot
lamps are usually connected as a parallel branch, so that the equipment
can function if the bulb burns out.

Table 8·2 Pilot-lamp data

| Lamp No. | Base | Rating | | Bead color |
		Volts	Amperes	
40	Screw	6–8	0.15	Brown
41	Screw	2.5	0.15	Brown
44	Bayonet	6–8	0.25	Blue
47	Bayonet	6–8	0.15	Brown
6 watts	Screw	120	0.05	

Table 8·3 Properties of conducting materials*

Material	Description	ρ = specific resistance, cir-mil ohms per ft at 20°C	Temperature coefficient, per °C (α)	Melting point °C
Aluminum	Element (Al)	17	0.004	660
Carbon	Element (C)	†	−0.0003	3000
Constantan	55% Cu, 45% Ni, alloy	295	0 (average)	1210
Copper	Element (Cu)	10.4	0.004	1083
Gold	Element (Au)	14	0.004	1063
Iron	Element (Fe)	58	0.006	1535
Manganin	84% Cu, 12% Mn, 4% Ni, alloy	270	0 (average)	910
Nichrome	65% Ni, 23% Fe, 12% Cr, alloy	676	0.0002	1350
Nickel	Element (Ni)	52	0.005	1452
Silver	Element (Ag)	9.8	0.004	961
Steel	99.5% Fe, 0.5% C, alloy	100	0.003	1480
Tungsten	Element (W)	33.8	0.005	3370

* Listings approximate only, since precise values depend on exact composition of material.
† Carbon has about 2,500 to 7,500 times the resistance of copper. Graphite is a form of carbon.

8·7 Wire resistance

The longer a wire, the higher is its resistance, since more work must be done to make electrons drift from one end to the other. However, the thicker the wire is, the less the resistance, since there are more free electrons in the cross-sectional area. This law can be stated as a formula.

$$R = \rho \frac{l}{A} \tag{8·1}$$

where R is the total resistance, l the length, A the cross-sectional area, and ρ the specific resistance or resistivity.[2] The factor ρ then enables different materials to be compared in resistance according to their nature without regard to different lengths or areas. Higher values of ρ mean more resistance.

Specific resistance. Table 8·3 lists resistance values for different metals having the standard size of a 1-ft length with a cross-sectional area of 1 cir mil. This rating is the *specific resistance* of the metal, in cir-mil ohms per foot. Since silver, copper, gold, and aluminum are the best conductors, they have the lowest values of specific resistance. Tungsten and iron have much higher resistance.

Example 2. How much is the resistance of 100 ft of No. 20 copper wire?
From Table 8·1, the cross-sectional area is 1,022 cir mils; from Table 8·3 ρ for copper is 10.4. Using formula (8·1) gives

---

[2] ρ is Greek letter "rho," corresponding to r.

Table 8·4   Comparison of specific resistances

Material	Resistivity	Description
Silver	1.6×10^{-6} ohm-cm	Conductor
Germanium	55 ohm-cm	Semiconductor
Silicon	55,000 ohm-cm	Semiconductor
Mica	2×10^{12} ohm-cm	Insulator

Answer. $R = \rho \dfrac{l}{A} = 10.4 \dfrac{\text{cir-mil ohms}}{\text{ft}} \times \dfrac{100 \text{ ft}}{1{,}022 \text{ cir mil}} = \mathbf{1 \ ohm}$ (approx)

Note that this is approximately ⅒ the resistance of 1,000 ft of No. 20 copper wire listed in Table 8·1, showing that the resistance is proportional to length.

Example 3. How much is the resistance of a 100-ft length of No. 23 copper wire?

Answer. $R = \rho \dfrac{l}{A} = 10.4 \dfrac{\text{cir-mil ohms}}{\text{ft}} \times \dfrac{100 \text{ ft}}{509.5 \text{ cir mils}} = \mathbf{2 \ ohms}$ (approx)

Note that the increase of 3 in gage size provides one-half the circular area and double the resistance, approximately, for the same wire length.

For materials other than wire conductors, the specific resistance ρ is usually compared for the standard size of a 1-centimeter cube. Then, ρ for a unit area of 1 cm² is specified in ohm-cm. For instance, pure germanium at 25°C has a specific resistance of 55 ohm-cm; for silicon, ρ is 55,000 ohm-cm. Table 8·4 compares the resistivity of these semiconductors with conductors and insulators.

Example 4. How much is the resistance for a slab of germanium 0.2 cm long, with a cross-sectional area of 1 cm²?

Answer. $R = \rho \dfrac{l}{A} = 55 \text{ ohm-cm} \times \dfrac{0.2 \text{ cm}}{1 \text{ cm}^2}$

$R = \mathbf{11 \ ohms}$

Types of resistance wire. For applications in heating elements, as in a toaster, an incandescent light bulb, or a heater, it is necessary to use wire that has more resistance than good conductors like silver, copper, or aluminum. Higher resistance is preferable so that the required amount of I^2R power dissipated as heat in the wire can be obtained without excessive current. Typical materials for resistance wire are the elements tungsten, nickel, or iron and alloys[3] such as manganin, Nichrome, and constantan.

[3] An *alloy* is a fusion of elements, without chemical action between them. Metals are commonly alloyed to alter their physical characteristics.

Temperature coefficient of resistance. This factor states how much the resistance changes for a change in temperature. A positive temperature coefficient α means the resistance increases for higher temperatures. With a negative α, the resistance decreases. Table 8·3 lists typical values of α, in the fourth column, comparing the resistance changes with temperature for different materials. The value of α is significant in determining exact resistance values, as the temperature will increase with normal load current because of the I^2R power dissipated.

All the pure metals have a positive temperature coefficient. The α for tungsten, for instance, is 0.005. This means the resistance of tungsten increases by 0.5 per cent for each degree centigrade increase in temperature. As an example, a tungsten wire with a resistance of 14 ohms at 20°C will have a resistance 50 per cent higher at a temperature of 120°C, because of the 100° temperature increase. The hot resistance then is $14 + 7$ or 21 ohms at 120°C.

Note that carbon has a negative temperature coefficient. In general, α is negative for all semiconductors, including germanium and silicon. The negative α means less resistance at higher temperatures. This principle is applied in the use of carbon *thermistors*. The thermistor can be connected as a series component to decrease its resistance to compensate for the increased hot resistance of wire conductors.

A value of zero for α means the resistance is constant with changes in temperature. The metal alloys constantan and manganin, as examples, have a zero temperature coefficient. They can be used for precision wire-wound resistors, which do not change their resistance when the temperature increases.

Hot resistance. With resistance wire made of tungsten, Nichrome, iron, or nickel, there is usually a big difference in the amount of resistance the wire has when hot in normal operation and cold without its normal load current. The reason why is that the resistance increases for higher temperatures, with a positive temperature coefficient for these materials, as shown in Table 8·3.

As an example, the tungsten filament of a 100-watt 120-volt incandescent bulb has a current of 0.833 amp when the bulb lights with normal brilliance at its rated power, since $I = P/E$. By Ohm's law, the hot resistance is E/I, or 120 volts/0.833 amp, which equals 144 ohms. If, however, the filament

Fig. 8·11   Formation of ions. (a) Normal sodium (Na) atom. (b) Positively charged sodium (Na$^+$) ion.

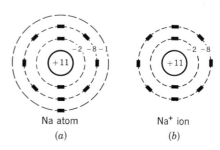

Na atom

(a)

Na$^+$ ion

(b)

resistance is measured with an ohmmeter when the bulb is not lit, the cold resistance is only about 10 ohms.

The Nichrome heater elements in appliances and the tungsten heaters in vacuum tubes also become several hundred degrees hotter in normal operation. In these cases, only the cold resistance can be measured with an ohmmeter; the hot resistance must be calculated from voltage and current measurements with the normal value of load current.

Example 5. The heater of a vacuum tube has 6.3 volts with its normal load current of 0.3 amp. How much is the hot resistance?

Answer.
$$R = \frac{E}{I} = \frac{6.3}{0.3} = \textbf{21 ohms}$$

It should be noted that the cold resistance of this heater measured with an ohmmeter equals 2 ohms, which is about one-tenth of the hot resistance.

8·8   Ion current in liquids and gases

We usually think of metal wire for a conductor, but there are other possibilities. Liquids such as salt water or dilute sulfuric acid can also allow the movement of electrical charges. For gases, consider the neon glow lamp, where neon serves as a conductor. The mechanism may be different for conduction in metal wire, liquids, or gases, but in any case the current is a motion of charges. Furthermore, either positive or negative charges can be the carriers that provide electrical current. The amount of current is Q/T. For 1 coul per sec the current is 1 amp.

In solid materials like the metals, the atoms are not free to move among each other. Therefore, conduction of electricity must take place by the drift of free electrons. Each atom remains neutral, neither gaining nor losing charge, but the metals are good conductors because they have plenty of free electrons that can be forced to drift through the solid substance.

In liquids and gases, however, each atom is able to move freely among all the other atoms because the substance is not solid. As a result, the atoms can easily take on electrons or lose electrons, particularly the valence electrons in the outside shell. The result is an atom that is no longer electrically neutral. Adding one or more electrons produces a negative charge; the loss of one or more electrons results in a positive charge. The charged atoms are called *ions*. Such charged particles are commonly formed in liquids and gases.

The ion. An ion is an atom that has a net electrical charge, either positive or negative, resulting from a loss or gain of electrons. See Fig. 8·11. In *a*, the sodium atom is neutral, with 11 positive charges in the nucleus balanced by 11 electrons in the outside shells. This atom has only 1 electron in the shell farthest from the nucleus. When the sodium is in a liquid solution, this one electron can easily leave the atom. The reason may be another atom close by that needs 1 electron for a stable ring of 8 electrons in its outside shell. Notice that if the sodium atom loses 1 valence electron, the atom will still have an outside ring of 8 electrons, as shown in *b*. This sodium atom now is a positive ion, with a charge equal to 1 proton.

Different ions can have a negative charge with an excess of electrons, just as the sodium ion is positive because it is missing an electron. The amount of charge, either positive or negative, can be equal to 1 electron or more. As an example, 1 sodium atom with a deficiency of 1 electron has the charge of 0.16×10^{-18} coul. With 6.25×10^{18} ions, their total charge equals 1 coul.

Current of ions. Just as in electron flow, opposite ion charges are attracted to each other, while like charges repel. The resultant motion of ions provides electrical current. In liquids and gases, therefore, conduction of electricity results mainly from the movement of ions. This motion of ion charges is called *ionization current*. Since an ion includes the nucleus of the atom, the ion charge is much heavier than an electron charge and moves with less velocity. We can say that ion charges are less mobile than electron charges.

It should be noted that the direction of ionization current can be the same as electron flow or the opposite. When negative ions move, they are attracted to the positive terminal of an applied voltage, in the same direction as electron flow. However, when positive ions move, this ionization current is in the opposite direction, toward the negative terminal of an applied voltage.

For either direction, though, the amount of ionization current is determined by the rate at which the charge moves. If 3 coul of positive ion charges move past a given point per second, the current is 3 amp, the same as 3 coul of negative ions or 3 coul of electron charges.

Ionization in liquids. Ions are usually formed in liquids when salts or acids are dissolved in water. Salt water is a good conductor because of ionization, but pure distilled water is an insulator. In addition, metals immersed in acids or alkaline solutions produce ionization. Lead immersed in sulfuric acid, for instance, results in hydrogen ions and sulfate ions.

Liquids that are good conductors because of ionization are called *electrolytes*. Acid and salt solutions in water can be classified as electrolytes. The process of producing a chemical change in a material by allowing ionization current to flow in an electrolyte is *electrolysis*. The gases hydrogen and oxygen, for instance, can be produced by electrolysis of water. A case of undesired electrolysis results with dissimilar metals joined mechanically, such as an iron bolt and brass nut; the materials can disintegrate because of electrolysis at the junction when the metals become wet. For *electroplating*, as in chromium-plated copper, a very thin coating of chromium is deposited on the copper base by means of ionization current in an electrolyte bath. Electrolytes, in general, have a negative temperature coefficient of resistance, as they conduct better when warm.

Ionization in gases. Gases have a minimum striking or ionization potential, which is the lowest applied voltage that will ionize the gas. Before

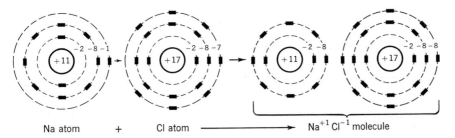

Fig. 8·12 *Ionic bond between atoms of sodium (Na) and chlorine (Cl) to form a molecule of sodium chloride (NaCl).*

ionization the gas is an insulator, but the ionization current makes the ionized gas a low resistance. The ionized gas usually glows. Argon, for instance, emits blue light when the gas is ionized. Ionized neon gas glows red. The amount of voltage needed to reach the striking potential varies with different gases and depends on the gas pressure. For example, a neon glow lamp for use as a night light ionizes at approximately 70 volts.

Ionic bonds. The sodium ion in Fig. 8·11 has a charge of $+1$ because it is missing 1 electron. If such positive ions are placed near negative ions with a charge of -1, there will be an electrical attraction to form an ionic bond. A common example is the combination of sodium (Na) ions and chlorine (Cl) ions to form table salt (NaCl), as shown in Fig. 8·12. Notice that the 1 outer electron of the Na atom can fit into the 7-electron shell of the Cl atom. When these two elements are combined, the Na atom gives up 1 electron to form a positive ion, with a stable L shell having 8 electrons; also the Cl atom adds this 1 electron to form a negative ion, with a stable M shell having 8 electrons. The two opposite types of ions are bound in NaCl because of the strong attractive force between opposite charges close together.

The ions in NaCl can separate in water to make salt water a conductor of electricity, while pure water is not. When current flows in salt water, then, the moving charges must be ions, as another example of ionization current.

Note the following definitions for atoms and molecules with reference to Fig. 8·12. The Na and Cl atoms at the left are neutral atoms because the charges are balanced. The charged atoms in NaCl at the right are ions. The combination of two or more atoms forms a molecule. When the combined atoms form a new substance, the result is a molecule of a new compound. One molecule of NaCl is shown here. However, two or more atoms of the same element can also be grouped to form a molecule of the element.

8·9 *Electrons and hole charges in semiconductors*

The semiconductor materials like germanium and silicon are in a class by themselves as conductors, as the charge carriers for current flow are neither ions nor free valence electrons. With a valence of ± 4 for these elements, the tendency to gain or lose electrons to form a stable 8 shell is the same either way. As a result, these elements tend to share their outer electrons in pairs of atoms. An example is illustrated in Fig. 8 · 13, for two silicon (Si) atoms, each sharing its 4 valence electrons with the other atom, to form one Si_2 molecule. This type of combination of atoms sharing their outer electrons to form a stable molecule is called a *covalent bond.*

The covalent-bond structure in germanium and silicon is the basis for their use in transistors. The reason why is that, although the covalent-bond structure is electrically neutral, it permits charges to be added by *doping* the semiconductor with a small amount of impurity atoms. As a specific example, germanium with a valence of 4 is combined with arsenic having a valence of 5. Then the doped germanium has covalent bonds with an excess of 1 electron for each impurity atom of arsenic. The result is a negative, or N-type, semiconductor.

For the opposite case, germanium can be doped with gallium, which has a valence of 3. Then covalent bonds formed with the impurity atoms have 7 outer electrons, instead of the 8 of 2 germanium atoms. The 1 missing electron for each covalent bond with an impurity atom corresponds to a positive charge called a *hole.* The amount of charge for each hole is 0.16×10^{-18} coul, the same as an electron, but of opposite polarity. This type of doping results in a P-type semiconductor with positive hole charges.

For either N-type or P-type semiconductors the charges can be made to move by an applied voltage to produce current. When electrons move, the current direction is the same as for electron flow. When the positive hole charges move, the direction is opposite from electron current. For either electrons or hole charges, when 1 coul moves past a given point in 1 sec, the amount of current is 1 amp.

For transistors, the negative and positive types of semiconductors are combined. In a PNP transistor, the N type is sandwiched between two P types. The opposite case, a P type between two N types, results in the NPN transistor. More details of semiconductors in general as important solid-state components and transistors in particular as commonly used for amplifier circuits are explained in Chap. 25 on Transistors.

8 · 10 *Insulators*

Substances that have very high resistance, in the order of many megohms, are classed as insulators. With such high resistance, an insulator cannot conduct appreciable current when voltage is applied. As a result, insulators can have either of two functions. One is to isolate conductors to eliminate conduction between them. The other is to store an electric charge when voltage is applied. An insulator maintains its charge because electrons cannot flow to neutralize the charge. The insulators are commonly called *dielectric materials,* therefore, meaning that they can store a charge. Among the best insulators, or dielectrics, are air, vacuum, rubber, wax, shellac, glass, mica, porcelain, oil, dry paper, textile fibers, and plastics

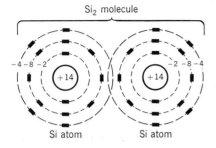

Si₂ molecule

Si atom   Si atom

Fig. 8·13   Covalent bond between silicon (Si) atoms.

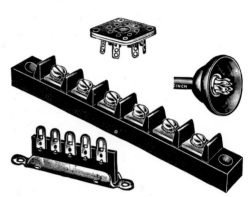

Fig. 8·14   Types of insulating materials. At top are plastic electron-tube socket and rubber cover for high-voltage connector. Plastic terminal strips below. (Cinch Mfg. Corp.)

such as Bakelite, formica, and polystyrene. Pure water is a good insulator, but salt water is not. Moist earth is a fairly good conductor, while dry, sandy earth is an insulator. Figure 8·14 shows some common insulators.

For any insulator, a high enough voltage can be applied to break down the internal structure of the material, forcing the dielectric to conduct. This dielectric breakdown is usually the result of an arc, which ruptures the physical structure of the material, making it useless as an insulator. Table 8·5 compares several insulators in terms of dielectric strength, which is the voltage breakdown rating. The higher the dielectric strength is, the better the insulator, since it is less likely to break down with a high value of applied voltage. The breakdown voltages in Table 8·5 are approximate values for the standard thickness of 1 mil, or 0.001 in. More thickness allows a higher breakdown-voltage rating.

Insulator discharge current. An insulator in contact with a voltage source stores charge, producing a potential on the insulator. The charge

Table 8·5   Voltage breakdown of insulators

Material	Dielectric strength, volts/mil	Material	Dielectric strength, volts/mil
Air or vacuum	20	Paraffin wax	200–300
Bakelite	300–550	Phenol, molded	300–700
Fiber	150–180	Polystyrene	500–760
Glass	335–2,000	Porcelain	40–150
Mica	600–1,500	Rubber, hard	450
Paper	1,250	Shellac	900
Paraffin oil	380		

tends to remain on the insulator but it can be discharged by one of the following methods:

1. Conduction through a conducting path. For instance, a wire across the charged insulator provides a discharge path. Then the discharged dielectric has no potential.
2. Brush discharge. As an example, high voltage on a sharp pointed wire can discharge through the surrounding atmosphere by ionization of the air molecules. This may be visible in the dark as a bluish or reddish glow, called *corona effect.*
3. Spark discharge. This is a result of breakdown in the insulator because of a high potential difference, rupturing the dielectric. The current that flows across the insulator at the instant of breakdown causes the spark.

Corona is undesirable as it reduces the potential by brush discharge into the surrounding air. In addition, the corona often indicates the beginning of a spark discharge. A potential in the order of kilovolts is usually necessary for corona, as the breakdown voltage for air is approximately 20 kv per in. To reduce the corona effect conductors that have high voltage should be smooth, rounded, and thick. This equalizes the potential difference from all points on the conductor to the surrounding air. Any sharp point can have a more intense field, making it more susceptible to corona and eventual spark discharge.

SUMMARY

1. A conductor has very low resistance. All the metals are good conductors, the best being silver, copper, and aluminum. Copper is generally used for wire conductors.
2. The sizes for copper wire are specified by the American Wire Gage. Higher gage numbers mean thinner wire. Typical sizes are No. 22 gage hookup wire for electronic circuits and No. 10 for house wiring.
3. The cross-sectional area of round wire is measured in circular mils. One mil is 0.001 in. The area in circular mils equals the diameter in mils squared.
4. $R = \rho(l/A)$. The factor ρ is specific resistance. Wire resistance increases directly with length (l), but decreases inversely with the cross-sectional area (A), or the square of the diameter.
5. A switch inserted in one side of a circuit opens the entire series circuit. When open, the switch has the applied voltage across it.
6. A fuse protects the circuit components against overload, as excessive current melts the fuse element to open the entire series circuit. A good fuse has very low resistance and practically zero voltage across it.
7. Ionization in liquids and gases produces atoms that are not electrically neutral. These are ions. Negative ions have an excess of electrons; positive ions have a deficiency of electrons. In liquids and gases, electrical current is a result of movement by the ions.
8. In the semiconductors, such as germanium and silicon, the charge carriers are electrons in N type and positive hole charges in P type. One hole charge is 0.16×10^{-18} coul, the same as 1 electron.
9. An insulator has very high resistance. Common insulating materials are air, vacuum, rubber, paper, glass, porcelain, shellac, and plastics. Insulators are also called dielectrics. A higher value of dielectric strength means the insulator can withstand higher voltages without breaking down.

SELF-EXAMINATION (*Answers at back of book.*)

Here's a chance to find out how well you have learned the material in this chapter. These exercises are for your self-testing only.

1. A 10-ft length of copper wire conductor gage No. 20 has a total resistance of (*a*) less than 1 ohm; (*b*) 5 ohms; (*c*) 10.4 ohms; (*d*) approximately 1 M.
2. A copper wire conductor with 0.2-in. diameter has an area of (*a*) 200 cir mils; (*b*) 400 cir mils; (*c*) 20,000 cir mils; (*d*) 40,000 cir mils.
3. If a wire conductor of 0.1-ohm resistance is doubled in length, its resistance becomes (*a*) 0.01 ohm; (*b*) 0.02 ohm; (*c*) 0.05 ohm; (*d*) 0.2 ohm.
4. If two wire conductors are tied in parallel, their total resistance is (*a*) double the resistance of one wire; (*b*) one-half the resistance of one wire; (*c*) the same as one wire; (*d*) two-thirds the resistance of one wire.
5. The hot resistance of the tungsten filament in a bulb is higher than its cold resistance because the filament's temperature coefficient is (*a*) negative; (*b*) positive; (*c*) zero; (*d*) about 10 ohms per degree.
6. A closed switch has a resistance of (*a*) zero; (*b*) infinity; (*c*) about 100 ohms at room temperature; (*d*) at least 1,000 ohms.
7. An open fuse has a resistance of (*a*) zero; (*b*) infinity; (*c*) about 100 ohms at room temperature; (*d*) at least 1,000 ohms.
8. Insulating materials have the function of (*a*) conducting very large currents; (*b*) preventing an open circuit between the voltage source and the load; (*c*) preventing a short circuit between conducting wires; (*d*) storing very high currents.
9. An ion is (*a*) a free electron; (*b*) a proton; (*c*) an atom with unbalanced charges; (*d*) a nucleus without protons.
10. Ionization current in liquids and gases results from a flow of (*a*) free electrons; (*b*) protons; (*c*) positive or negative ions; (*d*) ions that are lighter in weight than electrons.

ESSAY QUESTIONS

1. Name three good metal conductors, in their order of resistance. Give one application.
2. Name four insulators. Give one application.
3. Name two semiconductors. Give one application.
4. Name two types of resistance wire. Give one application.
5. What is meant by the dielectric strength of an insulator?
6. Why does ionization occur more readily in liquids and gases, compared with the solid metals? Give an example of ionization current.
7. Define the following: ion, ionic bond, covalent bond, molecule.
8. Draw a circuit with two bulbs, a battery, and an SPDT switch that determines which bulb lights.
9. Why is it not possible to measure the hot resistance of a filament with an ohmmeter?
10. Give one way in which negative ion charges are similar to electron charges and one way in which they are different.

PROBLEMS (*Answers to selected problems at back of book.*)

1. A copper wire has a diameter of 0.032 in. (*a*) How much is its circular-mil area? (*b*) What is its AWG size? (*c*) How much is the resistance of a 100-ft length?
2. Draw the schematic diagram of a resistance in series with an open SPST switch and 100-volt source. (*a*) With the switch open how much is the voltage across the resistance? How much across the open switch? (*b*) With the switch closed, how much is the voltage across the switch and across the resistance? (*c*) Do the voltage drops around the series circuit add to equal the applied voltage in both cases?
3. Draw the schematic diagram of a fuse in series with the resistance of a 100-watt 120-volt bulb

connected to a 120-volt source. (*a*) What size fuse can be used? (*b*) How much is the voltage across the good fuse? (*c*) How much is the voltage across the fuse if it is open?

4. Compare the resistance of two conductors; 100 ft of No. 10 gage copper wire and 200 ft of No. 7 gage copper wire.

5. How much is the hot resistance, approximately, of a No. 47 dial lamp?

6. How much is the resistance of a slab of silicon 0.1 cm long with a cross-sectional area of 1 cm²?

7. (*a*) How many hole charges are needed to equal 1 coul? (*b*) How many electrons? (*c*) How many ions with a negative charge of 1 electron?

8. A cable with two lengths of No. 10 copper wire is shorted at one end. The resistance reading at the open end is 10 ohms. What is the cable length in feet? (Temperature is 25°C.)

9. (*a*) If a copper wire has a resistance of 4 ohms at 25°C, how much is its resistance at 75°C? (*b*) If the wire is No. 10 gage, what is its length in feet?

10. A coil is wound with 3,000 turns of No. 20 wire. If the average amount of wire in a turn is 4 in., how much is the total resistance of the coil? What will be its resistance if No. 30 wire is used instead? (Temperature is 25°C.)

11. Calculate the voltage drop across 1,000 ft of No. 10 gage wire connected to a 2-amp load.

12. What is the smallest size of copper wire that will limit the line drop to 5 volts, with 120 volts applied and a 6-amp load? The total line length is 200 ft.

Chapter 9 Resistors

In many applications, resistance must be inserted into a circuit, either to reduce the current to a desired value or to produce a specific IR voltage drop. The components for these uses, manufactured with a specific value of resistance, are *resistors*. Actually, resistors are possibly the most common component in all kinds of electronic equipment. The main features of resistors are described in the following topics:

9·1   Resistor types
9·2   Variable resistors
9·3   Resistor color coding
9·4   Power rating of resistors
9·5   Choosing the resistor for a circuit
9·6   Series and parallel combinations of resistors
9·7   Resistors for specialized applications
9·8   Resistor troubles

9·1   Resistor types

Figure 9·1 shows typical examples of wirewound resistors, and Fig. 9·2 shows the carbon-composition type. These are the two main types of resistors commonly used. Resistors are available in a wide range of values, from a fraction of an ohm to many megohms, with a power rating of several hundred watts down to a value as low as ⅒ watt. The power rating indicates the maximum amount of watts the resistor can dissipate without excessive heat. Dissipation means that the power is wasted as I^2R loss, since the resultant heat is not used.

Wirewound resistors are used for applications where the power dissipation in the resistor is about 5 watts or more. For 2 watts or less, the carbon-composition type is preferable because it is smaller and costs less. Most of

Fig. 9·1   *Wirewound resistors. Resistor with variable tap at left; fixed resistor at center—both 5 in. long; variable resistor at right, 2-in. diameter. All have 50-watt rating.* (P. R. Mallory & Co., Inc.)

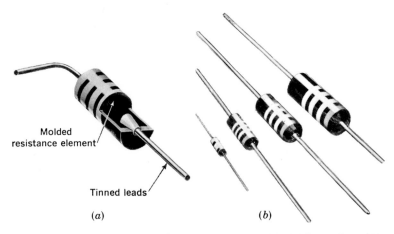

Molded resistance element

Tinned leads

(a)   (b)

Fig. 9·2   *Carbon-composition resistors. (a) Internal construction. (b) Sizes of ¼, ½, 1, 2 watts. Length is 0.7 in. for 2-watt size.* (Allen-Bradley Company.)

the resistors in radio, television, and electronic equipment are carbon-composition. Both types can be either fixed or variable. Fixed resistors have a specific amount of resistance that cannot be adjusted. A variable resistor can be adjusted for one value between zero ohms and its maximum resistance. Carbon-composition variable resistors are commonly used for controls, such as the volume control in a receiver. A common application for variable wirewound resistors is to divide the voltage from a power supply.

Wirewound resistors. In this construction, resistance wire such as Advance or manganin is wrapped around an insulating core. Insulating materials commonly used are porcelain, cement, phenolic materials like Bakelite, or just plain pressed paper. The wire is bare, but usually the entire unit is encased in an insulator. Several examples are shown in Fig. 9·1. The length of wire used and its specific resistivity determine the resistance of the unit.

Since they are generally for low-resistance high-power applications, wirewound resistors are available in power ratings from 3 watts to several hundred watts, with a resistance range of less than 1 ohm to several thousand ohms. Also, wirewound precision resistors are used where accurate, stable resistance values are required, as for meter shunts and multipliers.

Carbon-composition resistors. This type is made of finely divided carbon or graphite mixed with a powdered insulating material in the proportions needed for the desired resistance value. As shown in Fig. 9·2, the resistor element is usually enclosed in a plastic case for insulation and mechanical strength. Joined to the two ends of the carbon resistance element are metal caps with leads of tinned copper wire for soldering the resistor connections into a circuit. These are called *axial leads* because they come straight out from the ends. Carbon resistors are commonly available in resistance values of 1 ohm to 20 M. Their power rating is generally ¹⁄₁₀, ¼, ½, 1, or 2 watts.

9·2 Variable resistors

These can be wirewound, as in Fig. 9·1, or the carbon type in Fig. 9·3. Inside the metal case shown in Fig. 9·3, the control has a circular disk that is the carbon-composition resistance element. Joined to the two ends are the outside soldering-lug terminals 1 and 3. The middle lug 2 is connected to the variable arm contacting the resistor element by a metal spring wiper. As the shaft of the control is rotated, the variable arm moves the wiper to make contact at different points. When the contact moves closer to one end, the resistance decreases between this end and the variable arm. The variable resistance is zero when the wiper contacts this end but is maximum with the variable arm at the opposite end. Between the two outside ends, the resistance is not variable but always has the maximum resistance of the control.

Carbon controls are available with a total resistance value from 1,000 ohms to 5 M, approximately. Their power rating is usually ½ to 2 watts. A carbon control is often combined with an ON-OFF switch, which is a separate unit operated by the control shaft. A common example is the power ON-OFF switch and volume control for a receiver.

Potentiometers and rheostats. These are variable resistance controls, either carbon-composition or wirewound, used for varying the voltage and current in a circuit. A rheostat is a variable resistance with two terminals connected in series in a circuit to vary the current. A potentiometer has three terminals. The fixed maximum resistance between the two end terminals is connected across a voltage source and the variable arm used to vary the voltage division.

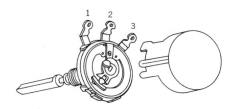

Fig. 9·3 Variable carbon resistance control. Diameter about 1 in.

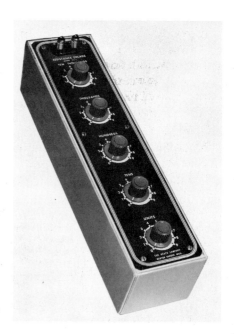

Fig. 9·4 Decade resistance box. (Heath Company.)

Decade resistance box. As shown in Fig. 9·4 the *decade box* is a convenient arrangement for obtaining any one resistance within a wide range of values. Inside the box are five series strings of resistors, with one string for each dial switch. The first dial connects in resistances of 1 to 9 ohms and is the *units* dial. The second dial has units of ten from 10 to 90 ohms and is the *tens* dial. The *hundreds* dial has resistances from 100 to 900 ohms, the fourth dial provides a resistance of 1,000 to 9,000 ohms, and the top dial is 10,000 to 90,000 ohms. The five dial sections are connected in series. Then any value from 1 to 99,999 ohms can be obtained. For instance, dial "five" on 5 means 50,000 ohms; dial "four" on 4 means 4,000 ohms; dial "three" on 3 equals 300 ohms; dial "two" on 2 is 20 ohms; dial "one" on 1 is 1 ohm. The total resistance is the sum of these series resistances:

$$50,000 + 4,000 + 300 + 20 + 1 = 54,321 \text{ ohms}$$

which is the amount of resistance connected internally across the terminals of the decade box. For other values the dials can be set for any resistance of 1 to 99,999 ohms.

9·3 Resistor color coding

Because carbon resistors are small physically, they are color-coded to indicate their resistance value in ohms. The basis of this system is the use of colors for numerical values, as listed in Table 9·1. In memorizing these colors, remember that the dark colors, black and brown, correspond to the lowest numbers, zero and one, through lighter colors, to white for nine.

Table 9·1   Color code

Color	Value	Color	Value
Black	0	Green	5
Brown	1	Blue	6
Red	2	Violet	7
Orange	3	Gray	8
Yellow	4	White	9

The color coding is standardized by the Electronics Industries Association (EIA). These codes are summarized in Appendix G.

Resistance color bands. This code is the most common system used for color-coding insulated carbon resistors having axial leads, as illustrated in Fig. 9·5. Color bands are printed at one end of the insulating body, which is usually tan. Reading from left to right, the first color band close to the edge indicates the first digit in the numerical value of resistance. The second band gives the second digit. The third band is the decimal multiplier, giving the number of zeros after the two digits. The resulting number is the resistance in ohms. As examples, in Fig. 9·6a the first stripe is yellow for 4; the second stripe is violet for 7; the orange multiplier means "add three zeros to 47." Therefore, this resistance value is 47,000 ohms. The example in Fig. 9·6b illustrates that black for the third stripe just means "do not add any zeros to the first two figures." This resistor has yellow, violet, and black for the resistance value of 47 ohms.

Resistors under 10 ohms. These resistors have a third stripe of gold or silver which are fractional decimal multipliers. When the third stripe is

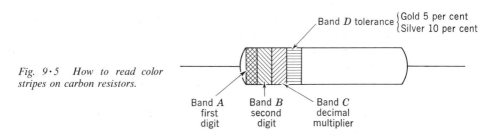

Fig. 9·5   How to read color stripes on carbon resistors.

Band D tolerance { Gold 5 per cent / Silver 10 per cent

Band A first digit   Band B second digit   Band C decimal multiplier

Fig. 9·6   Examples of color-coded resistance values.

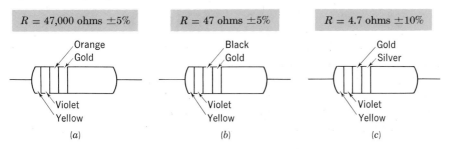

R = 47,000 ohms ±5%

Orange
Gold
Violet
Yellow
(a)

R = 47 ohms ±5%

Black
Gold
Violet
Yellow
(b)

R = 4.7 ohms ±10%

Gold
Silver
Violet
Yellow
(c)

gold, multiply the first two digits by 0.1; silver is 0.01 as a multiplier. For example, in Fig. 9·6c the color stripes are yellow, violet, and gold. The resistance is 47 × 0.1, therefore, which equals 4.7 ohms. If the multiplier were silver, the resistance would be 47 × 0.01, or 0.47 ohms. Gold and silver are fractional multipliers only in the third stripe. Gold and silver are most often used, however, as a fourth stripe to indicate how accurate the resistance value is.

Resistor tolerance. The amount by which the actual resistance can be different from the color-coded value is the *tolerance,* usually given in per cent. For instance, a 100,000-ohm resistor with ±10 per cent tolerance can have a resistance 10 per cent below or above the coded value. This resistance, therefore, is between 90,000 and 110,000 ohms. The inexact value of carbon resistors is a disadvantage resulting from their economical construction, but in most circuits 10 per cent variation in resistance can be tolerated.

As illustrated in Fig. 9·6, silver in the fourth band indicates a tolerance of ±10 per cent; gold is ±5 per cent. When there is no fourth stripe, the tolerance is ±20 per cent. The smaller the tolerance, the more accurate the resistance value and the higher is its cost.

Wirewound resistor marking. Usually, wirewound resistors are physically big enough to have their resistance value and tolerance printed on the insulating case. The tolerance of most is ±5 per cent, except for precision resistors, which have a tolerance of ±1 per cent or less. Some small wirewound resistors may be coded with stripes, however, as for carbon resistors. In this case, the first stripe is double the width of the others to indicate a wirewound resistor.

Preferred resistance values. In order to minimize the problem of manufacturing different resistance values for an almost unlimited variety of circuits, certain values of fixed carbon-composition resistors are manufactured in large quantities so that they are cheaper and more easily available than unusual sizes. For resistors of ±10 per cent tolerance, the preferred values are 10, 12, 15, 18, 22, 27, 33, 39, 47, 56, 68, and 82 and their decimal multiples, such as 820, 8,200, 82,000, or 820,000. This way, a preferred value is available for any resistance within 10 per cent. For more accurate resistors of low tolerance, there are additional preferred values. (See Appendix, Table G-4.)

9·4   Power rating of resistors

In addition to having the required ohms value, a resistor should have a wattage rating high enough to dissipate the I^2R power produced by the current flowing through the resistance, without becoming too hot. Carbon resistors in normal operation are often quite warm, up to a maximum temperature of about 85°C, which is close to the 100°C boiling point of water. Carbon resistors should not be so hot, however, that they "sweat" beads of liquid on the insulating case. Wirewound resistors operate very hot, a

typical value being 300°C for the maximum temperature. If a resistor becomes too hot because of excessive power dissipation, it can change appreciably in resistance value or burn open.

The power rating is a physical property depending on the resistor construction, especially physical size. Note the following:

1. A larger physical size indicates a higher power rating.
2. Higher-wattage resistors can operate at higher temperatures.
3. Wirewound resistors are physically larger with higher wattage ratings
   than carbon resistors.

For both types, a higher power rating allows a higher voltage rating.
This rating gives the highest voltage that may be applied across the
resistor without internal arcing. In wirewound resistors, excessive voltage
can produce an arc between turns; in carbon resistors the arc is between
carbon granules.

Derating curves. The power ratings for resistors are based on adequate
ventilation to remove heat. Usually an *ambient temperature* for the surrounding air is specified at 25 or 40°C. At higher ambient temperatures
the nominal power rating must be reduced to prevent excessive change of
resistance or damage to the resistor. This reduction in power rating for
higher ambient temperature is usually shown by a derating curve, as in
Fig. 9·7. Derating applies to wirewound and carbon-composition types
but the graph here illustrates a specific example for ½-watt carbon resistors.
This curve shows that the power is derated 50 per cent at an ambient temperature of about 70°C. In practice, then, a nominal ½-watt resistor with
this derating curve should be used as a ¼-watt resistor where the surrounding temperature of the resistor in the equipment rises to 70°C. It should be
noted, though, that resistors with different construction can have different
derating curves.

Fig. 9·7 Derating curve of ½-watt carbon-
composition resistor, showing how power
rating is reduced for higher ambient temperatures.

Fig. 9·8 Load characteristic of carbon-composition resistors, showing how resistance decreases with more load
current as the resistor dissipates a greater percentage of
its rated power.

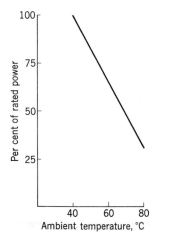

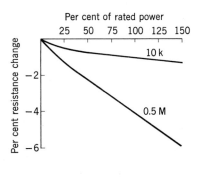

Load characteristic. When normal load current flows in a resistor, its resistance can change because of the temperature rise. In wirewound resistors, this effect depends on the type of wire. For carbon resistors the resistance decreases at high temperatures. A typical characteristic is shown by the graph in Fig. 9·8 for ½-watt carbon resistors. The curve for the 0.5-M resistor shows that at full rated load of 100 per cent, the resistance is reduced by 4 per cent. This load characteristic is the reason why carbon resistors are generally used with a safety factor of 2 for the power rating. If the actual power dissipated is 1 watt, a 2-watt resistor would normally be used. Then the resistor operates at 50 per cent of full rated load. This safety factor is in addition to any derating that may be required for high ambient temperature.

Shelf life. Resistors keep their characteristics almost indefinitely, when not used. Without any current in a circuit to heat the resistor, the resistor has practically no change with age. The shelf life of resistors is usually no problem, therefore. Actually, the only components that should be used fresh from manufacture are batteries and electrolytic capacitors.

9·5   Choosing the resistor for a circuit

In determining what size resistor to use, the first requirement is to have the amount of resistance needed. In Fig. 9·9a, for example, suppose that a resistor is to be inserted in series with R_1 for the purpose of limiting the current through the 900-ohm resistance to 0.1 amp with a 100-volt source. Since the total resistance required is 1,000 ohms, the 100-ohm resistor R_2 is added in series with R_1. The current through both R_1 and R_2 is then 0.1 amp. The I^2R power dissipated in R_2 is 1 watt, but a 2-watt resistor would normally be used. This safety factor of 2 in the power rating is common practice with carbon resistors, so that they will not become too hot in normal operation. A resistor with a higher wattage rating but the same resistance would allow the circuit to operate normally and last longer without breaking down, but it can be inconvenient when the next larger size is wirewound and physically bigger. Wirewound resistors can operate closer to their power rating, assuming adequate ventilation, because of their higher maximum operating temperature, compared with carbon resistors.

In Fig. 9·9b, the 10-M resistor R_4 is used with the resistance of R_3 to provide an IR voltage drop equal to one-half the applied voltage of 400 volts. Since R_3 and R_4 are equal, each has an IR voltage drop of 200 volts. Their total series resistance of 20 M limits the current in the circuit to 20 μa. The I^2R power dissipated in R_4 is 4 mw, but the wattage rating used is ¼ watt. In this case, the wattage rating is much higher than the actual amount of power dissipated in the resistor. Notice the small amount of power dissipated in this circuit, with an applied voltage of 400 volts, since the very high resistance limits the current to a low value.

In general, using a resistor with a high enough wattage rating automatically provides the required voltage rating. The exception, however,

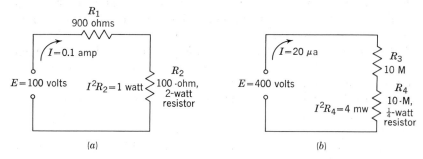

Fig. 9·9   *Power rating of resistors. (a)* R_2 *dissipates 1 watt, but 2-watt resistor is used for safety factor of 2. (b)* R_4 *dissipates 0.004 watt, but ¼ watt is used.*

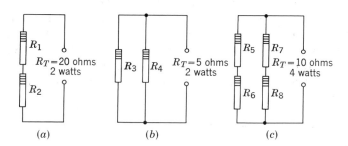

Fig. 9·10   *Total resistance and wattage rating for series and parallel combinations. All resistors are 10 ohms with 1-watt rating.*

is a low-current high-voltage circuit where the applied voltage is in the order of a kilovolt or more.

9·6   *Series and parallel combinations of resistors*

In some cases two or more resistors are combined in series or parallel to obtain a desired resistance value with a higher wattage rating. Several examples are shown in Fig. 9·10. The total resistance depends on the series and parallel combinations. The combination, however, has a power rating equal to the sum of the individual wattage ratings, whether the resistors are in series or in parallel, because the total physical size of the combination increases with each added resistor. In *a* the two resistors in series double the resistance with twice the power rating. The two parallel resistors in *b* have one-half the resistance but double the power rating. The series-parallel combination of four resistors in *c* has the same resistance as one unit and four times the power rating. Such resistor combinations are generally used to obtain a higher power rating with carbon resistors.

9·7   *Resistors for specialized applications*

In addition to wirewound and carbon-composition resistors for general use, there are special types for particular applications. Some examples are shown in Fig. 9·11. These types include:

1. *Deposited-film resistors.* These resistors have a crystalline carbon film deposited on a ceramic shell. The features include greater accuracy and better stability with changes in temperature and moisture.

2. *High-voltage resistors.* The carbon-composition coating is applied on a long ceramic tube. Constant spacing of the turns allows uniform voltage drop through the length of the resistor.

3. *Insulated wirewound resistors.* These resistors look like carbon resistors and have the same color coding except that a wide band is used for the first digit. Power ratings are ½ to 3 or 4 watts.

4. *Bobbin wirewound resistors.* These precision resistors are often used for meter shunts and multipliers.

5. *Thermistors.* These resistors provide a controlled amount of resistance change according to the amount of current flowing in the resistor. Thermistors usually have a negative temperature coefficient. Their cold resistance is therefore more than the hot resistance. One use is limiting the heater current in tubes before the tungsten filaments reach operating temperature. In this application, the thermistor is called a *tube saver.*

6. *Fusible resistors.* These low resistances are made to open readily with excessive current, serving the dual functions of a current-limiting resistance and a fuse.

9·8   Resistor troubles

The most common trouble in resistors is an open. When the open resistor is a series component, there is no current in the entire series circuit and it cannot operate.

Crystallized resistors. An open resistor is often just the result of constant use. The resistor expands slightly as it becomes hot with current and contracts as it cools off when power is off. Over a period of years the resistance element becomes crystallized. Then it can open when hot, or because of mechanical jarring. Resistors in high-power circuits are more likely to develop the trouble of an open because they are usually very hot in normal operation. The safety factor of a wattage rating double the actual power

Fig. 9·11   Specialized resistors. Bobbin-type precision resistor at left; high-voltage resistor at center; deposited-carbon resistor below. (International Resistance Company.)

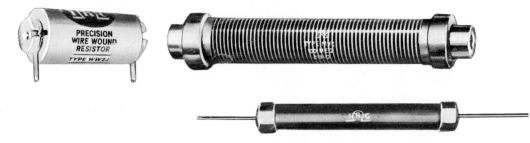

dissipation, or more, allows the resistor to operate for a longer time without trouble.

Noisy controls. In applications such as volume and tone controls, carbon controls are preferred because the smoother change in resistance results in less noise when the variable arm is rotated. With use, however, the resistance element becomes worn by the wiper contact, making the control noisy. When a volume or tone control makes a scratchy noise as the shaft is rotated, it indicates a worn-out resistance element.

Burned resistors. Excessive current can make the resistor hot enough actually to burn. The resistance element then will become charred, break apart, and be open, resulting in no current through the resistor. Usually, the excessive current results from a short in a series-parallel circuit, as illustrated in Fig. 9·12. In *a*, R_1 has its normal current, since the high resistance of R_2 limits the current to 1 ma. When R_2 is shorted by a parallel branch as in *b*, however, the current through R_1 increases to 1 amp. If R_1 is a carbon resistor, this is enough current to make it burn.

Changed resistance value. Carbon-composition resistors can change appreciably in resistance. Since carbon has a negative temperature coefficient, the resistance decreases with increasing temperature. The resistance will normally be within its tolerance, however, when the resistor has a wattage rating high enough to operate below its maximum temperature. What does happen often, though, is that the resistor crystallizes with constant use and its resistance becomes much higher than normal. Such a resistor can be considered as partially open.

Checking resistors with an ohmmeter. Since the ohmmeter has its own voltage source, it is always used without any external power applied to the resistance being measured. Just connect the ohmmeter leads across the resistance to be measured.

An open resistor reads infinitely high ohms. For some reason, infinite ohms is often confused with zero ohms. Remember, though, that infinite ohms means an open circuit. The current is zero but the resistance is

Fig. 9·12 *Short circuit causing excessive current through R_1. (a) Circuit normal with current through R_1 equal to 1 ma, approximately. (b) Switch shorts out R_2, resulting in excessive current of 1 amp through R_1.*

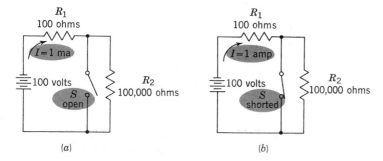

(a)　　　　　　　　(b)

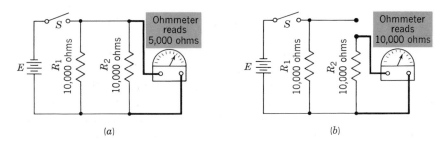

Fig. 9·13   *Parallel resistance of R_1 can lower reading for R_2. (a) R_1 and R_2 in parallel. (b) R_2 isolated from R_1.*

infinitely high. Furthermore, it is practically impossible for a resistor to become shorted in itself. The resistor may be shorted out by some other part of the circuit but the construction of resistors is such that the trouble they develop is an open, with infinitely high ohms.

The ohmmeter must have an ohms scale capable of reading the resistance value, or the resistor cannot be checked. In checking a 10-M resistor, for instance, if the highest reading is 1 M, the ohmmeter will indicate infinite resistance, even if the resistor has its normal value of 10 M. An ohms scale of 100 M or more should be used for checking such high resistances. Similarly, in checking resistance values less than 10 ohms, a low-ohms scale of about 100 ohms or less is necessary. Otherwise, the ohmmeter will read a normally low resistance value as zero ohms.

When checking resistance in a circuit, it is important to be sure there are no parallel paths across the resistor being measured. Otherwise, the measured resistance can be much lower than the actual resistor value, as illustrated in Fig. 9·13a. Here, the ohmmeter reads the resistance of R_2 in parallel with R_1. To check across R_2 alone, one end is disconnected as in Fig. 9·13b. For very high resistances, it is important not to touch the meter leads, since the body resistance of about 50,000 ohms as a parallel path lowers the ohmmeter reading.

SUMMARY

1. The two main types of resistors are carbon-composition and wirewound. Their characteristics are compared in Table 9·2.
2. A rheostat is a variable series resistance with two terminals to adjust the amount of current in a circuit.
3. A potentiometer is a variable voltage divider with three terminals.
4. Carbon resistors are practically always color-coded, as in Figs. 9·5 and 9·6, to indicate the resistance value.
5. The wattage rating of carbon resistors depends mainly on their physical size, larger resistors being able to dissipate more power. The power rating is not part of the color coding but may be printed on the resistor or judged from its size. A 2-watt carbon resistor is about 1 in. long with ¼ in. diameter.
6. With carbon resistors the wattage rating should be about double the actual I^2R power dissipation for a safety factor of 2 or more. The wattage rating does not affect the amount of current in the circuit, but only allows the resistor to have its normal current without excessive heat.

Table 9·2 *Comparison of resistor types*

CARBON-COMPOSITION	WIREWOUND
Carbon granules in resinous binder	Turns of resistance wire
Resistance values up to 20 M	Resistance values down to a fraction of 1 ohm
Color-coded for resistance value	Resistance usually printed on unit
For low-current circuits; power ratings of ⅒ to 2 watts	For high-current circuits; power rating of 3 to over 100 watts
Variable potentiometers up to 5 M for controls such as volume and tone in receivers	Low-resistance rheostats for varying current; potentiometers up to 50 K for voltage divider in power supply

7. Carbon resistors can be combined for a higher wattage rating. The total power rating is the sum of the individual wattage values, whether in series or parallel. In series, though, the total resistance increases; in parallel the combined resistance decreases.
8. The most common trouble in resistors is an open. An ohmmeter reads infinite ohms across the open resistor, assuming no parallel path.

SELF-EXAMINATION (*Answers at back of book.*)

Here's a chance to find out how well you have learned the material in this chapter. These exercises are for your self-testing only.

1. Which of the following are typical resistance and power-dissipation values for a wirewound resistor? (*a*) 1 M, ⅓ watt; (*b*) 500 ohms, 1 watt; (*c*) 50,000 ohms, 1 watt; (*d*) 10 ohms, 50 watts.
2. Which of the following are typical resistance and power-dissipation values for a carbon-composition resistor? (*a*) 100,000 ohms, 1 watt; (*b*) 10,000 ohms, 10 watts; (*c*) 5 ohms, 5 watts; (*d*) 1,000 ohms, 100 watts.
3. For a carbon-composition resistor color-coded with yellow, violet, orange, and silver stripes from left to right, the resistance and tolerance are (*a*) 740 ohms ±5 per cent; (*b*) 4,700 ohms ±10 per cent; (*c*) 7,400 ohms ±1 per cent; (*d*) 47,000 ohms ±10 per cent.
4. For a carbon-composition resistor color-coded with green, black, gold, and silver stripes from left to right, the resistance and tolerance are (*a*) 0.5 ohm ±5 per cent; (*b*) 0.5 ohm ±10 per cent; (*c*) 5 ohms ±10 per cent; (*d*) 50 ohms ±10 per cent.
5. A resistor with the color-coded value of 100 ohms and ±20 per cent tolerance can have an actual resistance between (*a*) 80 and 120 ohms; (*b*) 90 and 110 ohms; (*c*) 98 and 102 ohms; (*d*) 100 and 120 ohms.
6. Two 1,000-ohm 1-watt resistors are connected in parallel. Their combined resistance value and wattage rating is (*a*) 500 ohms, 1 watt; (*b*) 500 ohms, 2 watts; (*c*) 1,000 ohms, 2 watts; (*d*) 2,000 ohms, 2 watts.
7. A resistor is to be connected across a 45-volt battery to provide 1 ma of current. The required resistance with a suitable wattage rating is (*a*) 4.5 ohms, 1 watt; (*b*) 45 ohms, 10 watts; (*c*) 450 ohms, 2 watts; (*d*) 45,000 ohms, ⅓ watt.
8. Which of the following is a preferred resistor value? (*a*) 47; (*b*) 520; (*c*) 43,000; (*d*) 54,321.
9. When checked with an ohmmeter, an open resistor reads (*a*) zero; (*b*) infinite; (*c*) high but within the tolerance; (*d*) low but not zero.
10. One precaution in checking resistors with an ohmmeter is (*a*) Check high resistances on the lowest ohms range. (*b*) Check low resistances on the highest ohms range. (*c*) Disconnect all parallel resistance paths. (*d*) Check high resistances with your fingers touching the test leads.

ESSAY QUESTIONS

1. Show how to connect two 1,000-ohm 1-watt resistors to obtain 2,000 ohms with a power rating of 2 watts.
2. State the colors corresponding to the digits 1 to 9, inclusive.
3. Give the color coding for the following ohms values: 1 M, 33,000, 8,200, 150, and 68.
4. A 50-ohm rheostat R_1 is in series with 25-ohm R_2, with 50-volt E. Draw a graph of I against R_1 as it is varied in 10-ohm steps.
5. Why do high-resistance carbon-composition resistors, in the order of megohms, usually have a low power rating of 1 watt or less?
6. Name three factors that determine the resistance of a wirewound resistor.
7. Describe briefly how you would check a 5-M resistor to see if it is open. State two precautions to make sure the check is not misleading.
8. Show how to connect resistors for the following examples: (a) two 20-K 1-watt resistors for a total of 10,000 ohms with a power rating of 2 watts; (b) Two 20-K 1-watt resistors for a total of 40,000 ohms with a power rating of 2 watts; (c) Four 10-K 1-watt resistors for a total of 10,000 ohms with a power rating of 4 watts; (d) Three 10-K resistors for a total of 15,000 ohms.

PROBLEMS (*Answers to selected problems at back of book.*)

1. A current of 1 ma flows through a 1-M 2-watt carbon resistor. (a) How much power is dissipated as heat in the resistor? (b) How much is the maximum power that can be dissipated without excessive heat?
2. A resistor is to be connected across a 10-volt battery for the desired current of 1 ma. (a) What size resistance is required? (b) How much is its power dissipation in this circuit? (c) State the wattage rating of the resistor to be used. (d) Can this be a carbon resistor?
3. Give the resistance and tolerance for the following examples of resistors with color stripes: (a) yellow, violet, yellow, and silver; (b) red, red, green, and silver; (c) orange, orange, black, and gold; (d) white, brown, brown, and gold; (e) red, red, gold, and gold; (f) brown, black, orange, no tolerance band.
4. For resistors color-coded in the body-end-dot system shown in Appendix G, what is the resistance for the following: (a) body brown, end black, dot orange; (b) resistor completely red?
5. Fill in the resistance values for the following dial settings on the decade resistance in Fig. 9·4.

Dial settings

$R \times 10^4$	$R \times 10^3$	$R \times 10^2$	$R \times 10$	R	Total R
9	6	7	4	2	
0	5	6	8	3	
6	7	0	5	4	
1	2	3	4	5	
5	4	3	2	1	

6. Referring to the derating graph in Fig. 9·7, how much is the power rating of a ½-watt 0.5-M resistor at an ambient temperature of (a) 50°C; (b) 80°C?
7. Referring to the load characteristic in Fig. 9·8, find the resistance of a 0.5-M ½-watt resistor that is actually dissipating (a) ¼ watt; (b) 1 watt; (c) 1.5 watt.
8. Determine the resistance and power rating of a carbon-composition resistor to fit the following requirements: 5-volt *IR* drop, with 100 ma current, in an ambient temperature of 70°, with a safety factor of 2 for power dissipation.

Chapter 10 Batteries

A battery is a group of chemical cells that convert chemical energy to electrical energy. Specifically, the battery is a source of steady d-c voltage. This unit describes the main types, such as dry batteries for portable equipment, including miniature batteries for transistor radios, and the lead-acid wet cell generally used in automobile batteries and many industrial applications. More generally, a battery is a good example of a d-c generator supplying power to a load resistance. The topics are:

10·1 Functions of batteries
10·2 The voltaic cell
10·3 The dry cell
10·4 Series and parallel cells
10·5 Lead-acid batteries
10·6 Types of electromotive cells
10·7 Internal resistance of a generator
10·8 Matching a load resistance to a generator

10·1 Functions of batteries

The chemical battery has always been important as a d-c voltage source to supply power for operating radio and electronic equipment. Originally, all radio receivers used batteries. Then rectifier power supplies were developed to convert the a-c power-line voltage to d-c voltage. Now batteries are used mainly for portable equipment, which can operate without being connected to the a-c power line. Especially with miniaturized transistor equipment, the power requirements are easily supplied by a battery.

Even now, dry batteries for portable radios are called A, B, or C batteries, according to their original functions in vacuum-tube operation. The A battery supplies current to heat the filament so that electrons can be

Fig. 10·1 Typical batteries. (a) Radio A and B batteries. (b) Miniature
battery for transistor radios. (c) Twelve-volt lead-acid automobile battery,
with six cells in series.

emitted from the cathode. Generally, the required heater voltage is 1.5 to
4.5 volts, with a load current of 50 to 150 ma. However, the A battery is
seldom necessary any more, as a power supply can provide a-c voltage for
the heaters, while the transistor does not have any heater. The C battery
was used for a small negative grid bias of −1.5 to −7.5 volt, with practically no current drain. C batteries are seldom used now, though, because
the amplifier circuit can be arranged to provide its own C-bias voltage.

The function of the B-battery voltage is the same now as always. For a
vacuum-tube amplifier, the B battery supplies positive d-c plate voltage
to attract the electrons emitted from the cathode. This attraction of electrons to the anode or plate is necessary for current flow. In fact, the plate
supply for amplifier tubes is still called B+ voltage, whether from a battery
or rectifier power supply. A typical B battery for tubes supplies 60 to 90
volts with a load current of about 70 ma. Transistor radios can use smaller
batteries with an output voltage of 3 to 22.5 volts. Although the function
is the same as B+ voltage for tubes, the d-c voltage for transistors may be
of either polarity, depending on whether PNP or NPN transistors are used.
Some typical batteries are shown in Fig. 10·1, with more types listed in
Table 10·2.

10·2 The voltaic cell

When two different conducting materials are immersed in an electrolyte,
as illustrated in Fig. 10·2a, the chemical reaction of forming a new solution results in separation of charges. This arrangement for converting
chemical energy into electrical energy is a *voltaic cell.* The charged conductors are the electrodes, serving as the terminals of the cell for connection
to an external circuit. Then the potential difference resulting from the
separated charges enables the cell to function as a source of applied
voltage. As shown in Fig. 10·2b, the voltage E across the cell's terminals

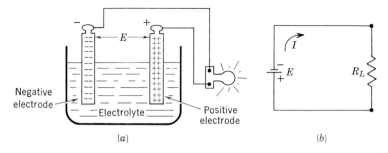

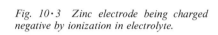

(a)   (b)

Fig. 10·2 Voltaic cell converting chemical energy into
electrical energy. (a) Physical arrangement. (b) Schematic
diagram. R_L is the resistance of the bulb filament.

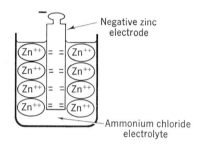

Fig. 10·3 Zinc electrode being charged
negative by ionization in electrolyte.

forces current to flow in the external circuit to light the bulb. Electrons
from the negative terminal of the cell flow through the external circuit and
return to the positive terminal. The chemical action in the cell continuously
separates charges to maintain the terminal voltage that produces current
in the circuit.

Separation of charges in the cell. When metals dissolve in water or an
electrolyte, the chemical action of forming the solution causes separation
or dissociation of molecules, which results in electrically charged ions.
Figure 10·3 illustrates the action of zinc dissolving in an ammonium
chloride solution as the electrolyte. Where the electrode contacts the solution, molecules of zinc dissolve to form a different compound, which is
zinc ammonium chloride. This chemical reaction requires zinc ions. Each
zinc ion in solution is positive, with a deficiency of 2 electrons. In the solution process, then, each molecule of zinc dissolving in the electrolyte leaves
2 surplus electrons on the zinc electrode.

In Fig. 10·3, zinc ions are shown in solution with two positive charges,
corresponding to 2 electrons left behind. As a result, the entire solid zinc
conductor has excess electrons that make the electrode negative with
respect to the solution. With a second electrode, other than zinc, immersed
in the electrolyte, the result is a voltaic cell with a difference of potential
between the two electrodes.

When the potential difference of a cell is used to produce current in an
external circuit, electrons leave the negative electrode, go through the external load resistance, and are added to the positive electrode. This current
tends to neutralize the charges generated by the cell. The chemical reaction

can increase, however, to maintain the separation of charges as the cell works harder to produce its output voltage. With the negative zinc electrode in Fig. 10·3, as more electrons are lost through the external circuit, more ions can be formed by the zinc dissolving in solution. Eventually, all the zinc will dissolve, and the cell then cannot separate charges to produce output voltage.

Primary cells. In a primary cell, the chemical process of forming the solution is not reversible. For instance, zinc can dissolve in ammonium chloride, but the process cannot be reversed to form the zinc electrode from the solution. The many forms of dry cells, such as the flashlight cell, are examples of a primary cell.

Secondary cells. Here the chemical action is reversible. The electrodes can dissolve in solution with current in one direction, or the current can be reversed to make the solution build up the electrodes. When the electrodes are going into solution, the cell is *discharging* as the current tends to neutralize the separated charges. Then the cell is used as a voltage source to produce current in a load resistance. For the opposite case, reversing the current to re-form the plates is *charging* the cell. The charging current must be supplied by an external voltage source, with the cell then serving just as a load resistance. Since a secondary cell can be recharged, it is also a *storage cell.* The most common form of storage cell is the lead–sulfuric acid cell generally used in automobile batteries.

Cell requirements. The two conductors used for electrodes in the electrolyte must be different to form a voltaic cell. With the same electrodes, each could become charged, but there would be no difference of potential across the terminals. The voltage output of one voltaic cell is approximately 1 to 2 volts, depending only on the materials used for the electrodes and the electrolyte. The physical size of the cell determines its current capacity, since larger electrodes can supply more current. The metals are commonly used for electrodes because they produce a relatively high charge when going into solution. Batteries with an output higher than 1 to 2 volts contain cells in series.

Table 10·1   Electromotive Series

ELEMENT	POTENTIAL, VOLTS
Lithium	−2.96
Magnesium	−2.40
Aluminum	−1.70
Zinc	−0.76
Cadmium	−0.40
Nickel	−0.23
Lead	−0.13
Hydrogen	0.00
Copper	+0.35
Mercury	+0.80
Silver	+0.80
Gold	+1.36

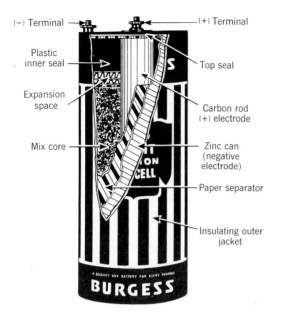

(−) Terminal

(+) Terminal

Plastic inner seal

Top seal

Expansion space

Carbon rod (+) electrode

Mix core

Zinc can (negative electrode)

Paper separator

Insulating outer jacket

BURGESS

Fig. 10·4 Internal view of zinc-carbon dry cell. This is No. 6 standard dry cell, 6 in. high. (Burgess Battery Co.)

Electromotive series. The fact that the voltage output of a cell depends only on its elements can be seen from Table 10·1. This list, called the *Electrochemical series* or *Electromotive series,* gives the relative activity for some of the metal elements in forming ions. The potential for each element lists the voltage with respect to hydrogen as a zero reference. The difference between two potentials for two metals indicates the voltage of an ideal cell using these electrodes. The more negative element will be the negative electrode of the voltaic cell. It should be noted, though, that other factors such as cost, stability, and long life are important for the construction of commercial batteries.

10·3 The dry cell

Figure 10·4 shows an internal view of a dry cell. The can is zinc, which functions both as a container to hold the electrolyte and as the negative electrode. The positive electrode is a carbon rod down the center but not low enough to touch the zinc. The electrolyte is a solution of ammonium chloride, called *sal ammoniac,* with water. The electrolyte is not in liquid form, however, but is a paste produced by the saturation of granulated carbon and powdered manganese dioxide with the ammonium chloride solution. Although not completely dry, the cell can be mounted in any position, while a cell with liquid electrolyte must be upright.

Polarization. When zinc dissolves in ammonium chloride, the ammonia molecules, which contain nitrogen and hydrogen, release hydrogen. The resulting collection of hydrogen around the carbon electrode is called *polarization* of the cell. Polarization reduces the output voltage of the dry cell. To minimize polarization, hydrogen gas must be removed from the carbon electrode. This is the function of the manganese dioxide, which is the *depolarizer* or depolarizing agent, in the dry cell. Rich in oxygen, the

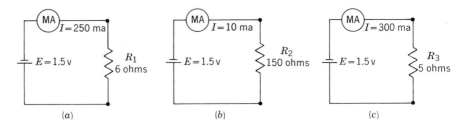

Fig. 10·5   *The current drain from the cell depends upon the load resistance. (a) E/R equals the normal current rating of ¼ amp, or 250 ma. (b) E/R equals 10 ma. (c) E/R equals 300 ma.*

manganese dioxide releases oxygen that combines with the hydrogen to form water. As a result, the dry cell can supply more output voltage, without the collection of hydrogen gas around the carbon.

Local action. If the zinc electrode contains impurities, such as iron and carbon, small voltaic cells are formed that do not add to the ouput voltage of the cell. This local action at the zinc electrode does use up the zinc, however. To minimize local action, the zinc electrode is generally coated with mercury, a process called *amalgamation.*

Shelf life. Because of local action and drying of the paste electrolyte, a dry cell slowly loses its ability to produce output voltage, even when out of use and stored on a shelf. For this reason, dry cells are usually dated and should be used when fresh from manufacture. The shelf life for dry cells of medium size is about a year. For very small sizes, such as pen-light cells, the shelf life may be only a few months.

Operating characteristics. The output voltage of a carbon–zinc–sal ammoniac dry cell is 1.4 to 1.6 volts, regardless of size, but larger sizes with more zinc, electrolyte, and depolarizer have a higher current rating. Maximum ratings for continuous operation range from a few milliamperes for the very small cells to ¼ amp[1] for the relatively large No. 6 dry cell. The size D flashlight cell has a current rating of 50 ma for approximately 60 hr of service.

Current drain depends on the load resistance. It is important to note that the current rating is only a guide to typical values permissible for normal service life. The amount of current produced by a cell connected to a load resistance equals E/R, by Ohm's law. Figure 10·5 illustrates three different cases of using the applied voltage of 1.5 volts from a No. 6 dry cell. In *a*, the load resistance R_1 of 6 ohms across the 1.5-volt source voltage allows a value of current equal to 1.5/6, which is 0.25 amp, or 250 ma. This value happens to be the same as the maximum current rating. In *b*, though, the higher value of R_2, as the load resistance, limits the current to 1.5/150, equal to 0.010 amp, or 10 ma. This value is less than the current rating, which means only that the cell can be in service a longer time, since it need

[1] Based on 145 hr of service, 24 hr a day, reducing terminal voltage to 1.0 volt, at 70°F.

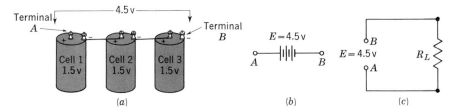

Fig. 10·6   Cells in series. (a) Wiring. (b) Schematic battery symbol. (c) Battery connected to load resistance.

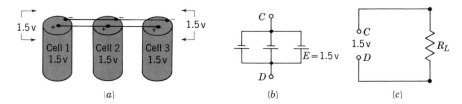

Fig. 10·7   Cells in parallel. (a) Wiring. (b) Schematic battery
symbol. (c) Battery connected to load resistance.

not work so hard to produce the 1.5-volt output with less current drain.
In *c*, the load resistance R_3 is low enough to result in more current than the
rated value of the cell. This much current is not desirable for long cell life,
but assuming that the 1.5-volt output is maintained, the current in the
circuit must be 1.5 volts/5 ohms, which equals 0.3 amp. In summary, then,
the current drain in a cell connected to a load resistance is equal to the
output voltage of the cell divided by the resistance in the circuit.

10·4   Series and parallel cells

An applied voltage higher than the emf of one cell can be obtained by
connecting cells in series. The total voltage available across the battery of
cells is equal to the sum of the individual values for each cell. Figure 10·6
shows the series connections for three dry cells. Here the three 1.5-volt
cells in series provide a total battery voltage of 4.5 volts. Notice that the
two end terminals, *A* and *B*, are left open to serve as the plus and minus
terminals of the battery. These terminals are used for connecting the battery to the load circuit, as shown in *c*. In the lead-acid battery in Fig. 10·1*c*,
short heavy metal straps connect the cells in series. The current capacity of
a battery with series cells is the same as for one cell because the same current flows through all the series cells.

For more current capacity, the battery has cells in parallel, as shown in
Fig. 10·7. All the positive terminals are strapped together, as are all the
negative terminals. Any point on the positive side can be the plus terminal
of the battery and any point on the negative side is the negative terminal.

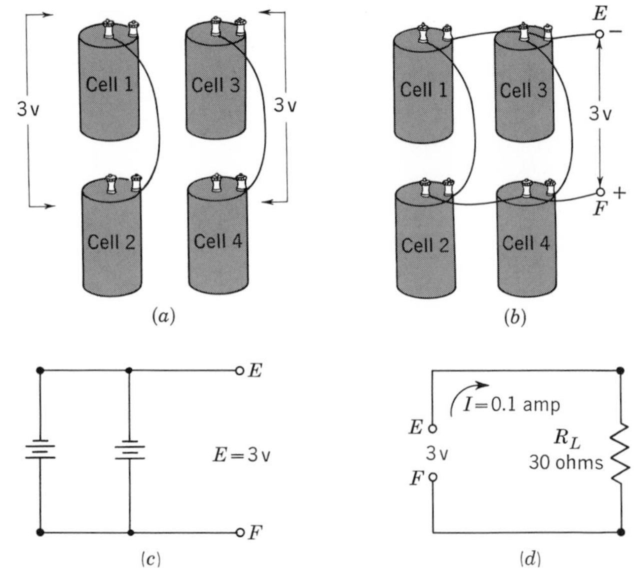

Fig. 10·8 Cells in series-parallel. (a) Wiring two strings, each with two 1.5-volt cells in series. (b) Wiring the two strings in parallel. (c) Schematic symbol. (d) Battery connected to load resistance.

The parallel connection is equivalent to increasing the size of the electrodes and electrolyte, which increases the current capacity. The voltage output of the battery, however, is the same as for one cell.

Identical cells in parallel all supply equal parts of the load current. For example, with three identical parallel cells producing a load current of 300 ma, each cell has a drain of 100 ma. Bad cells should not be connected in parallel with good cells, however, since the cells in good condition will supply more current, which may overload the good cells. In addition, a cell with lower output voltage will act as a load resistance, draining excessive current from the cells that have higher output voltage.

In order to provide higher output voltage and more current capacity, cells can be connected in series-parallel combinations. Figure 10·8 shows four No. 6 cells in series-parallel to form a battery that has 3-volt output with a current capacity of ½ amp. Two of the 1.5-volt cells in series provide 3 volts total output voltage. This series string has a current capacity of ¼ amp, however, as for one cell. To double the current capacity, another string is connected in parallel. The two strings in parallel have the same 3-volt output as one string, with a current capacity of ½ amp. Referring to the circuit in Fig. 10·8d note that the 3-volt source produces only 100 ma, or 0.1 amp, equal to 3 volts/30 ohms, although the rated current capacity is 500 ma.

10·5   The lead-acid cell

Where high values of load current are necessary, the lead-acid cell is the type most commonly used. In the application of battery power to start an automobile, for example, the load current at starting time is 200 to

300 amp. One lead-acid cell has an output of 2 to 2.2 volts, but they are generally used in a series combination of three for a 6-volt battery and six in series for a 12-volt battery. Since it is a storage cell, charging can be done repeatedly to restore the output voltage, as long as the cell is in good physical condition. Heat with excessive discharging and charging, however, shortens the useful life to about 3 years for an automobile battery.

Construction. The cutaway view of a lead-acid cell (Fig. 10·9) shows the component parts and how they are assembled. Inside the cell, the positive and negative electrodes consist of a group of plates welded to a connecting strap. The plates are immersed in a dilute solution of sulfuric acid for the electrolyte, which contains 8 parts of water to 3 parts of concentrated sulfuric acid. Each plate is a grid or framework, made of a lead-antimony alloy. This construction enables the active material, which is lead oxide, to be pasted into the grid. In manufacture of the cell, after the plates are dried, a forming charge produces the positive and negative electrodes. In the forming process, the active material in the positive plate is changed to lead peroxide to produce the positive electrode. The negative electrode is spongy lead.

Chemical action. Sulfuric acid is a combination of hydrogen and sulfate ions. When the cell discharges, lead peroxide of the positive electrode unites with hydrogen ions to form water and with the sulfate ions to form lead sulfate. The lead sulfate is also produced by the combining of lead on the negative plate with sulfate ions. Therefore, the net result of discharge is to produce more water, which dilutes the electrolyte, and to form lead sulfate on the plates. As discharge continues, the sulfate fills the pores of the grids, retarding circulation of acid in the active material. Lead sulfate is the white powder often seen on the outside of old batteries. When the

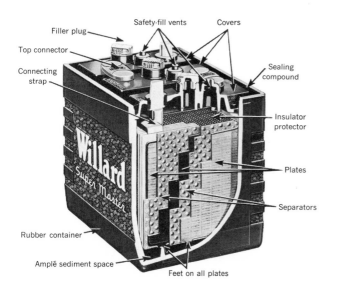

Filler plug

Top connector

Connecting strap

Safety-fill vents

Covers

Sealing compound

Insulator protector

Plates

Separators

Rubber container

Amplē sediment space

Feet on all plates

Fig. 10·9 Construction of lead-acid cell. (The Electric Storage Battery Co.)

combination of weak electrolyte and sulfation on the plates lowers the output voltage, charging is necessary.

On charge, the reversed direction of the ions flowing in the electrolyte results in a reversal of the chemical reactions. Now the lead sulfate on the positive plate reacts with the water and sulfate ions to produce lead peroxide and sulfuric acid. This action re-forms the positive electrode and strengthens the electrolyte by adding sulfuric acid. At the same time, charging enables the lead sulfate on the negative plate to react with hydrogen ions, which also forms sulfuric acid, while re-forming lead on the negative electrode. As a result, the charging current can restore the cell to full output with lead peroxide on the positive plates, spongy lead on the negative plates, and the required concentration of sulfuric acid in the electrolyte.

The chemical formula for the lead-acid cell is

$$Pb + PbO_2 + 2\,H_2SO_4 \underset{\text{Discharge}}{\overset{\text{Charge}}{\rightleftarrows}} 2\,PbSO_4 + 2\,H_2O$$

On discharge, the lead (Pb) and lead peroxide (PbO_2) electrodes supply Pb ions that combine with the sulfate ions (SO_4) to form lead sulfate ($PbSO_4$) and water (H_2O). On charge, with reverse current through the electrolyte, the chemical action is reversed. Then the Pb ions from the lead sulfate re-form the lead electrode. Also, Pb ions with O_2 ions from the water re-form the lead peroxide electrode and the SO_4 ions combine with H_2 ions to produce more sulfuric acid.

Current ratings. Lead-acid batteries are rated in terms of how much discharge current can be supplied continuously for a specified period of time. The output voltage must be maintained above a minimum level, which is 1.5 to 1.8 volts per cell. A common rating is ampere-hours based on 8-hr discharge. Typical values are 100 to 300 amp-hr. For example, a 120-amp-hr battery can supply load current of $^{12}\%$, or 15 amp, based on 8-hr discharge. The battery can supply less current for a longer time or more current for a shorter time. With heavy-duty batteries, the ampere-hour rating may be specified for more than 8 hr.

Note that the amp-hr unit specifies coulombs of charge. As an example, 200 amp-hr corresponds to 200 amp $\times$ 3,600 sec, which equals 720,000 amp-sec or 7.2×10^5 coul.

The ratings of a lead-acid battery are for a temperature of 80° F, approximately. Higher temperatures increase the chemical reaction, but operation above 110°F shortens the battery life. Lower temperatures reduce the voltage and current output. The ampere-hour capacity is reduced approximately 0.75 per cent for each decrease of one degree Fahrenheit. At 0°F the available output is only 60 per cent of the rating. In cold weather, therefore, it is important to have an automobile battery up to full charge. In addition, the electrolyte freezes more easily when diluted by water in the discharged condition.

Specific gravity. The state of discharge for a lead-acid cell is generally checked by measuring the *specific gravity* of the electrolyte. This is a ratio

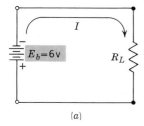
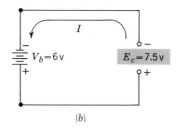

(a)   (b)

Fig. 10·10   *Reversed directions of charge and discharge current.*
(a) Battery voltage E_b supplies discharge current to R_L. (b) Battery is
load resistance for charging voltage E_c.

comparing the weight of a substance with the weight of water. For instance,
concentrated sulfuric acid is 1.835 times as heavy as an equal volume of
water. Therefore, its specific gravity is 1.835. The specific gravity of water
is 1, since it is the reference. In a fully charged cell, the mixture of water
and sulfuric acid results in a specific gravity of 1.280, approximately, at
room temperatures of 70 to 80°F. As the cell discharges, the water formed
dilutes the acid and lowers the specific gravity. When the specific gravity
is down to about 1.150, the cell is completely discharged.

Specific-gravity readings are taken with a battery hydrometer, which
has a calibrated float that will rest higher in electrolyte of higher specific
gravity. The decimal point is usually omitted for convenience. For example, a specific-gravity value of 1.250 is simply "twelve-fifty." A hydrometer reading of 1260 to 1280 indicates full charge; approximately 1250 is
half-charge, and 1150 to 1200 complete discharge.

Charging the lead-acid battery. The requirements are illustrated in
Fig. 10·10. An external d-c voltage source is necessary to produce current
in one direction. Also, the charging voltage must be more than the battery
emf. Approximately 2.5 volts per cell is enough to overcome the cell emf
so that the charging voltage can produce current opposite to the direction
of discharge current.

The reversed directions of charge current and discharge current are
shown in Fig. 10·10a and b. In a, the battery is the voltage source E_b producing current in the load resistance R_L. The direction of electrons in the
external circuit is from the negative battery terminal, through R_L, and back
to the positive terminal. Inside the battery, the ion current is from the positive electrode to the negative electrode. In b, however, the battery is effectively a load resistance across the external charging voltage source E_c. The
net voltage available to produce charging current is the difference between
the source voltage and the battery voltage, which equals 1.5 volts here. The
resultant electron current flows from the negative terminal of the charging
voltage E_c to the less negative electrode of the battery and returns from the
positive electrode of the battery to the more positive terminal of the charging voltage. In the circuit outside the battery, the current in b is in the reverse direction from a. Inside the battery, the ion current produced in the

Fig. 10·11 Battery eliminator or charger. (Heath Company.)

electrolyte by the charging voltage is also opposite to the direction of ion current on discharge.

Note that the reversal of current is obtained just by connecting the battery and charging voltage with + to + and − to − as shown in *b*. The charging current is reversed because the battery effectively becomes a load resistance for the charging voltage source when E_c is higher than V_b.

Battery chargers. There are many commercial types of battery chargers, which can be plugged into the a-c power line to convert 120-volt a-c input

Table 10·2   Types of electromotive cells

Name	+ terminal	− terminal	Electrolyte
Carbon-zinc (Leclanche)	Carbon	Zinc	Sal ammoniac
Alkaline dry cells	Manganese dioxide	Zinc	Potassium hydroxide
	Manganese dioxide	Zinc	Potassium hydroxide
Lead-acid	Lead peroxide	Lead	Sulfuric acid
Edison	Nickel	Iron	Potassium and lithium hydroxides
Mercury	Amalgamated zinc	Mercuric oxide	Potassium hydroxide
Nickel-cadmium	Nickel	Cadmium hydroxide	Potassium hydroxide

to the d-c voltage output required for charging. Figure 10·11 shows one type that supplies 6- to 12-volt d-c output. Since automobile radios operate on this battery voltage, the 6- to 12-volt output of the eliminator can serve as a voltage source for testing these receivers on the service bench without a battery. In addition, the d-c voltage output can be used to charge a battery.

Maintenance of lead-acid batteries. To obtain long life and efficient service, the most important requirements are:

1. The level of the liquid electrolyte must always be above the plates.
2. Keep the battery near full charge with the specific gravity 1250 or higher.

The required level of the electrolyte is generally ⅜ in. above the plates. Water is added to maintain the liquid level. Pure distilled water is generally preferred, but any water suitable for drinking is considered satisfactory. Sulfuric acid is never added unless it is known to have been lost by spilling.

Overcharging can be harmful to the battery, as internal heat makes the separators buckle. The result can be an internal short circuit, in one or more cells, lowering the output voltage. Fast charging can cause the same problems. A slow *trickle* charge is preferable, with a charging current of 2 to 8 amp. Note that for a 5-amp charging rate, it will take 30 hr to put back 150 amp-hr of charge into the battery.

Lead-acid batteries should not be stored with electrolyte in the cells if

Primary or secondary type	Wet or dry	Voltage output	Notes
Primary	Dry	1.5	Used for A, B, and C batteries
Primary	Dry	1.5	For currents above 300 ma
Secondary	Dry	1.5	Can be recharged about 50 times
Secondary	Wet	2.2	6- and 12-volt batteries for autos; very low r_i
Secondary	Wet	1.4	Rugged construction for industrial uses
Primary	Dry	1.345	Miniature construction
Secondary	Dry	1.345	
Secondary	Dry	1.25	Miniature construction

they are in a discharged condition, since the lead sulfate changes gradually to an insoluble form which may make recharging impossible. For this reason, manufacturers often supply new batteries dry, with separate electrolyte. This allows a long shelf life. The electrolyte is added when the battery is installed in service.

10·6 Types of electromotive cells

Probably most common are the zinc-carbon dry cell and lead-acid wet cell, but additional types are listed in Table 10·2. Note that the alkaline cells use an electrolyte with negative hydroxyl (OH) ions, while an acid solution contains positive H ions. The lead-acid cell and Edison cell are both heavy-duty rechargeable wet cells, although the Edison cell uses an alkaline electrolyte. Recently developed dry types are the alkaline cell, mercury cell, and nickel-cadmium cell. The alkaline cell has improved depolarization for greater power output. The mercury cell features constant voltage output and long shelf life. The nickel-cadmium cell is a true rechargeable cell with a completely reversible chemical reaction. These dry cells are shown in Figs. 10·12 and 10·13.

A completely different type is the sun, or solar, battery, which contains photosensitive silicon cells. Exposed to bright sunlight or artificial light, the cell's output is typically 0.26 volt. With a miniature storage battery that can be charged by the sun battery, continuous power is available for the times when there is no light. Additional types of photovoltaic cells use selenium and cadmium sulfide.

Fig. 10·12 (a) Alkaline battery. (b) Nickel-cadmium battery. (Union Carbide Corporation.)

(a)

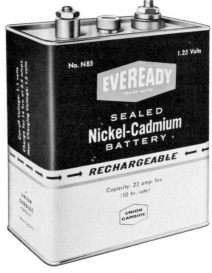

(b)

Fig. 10·13   Mercury battery. (P. R. Mallory & Co., Inc.)

Fig. 10·14   Internal resistance r_i is in series with the generated voltage E_g. (a) Physical arrangement in cell. (b) Schematic. (c) Equivalent circuit.

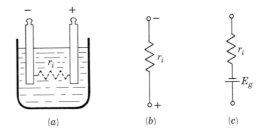

10·7   Internal resistance of a generator

Any source that produces voltage output continuously is a generator. It may be a cell separating charges by chemical action or a rotary generator converting motion and magnetism into voltage output, as common examples. In any case, all generators have internal resistance, which is labeled r_i in Fig. 10·14.

The internal resistance r_i is important when a generator supplies load current because its internal Ir_i drop subtracts from the generated emf, resulting in lower voltage across the output terminals. Physically, r_i may be the resistance of the wire in a rotary generator; or in a chemical cell the resistance of the electrolyte between electrodes is the internal resistance. More generally, the internal resistance r_i is the opposition to load current inside the generator.

Since any current in the generator must flow through the internal resistance, r_i is in series with the generated voltage, as shown in Fig. 10·14c. It may be of interest to note that, with just one load resistance connected across a generator, they are in series with each other because R_L is in series with r_i.

Figure 10·15 illustrates how the output of a 100-volt dry battery can drop to 90 volts because of the internal 10-volt Ir_i drop. In *a*, the voltage across the output terminals E is equal to the generated voltage E_g because there is no load current on open circuit. With no current, the voltage drop across r_i is zero, allowing the full generated voltage to be developed across the output terminals. This is the *generated emf, open-circuit voltage*, or *no-load voltage*. In *b*, however, the load current of 0.1 amp flows to produce a drop of 10 volts across the 100-ohm r_i. Note that R_T is 900 + 100 or 1,000 ohms, resulting in I_L equal to 100/1,000, which is 0.1 amp. As a result,

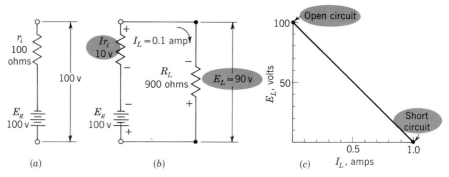

Fig. 10·15   Internal Ir drop decreases terminal voltage of a generator.
(a) Open-circuit voltage equals E_g of 100 volts. (b) Terminal voltage reduced
to 90 volts because of 10-volt internal Ir drop. (c) Graph of decreasing terminal
voltage with increasing load current.

the voltage output E_L equals 100 − 10 or 90 volts. This *terminal voltage* or
load voltage is available across the output terminals when the generator is
in a closed circuit with load current.

The graph in Fig. 10·15c shows how the terminal voltage E_L drops with
increasing load current I_L because of the internal voltage drop across r_i.
Note that the short-circuit current of 1 amp results in zero output voltage,
as the entire generator voltage is dropped across the internal resistance.
Or, we can say that, with a short circuit of zero ohms across the load, the
current is limited to E_g/r_i.

The lower the internal resistance of a generator, the better it is in terms
of being able to produce full output voltage when supplying current for a
load. For example, the very low r_i, about 0.01 ohm for a 12-volt lead-acid
battery, is the reason it can supply high values of load current and maintain
its output voltage. For the opposite case, a higher r_i means that the terminal
voltage of a generator is much less with load current. As an example, an
old dry battery with 500-ohm r_i would appear normal when measured by
a voltmeter but be useless because of low voltage when normal load current
flows in an actual circuit.

How to measure r_i. The internal resistance of any generator can be
measured indirectly by determining how much the output voltage drops
for a specified amount of load current. The difference between the no-load
voltage and the load voltage is the amount of internal *Ir* voltage drop. As
a formula,

$$r_i = \frac{E_{NL} - E_L}{I_L} \qquad (10 \cdot 1)$$

Example 1. Calculate r_i if the output of a generator drops from 100 volts with
no load current to 80 volts with 2-amp I_L.

$$r_i = \frac{100 - 80}{2} = \frac{20}{2} = \textbf{10 ohms}$$

A convenient technique for measuring r_i is to use a variable load resistance R_L. Vary R_L until the load voltage is one-half the no-load voltage. This value of R_L is also the value of r_i, as they must be equal to divide the generator voltage equally. For the same 100-volt generator with 10-ohm r_i in Example 1, if a 10-ohm R_L were used, the load voltage would be 50 volts, equal to one-half the no-load voltage. You can solve this circuit by Ohm's law to see that I_L is 5 amp with 20-ohm R_T, and the two voltage drops of 50 volts each add to equal the 100 volts of the generator.

Constant-voltage generator. A generator with very low internal resistance is considered a constant-voltage source. Then the output voltage remains essentially the same when the load current changes. This idea is illustrated in Fig. 10·16a for a 6-volt lead-acid battery with r_i of 0.005 ohm. If the load current varies over the wide range of 1 to 100 amp, for any of these values the internal Ir drop across 0.005 ohm is less than 0.5 volt. The voltage output of 5.5 to 6.0 volts can be considered constant, compared with the wide variations in load current, as shown by the graph in *b*.

Constant-current generator. The opposite case is a generator that has very high resistance compared with the external load resistance, resulting in constant current although the output voltage varies. Examples are found in vacuum-tube circuits, where a tube can be a generator having internal resistance as high as 1 M. The constant-current generator in Fig. 10·17a has such high resistance, with an r_i of 0.9 M, that it is the main factor determining how much current can be produced by E_g. Here R_L varies over a 3:1 range from 50 to 150 K, but since the current is determined by the total

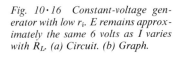

Fig. 10·16 *Constant-voltage generator with low r_i. E remains approximately the same 6 volts as I varies with R_L. (a) Circuit. (b) Graph.*

Fig. 10·17 *Constant-current generator with high r_i. I remains approximately the same, as E varies with R_L. (a) Circuit. (b) Graph.*

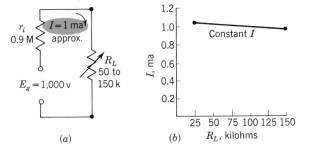

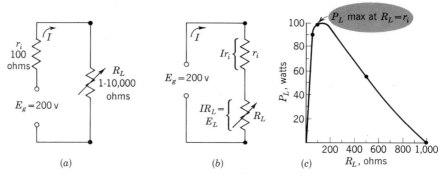

Fig. 10·18   *Circuit for varying R_L to match r_i. (a) Schematic diagram.
(b) Equivalent divider circuit for voltage output across R_L. (c) Graph of
power output P_L.*

resistance of R_L and r_i in series, I is essentially constant at 1.05 to 0.95 ma,
or approximately 1 ma, as shown by the graph in *b*.

Note that the terminal voltage E_L varies approximately in the same 3:1
range as R_L. Also, the output voltage is much less than the generator voltage because of its high internal resistance compared with R_L. This is a
necessary condition, however, in a circuit with a constant-current
generator.

10·8   Matching a load resistance to a generator

In the diagram in Fig. 10·18 when R_L equals r_i, the load and generator
are matched. The matching is significant because the generator then produces maximum power in R_L, as verified by the values listed in Table 10·3.
When R_L is 100 ohms, matching the 100 ohms of r_i, maximum power is
transferred from the generator to the load. With higher resistance for R_L,
the output voltage E_L is higher, but the current is reduced. Lower resistance
for R_L allows more current but E_L is less. When r_i and R_L equal 100 ohms,
the combination of current and voltage produces the maximum power of
100 watts across R_L.

Table 10·3   *Effect of load resistance on generator output**

R_L, ohms	$I = E_g/(r_i + R_L)$, amp	Ir_i, volts	$IR_L = E_L$ volts	P_L, watts	P_i, watts	$P_T = P_L + P_i$, watts	Efficiency = P_L/P_T, per cent
1	1.98	198	2	4	396	400	1
50	1.33	133	67	89	178	267	33
100	1	100	100	100	100	200	50
500	0.33	33	167	55	11	66	83
1,000	0.18	18	180	32	3.24	35.24	91
10,000	0.02	2	198	4	0.04	4.04	99

$R_L = r_i \rightarrow$ (points to the 100 ohms row)

* Values calculated for circuit in Fig. 10·18, with $E_g = 200$ volts and $r_i = 100$ ohms.

With generators having very low resistance, however, matching is often impractical. For example, if a 6-volt lead-acid battery with 0.003-ohm internal resistance were connected to 0.003-ohm load resistance, the battery could be damaged by excessive current as high as 1,000 amp.

In addition, if maximum voltage across R_L is desired rather than power, the load should have as high a resistance as possible. Note that R_L and r_i form a voltage divider for the generator voltage, as illustrated in Fig. $10 \cdot 18b$. The values tabulated for IR_L in Table $10 \cdot 3$ show how the output voltage E_L increases with higher values of R_L.

Note also that the efficiency increases as R_L increases because there is less current, resulting in less power lost in r_i. When R_L equals r_i, the efficiency is only 50 per cent, since one-half the total generated power is dissipated in r_i, the internal resistance of the generator. In conclusion, then, matching the load and generator resistances is desirable when the load requires maximum power, rather than voltage or efficiency, assuming that the match does not result in excessive current.

SUMMARY

1. A voltaic cell consists of two different conductors as electrodes immersed in an electrolyte. The voltage output depends only on the chemicals in the cell; the current capacity increases with larger sizes. A primary cell cannot be recharged. A secondary or storage cell can be recharged.
2. A battery is a group of cells in series or in parallel. With cells in series, their voltages add, but the current capacity is the same as one cell. With cells in parallel, the voltage output is the same as one cell, but the total current capacity is the sum of the individual values.
3. The zinc–carbon–sal ammoniac dry cell is the most common type of primary cell. Zinc is the negative electrode; carbon is the positive electrode. Its output voltage is approximately 1.5 volts.
4. The lead-acid cell is the most common form of storage battery. The positive electrode is lead peroxide, spongy lead is the negative electrode, and both are in a dilute solution of sulfuric acid for the electrolyte. The voltage output is approximately 2.2 volts per cell. A 6-volt automobile battery has three cells in series; the 12-volt battery has six cells in series. The feature of a lead-acid battery is its very low internal resistance, allowing several hundred amperes of load current without excessive drop in output voltage.
5. To charge a lead-acid battery, connect it to a d-c voltage equal to approximately 2.5 volts per cell. Connecting the positive terminal of the battery to the positive side of the charging source and minus to minus results in charging current through the battery.
6. A constant-voltage generator has very low internal resistance, resulting in output voltage that is relatively constant with changing values of load because of the small internal IR drop. A constant-current generator has a very high internal resistance, which determines the constant value of current in the generator circuit relatively independent of the load resistance.
7. When load current makes the terminal voltage drop to one-half the no-load voltage, the resistance of the external load equals the internal resistance of the generator.
8. Matching a load to a generator means making the load resistance equal to the generator's internal resistance and results in maximum power delivered to the load from the generator.

SELF-EXAMINATION QUESTIONS (*Answers at back of book.*)

Here's a chance to see how well you have learned the material in this chapter. These exercises are for your self-testing only.

1. Which of the following is false? (*a*) A lead-acid cell can be recharged. (*b*) A primary cell

has a reversible chemical reaction. (*c*) A storage cell has a reversible chemical reaction. (*d*) A carbon-zinc cell has unlimited shelf life.

2. The output of a lead-acid cell is (*a*) 1.25 volts; (*b*) 1.345 volts; (*c*) 2.2 volts; (*d*) 6 volts.
3. The current in a chemical cell is a movement of (*a*) positive hole charges; (*b*) positive and negative ions; (*c*) positive ions only; (*d*) negative ions only.
4. Cells are connected in series to (*a*) increase the voltage output; (*b*) decrease the voltage output; (*c*) decrease the internal resistance; (*d*) increase the current capacity.
5. Cells are connected in parallel to (*a*) increase the voltage output; (*b*) increase the internal resistances; (*c*) decrease the current capacity; (*d*) increase the current capacity.
6. Which of the following is a dry storage cell? (*a*) Edison; (*b*) carbon-zinc; (*c*) mercury; (*d*) nickel-cadmium.
7. When R_L equals the generator r_i, which of the following is maximum? (*a*) Power in R_L; (*b*) current; (*c*) voltage across R_L; (*d*) efficiency of the circuit.
8. Five carbon-zinc cells in series have an output of (*a*) 1.5 volts; (*b*) 5.0 volts; (*c*) 7.5 volts; (*d*) 11.0 volts.
9. A constant-voltage generator has (*a*) low internal resistance; (*b*) high internal resistance; (*c*) minimum efficiency; (*d*) minimum current capacity.
10. A generator has 100 volts output on open circuit, which drops to 50 volts with a load current of 50 ma and R_L of 1,000 ohms. The internal resistance r_i equals (*a*) 25 ohms; (*b*) 50 ohms; (*c*) 100 ohms; (*d*) 1,000 ohms.

ESSAY QUESTIONS

1. Draw a sketch illustrating construction of a zinc-carbon dry cell. Indicate the negative and positive electrodes and the electrolyte.
2. Draw a sketch illustrating construction of the lead-acid cell. Indicate the negative and positive electrodes and the electrolyte.
3. Show the wiring for the following batteries: (*a*) six lead-acid cells for a voltage output of approximately 12 volts; (*b*) six standard No. 6 dry cells for voltage output of 4.5 volts with a current capacity of ½ amp.
4. (*a*) What is the advantage of connecting cells in series? (*b*) What is connected to the end terminals of the series cells?
5. (*a*) What is the advantage of connecting cells in parallel? (*b*) Why can the load be connected across any one of the parallel cells?
6. How many cells are necessary in a battery to double the voltage and current rating of a single cell? Show the wiring diagram.
7. Draw a diagram showing two 6-volt lead-acid batteries being charged by a 7.5-volt source.
8. Why is a generator with very low internal resistance called a constant-voltage source?
9. Why does discharge current lower the specific gravity in a lead-acid cell?
10. Would you consider the lead-acid battery a constant-current source or constant-voltage source? Why?
11. Referring to Fig. 10·16*b*, draw the corresponding graph that shows how *I* varies with R_L.
12. Referring to Fig. 10·17*b*, draw the corresponding graph that shows how E_L varies with R_L.
13. Referring to Fig. 10·18*c*, draw the corresponding graph that shows how E_L varies with R_L.
14. List five types of chemical cells, giving two features of each.

PROBLEMS (*Answers to selected problems at back of book.*)

1. A No. 6 carbon-zinc dry cell is connected across a resistance of 1,000 ohms. How much current flows in the circuit?
2. Draw the wiring diagram for six No. 6 cells providing 3 volts output with a current capacity of ¾ amp. Draw the schematic diagram of this battery connected across a 10-ohm resistance: (*a*) How much current flows in the circuit? (*b*) How much power is dissipated in the resistance? (*c*) How much power is supplied by the battery?

3. A 6-volt lead-acid battery has an internal resistance of 0.01 ohm. How much current will flow if the battery has a short circuit across the two terminals?

4. How much is the specific gravity of a solution with equal parts of sulfuric acid and water?

5. A lead-acid battery discharges at the rate of 8 amp for 10 hr. (*a*) How many coulombs of charge must be put back into the battery to restore the original charge, assuming 100 per cent efficiency? (*b*) How long will this recharging take, with a trickle charging current of 2 amp?

6. The output voltage of a battery drops from 90 volts at no load to 60 volts with a load current of 50 ma. (*a*) How much is the internal r_i of the battery? (*b*) How much is R_L for this load current? (*c*) How much R_L would be needed to reduce the load voltage to one-half the no-load voltage?

7. A 100-volt source with internal resistance of 10,000 ohms is connected to a variable load resistance R_L. Tabulate I, E_{RL}, and power in R_L for values of 1,000 ohms, 5,000 ohms, 10,000 ohms, 15,000 ohms, and 20,000 ohms.

8. The output voltage of a source reads 60 volts with a VTVM. When a meter with 1,000 ohms-per-volt sensitivity is used, the reading is 50 volts on the 100-volt range. How much is the internal resistance of the source?

Review of chapters *to*

SUMMARY

1. A milliammeter or ammeter is a low-resistance meter connected in series in a circuit to measure its current. Different current ranges are obtained by meter shunts.
2. A voltmeter is a high-resistance meter connected across the circuit to measure its voltage. Different voltage ranges are obtained by multipliers.
3. An ohmmeter has an internal battery to indicate the resistance of a component across its two terminals, with external power off.
4. The VTVM is a multimeter featuring very high input resistance for d-c voltages and very high ohms ranges for resistance measurements.
5. In making voltage tests, remember that the voltage across a short circuit is zero, but the voltage across an open circuit equals the full applied voltage.
6. In making resistance tests remember that the resistance of a short circuit is zero, but the resistance of an open circuit is infinite.
7. A conductor has very low resistance. Silver, copper, and aluminum are the best conductors with copper generally used for wire conductors.
8. Resistance wire for heating elements and filaments has a much higher resistance when hot than its cold resistance. The hot resistance, equal to E/I with normal load current, cannot be measured with an ohmmeter.
9. A potential difference can produce charged ions in liquids and gases. The ions may be positive or negative. Movement of the ions is ionization current.
10. Insulators or dielectrics have very high resistance. Examples are air, vacuum, paper, glass, rubber, shellac, wood, and plastics.
11. The two main types of resistors are wirewound and carbon-composition. The wirewound type generally has relatively low resistance for power applications up to several hundred watts; the carbon type can have very high resistance values with wattage ratings up to 2 watts.
12. The color coding of carbon resistors is illustrated in Figs. 9·5 and 9·6.
13. An open resistor reads infinite ohms with an ohmmeter.
14. The two main types of cells used for batteries are the dry cell and lead-acid cell. Dry batteries are for relatively low-power applications, while the lead-acid battery can supply current up to several hundred amperes.
15. With cells or batteries connected in series, the total voltage equals the sum of the individual values, while the current rating is the same as one; in parallel, the voltage across all is the same, but the current rating equals the sum of the individual values.
16. Matching a load to the generator means making the load resistance equal to the generator internal resistance for maximum power at the load.

REFERENCES *(Additional references at back of book.)*

Books

Crouse, W. H., *Electrical Appliance Servicing*, McGraw-Hill Book Company, New York.
Richter, H. P., *Practical Electrical Wiring*, 6th ed., McGraw-Hill Book Company, New York.
Rider, J. F., *How to Use Meters*, John F. Rider, Publisher, Inc., New York.

Swiggett, R. L., *Introduction to Printed Circuits*, John F. Rider, Publisher, Inc., New York.
Timbie, W. H., *Elements of Electricity,* John Wiley & Sons, Inc., New York.

Pamphlets

National Electrical Code Standard of the National Board of Fire Underwriters for Electrical Wiring and Apparatus, National Board of Fire Underwriters, New York, Chicago, San Francisco.
Weston Electrical Instrument Corp., Newark, N.J., *The Instrument Sketch Book.*

REVIEW SELF-EXAMINATION (*Answers at back of book.*)

Here's another chance to check your progress. Work the exercises just as you did those at the end of each chapter and check your answers.

1. The internal resistance of a milliammeter must be very low in order to have (*a*) high sensitivity; (*b*) accuracy; (*c*) maximum voltage drop across the meter; (*d*) minimum effect on the current in the circuit.

2. The internal resistance of a voltmeter must be very high in order to have (*a*) low voltage ranges; (*b*) minimum current through the meter; (*c*) maximum loading effect; (*d*) more current supplied by the voltage source.

3. Which of the following ranges is best for checking a 1-M resistor for an open with power off? (*a*) $R \times 1$; (*b*) $R \times 1$ M; (*c*) 0 to 500 volts; (*d*) 0 to 50 ma.

4. A tungsten filament measures 10 ohms with an ohmmeter. In a circuit with 100 volts applied, 2 amp flows. The hot resistance of the filament equals (*a*) 2 ohms; (*b*) 10 ohms; (*c*) 50 ohms; (*d*) 100 ohms.

5. Three resistors R_1, R_2, and R_3 are in series across a 100-volt source. If R_2 opens, the (*a*) voltage across R_2 is zero; (*b*) total resistance of R_1, R_2, and R_3 decreases; (*c*) voltage across R_1 is 100 volts; (*d*) voltage across R_2 is 100 volts.

6. The current flowing between electrodes inside a lead-acid battery is (*a*) electron current; (*b*) proton current; (*c*) ionization current; (*d*) polarization current.

7. With 300 volts applied across two equal resistors in series, 1 ma of current flows. Typical values for each resistor to be used here are (*a*) 100,000 ohms, 1 watt; (*b*) 150,000 ohms, ½ watt; (*c*) 150,000 ohms, 50 watts; (*d*) 300,000 ohms, 2 watts.

8. A carbon resistor is coded with brown, green, yellow, and gold stripes from left to right. Its resistance value is (*a*) 15,000 ohms ±10 per cent; (*b*) 68,000 ohms ±10 per cent; (*c*) 150,000 ohms ±5 per cent; (*d*) 500,000 ohms ±5 per cent.

9. Thirty zinc-carbon dry cells are connected in series. The total voltage output is (*a*) 1.5 volts; (*b*) 30 volts; (*c*) 45 volts; (*d*) 60 volts.

10. A 45-volt source with an internal resistance of 2 ohms is connected across a wirewound resistor. Maximum power will be dissipated in the resistor when its resistance equals (*a*) zero; (*b*) 2 ohms; (*c*) 45 ohms; (*d*) infinity.

Chapter 11 Magnetism

Electrical effects exist in two forms, voltage and current. In terms of voltage, separated electric charges have the potential to do mechanical work in attracting or repelling charges. Similarly, any electrical current has an associated magnetic field that can do the work of attraction or repulsion. Materials made of iron, nickel, and cobalt, particularly, concentrate their magnetic effects at opposite ends. As shown in Fig. 11·1, these points of concentrated magnetic strength are north and south poles, corresponding to opposite polarities of electric charges. The name *magnetism* is derived from the iron oxide mineral *magnetite*. Ferromagnetism specifically refers to the magnetic properties of iron. The topics explained here are:

11·1 The magnetic field
11·2 Induction by the magnetic field
11·3 Air gap of a magnet
11·4 Types of magnets
11·5 Ampere-turns of magnetizing force
11·6 Field intensity *H*
11·7 *B-H* magnetization curve
11·8 Magnetic hysteresis
11·9 Ohm's law for magnetic circuits
11·10 Magnetic shielding

11·1 The magnetic field

The practical effects of ferromagnetism result from the magnetic field of force between the two poles at opposite ends of the magnet. Although the magnetic field is invisible, evidence of its force can be seen when small iron filings are sprinkled on a glass or paper sheet placed over a bar magnet, as illustrated in Fig. 11·2*a*. Each iron filing becomes a small bar magnet.

If the sheet is tapped gently to overcome friction so that the filings can move, they become aligned by the magnetic field. Many filings cling to the ends of the magnet, showing that the magnetic field is strongest at the poles. The field exists in all directions but decreases in strength inversely as the square of the distance from the poles of the magnet.

Field lines. In order to visualize the magnetic field without iron filings, it is conventional practice to show the field as lines of force, as in Fig. 11·2*b*. The direction of the lines outside the magnet shows the path a north pole would follow in the field, repelled away from the north pole of the magnet and attracted to its south pole. Inside the magnet, which is the generator for the magnetic field, the lines are from south pole to north pole.

Magnetic field lines are unaffected by nonmagnetic materials such as air, vacuum, paper, glass, or wood. When these materials are placed in the magnetic field of a magnet, the field lines are the same as though the material were not there.

The magnetic field lines become concentrated, however, when a magnetic substance like iron is placed in the field. Inside the iron, the field lines are more dense, compared with the field in air. There are two effects, as the iron in the field becomes a magnet itself. Then its poles concentrate lines of force from the external field. Also the magnetic lines between the poles inside the iron are in the same direction as the external field. As a result, a magnetic material like iron in a magnetic field has the effect of concentrating magnetic lines, to increase the field intensity in the iron.

North and south magnetic poles. The earth itself is a huge natural magnet, with its greatest strength at the north and south poles. Because of the earth's magnetic poles, if a small bar magnet is suspended so that it can

Fig. 11·1 Poles of a magnet. (a) Electromagnet (EM) produced by current from battery. (b) Permanent magnet (PM) without any external current source.

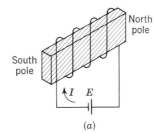

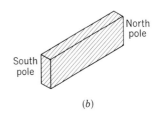

(a)

(b)

Fig. 11·2 Magnetic field of force around a bar magnet. (a) Field outlined by iron filings. (b) Field indicated by lines of force.

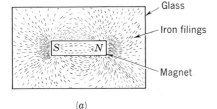

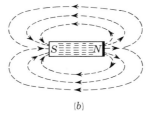

(a)

(b)

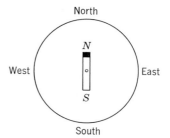

Fig. 11·3 Definition of north and south poles on bar magnet.

turn easily, one end will always point north. This end of the bar magnet is defined as the *north-seeking pole,* as shown in Fig. 11·3. The opposite end is the *south-seeking pole.* When polarity is indicated on a magnet, the north-seeking end is the north pole (N) and the opposite end is the south pole (S).

Similar to the force between electric charges is a force between magnetic poles causing attraction of opposite poles and repulsion between similar poles:

1. A north pole (N) and south pole (S) tend to attract each other.
2. A north pole (N) tends to repel another north pole (N), while a south (S) pole tends to repel another south pole (S).

Units of magnetic flux. The entire group of magnetic field lines, which can be considered to flow outward from the north pole of a magnet, is called magnetic flux. Its symbol is the Greek letter ϕ (phi). The unit of flux is the maxwell[1] in the cgs system.[2] One maxwell equals one magnetic field line. In Fig. 11·4a, for example, the flux illustrated is 6 maxwells because there are 6 field lines flowing in or out for each pole. In English units, flux is measured simply in total number of lines, or kilolines. One kiloline equals 1,000 lines. For example, a 1-lb magnet can provide the magnetic flux ϕ of about 5,000 lines, which equals 5 kilolines, or 5,000 maxwells.

In the mks system, the unit of magnetic flux is the weber.[3] One weber equals 1×10^8 lines or maxwells. Since the weber is relatively large, it is commonly used in microweber units. Then 1 μweber = 100 lines or 100 maxwells. For the same 1-lb magnet producing the magnetic flux of 5,000 maxwells, this corresponds to 50 μwebers.

Flux density B. As shown in Fig. 11·4, flux density is the number of magnetic field lines per unit area of a section perpendicular to the direction of flux. The symbol is B. The unit is lines per square inch in the English system, or lines per square centimeter in the cgs system. One line per square centimeter is called a gauss.[4]

[1] Named for James Clerk Maxwell (1831–1879), an important Scottish mathematical physicist, who contributed much to electrical and radio theory.
[2] See Appendix D on Physics Units for definitions of centimeter-gram-second (cgs) and meter-kilogram-second (mks) systems.
[3] Named for Wilhelm Weber, a German physicist (1804–1890).
[4] Named for Karl F. Gauss (1777–1855), a German mathematician.

In Fig. 11·4a, the total flux ϕ of 6 lines, or 6 maxwells, has a flux density B of 2 gauss at point P in the field, since there are 2 lines per cm². The flux density has a higher value close to the poles where the flux lines are more crowded. As a typical value, the flux density for a 1-lb magnet would be about 1,000 gauss at the poles.

Example 1. With a flux of 10,000 maxwells through a perpendicular area of 5 cm², what is the flux density in gauss?

Answer. $B = \dfrac{\phi}{A} = \dfrac{10{,}000 \text{ maxwells}}{5 \text{ cm}^2} = 2{,}000\,\dfrac{\text{maxwells}}{\text{cm}^2} = \textbf{2,000 gauss}$

In the mks system the unit of flux density is webers per square meter (webers per m²). Since this unit is much larger than the gauss, 1 weber per m² equals 1×10^4 gauss. For the value of B equal to 2,000 gauss in the previous example, in mks units the flux density is 2,000/10,000 or 0.2 weber per m².

Example 2. With a flux of 100 μwebers through an area of 0.0005 m², what is the flux density in webers per m²?

Answer.
$$B = \frac{\phi}{A} = \frac{100 \times 10^{-6} \text{ weber}}{5 \times 10^{-4} \text{ m}^2} = \frac{100}{5} \times 10^{-2} = 20 \times 10^{-2} = \textbf{0.2}\,\frac{\textbf{weber}}{\textbf{m}^2}$$

It should be noted that all these units for flux or flux density apply to the magnetic field produced either by a permanent magnet or by an electromagnet. Also, the weber in the mks system is a practical unit of magnetism closely related to the practical volt and ampere units in electricity.

Fig. 11·4   Total magnetic flux ϕ compared with flux density B. (a) The total ϕ is 6 lines or 6 maxwells. Density at P is 2 lines per cm² or 2 gauss. (b) ϕ for total area is 144 maxwells. B is 16 gauss.

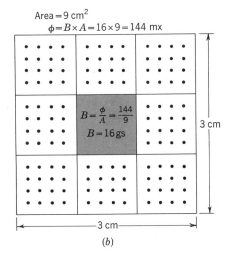

Area = 9 cm²
$\phi = B \times A = 16 \times 9 = 144$ mx

$B = \dfrac{\phi}{A} = \dfrac{144}{9}$
$B = 16\,\text{gs}$

3 cm

3 cm

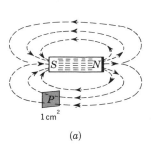

1 cm²

(a)

(b)

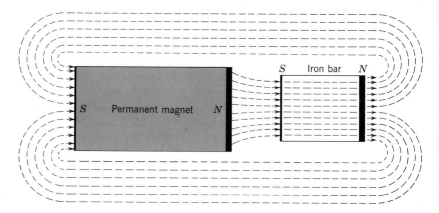

Fig. 11·5 *Magnetizing an iron bar by induction.*

It is important to remember that the flux ϕ includes total area, while the flux density B is for a specified unit area. The difference between ϕ and B is illustrated in Fig. 11·4b with cgs units. The total area A here is 9 cm², equal to 3 cm × 3 cm. For one unit box of 1 cm², 16 lines are shown. Therefore, the flux density B is 16 lines or maxwells per cm², which equals 16 gauss. The total area includes nine of these boxes. Therefore, the total flux ϕ is 144 lines or maxwells, equal to 9 × 16 for $B \times A$. Conversely, if the total flux ϕ is given as 144 lines or maxwells, the flux density is found by dividing 144 by 9 cm², which equals 16 lines or maxwells per cm², or 16 gauss for B.

11·2 Induction by the magnetic field

The electrical effect of one body on another without any physical contact between them is called induction. For instance, a permanent magnet can induce an unmagnetized iron bar to become a magnet, without the two touching. The iron bar then becomes a magnet, as shown in Fig. 11·5. What happens is that the magnetic lines of force generated by the permanent magnet make the internal molecular magnets in the iron bar line up in the same direction, instead of the random directions in unmagnetized iron. The magnetized iron bar then has magnetic poles at the ends, as a result of the magnetic induction. Note that the induced poles in the iron have opposite polarity from the poles of the magnet. Since opposite poles attract, the iron bar will be attracted to the permanent magnet. Any magnet attracts to itself all magnetic materials by induction.

Although the two bars in Fig. 11·5 are not touching, the iron bar is in the magnetic flux of the permanent magnet. It is the invisible magnetic field that links the two magnets, enabling one to affect the other. Actually, this idea of magnetic flux extending outward from the magnetic poles is the basis for many inductive effects in a-c circuits. More generally, the magnetic field between magnetic poles and the electric field between static charges form the basis for wireless radio transmission and reception.

The strength of the magnetic flux in Fig. 11·5 can be determined from the number of lines shown, as an example of calculating ϕ and B. Because of the small values, cgs units will be used. With 10 lines of force in the field, the flux ϕ is 10 lines or maxwells. If the area of a pole at the end of the permanent magnet is taken as 2 cm^2, then the flux density equals $^{10}\!/_2$ or 5 gauss for B at the pole. For a cross-sectional area of 0.5 cm^2 for a pole at the end of the iron bar, here the flux density B equals 10/0.5 or 20 gauss. The same number of magnetic lines provides a greater flux density because of the smaller area.

Polarity of induced poles. Note that the north pole of the permanent magnet in Fig. 11·5 induces an opposite south pole at this end of the iron bar. If the permanent magnet were reversed, its south pole would induce a north pole. The closest induced pole will always be of opposite polarity. This is the reason why either end of a magnet can attract another magnetic material to itself. No matter which pole is used, it will induce an opposite pole and the opposite poles are attracted.

Permeability. Soft iron, as an example, is very effective in concentrating magnetic field lines, by induction in the iron. This ability to concentrate magnetic flux is called permeability. Any material that is easily magnetized has high permeability, therefore, as the field lines are concentrated because of induction. The permeability of materials for magnetic flux corresponds to the conductance of a conductor for electrical current. High permeability means a relatively large amount of flux can be produced by the magnetizing force. This idea is similar to conductance allowing a large amount of current for an applied electromotive force.

Numerical values of permeability for different materials can be assigned in comparison with air or vacuum. Since air, vacuum, or any nonmagnetic material cannot affect a magnetic field by induction, they have the reference value of 1 for permeability. For example, if the flux density in air is 1 gauss but an iron coil in the same position in the same field has a flux density of 200 gauss, the permeability of the iron coil equals $^{200}\!/_1$ or 200. The symbol is μ (mu) for permeability. Typical values are 100 to 9,000 for iron and steel.

11·3 Air gap of a magnet

As shown in Fig. 11·6, the air space between poles of a magnet is its air gap. The shorter the air gap, the stronger is the field in the gap for a given pole strength. Since air is not magnetic and cannot concentrate magnetic lines, a larger air gap only provides additional space for the magnetic lines to spread out. Referring to Fig. 11·6a, note that the horseshoe magnet has more crowded magnetic lines in the air gap, compared with the widely separated lines around the bar magnet in b. Actually, the horseshoe magnet can be considered as a bar magnet bent around to place the opposite poles closer, so that both poles provide magnetic lines that reinforce each other in the air gap. The purpose of a short air gap is to concentrate the magnetic field outside the magnet, for maximum induction in a magnetic material placed in the gap.

Fig. 11·6   The horseshoe magnet in (a) has a smaller air gap than the bar magnet in (b).

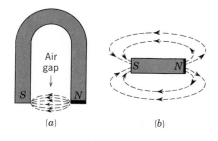

Fig. 11·7   (a) Air gap in record-playback head for magnetic tape. (b) Magnetized tape with pattern visible with a coating of carbonyl iron particles. (Minnesota Mining and Mfg. Co.)

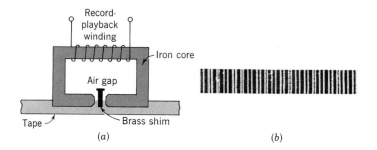

Magnetic-tape recording. An example of using a short air gap can be seen in Fig. 11·7a illustrating the magnetic head of a tape recorder. In this application, the magnetic tape must pass through a very narrow air gap on the head. Then very small areas of the tape become magnetized by induction for recording. The magnetizing field results from current in the winding. On playback, the magnetized tape induces current in the same winding. The extremely narrow air gap can be provided by a brass insert with a thin slit.

The magnetization of the tape can be made visible by a coating of extremely small carbonyl iron particles. This technique corresponds to the idea of sprinkling iron filings around a magnet to see its field pattern. The photograph in Fig. 11·7b shows a typical sound-track pattern of magnetization. Note that the lines across the tape have variable spacing and different intensities, which indicate the magnetization on the tape.

Ring magnet without air gap. When it is desired to concentrate magnetic lines within a magnet, however, it can be formed as a closed magnetic loop. This method is illustrated in Fig. 11·8a by the two permanent horseshoe magnets placed in a closed loop with opposite poles touching. Since the loop has no open ends, there can be no air gap and no poles. The north and south poles of each magnet cancel as opposite poles touch. Each magnet has its magnetic lines inside, plus the magnetic lines of the other magnet, but outside the magnets the lines cancel because they are in opposite directions. The effect of the closed magnetic loop, therefore, is maximum concentration of magnetic lines in the magnet with minimum lines outside.

The same effect of a closed magnetic loop is obtained with the *toroid* or ring magnet in Fig. 11·8b, made in the form of a doughnut. Iron is often used for the core. This type of electromagnet has maximum strength in the iron ring, with little flux outside. As a result, the toroidal magnet is less sensitive to induction from external magnetic fields and, conversely, has little magnetic effect outside the coil.

Keeper for a magnet. The principle of the closed magnetic ring is used to protect permanent magnets in storage. In Fig. 11·9*a*, four PM bar magnets are in a closed loop while *b* shows a stacked pair. Additional even pairs can be stacked this way with opposite poles touching. The closed loop in *c* shows one permanent horseshoe magnet with a soft iron *keeper* across the air gap. The keeper maintains the strength of the permanent magnet as it becomes magnetized by induction to form a closed loop. Then any external magnetic field is just concentrated in the closed loop without inducing opposite poles in the permanent magnet. If permanent magnets are not stored this way, the polarity can be reversed with induced poles produced by a strong external field from a d-c source; an alternating field can demagnetize the magnet.

11·4   Types of magnets

The two broad classes are permanent magnets and electromagnets. An electromagnet needs current from an external source to maintain its magnetic field. With a permanent magnet, not only is its magnetic field present without any external current, but the magnet can maintain its strength indefinitely.

Electromagnets. Current in a wire conductor has an associated magnetic field. If the wire is wrapped in the form of a coil, as in Fig. 11·10, the cur-

Fig. 11·8   Examples of a closed magnetic ring without any air gap. (a) Two PM horse-shoe magnets with opposite poles touching. (b) Toroid electromagnet.

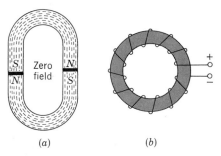

(a)   (b)

Fig. 11·9   Storing permanent magnets in a closed loop, with opposite poles touching. (a) Four bar magnets. (b) Two bars. (c) Horseshoe with iron keeper across air gap.

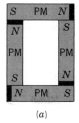

(a)   (b)   (c)

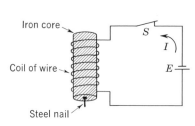

Iron core

Coil of wire

Steel nail

Fig. 11·10   Electromagnet holding nail when S is closed for current in coil.

Fig. 11·11   PM loudspeaker.

rent and its magnetic field become concentrated in a smaller space, resulting in a stronger field. With the length much greater than its width, the coil is called a *solenoid.* It acts like a bar magnet, with opposite poles at the ends. More current and more turns make a stronger magnetic field. Also, the iron core concentrates magnetic lines inside the coil. Soft iron is generally used for the core because it is easily magnetized and demagnetized.

The coil in Fig. 11·10, with the switch closed and current in the coil, is an electromagnet that can pick up the steel nail shown. If the switch is opened, the magnetic field is reduced to zero and the nail will drop off. This ability of an electromagnet to provide a strong magnetic force of attraction that can be turned on or off easily has many applications in lifting magnets, buzzers, bells or chimes, and relays. A relay is a switch with contacts that are opened or closed by an electromagnet.

Permanent magnets. These are made of hard magnetic materials, like cobalt steel, magnetized by induction in the manufacturing process. A very strong field is needed for induction in these materials. When the magnetizing field is removed, however, a residual induction makes the material a permanent magnet. A common PM material is *alnico,* a commercial alloy of aluminum, nickel, and iron, with cobalt, copper, and titanium added to produce about 12 grades. The Alnico V grade is often used for PM loudspeakers (Fig. 11·11). In this application, a typical size of PM slug for a steady magnetic field is a few ounces to about 5 lb, with a flux B of 500 to 25,000 lines or maxwells. One advantage of a PM loudspeaker is that only two connecting leads are needed for the voice coil, as the steady magnetic field of the PM slug is obtained without any field-coil winding.

Commercial permanent magnets will last indefinitely if not subject to high temperatures or to a strong magnetizing field. If the magnet becomes hot, however, the molecular structure can be rearranged, resulting in loss of magnetism that is not recovered after cooling. A permanent magnet does not become exhausted with use, as its magnetic properties are determined by the structure of the internal atoms and molecules.

Classification of magnetic materials. When we consider materials simply as either magnetic or nonmagnetic, this division is really based on the strong magnetic properties of iron. However, weak magnetic materials can be important in some applications. For this reason, a more exact classification includes the following three groups:

1. *Ferromagnetic materials.* These include iron, steel, nickel, cobalt, and commercial alloys such as alnico and Permalloy. They become strongly magnetized, in the same direction as the magnetizing field, with high values of permeability from 50 to 5,000. Permalloy has a μ of 100,000 but is easily saturated at relatively low values of flux density.

2. *Paramagnetic materials.* These include aluminum, platinum, manganese, and chromium. The permeability is slightly more than 1. They become weakly magnetized in the same direction as the magnetizing field.

3. *Diamagnetic materials.* These include bismuth, antimony, copper, zinc, mercury, gold, and silver. The permeability is less than 1 because they become weakly magnetized but in the opposite direction from the magnetizing field.

The basis of all magnetic effects is the magnetic field associated with electric charges in motion. Within the atom, the motion of its orbital electrons generates a magnetic field. There are two kinds of electron motion in the atom. First is the electron revolving in its orbit. This motion provides a diamagnetic effect. However, this magnetic effect is weak because thermal agitation at normal room temperature results in random directions that neutralize each other.

More effective is the magnetic effect from the motion of each electron spinning on its own axis. The spinning electron serves as a tiny permanent magnet. Opposite spins provide opposite polarities. Two electrons spinning in opposite directions form a pair, neutralizing the magnetic fields. In the atoms of ferromagnetic materials, however, there are many unpaired electrons with spins in the same direction, resulting in a strong magnetic effect.

In terms of molecular structure, iron atoms are grouped in microscopically small arrangements called *domains*. Each domain is an elementary *dipole magnet*, with two opposite poles. In crystal form, the iron atoms form domains that are parallel to the axes of the crystal. Still, the domains can point in different directions, because of the different axes. When the material becomes magnetized by an external magnetic field, though, the domains become aligned in the same direction. With PM materials, the alignment remains after the external field is removed.

Magnetostriction. The action of forcing the magnetic domains to become aligned in a ferromagnetic material causes a slight change in its physical dimensions, which is called magnetostriction. Conversely, a physical force applied to the magnetic material can change its field strength. The effect is small. For nickel, as an example, the length is reduced about 20 parts in a million by a very strong magnetizing force of 6,000 amp-turns per m.

Ferrites. This is the name for recently developed ceramic materials having the ferromagnetic properties of iron. The ferrites feature high permeability, like iron, but the ceramic material is an insulator while iron is a conductor. A ferrite coil is much more efficient in a coil when the current alternates very rapidly, since the I^2R power lost by eddy currents in the magnetic coil is then less because of the high resistance. However, the ferrites are easily saturated, at relatively low values of magnetizing current.

11·5 Ampere-turns of magnetizing force

With an electromagnet, it is convenient to consider the strength of its magnetic field in terms of current in the turns of the coil. The more current and the more turns, the stronger is the magnetic field. The coil serves as a bar magnet, with poles at the ends, providing a magnetic field proportional to the ampere-turns. Specifically,

$$\text{Ampere-turns} = NI \qquad (11·1)$$

where N is the number of turns and I is the current in amperes.

As shown in Fig. 11·12, a solenoid with 5 turns and 2-amp I has the same magnetizing force as 10 turns with 1 amp, as the product of the amperes and turns is 10 for both cases. With thinner wire, more turns can be used in a given space. The amount of current is determined by the resistance of the wire and the source voltage. How many ampere-turns are necessary depends on the required magnetic field strength.

Example 3. Calculate the ampere-turns for a coil with 2,000 turns and 5 ma current.

Answer. $NI = 2,000 \times 5 \times 10^{-3} = $ **10 amp-turns**

Example 4. The wire in a solenoid of 250 turns has a resistance of 3 ohms. (*a*) How much is the current with the coil connected to a 6-volt battery? (*b*) Calculate the ampere-turns.

Answer. (*a*) $I = \dfrac{E}{R} = \dfrac{6}{3} = $ **2 amp**

(*b*) $NI = 250 \times 2 = $ **500 amp-turns**

Example 5. A coil with 4-amp I is to provide the magnetizing force of 600 amp-turns. How many turns are necessary?

Answer. $N = \dfrac{NI}{I} = \dfrac{600}{4} = $ **150 turns**

Example 6. A coil with 400 turns must provide 800 amp-turns of magnetizing force. How much current is necessary?

Answer. $I = \dfrac{NI}{N} = \dfrac{800}{400} = $ **2 amp**

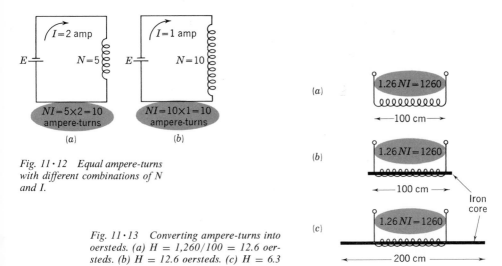

Fig. 11·12 Equal ampere-turns with different combinations of N and I.

Fig. 11·13 Converting ampere-turns into oersteds. (a) H = 1,260/100 = 12.6 oersteds. (b) H = 12.6 oersteds. (c) H = 6.3 oersteds.

11·6   Field intensity H

The ampere-turn unit indicates the magnetizing force for an electromagnet, but different units are used for the intensity of the magnetic field. In cgs units, the *oersted* measures magnetic field intensity. The symbol is *H*. When the magnetic field exerts a force of one dyne[5] on a standard north pole, the field intensity *H* at that point in the field is one oersted. By means of units for *H*, the magnetic field intensity can be stated for either electromagnets or permanent magnets, since both provide the same kind of magnetic field.

For an electromagnet in the form of a solenoid, ampere-turns of magnetizing force and oersteds of field intensity are related as follows:

$$H = \frac{1.256 \, NI}{\text{length (cm)}} \qquad \text{oersteds} \qquad (11·2)$$

NI is the ampere-turns value. The factor 1.256 is equal to $4\pi/10$, derived from the geometry of a solenoid. Note that this value is double 6.28 for 2π, or 12.56, divided by 10 to equal 1.256. The length *l* is the distance from pole to pole, in centimeters.

As an example, Fig. 11·13a shows an air-core coil having 1,000 amp-turns, or 1,256 for 1.256 *NI*. Dividing 1,256 by the length of 100 cm results in 12.56 oersteds for the field intensity. This value is for *H* at the center of the air-core solenoid.

When the coil has an iron core, the length of the iron path is divided into 1.256 *NI*. In *b*, the length of iron is the same as the coil length, resulting

[5] See Appendix D, Physics Units.

in 1,256/100 or 12.56 oersteds for H. This answer is the same as for *a*. However, this value of H is the field intensity throughout the entire length of the iron core.

Notice that in *c* the iron path of 200 cm is double the coil length of 100 cm, with the same ampere-turns. The larger magnetic path results in a field intensity of 1,256/200 or 6.28 oersteds for H throughout the iron core.

Example 7. What is the field intensity H in oersteds in an iron core 10 cm long with 100 amp-turns in the coil?

Answer. $$H = \frac{1.256\ NI}{l} = \frac{125.6}{10} = \textbf{12.56 oersteds}$$

This is the same value of H as in Fig. 11·13*b*, but with a shorter magnetic path and fewer ampere-turns.

Note that the dimensions of the oersted unit are basically ampere-turns per unit of length. For a length of 1 cm and magnetizing of force of 1 amp-turn, $H = 1.256$ oersteds in the cgs system.

In the mks system the unit for field intensity H is ampere-turns per meter. There is no common name for this unit. One ampere-turn per meter equals 0.01256 oersted, or 1 oersted equals 79.6 amp-turns per meter. The ampere-turn per meter is a smaller unit of H because of the greater length l. The different magnetic units are summarized in Table 11·2 at the end of the chapter.

Example 8. Convert 2 oersteds to amp-turns per meter units.

Answer. $H = 2$ oersteds $= 2 \times 79.6$ amp-turns per m $= \textbf{159.2 amp-turns}$
per m

11·7   B-H magnetization curve

As shown in Fig. 11·14, the *B-H* curve is commonly used to show how much flux density *B* results from increasing amounts of field intensity *H*.

Fig. 11·14   B-H magnetization curve for soft iron. The curve is nonlinear at the top because the permeability decreases at saturation.

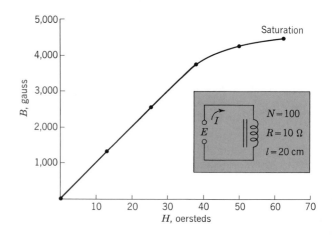

Table 11·1   B-H values for Fig. 11·14

E, volts	R, ohms	I, amp = E/R	N, turns	NI, amp-turns	l, cm	H, oersteds = 1.256NI/cm	μ	B, gauss = μH
20	10	2	100	200	20	12.56	100	1,256
40	10	4	100	400	20	25.12	100	2,512
60	10	6	100	600	20	37.68	100	3,768
80	10	8	100	800	20	50.24	85	4,260
100	10	10	100	1,000	20	62.80	70	4,396

This curve is for soft iron, plotted for the values in Table 11·1, but similar curves can be obtained for all magnetic materials. The values for the circuit shown in the graph are derived as follows:

1. The current I in the coil equals E/R. For 10-ohm coil resistance and 20 volts applied, I is 2 amp, as listed in the top row of Table 11·1. Increasing values of E produce more current in the coil.

2. The ampere-turns (NI) of magnetizing force increase with more current. Since the turns are constant at 100, the values of NI in the third column increase from 200 for 2 amp in the top row to 1,000 for 10 amp in the bottom row.

3. The field intensity H increases with higher values of NI. In the fourth column, the increasing values of H are in oersted units. Since oersteds equal 1.256 amp-turns per cm, the value of 1,000 for NI in the bottom row corresponds to 1,256/20 or 62.8 oersteds, as the coil length is 20 cm.

4. The flux density B depends on the field intensity H and permeability $μ$ of the iron. The values of B in the last column are obtained by multiplying $μ \times H$. Note that the values of $μ$ decrease for higher values of H because of saturation in the iron core. With less permeability, the iron cannot provide proportional increases in B for increasing values of H.

Relation between B and H. If we compare field intensity H with flux density B, oersteds of H can be considered the cause, while gauss of flux density correspond to the effect. This difference matters when comparing a magnetic material such as iron with air, when they are in a magnetic field. Because of its permeability, iron concentrates magnetic lines of force, providing greater flux density than would exist in air. However, the magnetic field intensity H can be the same for both cases. The permeability, then, determines how much flux density B is produced by a given field intensity H. Specifically,

$$B = μ \times H \qquad\qquad (11·3)$$

As an example, for the $μ$ of 100 and H of 12.56 oersteds in the top row of Table 11·1,

$$B = μ \times H = 100 \times 12.56 = \textbf{1,256 gauss}$$

With a material of high μ in the field, H produces a large value of B. In air or vacuum, however, with μ equal to 1, the numerical value of B is the same as H. Still, the units for B and H have different dimensions. For H equal to 100 oersteds in air, as an example, B would be 100 gauss.

In a comparison of the permeability for different magnetic materials with each other, rather than using air as a reference, the value of μ can be specified as B/H. Then μ states how much flux density B can be produced for a given field intensity H. A higher value of μ can provide more flux density. As an example, the μ of 5,000 gauss/50 oersteds means that the field intensity H of 50 oersteds produces 5,000 gauss for the flux density B. The value of μ is generally specified for the highest flux density before saturation.

Saturation on the B-H curve. The curve in Fig. 11·14 with flux density B rising for increasing field intensity H is a characteristic of the magnetic material, showing its ability to concentrate flux. However, notice that for values of H greater than 50 oersteds, approximately, the B values of flux density increase at a much slower rate. This effect of little change in flux density when the field-intensity force increases is called *saturation*. The reason is that the iron becomes saturated with magnetic lines of induction. After most of the molecular dipoles in the magnetic domains are aligned by the magnetizing force, very little additional induction can be produced.

11·8   Magnetic hysteresis

Hysteresis means "a lagging behind." With respect to the magnetic flux in an iron core of an electromagnet, the flux lags the increases or decreases of magnetizing force. The hysteresis results from the fact that the magnetic dipoles are not perfectly elastic. Once aligned by an external magnetizing force, the dipoles do not return exactly to their original positions when the force is removed. The effect is the same as if the dipoles were forced to move against an internal friction between molecules. Furthermore, if the magnetizing force is reversed in direction by reversal of the current in an electromagnet, the flux produced in the opposite direction lags behind the reversed magnetizing force.

Hysteresis loss. When the magnetizing force reverses thousands or millions of times per second, as with rapidly reversing alternating current, the hysteresis can cause a considerable loss of energy. A large part of the magnetizing force is then used just for overcoming the internal friction of the molecular dipoles. The work done by the magnetizing force against this internal friction produces heat. This energy wasted in heat as the molecular dipoles lag the magnetizing force is called hysteresis loss. For steel and other hard magnetic materials, the hysteresis losses are much higher than in soft magnetic materials like iron.

When the magnetizing force varies at a slow rate, the hysteresis losses can be considered negligible. An example is an electromagnet with direct current that is simply turned on and off, or the magnetizing force of an alternating current that reverses 60 times per second or less. The faster the magnetizing force changes, however, the greater is the hysteresis effect.

Hysteresis loop. To show the hysteresis characteristics of a magnetic material, its values of flux density B are plotted for a periodically reversing magnetizing force, as Fig. 11·15. This curve is the hysteresis loop of the material. The larger the area enclosed by the curve, the greater is the hysteresis loss.

The hysteresis loop is actually a B-H curve with an a-c magnetizing force. On the vertical axis, values of flux density B are indicated. The units can be gauss, or webers per m². The horizontal axis indicates values of field intensity H. On this axis the units can be oersteds, amp-turns per m, amp-turns, or just magnetizing current, as all factors are constant except I. Opposite directions of current result in the opposite directions of $+H$ and $-H$ for the field lines. Similarly, opposite polarities are indicated for flux density as $+B$ or $-B$.

The current starts from 0 at the center, when the material is unmagnetized. Then positive H values increase B to saturation at $+B_{\max}$. Next H decreases to 0 but B drops to the value of B_R, instead of 0, because of hysteresis. When H becomes negative, B drops to zero and continues to $-B_{\max}$, which is saturation in the opposite direction from $+B_{\max}$ because of the reversed magnetizing current.

Then as the $-H$ values decrease, the flux density is reduced to $-B_R$. Finally, the loop is completed with positive values of H producing saturation at $B_{\max}$ again. The curve does not return to the zero origin at the center because of hysteresis. As the magnetizing force periodically reverses, the values of flux density are repeated to trace out the hysteresis loop.

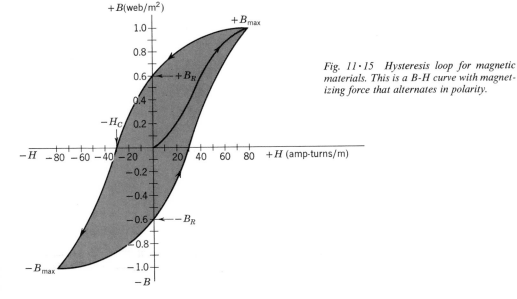

Fig. 11·15 *Hysteresis loop for magnetic materials. This is a B-H curve with magnetizing force that alternates in polarity.*

The value of either $+B_R$ or $-B_R$, which is the flux density remaining after the magnetizing force has been reduced to zero, is the *residual induction* of a magnetic material, also called its *retentivity*. In Fig. 11·15, the residual induction is 0.6 weber per m².

The value of $-H_c$, which equals the magnetizing force that must be applied in the reverse direction to reduce the flux density to zero, is the *coercive force* of the material. In Fig. 11·15, the coercive force $-H_c$ is 30 amp-turns per m.

It should be noted that the values shown here are typical for an iron sample, but different magnetic materials will have different values for the hysteresis loop. For power applications in general, the desired shape of the hysteresis loop is to have it as small as possible for minimum losses, with a high value of $B_{\max}$ at saturation so that the required magnetizing current will be small for the desired flux.

Demagnetization. In order to demagnetize a magnetic material completely, the residual induction B_R must be reduced to zero. This cannot be accomplished by a reversed d-c magnetizing force usually, because the material then would just become magnetized with opposite polarity. The practical way is to magnetize and demagnetize the material with a continuously decreasing hysteresis loop. This can be done with a magnetic field produced by alternating current. Then as the magnetic field and the material are moved away from each other, or the current amplitude is reduced, the hysteresis loop becomes smaller and smaller. Finally, with the weakest field, the loop collapses practically to zero, resulting in zero residual induction. This method of *demagnetization* is also called *degaussing*. One application is degaussing the metal electrodes in a color picture tube, with a degaussing coil providing 60-cycle alternating current from the power line. Another example is erasing the recorded signal on magnetic tape by demagnetizing with the a-c bias current.

11·9   Ohm's law for magnetic circuits

In analysis of electromagnets, it can be helpful to make some comparisons with electric circuits. Magnetic flux corresponds to current. The

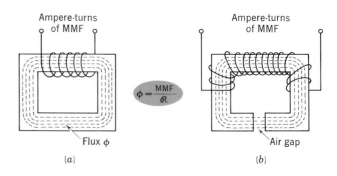

Fig. 11·16 Magnetic circuit. (a) Closed iron path having low reluctance requiring little mmf. (b) Higher reluctance path with air gap, requiring more mmf.

Ampere-turns of MMF

$\phi = \dfrac{MMF}{\mathcal{R}}$

Flux ϕ

(a)

Ampere-turns of MMF

Air gap

(b)

flux is produced by ampere-turns. Therefore, the ampere-turns correspond to voltage.

Opposition to the production of flux in a material is called its *reluctance*, comparable with resistance. The symbol for reluctance is $\mathcal{R}$. Reluctance is inversely proportional to permeability. Iron has high permeability and low reluctance. Air or vacuum has low permeability and high reluctance.

In Fig. 11·16, the ampere-turns of the coil produce magnetic flux throughout the magnetic path. The reluctance is the total opposition to the flux ϕ. In *a* there is little reluctance in the closed iron path, and few ampere-turns are necessary. In *b*, however, the air gap has high reluctance, requiring many more ampere-turns for the same flux as in *a*.

The three factors—flux, ampere-turns, and reluctance—are related as follows:

$$\phi = \frac{\text{mmf}}{\mathcal{R}} \qquad (11 \cdot 4)$$

which is known as Ohm's law for magnetic circuits, corresponding to $I = E/R$. The ampere-turns factor is called magnetomotive force, or mmf, comparable with emf in an electric circuit. In the form of Ohm's law for magnetic circuits, the mmf is considered to produce flux ϕ in a magnetic material against the opposition of its reluctance $\mathcal{R}$. This relationship corresponds to emf or voltage producing current in a conducting material against the opposition of its resistance.

Remember that the units for the flux ϕ are maxwells, kilolines, webers, or microwebers. These units measure total lines, as distinguished from flux density B, which equals lines per unit area.

The unit of mmf in the mks system is simply ampere-turns. There is no dimension of length for mmf, which corresponds to the idea of potential difference which is also independent of distance.

In the cgs system the unit of mmf is the gilbert.[6] One amp-turn equals 1.256 gilberts. As an example, the mmf of 100 amp-turns in mks units is the same as 125.6 gilberts in cgs units. The gilbert is a smaller unit than the amp-turn.

Note how the dimensions of mmf, which is independent of length for either ampere-turns or gilberts, differ from field intensity H, which is ampere-turns per meter in mks units or oersteds in cgs units. One gilbert per centimeter of mmf corresponds to one oersted of H.

There are no units for reluctance, but it can be considered as an mmf/ϕ ratio, just as resistance is an E/I ratio. Then $\mathcal{R}$ is ampere-turns per weber in the mks system, or gilberts per maxwell in the cgs system.

---

[6] William Gilbert (1540–1603), an English scientist who investigated the magnetism of the earth.

Example 9. For a coil having 50 turns with 2-amp I, how much is the mmf in (*a*) mks units and (*b*) cgs units?

Answer. (*a*) In mks units, mmf = NI amp-turns
$$\text{mmf} = 50 \times 2 = \textbf{100 amp-turns}$$
(*b*) In cgs units, mmf = 1.256 NI gilberts
$$\text{mmf} = 1.256 \times 100 = \textbf{125.6 gilberts}$$

This is an example of using the ampere-turns of the coil magnet to calculate the amount of mmf producing the magnetic field.

Example 10. If this coil is on an iron core with a length of 20 cm, or 0.2 m, how much is the field intensity H throughout the iron in (*a*) mks units and (*b*) cgs units?

Answer. (*a*) In mks units, $H = \dfrac{\text{amp-turn}}{\text{meter}}$

$$H = \frac{100}{0.2} = \textbf{500 amp-turns per m}$$

(*b*) In cgs units, $H = \dfrac{1.256\ NI}{\text{cm}} = \dfrac{\text{gilberts}}{\text{cm}} = \text{oersteds}$

$$H = \frac{1.256 \times 100}{20} = \frac{125.6}{20} = \textbf{6.28 oersteds}$$

This is an example of calculating the field intensity of the magnetic field from the mmf of the coil magnet.

The following examples are calculated in the cgs system, to show the relations between B, ϕ, mmf, and $\Re$.

Example 11. If the iron coil in the previous example with H of 6.28 oersteds has a permeability μ of 100 gauss per oersted, calculate the flux density B.

Answer. $\qquad B = \mu H = 100\,\dfrac{\text{gauss}}{\text{oersted}} \times 6.28\ \text{oersteds}$

$$B = \textbf{628 gauss}$$

Example 12. If the iron core in Fig. 11·16*a* has this flux density B of 628 gauss and its cross-sectional area A is 2 cm², calculate the flux ϕ in the core.

Answer. $\qquad B = 628\ \text{gauss} = 628\ \text{lines per cm}^2 = \phi/A$

or, $\qquad \phi = B \times A$

then, $\qquad \phi = 628\ \dfrac{\text{lines}}{\text{cm}^2} \times 2\ \text{cm}^2 = \textbf{1,256 lines or maxwells}$

Example 13. With an mmf of 125.6 gilberts for the coil in Fig. 11·16*a* and flux ϕ of 1,256 lines or maxwells, calculate the reluctance $\Re$ of the iron core.

Answer. $\quad \phi = \dfrac{\text{mmf}}{\Re} \quad$ or $\quad \Re = \dfrac{\text{mmf}}{\phi} = \dfrac{125.6\ \text{gilberts}}{1,256\ \text{maxwells}}$

$$\Re = \textbf{0.1 gilbert per maxwell}$$

Example 14. If the reluctance of the path with an air gap in Fig. 11·16*b* is 10 gilberts per maxwell, how much mmf is required for the same flux of 1,256 maxwells?

Answer. $$\phi = \frac{\text{mmf}}{\mathcal{R}} \quad \text{or} \quad \text{mmf} = \phi \times \mathcal{R}$$

$$\text{mmf} = 1{,}256 \text{ maxwells} \times 10 \frac{\text{gilberts}}{\text{maxwell}} = \textbf{12,560 gilberts}$$

Note that 100 times more mmf is necessary for the same flux because the reluctance is 100 times greater, compared with Example 13. This idea corresponds to the higher voltage needed to produce the same current in a higher resistance. Also, $\phi \times \mathcal{R}$ can be considered a reluctance drop in magnetic circuits, similar to an *IR* drop in electric circuits.

11·10   Magnetic shielding

The idea of preventing one component from affecting another through their common electric or magnetic field is called *shielding*. Examples are the metal cover on a vacuum tube, the braided copper-wire shield enclosing the inner conductor of a coaxial cable, or a shield of magnetic material enclosing a cathode-ray tube.

The problem in shielding is to prevent one component from inducing an effect in the shielded component. The shielding materials are always metals, but there is a difference in using good conductors with low resistance like copper and aluminum, or magnetic materials with low reluctance like soft iron or Mumetal. A good conductor is best for two shielding functions. One is to prevent induction of static electric charges. The other is to shield against the induction of a varying magnetic field. For static charges, the shield provides opposite induced charges, which prevent induction inside the shield. For a varying magnetic field, the shield has induced currents that oppose the inducing field. Then there is little net field strength to produce induction inside the shield.

The best shield for a steady magnetic field is a good magnetic material of low reluctance. A steady field is produced by a permanent magnet, a coil with steady direct current, or the earth's magnetic field. With a magnetic shield of high permeability or low reluctance, it concentrates the magnetic flux. Then there is little flux to induce poles in a component inside the shield. As its reluctance approaches zero, the shield becomes more perfect.

Table 11·2   Magnetic units and definitions

Term	Description	Symbol	cgs units
Flux	Total lines	$\phi = \dfrac{mmf}{\mathfrak{R}}$	1 maxwell = 1 line
Flux density	Lines per unit area	$B = \dfrac{\phi}{A}$	$1\ \text{gauss} = \dfrac{1\ \text{maxwell}}{\text{cm}^2}$
Magnetomotive force	Total force producing flux	$mmf = \phi \times \mathfrak{R}$	gilberts = 1.256 × amp turns
Field intensity, or magnetizing force	Force per unit length of flux path	H	$1\ \text{oersted} = \dfrac{1\ \text{gilbert}}{\text{cm}}$
Reluctance*	Opposition to flux	$\mathfrak{R} = \dfrac{mmf}{\phi}$	$\dfrac{\text{gilbert}}{\text{maxwell}}$
Permeability	Ability to concentrate flux	$\mu = \dfrac{B}{H}$	$\dfrac{\text{gauss}}{\text{oersted}}$

*The reciprocal of reluctance is permeance = $1/\mathfrak{R}$, corresponding to conductance.
† Multiply μ by these factors to calculate B from H in mks or English units.

SUMMARY

Table 11·2 summarizes the magnetic units and their definitions.

SELF-EXAMINATION (*Answers at back of book.*)

Here's a chance to see how well you have learned the material in this chapter. These exercises are for your self-testing only.

Answer true or false.
1. Iron and steel are ferromagnetic materials with high permeability.
2. Ferrites are magnetic but have high resistance.
3. Air, vacuum, wood, and paper have practically no effect on magnetic flux.
4. Aluminum is paramagnetic, while nickel is ferromagnetic.
5. Magnetic poles exist on opposite sides of an air gap.
6. A closed magnetic ring has no poles and no air gap.
7. A magnet can pick up a steel nail by magnetic induction.
8. Induced poles are always opposite from the original field poles.
9. Soft iron concentrates magnetic flux by means of induction.
10. Without current, an electromagnet has practically no magnetic field.
11. The total flux ϕ of 5,000 lines equals 5,000 maxwells, 5 kilolines, or 50 μweber.
12. This flux ϕ through a cross-sectional area of 5 cm² has a flux density B of 1,000 gauss.
13. The flux density B of 1,000 gauss equals 1,000 lines per cm².
14. A current of 4 amp through 25 turns provides an mmf of 100 amp-turns.
15. For an mmf of 100 amp-turns through 50 turns, 2-amp current is necessary.
16. An mmf of 100 amp-turns in mks units corresponds to 125.6 gilberts in cgs units.
17. In Ohm's law for magnetic circuits, reluctance $\mathfrak{R}$ is the opposition to flux ϕ.
18. An mmf of 125.6 gilberts across a flux path 10 cm long produces the field intensity H of 12.56 oersteds.

mks units	English units	Notes
1 weber = 10^8 lines	1 kiloline = 10^3 lines	Corresponds to current, 1 μweber = 10^2 lines
$\dfrac{\text{weber}}{\text{m}^2}$	$\dfrac{\text{kilolines}}{\text{in.}^2}$	$1\ m^2 = 10^4\ cm^2$ $1\ in.^2 = 6.45\ cm^2$
amp-turn	amp-turn	Corresponds to voltage, independent of length; 0.796 = 1/1.256
$\dfrac{\text{amp-turn}}{\text{m}}$	$\dfrac{\text{amp-turn}}{\text{in.}}$	Corresponds to voltage per unit length; 1 in. = 2.54 cm
$\dfrac{\text{amp-turn}}{\text{weber}}$	$\dfrac{\text{amp-turns}}{\text{kiloline}}$	Corresponds to resistance
$1.256 \times 10^{-6}\ \mu\dagger$	$3.2 \times 10^{-3}\ \mu\dagger$	μ of air or vacuum is 1

19. The field intensity H of 12.56 oersteds will produce the flux density B of 2,512 gauss in an iron core with μ of 200.
20. In Ohm's law for magnetic circuits, ampere-turn units correspond to volts.
21. Hysteresis losses are greater in soft iron than in air.
22. A magnetic material with high μ is best for a shield against a steady magnetic field.
23. The units for a *B-H* curve can be webers/m² plotted against amp-turns.
24. The *B-H* curve shows saturation of a magnetic material when *B* does not increase in proportion to *H*.
25. An electromagnet that produces 2 webers with 80,000 amp-turns has a reluctance of 40,000 amp-turns/weber.

ESSAY QUESTIONS

1. Name two ferromagnetic materials and three nonmagnetic materials.
2. Explain briefly the difference between a permanent magnet and an electromagnet.
3. Draw a horseshoe magnet, with its magnetic field. Label the magnetic poles, indicate the air gap, and show the direction of flux in the gap.
4. Define the following: permeability, hysteresis losses, saturation, induction, shielding.
5. In Ohm's law for magnetic circuits, what cgs units correspond to voltage, current, and resistance?
6. Give the symbol and cgs unit for each of the following: flux, flux density, field intensity, permeability, and mmf.
7. What mks units correspond to the following cgs units: maxwell, gauss, gilbert, oersted?
8. Draw a *B-H* curve with μ, *N*, *l*, and *E* the same as in Fig. 11·14 but the coil resistance is 5 ohms.
9. Explain briefly how to demagnetize a metal object that has become temporarily magnetized.
10. What would be the cgs unit for a reluctance drop in magnetic circuits, corresponding to an *IR* drop in electric circuits?

11. What is the advantage of a ferrite core for an electromagnet, compared with an iron core? What is a disadvantage?
12. Why can reluctance and permeability be considered opposite characteristics?

PROBLEMS (*Answers to selected problems at back of book.*)

1. A magnetic pole produces 5,000 field lines. How much is the flux ϕ in maxwells, kilolines, and microweber units?
2. If the area of the pole in Prob. 1 is 5 cm², calculate the flux density B in gauss and webers per square meter.
3. For a flux density B of 3,000 gauss at a pole with a cross-sectional area of 8 cm², how much is the total flux in maxwell units?
4. Referring to the *B-H* curve in Fig. 11·14, calculate the μ of the iron core, with a magnetizing force of 30 oersteds. Also at 60 oersteds.
5. A coil of 800 turns has 100-ma current. (*a*) Calculate the ampere-turns. (*b*) With 100 turns how much current is necessary for the same *NI*?
6. A coil of 1,000 turns with 100 ma current is 20 cm long with an iron core of the same length. (*a*) Calculate the mmf in gilberts. (*b*) Calculate the field intensity H in oersteds. (*c*) If the μ of the iron core is 200, calculate its flux density B in gauss. (*d*) If the coil has an air core, calculate B.
7. Referring to the hysteresis loop in Fig. 11·15 give the values in mks units at the following points: (*a*) residual induction B_R; (*b*) coercive force $-H_c$.
8. Prove that the flux density B of 1 weber per m² is equivalent to 10,000 gauss.
9. The flux density of a magnetic field in air is 24 gauss. An iron bar in the same field has a flux density of 7,200 gauss. How much is the permeability of the iron?
10. A battery E is connected across a coil of 100 turns and 20-ohm resistance, with an iron core 20 cm long. (*a*) Draw the circuit diagram. (*b*) How much E is needed for 252 gilberts of mmf? (*c*) Calculate the field intensity H in the iron core, in oersted units. (*d*) Calculate the gauss of flux density B in the iron core if its μ is 300. (*e*) Calculate the total flux ϕ, in maxwells, at each pole if its area is 8 cm². (*f*) How much is the reluctance of the iron core, in gilberts per maxwell?

Chapter 12 Electromagnetic induction

The link between electricity and magnetism was discovered in 1824 by Oersted, who found that current in a wire could move a magnetic compass needle. A few years later the opposite effect was discovered: a magnetic field in motion forces electrons to move, producing current. This important effect was studied by Faraday, Henry, and Lenz.[1] Electromagnetism, therefore, includes the magnetic effects of electrical current. Electrons in motion have an associated magnetic field; a moving magnetic field forces electrons to move, producing current. These electromagnetic effects have many practical applications that are the basis for motors and generators and all electronic circuits with inductance. The details of electromagnetism are analyzed in the following topics:

12·1   Magnetic field around an electrical current
12·2   Magnetic polarity of a coil
12·3   Motor action between two magnetic fields
12·4   Induced current
12·5   Lenz's law
12·6   Generating an induced voltage
12·7   Faraday's law of induced voltage

12·1   Magnetic field around an electrical current

In Fig. 12·1, the iron filings aligned in concentric rings around the conductor show the magnetic field of the current in the wire. The iron filings are dense next to the conductor, showing the field is strongest at this point. Furthermore, the field strength decreases inversely as the square of the

---

[1] Michael Faraday (1791–1867), eminent British physicist and pioneer in electromagnetism; Joseph Henry (1797–1878), American physicist; H. F. E. Lenz (1804–1865), Russian physicist.

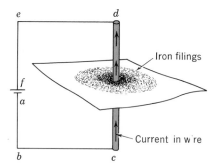

Fig. 12·1   Iron filings line up in magnetic field around conductor carrying current.

distance from the conductor. It is important to note the following two factors about the magnetic lines of force:

1. The magnetic lines are circular, as the field is symmetrical with respect to the wire in the center.
2. The magnetic field with circular lines of force is in a plane perpendicular to the current in the wire.

From points *c* to *d* in the wire, its circular magnetic field is in the horizontal plane because the wire is vertical. Also, the vertical conductor between points *ef* and *ab* has the associated magnetic field in the horizontal plane. Where the conductor is horizontal, as from *b* to *c* and *d* to *e*, the magnetic field is in a vertical plane.

These two requirements of a circular magnetic field in a perpendicular plane apply to any charge in motion. Whether electron flow or a motion of positive charges is considered, the associated magnetic field must be at right angles to the direction of current. In addition, the current need not be in a wire conductor. As an example, the beam of moving electrons in the vacuum of a cathode-ray tube has an associated magnetic field. In all cases, the magnetic field has circular lines of force in a plane perpendicular to the direction of motion of the electrical charge.

Clockwise and counterclockwise fields. With circular lines of force, the magnetic field would tend to move a north pole in a circular path. Therefore, the direction of the lines must be considered as either clockwise or counterclockwise. This idea is illustrated in Fig. 12·2, showing how a north pole would move in the circular field. The directions are tested with a magnetic compass needle. When the compass is in front of the wire, the north pole on the needle points up. On the opposite side, the compass points down. If the compass were placed at the top, its needle would point toward the back of the wire; below the wire, the compass would point forward. Combining all these directions, the result is the circular magnetic field shown, with counterclockwise lines of force. This direction has the magnetic lines upward at the front of the conductor and downward at the back.

Instead of testing every conductor with a magnetic compass, however,

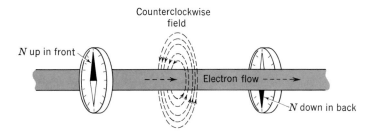

Fig. 12·2 Rule for determining counterclockwise
field around straight conductor. Reverse direction
of electron flow would provide clockwise field.

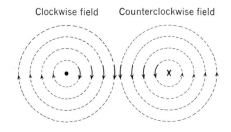

Fig. 12·3 Magnetic fields aiding between parallel
conductors with opposite directions of current.

we can use the following rule to determine the circular direction of the
magnetic field: *If you look along the wire in the direction of electron flow,
the magnetic field is counterclockwise.* In Fig. 12·2, the line of electron flow
is from left to right. Facing this way, you can assume the circular magnetic
flux in a perpendicular plane has lines of force in the counterclockwise
direction.

The opposite direction of current produces a reversed field. Then the
magnetic lines of force have clockwise rotation. If the charges were moving
from right to left in Fig. 12·2, the associated magnetic field would be in
the opposite direction, with clockwise lines of force.

Fields aiding or canceling. When the magnetic lines of two fields are in
the same direction, the lines of force aid each other, making the field
stronger. With magnetic lines in opposite directions, the fields cancel.

In Fig. 12·3 the fields are shown for two conductors with opposite directions of current. The dot in the middle of the field at the left indicates the
tip of an arrowhead to show current up from the paper. The cross symbolizes the back of an arrow to indicate current into the paper. Notice that
the magnetic lines are in the same direction between the conductors,
although one field is clockwise and the other counterclockwise. Therefore,
the fields aid here, making a stronger total field. On either side of the conductors, the two fields are opposite in direction and tend to cancel each
other. The net result, then, is to strengthen the field in the space between
the conductors.

12·2 Magnetic polarity of a coil

Bending a straight conductor around in the form of a loop, as shown in
Fig. 12·4, has two effects. First, the magnetic field lines are more dense

Fig. 12·4   *Magnetic poles of a current loop.*

inside the loop. The total number of lines is the same as for the straight conductor, but in the loop the lines are concentrated in a smaller space. Inside the loop, all the lines are aiding in the same direction. This makes the loop field effectively the same as a bar magnet with opposite poles at opposite faces of the loop.

Solenoid as a bar magnet. A coil of wire conductor with more than one turn is generally called a *solenoid.* An ideal solenoid, however, has a length much greater than its diameter. Like a single loop, the solenoid concentrates the magnetic field inside the coil and provides opposite magnetic poles at the ends. These effects are multiplied, however, by the number of turns as the magnetic field lines aid each other in the same direction inside the coil.

Outside the coil, the field corresponds to a bar magnet with north and

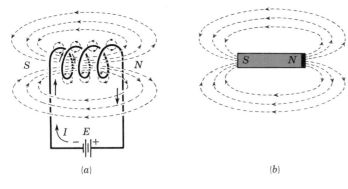

(a)   (b)

Fig. 12·5   *Magnetic poles of a solenoid. (a) Coil winding. (b) Equivalent bar magnet.*

Fig. 12·6   *Left-hand rule for determining north pole of a coil.*

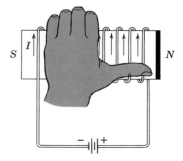

south poles at opposite ends, as illustrated in Fig. 12·5. To determine the magnetic polarity, use the *left-hand rule* illustrated in Fig. 12·6. The left hand is used because the current is electron flow. This rule is stated as follows: *If the coil is grasped with the fingers of the left hand curled in the direction of electron flow around the coil, the thumb points to the north pole of the coil.*

The magnetic polarity depends on two factors: the direction of electron flow and the direction of winding. The direction of electron flow is determined by the connections to the voltage source producing the current, since the electron current is from the negative side of the voltage source, through the coil, and back to the positive terminal. The direction of winding can be over and under, starting from one end of the coil, or under and over with respect to the same starting point. Reversing either the direction of winding or the direction of current reverses the magnetic poles of the solenoid. With both reversed the polarity is the same.

The solenoid acts like a bar magnet whether it has an iron core or not. Adding an iron core increases the flux density inside the coil. In addition, the field strength then is uniform for the entire length of the core. The polarity is the same, however, for air-core or iron-core coils.

12·3 Motor action between two magnetic fields

The physical motion resulting from the forces of magnetic fields is called *motor action*. One example is the simple attraction or repulsion between bar magnets. We know that like poles repel and unlike poles attract. It can also be considered that fields in the same direction repel and opposite fields attract. Consider the repulsion between two north poles illustrated in Fig. 12·7. Note that similar poles have fields in the same direction. Therefore, the similar fields of the two like poles repel each other.

A more fundamental reason for motor action, however, is the fact that the force in a magnetic field tends to produce motion from a stronger field toward a weaker field. In Fig. 12·7, note that the field intensity is greatest

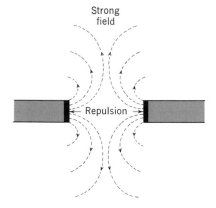

Fig. 12·7 *Repulsion between north poles of two bar magnets, showing motion from stronger field to weaker field.*

in the space between the two north poles, where the field lines reinforce in the same direction. Farther away the field intensity is less. As a result there is a difference in field strength, providing a net force that tends to produce motion. The direction of motion is always toward the weaker field.

To remember the directions, we can consider that the stronger field moves to the weaker field, tending to equalize the field intensity. Otherwise, the motion would make the strong field stronger and the weak field weaker, which must be impossible, because then the magnetic field would multiply its own strength without any work being added.

Force on a straight conductor in a magnetic field. Current in a conductor has its associated magnetic field. When this conductor is placed in another magnetic field from a separate source, the two fields can react to produce motor action. The conductor must be perpendicular to the magnetic field, however, as illustrated in Fig. 12·8. This way, the perpendicular magnetic field of the current then is in the same plane as the external magnetic field. Unless the two fields are in the same plane, they cannot affect each other. In the same plane, however, lines of force in the same direction reinforce to make a stronger field, while lines in opposite direction cancel and result in a weaker field.

To summarize these directions:

1. With the conductor at 90° or perpendicular to the external field, the reaction between the two magnetic fields is maximum.
2. With the conductor at 0° or parallel to the external field, there is no effect between them.
3. When the conductor is at an angle between 0 and 90°, only the perpendicular component is effective.

In Fig. 12·8, electrons flow in the wire conductor in the plane of the paper, from bottom to top of the page. This flow provides the counterclockwise field H_I around the wire, in a perpendicular plane cutting through the paper. The external field H_M has lines of force from left to right in the plane of the paper. Then lines of force in the two fields are parallel above and below the wire.

Below the conductor, its field lines are left to right in the same direction as the external field. Therefore, these lines reinforce to produce a stronger field. Above the conductor the lines of the two fields are in opposite directions, causing a weaker field. As a result, the net force of the stronger field makes the conductor move upward out of the page, toward the weaker field.

If electrons flow in the reverse direction in the conductor, or if the external field is reversed, the motor action will be in the opposite direction. Reversing both the field and the current results in the same direction of motion.

Rotation of a current loop in a magnetic field. In Fig. 12·9, current in the rectangular loop, as a simple coil, provides a magnetic field that reacts with the external field H_M. The result is a net force that makes the loop

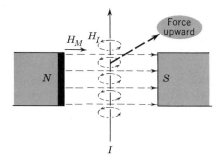

Fig. 12·8 *Motor action on current in a straight conductor in an external magnetic field. The net force of the resultant magnetic field here moves the conductor upward to the weaker field.*

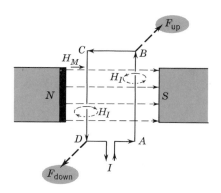

Fig. 12·9 *Motor action causing loop to rotate in magnetic field. AB is forced upward while CD moves downward, resulting in counterclockwise rotation.*

rotate. The rotation is a result of the upward force on the straight conductor AB of the loop, while conductor CD is forced to move downward by the motor action. Conductors BC and DA form a continuous loop for current flow, but they do not provide any motor action, because their magnetic fields are in a plane perpendicular to H_M.

Consider conductor AB: below the wire its counterclockwise field is in the same direction as H_M and they add. Above the wire AB, however, the fields cancel. The stronger field is below AB, therefore, and the net force tends to move this conductor AB upward to the weaker field. This case corresponds to Fig. 12·8. Now consider conductor CD: it has a clockwise field because its current is in the opposite direction. Here, the current's field aids H_M above the wire, and they cancel below. The net force tends to move conductor CD downward, therefore. As AB is forced upward and CD downward, the loop rotates.

The rotation of the loop here is counterclockwise around its long axis. This effect of a force in producing rotation is called *torque*. With more turns in the coil, the torque on the loop is multiplied by the number of turns. The rectangular loop is better than a circular or square shape because the rectangle allows more conductor length to be effective in producing motor action. The amount of torque also increases with the current, field strength H_M, and the area of the loop.

There are many useful applications of motor action producing rotational torque. One common example is the torque on a coil in an external magnetic field, which is the basis of electric motors. The moving-coil meter described in Sec. 7·1 is a similar application; since the torque can be made proportional to current, the amount of rotation indicates how much current flows through the coil.

12·4   *Induced current*

Just as electrons in motion provide an associated magnetic field, when magnetic flux moves, the motion of magnetic lines cutting across a conductor forces free electrons in the conductor to move, producing current. The process is called *induction* because there is no physical connection between the magnet and the conductor. The induced current is a result of generator action as the mechanical work put into moving the magnetic field is converted into electrical energy when current flows in the conductor.

Referring to Fig. 12·10, let the conductor *AB* be placed at right angles to the flux in the air gap of the horseshoe magnet. Then, when the magnet is moved up or down, its flux cuts across the conductor. The action of magnetic flux cutting across the conductor generates current. The fact that current flows is indicated by the microammeter. When the magnet is moved downward, current flows in the direction shown. If the magnet is moved upward, current will flow in the opposite direction. Without motion, there is no current.

Direction of motion. The motion is necessary in order to have the flux lines of the magnetic field cut across the conductor. This cutting can be accomplished by motion of either the field or the conductor. When the conductor is moved upward or downward, it cuts across the flux. The generator action is the same as moving the field, except that the relative motion is opposite. Moving the conductor upward, for instance, corresponds to moving the magnet downward.

Conductor perpendicular to external flux. In order to have electromagnetic induction, the conductor and the magnetic lines of flux must be perpendicular to each other. Then the motion makes the flux cut through the cross-sectional area of the conductor. As shown in Fig. 12·10, the conductor is at right angles to the lines of force in the field *H*. The reason the conductor must be perpendicular is to make its induced current have an associated magnetic field in the same plane as the external flux. If the field of the induced current does not react with the external field, there can be no induced current.

How induced current is generated. The induced current can be considered the result of motor action between the external field *H* and the

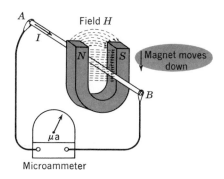

Fig. 12·10   *Induced current produced by magnetic flux cutting across a conductor.*

magnetic field of free electrons in every cross-sectional area of the wire. Without an external field, the free electrons move at random without any specific direction and they have no net magnetic field. When the conductor is in the magnetic field H, there still is no induction without relative motion, since the magnetic fields for the free electrons are not disturbed. When the field or conductor moves, however, there must be a reaction opposing the motion. The reaction is a flow of free electrons resulting from motor action on the electrons.

Referring to Fig. 12·10, for example, the induced current must flow in the direction shown because the field is moved downward, pulling the magnet away from the conductor. The induced current of electrons then has a clockwise field with lines of force aiding H above the conductor and canceling H below. With motor action between the two magnetic fields tending to move the conductor toward the weaker field, the conductor will be forced downward, staying with the magnet to oppose the work of pulling the magnet away from the conductor.

The effect of electromagnetic induction is increased where a coil is used for the conductor. Then the turns concentrate more conductor length in a smaller area. As illustrated in Fig. 12·11, moving the magnet into the coil enables the flux to cut across many turns of conductors.

12·5 Lenz's law

This basic principle is used to determine the direction of an induced voltage or current. Based on the principle of conservation of energy, Lenz's law simply states that the direction of the induced current must be such that its own magnetic field will oppose the action that produced the induced current. In Fig. 12·11, for example, the induced current has the direction that produces a north pole at the left to oppose the motion by repulsion of the north pole being moved in. This is why it takes some work to push the permanent magnet into the coil. The work expended in moving the permanent magnet is the source of energy for the current induced in the coil.

Using Lenz's law, we can start with the fact that the left end of the coil in Fig. 12·11 must be a north pole to oppose the motion. Then the direc-

Fig. 12·11 *Induced current produced by flux cutting across turns of wire in coil.*

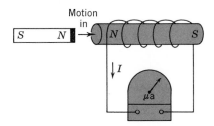

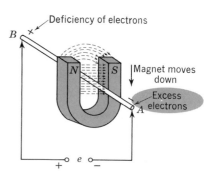

Fig. 12·12   Voltage induced across open ends of conductor cut by magnetic flux.

tion of the induced current is determined by the left-hand rule for electron flow. If the fingers coil around the direction of electron flow shown, under and over the winding, the thumb will point to the left for the north pole.

For the opposite case, suppose that the north pole of the permanent magnet in Fig. 12·11 is moved away from the coil. Then the induced pole at the left end of the coil must be a south pole, by Lenz's law. The induced south pole will attract the north pole to oppose the motion of the magnet being moved away. For a south pole at the left end of the coil, then, the electron flow will be reversed from the direction shown in Fig. 12·11.

12·6   Generating an induced voltage

Consider the case of magnetic flux cutting a conductor that is not in a closed circuit, as shown in Fig. 12·12. The motion of flux across the conductor forces free electrons to move, but with an open circuit, the displaced electrons produce opposite electric charges at the two open ends. For the directions shown, free electrons in the conductor are forced to move to point *A*. Since the end is open, electrons accumulate here. Point *A* then develops a negative potential. At the same time, point *B* loses electrons and becomes charged positive. The result is a potential difference across the two ends, provided by the separation of electric charges in the conductor.

The potential difference is an electromotive force, generated by the work of cutting across the flux. As a conductor cannot store electric charge, however, the emf is present only while the motion of flux cutting across the conductor is producing the induced voltage.

Induced voltage across a coil. With a coil, as in Fig. 12·13a, the induced emf is increased by the number of turns. Each turn cut by flux adds to the induced voltage, since they all force free electrons to accumulate at the negative end of the coil, with a deficiency of electrons at the positive end. The polarity of the induced voltage follows from the direction of induced current. The end of the conductor to which the electrons go and where they accumulate is the negative side of the induced voltage. The opposite end with a deficiency of electrons is the positive side. The total emf across the coil is the sum of the induced voltages, since all the turns are in series.

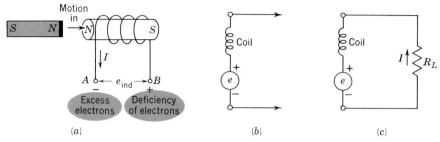

Fig. 12·13 *Voltage induced across coil cut by magnetic flux. (a) Motion of flux generating voltage across coil. (b) Induced voltage acts in series with coil. (c) Induced voltage is a source that can produce current in external load circuit connected across coil.*

Furthermore, the total induced voltage acts in series with the coil, as illustrated by the equivalent circuit in Fig. 12·13, showing the induced voltage as a separate generator. This generator represents a voltage source with a potential difference resulting from the separation of charges produced by electromagnetic induction. The voltage source e then can produce current in an external load circuit connected across the negative and positive terminals, as shown in Fig. 12·13c. The induced voltage is in series with the coil because current produced by the generated emf must flow through all the turns. An induced voltage of 10 volts, for example, with R_L equal to 5 ohms, results in a current of 2 amp, which flows through the coil, the equivalent generator e, and the load resistance R_L.

The direction of current in Fig. 12·13c shows electron flow around the circuit. Outside the source e, the electrons move from its negative terminal, through R_L, and back to the positive terminal of e because of its potential difference. Inside the generator, however, the electron flow is from the + terminal to the − terminal. The work put into inducing the voltage is separating charges to produce the potential difference that allows electrons to move around the external circuit. This direction of electron flow results from the fact that the left end of the coil in a must be a north pole by Lenz's law, to oppose the north pole being moved in.

Notice how motors and generators are similar in using the motion of a magnetic field, but with opposite applications. In a motor, current is supplied for an associated magnetic field to react with the external flux to produce motion of the conductor. In a generator, motion must be supplied so that the flux and conductor can cut across each other to induce voltage across the ends of the conductor.

12·7   Faraday's law of induced voltage

The voltage induced by magnetic flux cutting the turns of a coil depends upon the number of turns and how fast the flux moves across the conductor. Either the flux or the conductor can move. Specifically, the amount of induced voltage is determined by the following three factors:

1. *Amount of flux.* The more magnetic lines of force that cut across the conductor, the higher is the amount of induced voltage.

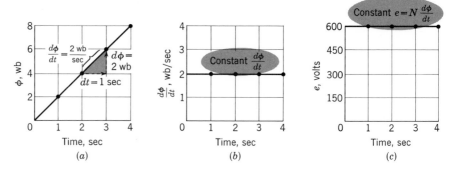

Fig. 12·14   Graphs of induced voltage e produced by flux changes dφ/dt in a coil with N of 300 turns. (a) Linear increase of flux φ. (b) Constant rate of change dφ/dt at 2 webers per sec. (c) Constant induced voltage e of 600 volts.

2. *Number of turns.* The more turns in a coil, the higher is the induced voltage, as the total e is the sum of all the individual voltages induced in each turn in series.

3. *Time rate of cutting.* The faster the flux cuts a conductor, the higher is the induced voltage. Then more lines of force cut the conductor within a specific period of time. These factors are of fundamental importance in many applications because any conductor with current will have voltage induced in it by a change in current and its associated magnetic flux.

The amount of induced voltage can be calculated by Faraday's law:

$$e \text{ (volts)} = N \frac{d\phi \text{ (webers)}}{dt \text{ (sec)}} \qquad (12 \cdot 1)$$

where e is the induced voltage, N the number of turns, and dφ/dt specifies how fast the flux φ cuts across the conductor. With dφ/dt in webers per second, the induced voltage e is in volt units. As an example, if the magnetic flux cuts across 300 turns at the rate of 2 webers per sec, the induced voltage equals 300 × 2 or 600 volts. It is assumed that all the flux links all the turns, which is true with an iron core.

Time rate of change. The symbol d in dφ and dt is an abbreviation for delta (Δ), which means a *change*.[2] The dφ means a change in the flux φ, while dt means a change in time. As an example, if the flux φ is 4 webers at one time but then changes to 6 webers, the change in flux is 2 webers for dφ. The same idea applies to a decrease as well as an increase. If the flux changed from 6 to 4 webers, dφ would still be 2 webers. However, an increase is usually considered a change in the positive direction, with an upward slope, while a decrease has a negative slope downward.

Similarly, dt means a change in time. If we consider the flux at a time

[2] In calculus, dt represents only an infinitesimally small change, but we are using this symbol for rate of change in general.

Table 12·1   Induced-voltage calculations for Fig. 12·14

ϕ, webers	$d\phi$, webers	t, sec	dt, sec	$d\phi/dt$, webers per sec	N, turns	$e = N\, d\phi/dt$, volts
2	2	1	1	2	300	600
4	2	2	1	2	300	600
6	2	3	1	2	300	600
8	2	4	1	2	300	600

2 sec after the start, and at a later time 3 sec after the start, the change in time is $3 - 2$ or 1 sec for dt. Time always increases in the positive direction. Combining the two factors of $d\phi$ and dt, we can say that for magnetic flux increasing by 2 webers per sec, $d\phi/dt$ equals $\frac{2}{1}$ or 2 webers per sec, which states the time rate of change of the magnetic flux. For 300 turns cut by the changing flux of 2 webers per sec, then, the induced voltage is 300×2 or 600 volts.

Analysis of induced voltage as $N\, d\phi/dt$. This fundamental concept of voltage induced by a change in flux is illustrated by the graphs in Fig. 12·14, for the values listed in Table 12·1. The linear rise in *a* shows values of flux ϕ increasing at a uniform rate. In this case, the curve goes up 2 webers for every 1-sec interval of time. The slope of this curve then, equal to $d\phi/dt$, is 2 webers per sec. Note that, although ϕ increases, the rate of change is constant because the linear rise has a constant slope.

For induced voltage, only the $d\phi/dt$ factor is important, not the actual value of flux. To emphasize this basic concept, the graph in *b* shows the $d\phi/dt$ values alone. This graph is just a straight horizontal line for the constant value of 2 webers per sec. The induced-voltage graph in *c* is also a straight horizontal line. Since $e = N\, d\phi/dt$, the graph of *e* values is just the $d\phi/dt$ values multiplied by the number of turns. The result is a constant induced voltage at 600 volts with 300 turns cut by flux changing at the constant rate of 2 webers per sec.

The example illustrated here can be different in several ways without changing the basic fact that the induced voltage *e* is equal to $N\, d\phi/dt$. First, the number of turns or the $d\phi/dt$ values can be greater than the values assumed here, or less. More turns will provide more induced voltage, while fewer turns mean less voltage. Similarly, a higher value for $d\phi/dt$ results in more induced voltage. Note that two factors are included in $d\phi/dt$. Its value can be increased by a higher value of $d\phi$, or a smaller value of dt. As an example, the value of 2 webers per sec for $d\phi/dt$ can be doubled by either increasing $d\phi$ to 4 webers or reducing dt to ½ sec. Then $d\phi/dt$ is $\frac{4}{1}$ or 2/0.5, which equals 4 webers per sec in either case. The same flux changing within a shorter time means a faster rate of flux cutting for a higher value of $d\phi/dt$ and more induced voltage.

For the opposite case, a smaller value of $d\phi/dt$, with less flux or a slower rate of change, results in a smaller value of induced voltage. When $d\phi/dt$

decreases, the induced voltage has opposite polarity, compared with an increase.

Finally, it should be noted that the $d\phi/dt$ graph in Fig. 12·14b has the constant value of 2 webers per sec because the flux is increasing at a linear rate. However, the flux need not have a uniform rate of change. Then the $d\phi/dt$ values will not be constant. In any case, though, the values of $d\phi/dt$ at all instants of time will determine the instantaneous values of e equal to $N\,d\phi/dt$.

Polarity of the induced voltage. The polarity is determined by Lenz's law. The induced voltage e has the polarity that opposes the change causing the induction. Sometimes this fact is indicated by using a negative sign for e in Eq. (12·1). However, the absolute polarity of e depends on whether the flux is increasing or decreasing, the method of winding, and which end of the coil is the reference. When all these factors are considered, e has the polarity such that the current it produces and the associated magnetic field will oppose the change in flux producing the induced voltage. If the external flux increases, the magnetic field of the induced current will be in the opposite direction. If the external field decreases, the magnetic field of the induced current will be in the same direction as the external field to oppose the change by sustaining the flux.

SUMMARY

1. Current in a straight conductor has an associated magnetic field with circular lines of force in a plane perpendicular to the conductor. The direction of the circular field is counterclockwise when you look along the conductor in the direction of electron flow. The opposite direction of current has a reverse field, in the clockwise direction.
2. With two fields in the same plane, produced by either current or a permanent magnet, lines of force in the same direction aid each other to provide a stronger field, while lines of force in opposite directions cancel and result in a weaker field.
3. A solenoid is a long, narrow coil of wire which concentrates the conductor and its associated magnetic field. Because the fields for all turns aid inside the coil and cancel outside, a solenoid has a resultant electromagnetic field like a bar magnet with north and south poles at opposite ends. The left-hand rule for polarity says that when your fingers curl around the turns in the direction of electron flow, the thumb points to the north pole.
4. Motor action is the motion that results from the net force of two fields that can aid or cancel each other. The direction of the resultant force is always from the stronger field to the weaker field.
5. Generator action refers to induced voltage. For N turns, $e = N\,d\phi/dt$, with $d\phi/dt$ in webers per second. There must be a change in the flux to produce induced voltage.
6. Lenz's law states that the polarity of the induced voltage will oppose the change in magnetic flux causing the induction.

SELF-EXAMINATION (*Answers at back of book.*)

Here's a chance to see how well you have learned the material in this chapter. These exercises are for your self-testing only.
   Answer true or false.
   1. A vertical wire with electron flow downward through this page has an associated magnetic field counterclockwise in the plane of the paper.
   2. Lines of force of two magnetic fields in the same direction aid each other to produce a stronger resultant field.

3. Motor action always tends to produce motion toward the weaker field.
4. In Fig. 12·6, if the battery connections are reversed the magnetic poles of the coil will be reversed.
5. A solenoid is a long, narrow coil that acts as a bar magnet only when current flows.
6. A torque is a force tending to cause rotation.
7. In Fig. 12·8, if the poles of the external field are reversed, the motor action will be downward.
8. In Fig. 12·10, if the conductor is moved down, instead of the magnet, the induced current flows in the opposite direction.
9. In Fig. 12·9, if the direction of current in the loop is reversed, the loop will rotate in the opposite direction.
10. Faraday's law determines the amount of induced voltage.
11. Lenz's law determines the polarity of an induced voltage.
12. Induced voltage increases with a faster rate of flux cutting.
13. An induced voltage is effectively in series with the turns of the coil in which the voltage is produced.
14. A decrease in flux will induce a voltage of opposite polarity from an increase in flux, with the same direction of field lines in both cases.
15. The flux of 1,000 lines increasing to 1,001 lines produces a flux change $d\phi/dt$ of 1 line per sec.
16. The flux of 2 lines increasing to 3 lines in 1 μsec corresponds to a flux change $d\phi/dt$ of 1,000,000 lines per sec.
17. In question 16, $d\phi/dt$ equals 0.01 weber per sec.
18. The induced voltage will be much greater for the example in question 16, compared with question 15, with the same number of turns in both cases.
19. The more turns in a coil, the higher is its induced voltage.
20. In Fig. 12·14, the flux ϕ is increasing but its rate of change $d\phi/dt$ is constant.

ESSAY QUESTIONS

1. Draw a diagram showing two conductors connecting a battery to a load resistance through a closed switch. (*a*) Show the magnetic field of the current in the negative side of the line and in the positive side. (*b*) Where do the two fields aid? Where do they oppose?
2. State the rule for determining the magnetic polarity of a solenoid. (*a*) How can the polarity be reversed? (*b*) Why are there no magnetic poles when the current through the coil is zero?
3. Why does the motor action between two magnetic fields result in motion toward the weaker field?
4. Why does current in a conductor perpendicular to this page have a magnetic field in the plane of the paper?
5. Why must the conductor and external field be perpendicular to each other in order to have either motor action or to generate induced voltage?
6. Explain briefly how either motor action or generator action can be obtained with the same conductor in a magnetic field.
7. Assume that a conductor being cut by the flux of an expanding magnetic field has 10 volts induced with the top end positive. Now analyze the effect of the following changes: (*a*) The magnetic flux continues to expand but at a slower rate. How does this affect the amount of induced voltage and its polarity? (*b*) The magnetic flux is constant, neither increasing nor decreasing. How much is the induced voltage? (*c*) The magnetic flux contracts, cutting across the conductor with the opposite direction of motion. How does this affect the polarity of the induced voltage?
8. Redraw the graph in Fig. 12·14c for the case of 500 turns, with all other factors the same.
9. Redraw the circuit with the coil and battery in Fig. 12·6, showing two different ways to reverse the magnetic polarity.
10. Referring to Fig. 12·14, suppose that the flux decreases from 8 webers to zero at the same rate as the increase. Tabulate all the values as in Table 12·1 and draw the three graphs corresponding to those in Fig. 12·14.

PROBLEMS (*Answers to selected problems at back of book.*)

1. A magnetic flux of 900 maxwells cuts across a coil of 1,000 turns in 1 μsec. How much is the voltage induced in the coil?
2. Refer to Fig. 12·12. (*a*) Show the induced voltage here connected to a load resistance R_L of 100 ohms. (*b*) If the induced voltage is 100 volts, how much current flows in R_L? (*c*) Give one way to reverse the polarity of the induced voltage. (*d*) Why will this method reverse the direction of current through R_L?
3. Calculate the rate of flux change $d\phi/dt$ for the following: (*a*) 6 webers increasing to 8 webers in 1 sec; (*b*) 8 webers decreasing to 6 webers in 1 sec; (*c*) 5,000 maxwells increasing to 6,000 maxwells in 1 sec; (*d*) 5,000 maxwells increasing to 6,000 maxwells in 5 μsec; (*e*) 5,000 maxwells increasing to 5,100 maxwells in 10 sec.
4. Calculate the induced voltage produced in 400 turns by each of the flux changes in Prob. 3.
5. Draw a circuit with a 20-volt battery connected to a 100-ohm coil of 400 turns with an iron core 20 cm long. Using cgs magnetic units, calculate (*a*) I; (*b*) NI; (*c*) mmf; (*d*) H in core; (*e*) flux density B in core with μ of 500; (*f*) flux ϕ at each pole with area of 6 cm²; (*g*) show direction of winding of coil and its magnetic polarity.
6. For the coil in Prob. 5: (*a*) If the iron core is removed, how much will the flux be in the air-core coil? (*b*) How much induced voltage would be produced by this change in flux while the core is being moved out in 1 sec? (*c*) How much is the induced voltage after the core is removed?

Chapter 13 *Alternating voltage and current*

This unit explains the characteristics of alternating voltage and current, such as the 60-cps a-c power line (Fig. 13·1). Also, audio and radio signals are examples of a-c voltage. Actually, there are many more applications for a-c circuits than for d-c circuits. We can consider the rules for d-c circuits as an introduction to the analysis of a-c circuits. All the d-c principles still apply, but the new factor to consider with an a-c source is the fact that the voltage alternately reverses its polarity, producing current that reverses in direction. Most important, the voltage and current are always changing, instead of remaining at a steady value. This characteristic of varying values is the reason why a-c circuits have so many useful applications. For instance, a transformer can operate only with alternating current, as its varying flux can produce induced voltage. The features of alternating voltage and current are explained in the following topics:

13·1 Alternating-voltage generator
13·2 The sine wave
13·3 Alternating current
13·4 Voltage and current values for a sine wave
13·5 Frequency
13·6 Period
13·7 Wavelength
13·8 Phase angle
13·9 The time factor in frequency and phase
13·10 A-c circuits with resistance
13·11 The 60-cps a-c power line
13·12 Motors and generators
13·13 Nonsinusoidal a-c waveforms

Fig. 13·1 Oscilloscope photograph of
60-cps alternating voltage. Four cycles
shown.

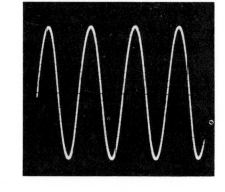

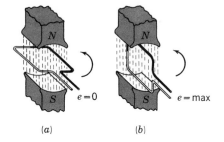

e = 0   e = max

(a)   (b)

Fig. 13·2 Loop rotating in magnetic field to produce
alternating induced voltage e. (a) Loop conductors moving
parallel to field resulting in zero voltage. (b) Loop connectors cutting across field resulting in maximum induced
voltage.

13·1 Alternating-voltage generator

We can define an a-c voltage as one that continuously varies in magnitude and periodically reverses in polarity. Figure 13·2 illustrates how
such a voltage waveform is produced by a rotary generator, as the conductor loop rotates through the magnetic field to generate the induced
voltage across its open terminals. The magnetic flux is vertical, with lines
of force down in the plane of the paper.

In *a* the loop is shown in its horizontal starting position in a plane perpendicular to the paper. When the loop rotates counterclockwise, the two
longer conductors move around a circle. Note that in the flat position
shown, the two long conductors of the loop move vertically up or down
through the paper but parallel to the vertical flux lines. In this position,
motion of the loop does not induce a voltage, because the conductors are
not cutting across the flux.

When the loop rotates through the upright position in *b*, however, the
conductors cut across the flux, producing maximum induced voltage. The
shorter connecting wires in the loop do not have any appreciable voltage
induced in them.

Each of the longer conductors has opposite polarity of induced voltage
because the one at the top is moving to the left while the bottom conductor
is moving to the right. The amount of voltage varies from zero to maximum as the loop moves from a flat position to upright, where it can cut
across the flux. Also the polarity at the terminals of the loop reverses as
the motion of each conductor reverses during each half-revolution.

With one revolution of the loop in a complete circle back to the starting
position, therefore, the induced voltage provides a potential difference *e*

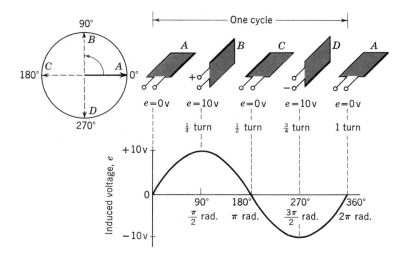

Fig. 13·3   One cycle of sine-wave alternating voltage generated by the loop. External field not shown is from top to bottom of the page as in Fig. 13·2.

across the loop, varying in the same way as the wave of voltage shown in Fig. 13·1. If the loop rotates at the speed of 60 revolutions per second, the a-c voltage will have the frequency of 60 cps.

The cycle. One complete revolution of the loop around the circle is a *cycle.* In Fig. 13·3, the generator loop is shown in its position at each quarter-turn during one complete cycle. The corresponding wave of induced voltage also goes through one cycle. Although not shown, the magnetic field is from top to bottom of the page as in Fig. 13·2.

At position *A* in Fig. 13·3, the loop is flat and moves parallel to the magnetic field, so that the induced voltage is zero. Counterclockwise rotation of the loop moves the dark conductor to the top at position *B*, where it cuts across the field to produce maximum induced voltage. The polarity of the induced voltage here makes the open end of the dark conductor positive. This conductor at the top is cutting across the flux from right to left. At the same time, the opposite conductor below is moving from left to right, causing its induced voltage to have opposite polarity. Therefore, maximum induced voltage is produced at this time across the two open ends of the loop. Now the top conductor is positive with respect to the bottom conductor.

In the graph of induced voltage values below the loop in Fig. 13·3, the polarity of the dark conductor is shown with respect to the other conductor. Positive voltage is shown above the zero axis in the graph. As the dark conductor rotates from its starting position parallel to the flux toward the top position, where it cuts maximum flux, more and more induced voltage is produced, with positive polarity.

When the loop rotates through the next quarter-turn, it returns to the flat position shown in *C*, where it cannot cut across flux. Therefore, the graph of induced voltage values decreases from its maximum value to zero at the half-turn, just as it is zero at the start. The half-cycle of revolution is called an *alternation.*

The next quarter-turn of the loop moves it to the position shown at *D* in Fig. 13·3, where the loop cuts across the flux again for maximum induced voltage. Note, however, that here the dark conductor is moving left to right at the bottom of the loop. This motion is reversed from the direction it had when it was at the top moving right to left. Because of the reversed direction of motion during the second half-revolution, the induced voltage has opposite polarity, with the dark conductor negative. This polarity is shown in the graph as negative voltage below the zero axis. The maximum value of induced voltage at the three-quarter turn is the same as at the first quarter-turn but with opposite polarity.

When the loop completes the last quarter-turn in the cycle, the induced voltage returns to zero as the loop returns to its flat position at *A*, the same as at the start. This cycle of values of induced voltage is repeated as the loop continues to rotate, with one complete cycle of voltage values, as shown, for each circle of revolution.

Note that zero at the start and zero after the half-turn of an alternation are not the same. At the start, the voltage is zero because the loop is flat, but the dark conductor is moving upward in the direction that produces positive voltage. After one half-cycle, the voltage is zero with the loop flat, but the dark conductor is moving downward in the direction that produces negative voltage. After one complete cycle, the loop and its corresponding waveform of induced voltage are the same as at the start. *A cycle can be defined, therefore, as including the variations between two points having the same value and varying in the same direction.*

Angular measure. Because the cycle of voltage in Fig. 13·3 corresponds to rotation of the loop around a circle, it is convenient to consider parts of the cycle in angles. The complete circle includes 360°. One half-cycle, or one alternation, is 180° of revolution. A quarter-turn is 90°. The circle next to the loop positions in Fig. 13·3 illustrates the angular rotation

Fig. 13·4   One radian is the angle equal to 57.3°. The complete circle includes 2π rad.

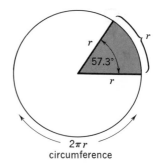

$2\pi r$
circumference

Table 13·1   Values in a sine wave

Angle	Sine	Loop voltage
0°	0	Zero
30°	0.500	50% of maximum
45°	0.707	70.7% of maximum
60°	0.866	86.6% of maximum
90°	1.000	Positive maximum value
180°	0	Zero
270°	−1.000	Negative maximum value
360°	0	Zero

of the dark conductor as it rotates counterclockwise from 0° to 90° to 180° for one half-cycle and then to 270°; returning to 360° to complete the cycle. Therefore, one cycle corresponds to 360°.

Radian measure. In angular measure it is convenient to use a specific unit angle called the *radian* (abbreviated rad), which is an angle equal to 57.3°. Its convenience is due to the fact that a radian is the angular part of the circle that includes an arc equal to the radius r of the circle, as shown in Fig. 13·4. The circumference around the circle equals $2\pi r$. A circle includes 2π rad, then, as each radian angle includes one length r of the circumference. Therefore, one cycle equals 2π rad.

As shown in the graph in Fig. 13·3, divisions of the cycle can be indicated by angles in either degrees or radians. Zero degrees is also zero rad, 360° is 2π rad, 180° is π rad, 90° is $\pi/2$ rad, and 270° is π rad plus $\pi/2$ rad, which equals $3\pi/2$ rad. The constant 2π in circular measure is numerically equal to 6.28. This is double the value of 3.14 for π, which is the ratio of the circumference to the diameter for any circle.

13·2   The sine wave

The voltage waveform in Figs. 13·1 and 13·3 is called a *sine wave, sinusoidal wave,* or *sinusoid* because the amount of induced voltage is proportional to the sine of the angle of rotation in the circular motion producing the voltage. The sine is a trigonometric function[1] of an angle equal to the ratio of the opposite side to the hypotenuse. This numerical ratio increases from zero for 0° to a maximum value of 1 for 90° as the side opposite the angle becomes larger.

The voltage waveform produced by circular motion of the loop is a sine wave because the induced voltage increases to maximum at 90° when the loop is vertical in the same way that the sine of the angle of rotation increases to a maximum for 90°. The induced voltage and sine of the angle correspond for the full 360° of the cycle. Table 13·1 lists the numerical values of the sine for several important angles, to illustrate the specific characteristics of a sine wave.

[1] See Appendix E, Mathematics, for more details of trigonometry.

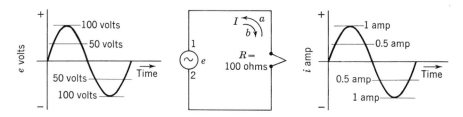

Fig. 13·5　*Sine wave of alternating voltage applied across R produces a sine wave of alternating current in the circuit.*

Notice that the sine wave reaches one-half its maximum value in 30°, which is only ⅓ of 90°. This fact means that the sine wave has a sharper slope of changing values when the wave is near the zero axis, compared with the more gradual changes near the maximum value.

The instantaneous value of a sine-wave voltage for any angle of rotation is expressed by the formula

$$e = E \sin \theta \qquad \text{volts}$$ (13·1)

where θ (Greek letter *theta*) is the angle, sin is the abbreviation for its sine, E is the maximum voltage value, and e is the instantaneous value for any angle.

> *Example 1.*　A sine wave of voltage varies from zero to a maximum of 100 volts. How much is the voltage at the instant of 30° of the cycle? 45°? 90°? 270°?

$$e = E \sin \theta$$

At 30°:　　　$e = E \sin 30° = 100 \times 0.5 = \mathbf{50 \text{ volts}}$
At 45°:　　　$e = E \sin 45° = 100 \times 0.707 = \mathbf{70.7 \text{ volts}}$
At 90°:　　　$e = E \sin 90° = 100 \times 1 = \mathbf{100 \text{ volts}}$
At 270°:　　 $e = E \sin 270° = 100 \times -1 = \mathbf{-100 \text{ volts}}$

The value of -100 volts at 270° is the same as at 90° but with opposite polarity.

13·3　Alternating current

When a sine-wave alternating voltage is connected across a load resistance, the current that flows in the circuit is also a sine wave (Fig. 13·5). Let the sine-wave voltage at the left in the diagram be applied across the resistance R of 100 ohms. The resulting sine wave of alternating current is shown at the right in the diagram.

During the first half-cycle of e in Fig. 13·5, terminal 1 is positive with respect to terminal 2. Since the direction of electron flow is from the negative side of e, through R, and back to the positive side of e, current flows in the direction indicated by arrow a for the first half-cycle. This direction is taken as the positive direction of current in the graph for 1, corresponding to positive values of *e*. The amount of current is equal to *e/R*. If several instantaneous values are taken, when *e* is zero, *i* is zero; when *e* is 50 volts, *i* equals 50 volts/100, or 0.5 amp; when *e* is 100 volts, *i* equals 100 volts/100, or 1 amp. For all values of applied voltage with positive polarity, therefore, the current is in one direction, increasing to its maximum value and decreasing to zero, just like the voltage.

On the next half-cycle, the polarity of the alternating voltage reverses. Then terminal 1 is negative with respect to terminal 2. With reversed voltage polarity, current flows in the opposite direction. Electron flow is from terminal 1 of the voltage source, which is now the negative side, through *R*, and back to terminal 2. This direction of current, as indicated by arrow *b* in Fig. 13·5, is negative. The negative values of *i* in the graph have the same values as in the first half-cycle, corresponding to the reversed values of applied voltage. As a result, the alternating current in the circuit has sine-wave variations corresponding exactly to the sine-wave alternating voltage. Only the waveforms for *e* and *i* can be compared. There is no comparison between relative values, because the current and voltage are different quantities.

It is important to note that the negative half-cycle of applied voltage is just as useful as the positive half-cycle in producing current. The only difference is that the reversed polarity of voltage produces the opposite direction of current. Furthermore, the negative half-cycle of current is just as effective as the positive values when heating the filament to light a bulb. With positive values, electrons flow through the filament in one direction. Negative values produce electron flow in the opposite direction. In both cases, electrons flow from the negative side of the voltage source, through the filament, and return to the positive side of the source. For either direction, the current heats the filament. The direction does not matter, since it is just the motion of electrons against resistance that produces power dissipation.

13·4   *Voltage and current values for a sine wave*

Since an alternating sine wave of voltage or current has many instantaneous values through the cycle, it is convenient to define specific magnitudes for comparing one wave with another. Peak, average, or RMS

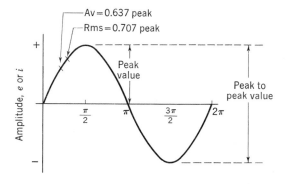

Fig. 13·6   *A-c values for a sine wave of voltage or current.*

value can be specified as indicated in Fig. 13·6 for either current or voltage.

Peak value. One characteristic commonly used is peak value, which is the maximum value of the wave. For example, specifying that a sine wave has a peak value of 170 volts states how much it is, since all other values during the cycle follow a sine wave. Sometimes the term *amplitude* is reserved for peak value, but usually the peak is stated as such. The peak value applies to either the positive or the negative peak, since they are the same amount. In order to include both peak amplitudes, the *peak-to-peak value* may be specified. For the same example, the peak-to-peak value is 340 volts, double the peak value of 170 volts, since the positive and negative peaks are symmetrical. It should be noted, though, that the two opposite peak values cannot occur at the same time. Also, in some waveforms the two peaks are not equal.

Average value. This value is an arithmetical average of all the values in a sine wave for one alternation, or half-cycle. The half-cycle is used for the average because over a full cycle the average value is zero, which has no use for comparison purposes. If the sine values for all angles up to 180°, for one alternation, are added and then divided by the number of values, this average equals 0.637. These calculations are shown in Table 13·2.

Since the peak value of the sine is 1 and the average equals 0.637, then

$$\text{Average value} = 0.637 \times \text{peak value} \qquad (13\cdot2)$$

With a peak of 170 volts, for example, the average value is 0.637 × 170, or 108 volts, approximately.

Root-mean-square, or effective, value. The most common method of specifying the amount of a sine wave of voltage or current is by stating its value at 45°, which is 70.7 per cent of the peak. This is its *root-mean-square* value, abbreviated RMS. Therefore,

$$\text{RMS value} = 0.707 \times \text{peak value} \qquad (13\cdot3)$$

or

$$E_{\text{RMS}} = 0.707\, E_{\text{max}} \qquad \text{and} \qquad I_{\text{RMS}} = 0.707\, I_{\text{max}}$$

With a peak of 170 volts, for example, the RMS value is 0.707 × 170, or 120 volts, approximately. This is the voltage of the commercial a-c power line, which is always given in RMS value.

It is often necessary to convert from RMS to peak value. This can be done by transposing formula (13·3), as follows:

$$\text{Peak value} = \frac{1}{0.707} \times \text{RMS value} = 1.414 \times \text{RMS value} \qquad (13\cdot4)$$

or

$$E_{\text{max}} = 1.414\, E_{\text{RMS}} \qquad \text{and} \qquad I_{\text{max}} = 1.414\, I_{\text{RMS}}$$

For example, the commercial power-line voltage with an RMS value of

Table 13·2 Derivation of average and RMS values for a sine-wave alternation

Interval	Angle θ	sin θ	(sin θ)²
1	15°	0.26	0.07
2	30°	0.50	0.25
3	45°	0.71	0.50
4	60°	0.87	0.75
5	75°	0.97	0.93
6	90°	1.00	1.00
7*	105°	0.97	0.93
8	120°	0.87	0.75
9	135°	0.71	0.50
10	150°	0.50	0.25
11	165°	0.26	0.07
12	180°	0.00	0.00
	Total	7.62	6.00
	Average →	$\dfrac{7.62}{12} = 0.635$†	$\sqrt{\dfrac{6}{12}} = \sqrt{0.5} = 0.707$

* For angles between 90 and 180°, sin θ = sin (180° − θ).
† More intervals and precise values are needed for the exact average of 0.637.

120 volts has a peak value of 120 × 1.414, which equals 170 volts, approximately. Its peak-to-peak value is 2 × 170, or 340 volts, which is double the peak value. As a formula,

$$\text{Peak-to-peak value} = 2.828 \times \text{RMS value} \qquad (13·5)$$

The factor 0.707 for RMS value is derived as the square root of the average (mean) of all the squares of the sine values. If we take the sine for each angle in the cycle, square each value, add all the squares, divide by the number of values added to obtain the average square, and then take the square root of this mean value, the answer is 0.707. These calculations are shown in Table 13·2 for one alternation from 0 to 180°. The results are the same for the opposite alternation.

The advantage of the RMS value derived in terms of the squares of the voltage or current values is that it provides a measure based on the ability of the sine wave to produce power, which is I^2R or E^2/R. As a result, the RMS value of an alternating sine wave corresponds to the same amount of direct current or voltage in heating power. An alternating voltage with an RMS value of 120 volts, for instance, is just as effective in heating the filament of a light bulb as 120 volts from a steady d-c voltage source. For this reason, the RMS value is also called *effective* value.

The factors 0.637 and 0.707 apply to either alternating current or voltage.

For instance, the RMS value of an alternating current equals 0.707 of the peak current. In addition, note that sine waves can have different amplitudes but still follow the sinusoidal waveform. Figure 13·7 compares a low-amplitude voltage with a high-amplitude voltage. Although different in amplitude, they are both sine waves. In each wave, the RMS value is 0.707 of its peak value.

13·5 Frequency

The number of cycles per second is the *frequency*. In Fig. 13·3, if the loop rotates through 60 complete revolutions, or cycles, during one second, the frequency of the generated voltage is 60 cps (cycles per second). You see only one cycle of the sine waveform, instead of 60 cycles, because the time interval shown here is $\frac{1}{60}$ sec. Note that the factor of time is involved. More cycles per second means a higher frequency and less time for one cycle, as illustrated in Fig. 13·8.

A complete cycle is measured between two successive points that have the same value and direction. In Fig. 13·8 the cycle is between successive points where the waveform is zero and ready to increase in the positive direction. Or the cycle can be measured between successive peaks.

On the time scale of one second, waveform *a* goes through one cycle, for a frequency of 1 cps, while waveform *b* has much faster variations with four complete cycles during one second, or a frequency of 4 cps. Both waveforms are sine waves, even though each has a different frequency.[2]

In comparing sine waves, the amplitude has no relation to frequency. Two waveforms can have the same frequency with different amplitudes

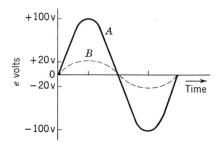

Fig. 13·7 *Waveforms A and B have different amplitudes, but both are sine waves.*

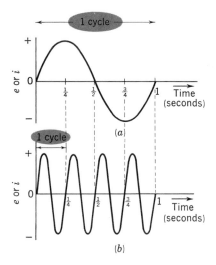

Fig. 13·8 *Number of cycles per second is the frequency. (a) Frequency of 1 cps. (b) Frequency of 4 cps.*

[2] A new unit called the *Hertz* (*Hz*) is also used for cps. Thus, 4 cps = 4 *Hz*.

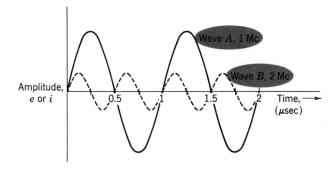

Fig. 13·9 Two sine waves with different amplitudes and different frequencies.

(Fig. 13·7), the same amplitude but different frequencies (Fig. 13·8), or different amplitudes and frequencies (Fig. 13·9). The amplitude indicates how much the voltage or current is, while the frequency indicates the time rate of change of the amplitude variations, in cycles per second.

Example 2. What is the frequency of (a) waveform A in Fig. 13·9 with 2 cycles in 2 μsec and (b) waveform B with 4 cycles in 2 μsec?

Answer.

(a) $\quad f = \dfrac{2 \text{ cycles}}{2 \text{ μsec}} = \dfrac{2 \text{ cycles}}{2 \times 10^{-6} \text{ sec}} = 1 \times 10^6 \dfrac{\text{cycles}}{\text{sec}} = 1 \times 10^6 \text{ cps}$

(b) $\quad f = \dfrac{4 \text{ cycles}}{2 \text{ μsec}} = \dfrac{4 \text{ cycles}}{2 \times 10^{-6} \text{ sec}} = 2 \times 10^6 \dfrac{\text{cycles}}{\text{sec}} = 2 \times 10^6 \text{ cps}$

Frequency units. The rotary generators for commercial electrical power produce a 60-cps alternating voltage. Electric circuits can, however, produce alternating voltage of either lower or higher frequencies. For high frequencies, kilocycles per second and megacycles per second are commonly used. The time factor of seconds is often omitted in these units:

One kilocycle per second = 1 kc = 10^3 cps
One megacycle per second = 1 Mc = 10^6 cps
One gigacycle per second = 1 Gc = 10^9 cps

Audio and radio frequencies. The entire frequency range of alternating voltage or current from one cycle to many megacycles can be considered in two broad groups: audio frequencies (a-f) and radio frequencies (r-f). The audio[3] range includes frequencies that can be heard in the form of sound waves for the human ear. This range of audible frequencies is approximately 16 to 16,000 cps. The higher the frequency, the higher the pitch

[3] *Audio* is a Latin word meaning "I hear."

or tone of the sound. High audio frequencies about 3,000 cps and above can be considered to provide *treble* tone. Low audio frequencies about 300 cps and below provide *bass* tone.

Loudness is determined by amplitude. The greater the amplitude of the a-f variation, the louder is its corresponding sound.

Alternating current and voltage above the audio range provide r-f variations, since electrical variations of high frequency can be transmitted by electromagnetic radio waves. Some of the more common frequency bands for radio broadcasting are listed in Table 13·3.

Sonic and supersonic frequencies. These terms refer to sound waves, which are variations in pressure generated by mechanical vibrations, rather than electrical variations. The velocity of transmission for sound waves equals 1,130 ft per sec, through dry air at 20°C. Sound waves above the audible range of frequencies are called *supersonic* waves. The range of frequencies for supersonic applications, therefore, is from 16,000 cycles up to several megacycles. Sound waves in the audible range of frequencies below 16,000 cps can be considered *sonic* or sound frequencies, reserving *audio* for electrical variations that can be heard when converted to sound waves.

Table 13·3   Frequency spectrum

Band	Abbreviation	Frequencies	Notes and applications
Direct current	d-c	0 cps	Frequencies less than 16 cps can be considered change in d-c level; d-c motors; relays
Audio frequencies	a-f	16–16,000 cps	Sound waves can be heard by human ear; phonographs; tape recorders
Radio frequencies	r-f	20 kc–300,000 Mc	Includes the bands listed below—
Low radio frequencies		20–300 kc	Used for long-distance radio transmission; radio navigation; maritime communications
Medium radio frequencies		300–3,000 kc	Includes standard radio broadcast band, 540–1,620 kc
High radio frequencies		3–30 Mc	Includes international shortwave broadcast band, 5.95–26.1 Mc; industrial, scientific, medical equipment; amateur radio
Very high radio frequencies	VHF	30–300 Mc	Includes television VHF channels 2 to 13; also FM broadcast band, 88–108 Mc; radio navigation; amateur radio
Ultrahigh radio frequencies	UHF	300–3,000 Mc	Includes television UHF channels 14 to 83; radar
Superhigh radio frequencies	SHF	3,000–30,000 Mc	Microwaves; wavelength 1–10 cm
Extrahigh radio frequencies	EHF	30–300 Gc	Microwaves; wavelength 0.1–1 cm

13·6 Period

The amount of time for one cycle is the *period.* Its symbol is T for time. With a frequency of 60 cps, as an example, the time for one cycle is ⅟₆₀ sec. Therefore, the period is ⅟₆₀ sec in this case. The frequency and period are reciprocals of each other:

$$T \text{ (sec)} = \frac{1}{f \text{ (cps)}} \quad \text{or} \quad f \text{ (cps)} = \frac{1}{T \text{ (sec)}} \quad (13 \cdot 6)$$

The higher the frequency, the shorter is the period. In Fig. 13 · 8, the period for wave *a* with a frequency of 1 cps is 1 sec, while the higher-frequency wave of 4 cps in *b* has the period of ¼ sec for a complete cycle.

Units of time. The second is the basic unit, but for higher frequencies and shorter periods, smaller units of time are convenient. Those used most often are:

$$T = 1 \text{ millisecond} = 1 \text{ msec} = 1 \times 10^{-3} \text{ sec}$$
$$T = 1 \text{ microsecond} = 1 \text{ } \mu\text{sec} = 1 \times 10^{-6} \text{ sec}$$
$$T = 1 \text{ nanosecond} = 1 \text{ nsec} = 1 \times 10^{-9} \text{ sec}$$

These units of time for period are reciprocals of the corresponding units for frequency. The reciprocal of frequency in kilocycles gives the period T in milliseconds; the reciprocal of megacycles is microseconds; the reciprocal of gigacycles is nanoseconds.

Example 3. An alternating current varies through one complete cycle in ⅟₁,₀₀₀ sec. Calculate the period and frequency.

$$T = \frac{1}{1,000} \text{ sec}$$

$$f = \frac{1}{T} = \frac{1}{⅟₁,₀₀₀} = \frac{1,000}{1} = 1,000 \text{ cps}$$

Example 4. Calculate the period for the two frequencies of 1 Mc and 2 Mc in Fig. 13 · 9.

(*a*) For 1 Mc, $\quad T = \dfrac{1}{1 \times 10^6} = 1 \times 10^{-6} = 1 \text{ } \mu\text{sec}$

(*b*) For 2 Mc, $\quad T = \dfrac{1}{2 \times 10^6} = 0.5 \times 10^{-6} = 0.5 \text{ } \mu\text{sec}$

13·7 Wavelength

When a periodic variation is considered with respect to distance, one cycle includes the *wavelength,* which is the length of one complete wave or cycle (Fig. 13 · 10). For example, when a radio wave is transmitted, variations in the electromagnetic field travel through space. Also, with sound

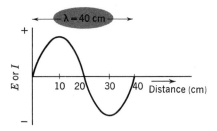

Fig. 13·10 Wavelength (λ) is the distance traveled by the wave in 1 cycle. Here the wavelength is 40 cm.

waves, the variations in air pressure corresponding to the sound wave move through air. In these applications, the distance traveled by the wave in one cycle is the wavelength. The wavelength depends upon the frequency of the variation and its velocity of transmission:

$$\lambda = \frac{\text{velocity}}{\text{frequency}} \qquad (13\cdot7)$$

where λ (lambda) is the symbol for one complete wavelength.

Wavelength of radio waves. For electromagnetic radio waves, the velocity in air or vacuum is 186,000 miles per sec or 3×10^{10} cm per sec, which is the speed of light. Therefore,

$$\lambda \text{ (cm)} = \frac{3 \times 10^{10} \text{ cm per sec}}{f \text{ (cps)}} \qquad (13\cdot8)$$

Note that the higher the frequency is, the shorter the wavelength. For instance, the short-wave radio broadcast band of 5.95 to 26.1 Mc includes higher frequencies than the standard radio broadcast band of 540 to 1,620 kc.

Example 5. What is the wavelength of an electromagnetic radio wave with a frequency of 30 Gc?

Answer. $\lambda = \dfrac{3 \times 10^{10} \text{ cm per sec}}{30 \times 10^9 \text{ cps}} = \dfrac{3}{30} \times 10 = 0.1 \times 10 = \mathbf{1\ cm}$

Such short wavelengths are called *microwaves.*

Example 6. The length of a television antenna is one half-wavelength for electromagnetic radio waves with a frequency of 60 Mc. What is the antenna length (*a*) in centimeters and (*b*) in feet?

Answer.

(*a*) $\qquad \lambda = \dfrac{3 \times 10^{10} \text{ cm per sec}}{60 \times 10^6 \text{ cps}} = \dfrac{1}{20} \times 10^4 = 0.05 \times 10^4 = \mathbf{500\ cm}$

For one half-wavelength,

$$\frac{\lambda}{2} = \frac{500}{2} = \mathbf{250\ cm}$$

(*b*) Since 2.54 cm = 1 in., $\qquad \dfrac{\lambda}{2} = \dfrac{250}{2.54} \text{ in.} = 100 \text{ in.} = \mathbf{8⅓\ ft}$ approx

Wavelength of sound waves. The velocity is much lower, compared with radio waves, because sound waves result from mechanical vibrations rather than electrical variations. For average conditions the velocity of sound waves in air equals 1,130 ft per sec. To calculate the wavelength, therefore,

$$\lambda = \frac{1,130 \text{ ft per sec}}{f \text{ (cps)}} \qquad (13 \cdot 9)$$

This formula can also be used for supersonic waves. Although their frequencies are too high to be audible, supersonic waves are still sound waves rather than radio waves.

Example 7. What is the wavelength of the sound waves produced by a loudspeaker at a frequency of 100 cps?

Answer. $\qquad \lambda = \dfrac{1,130 \text{ ft per sec}}{100 \text{ cps}} = \textbf{11.3 ft}$

Example 8. For supersonic waves at a frequency of 34.44 kc, calculate the wavelength in feet and in centimeters.

Answer. $\qquad \lambda = \dfrac{1,130}{34.44 \times 10^3} = 32.8 \times 10^{-3} = \textbf{0.0328 ft}$

To convert to inches: $0.0328 \text{ ft} \times 12 = 0.3936 \text{ in.}$

To convert to centimeters: $0.3936 \text{ in.} \times 2.54 = 1 \text{ cm approx}$

Note that for sound waves with a frequency of 34.44 kc in this example, the wavelength is the same 1 cm as radio waves with the much higher frequency of 30 Gc in Example 5.

13·8   Phase angle

Referring back to Fig. 13·3, suppose that the generator started its cycle at point B, where maximum voltage output is produced, instead of starting at the point of zero output. If we compare the two cases, the two output

Fig. 13·11   Two sine-wave voltages 90° out of phase. (a) Sine-wave voltage B leads voltage wave A by 90°. (b) Angle of 90° between phasors e_B and e_A representing the two voltages.

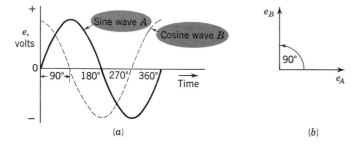

(a)   (b)

voltage waves would be as in Fig. 13·11. Each is the same waveform of alternating voltage, but wave *B* starts at maximum, while wave *A* starts at zero. The complete cycle of wave *B* through 360° takes it to the maximum value from which it started. Wave *A* starts and finishes its cycle at zero. With respect to time, therefore, wave *B* is ahead of wave *A* in its values of generated voltage. The amount it leads in time equals one quarter-revolution, which is 90°. This angular difference is the phase angle between waves *B* and *A*. Wave *B* leads wave *A* by the phase angle of 90°.

The 90° phase angle between waves *B* and *A* is maintained throughout the complete cycle and in all successive cycles, as long as they both have the same frequency. At any instant of time for wave *B*, it has the value that *A* will have 90° later. For instance, at 180° wave *A* is at zero, but *B* is already at its negative maximum value, where wave *A* will be later at 270°.

In order to compare the phase angle between two waves, they must have the same frequency. Otherwise, the relative phase keeps changing. Also, they must have sine-wave variations, as this is the only kind of waveform that is measured in angular units of time. The amplitudes can be different for the two waves, although they are shown the same here.

The 90° phase angle. The two waves in Fig. 13·11 represent a sine wave and a cosine wave 90° out of phase with each other. The 90° phase angle means that one has its maximum amplitude when the other is at zero value. Wave *A* starts at zero, corresponding to the sine of 0°, has its peak amplitude at 90 and 270°, and is back to zero after one cycle of 360°. Wave *B* starts at its peak value, corresponding to the cosine of 0°, has its zero value at 90 and 270°, and is back to the peak value after one cycle of 360°. Or, wave *B* can be considered a sine wave that starts 90° before wave *A*, in time. This phase angle of 90° for current and voltage waveforms has many applications in sine-wave a-c circuits with inductance or capacitance.

Phase-angle vectors or phasors. To compare phases of alternating currents and voltages, it is much more convenient to use vector diagrams corresponding to the voltage and current waveforms, as shown in Fig. 13·11*b*. The arrows here represent the vector quantities corresponding to the generator voltage. A vector is a quantity that has magnitude and direction. The length of the arrow indicates the magnitude of the alternating voltage, in RMS, peak, or any a-c value as long as the same measure is used for all the vectors. The angle of the arrow with respect to the horizontal axis indicates the phase angle.

The term vector is generally used to represent a quantity with direction in space. For phase angle directions, the term phasor is more specific to indicate the phase angle of a quantity.

The phasor corresponds to the entire cycle of voltage, but is shown only at one angle, such as the starting point, since the complete cycle is known to be a sine wave. Without the extra details of a whole cycle, phasors represent the alternating voltage or current in a compact form that is easier for comparing phase angles. In Fig. 13·11*b*, for instance, the phasor e_A represents the voltage of wave *A*, with a phase angle of 0°. This

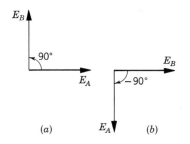

Fig. 13·12 Phase angle of 90° leading or lagging depending on reference. (a) E_A is reference and E_B leads E_A by 90°. (b) E_B is reference and E_A lags E_B by 90°.

angle can be considered as the plane of the loop in the rotary generator where it starts with zero output voltage. The phasor e_B is vertical to show the phase angle of 90° for this voltage wave, corresponding to the vertical generator loop at the start of its cycle. The angle between the two phasors is the phase angle of 90°.

Phase-angle reference. The phase angle of one wave can be specified only with respect to another as reference. How the phasors are drawn to show the phase angle depends on which phase is chosen as the reference. Generally, the reference phasor is horizontal, corresponding to 0°. Two possibilities are shown in Fig. 13·12. In *a*, the voltage wave *A* or its phasor E_A is the reference. Then the phasor E_B is 90° counterclockwise. This method is standard practice, using counterclockwise rotation as the positive direction for angles. Also, a leading angle is positive. In this case, then, E_B is 90° counterclockwise for the reference E_A to show that wave *B* leads wave *A* by 90°.

However, wave *B* is shown as the reference in *b*. Now E_B is the horizontal phasor. In order to have the same phase angle, E_A must be 90° clockwise, or −90° from E_B. This arrangement shows that negative angles, clockwise from the 0° reference, are used to show a lagging phase angle. The reference determines whether the phase angle is considered leading or lagging in time. However, the phase is not actually changed by the method of showing it. In Fig. 13·12, E_A and E_B are 90° out of phase with E_B 90° leading E_A

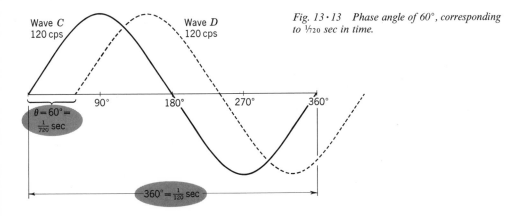

Fig. 13·13 Phase angle of 60°, corresponding to ¹⁄₇₂₀ sec in time.

in time, and there is no fundamental difference whether we say E_B is ahead of E_A by $+90°$ or E_A is behind E_B by $-90°$.

In-phase and out-of-phase waveforms. Two waves and their corresponding phasors can be out of phase by any angle, either less or more than $90°$. For instance, a phase angle of $60°$ is shown in Fig. $13 \cdot 13$. Note, though, that a phase angle of $0°$ means the two waves are in phase. Then the amplitudes add to make a resultant with larger values than either wave. For the opposite case, the angle of $180°$ means opposite phase or the two waves are out of phase. Then the amplitudes are opposing in the two waves. Equal values of opposite phase cancel each other. A $360°$ angle means an initial difference in starting time, but the two waves are in phase, with identical times for the zero and peak values.

$13 \cdot 9$ The time factor in frequency and phase

It is important to remember that the waveforms we are considering are just graphs drawn on paper. The physical factors represented are variations in amplitude, usually on the vertical scale, with respect to equal intervals on the horizontal scale, which can represent either distance or time. To show wavelength, as in Fig. $13 \cdot 10$, the cycles of amplitude variations are plotted against distance or length units. To show frequency, the cycles of amplitude variations are shown with respect to time. This time factor for frequency applies to Figs. $13 \cdot 7$ to $13 \cdot 9$ and to Fig. $13 \cdot 11$.

As an example of how frequency involves time, a waveform with stable frequency is actually used in electronic equipment as a clock reference for very small units of time. Assume a voltage waveform with the frequency of 10 Mc. The period T is 0.1 μsec. Every cycle is repeated at 0.1-μsec intervals, therefore. When each cycle of voltage variations is used to indicate time, then, the result is effectively a clock that measures 0.1-μsec units. Even smaller units of time can be measured with higher frequencies. In everyday applications, an electric clock connected to the power line keeps correct time because it is controlled by the exact frequency of 60 cps.

Furthermore, the phase angle between two waves of the same frequency indicates a difference in time. As an example, Fig. $13 \cdot 13$ shows a phase angle of $60°$, with wave C leading wave D. They both have the same frequency of 120 cps. The period T for each wave then is $\frac{1}{120}$ sec. Since $60°$ is one-sixth of the complete cycle of $360°$, this phase angle represents one-sixth of the complete period of $\frac{1}{120}$ sec. Multiplying $\frac{1}{6} \times \frac{1}{120}$, the answer is $\frac{1}{720}$ sec for the time corresponding to the phase angle of $60°$. If we consider wave D lagging wave C by $60°$, this lag is a time delay of $\frac{1}{720}$ sec.

More generally, the time for a phase angle θ can be calculated as

$$t = \frac{\theta}{360} \times \frac{1}{f} \qquad (13 \cdot 10)$$

With f in cps and θ in degrees, the time t is in seconds. The formula gives

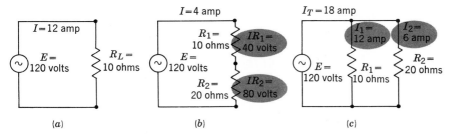

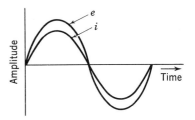

(a) (b) (c)

Fig. 13·14 A-c circuits with resistance. All values are RMS. (a) One resistance across voltage source. (b) Series circuit. (c) Parallel circuit.

Fig. 13·15. Current varying in phase with applied voltage in a-c circuit with resistance.

the time of the phase angle as its proportional part of the total period of one cycle. For the example of θ equal to 60° with f at 120 cps,

$$t = \frac{\theta}{360} \times \frac{1}{f} = \frac{60}{360} \times \frac{1}{120} = \frac{1}{6} \times \frac{1}{120} = \frac{1}{720} \text{ sec}$$

13·10 A-c circuits with resistance

An a-c circuit has an a-c voltage source. Note the symbol in Fig. 13·14 used for any source of sine-wave alternating voltage. This voltage connected across an external load resistance produces alternating current of the same waveform, frequency, and phase as the applied voltage. The amount of current equals E/R by Ohm's law. When E is an RMS value, I is also an RMS value. For any instantaneous value of E during the cycle, the value of I is for the corresponding instant of time.

In an a-c circuit with only resistance, the current variations i are in phase with the applied voltage e, as shown in Fig. 13·15. This in-phase relation between e and i means that such an a-c circuit can be analyzed by the same methods used for d-c circuits, since there is no phase angle to consider. However, when a-c circuits have inductance and capacitance, as explained in later chapters, there is usually a 90° phase angle that must be included in the calculations.

Generally, a-c circuits are considered in terms of RMS values, unless otherwise noted.[4] In Fig. 13·14a, for example, the applied RMS voltage of 120 volts across the 10-ohm resistance produces current equal to

---

[4] The capital letters E and I are generally used for RMS values and peak values, with e and i for instantaneous values.

120 volts/10, or 12 amp RMS. With I in RMS value, the RMS power dissipated is I^2R, which equals 144×10, or 1,440 watts.

Series circuit. With resistances in series, as in Fig. 13·14b, the total circuit resistance is the sum of the individual resistances. The total resistance of 30 ohms for R_1 and R_2 across 120 volts in this example results in a value of 4 amp for I. The current is the same in all parts of any series circuit. With 4 amp through the 10 ohms of R_1, its IR voltage drop equals 4×10, or 40 volts. The same 4 amp through 20 ohms in R_2 produces an IR voltage drop of 80 volts. Note that the sum of the series IR voltage drops equals the applied voltage of 120 volts.

Parallel circuit. With R_1 and R_2 in parallel across the a-c voltage source, as in Fig. 13·14c, the voltage across the parallel branches is the same as the applied voltage. Each branch current then is equal to the applied voltage divided by the branch resistance. For R_1, its branch current is 120 volts/10 ohms, which equals 12 amp. In the R_2 branch, the current equals 120 volts/20 ohms, or 6 amp. The total line current of 18 amp is the sum of the individual branch currents of 12 amp and 6 amp.

Series-parallel circuits. The results of analyzing a series-parallel a-c circuit with resistances only are shown in Fig. 13·16a. Note that the 20-ohm R_2 and 20-ohm R_L are in parallel for an equivalent bank resistance of 10 ohms. This 10-ohm bank is in series with the 20-ohm R_1 for a total of 30 ohms across the 90 volts applied by E_a. Therefore, the main-line current I_a equals $^{90}\!/_{30}$ or 3 amp.

The I_aR_1 voltage drop then is 3×20, or 60 volts. The remaining 30 volts is across the bank of R_2 and R_L in parallel. Finally, the 3-amp line current divides equally with 1.5 amp for the R_2 branch and 1.5 amp for the R_L branch as these branch resistances are equal. When we consider just R_L across the output terminals AB, the voltage across the 20-ohm R_L is 30 volts, with 1.5 amp through it.

The Thévenin equivalent circuit is shown in Fig. 13·16b. Here the voltage output across R_L between A and B is $^{20}\!/_{30}$ or $^2\!/_3$ of 45 volts, which equals

Fig. 13·16 *Series-parallel a-c circuit with resistances only.*
(a) Actual schematic. (b) Thévenin equivalent circuit. (c) Norton equivalent circuit.

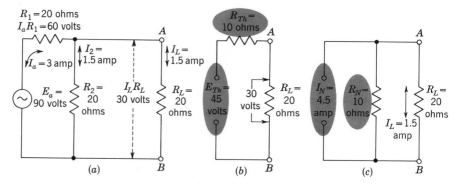

30 volts. For the Norton equivalent circuit in *c*, the current in the R_L branch between *A* and *B* is ⅓ of 4.5 amp, which equals 1.5 amp. These equivalent circuits are the same ones explained before as d-c circuits in Chap. 6. Note that R_{Th} and R_N have the same value of 10 ohms.

13·11   The 60-cps a-c power line

Although there are applications for commercial d-c power, practically all homes in the United States are supplied alternating voltage with a value of 110 to 120 volts RMS and a frequency of exactly 60 cps. This is a sine-wave voltage produced by a rotary generator. The electrical power is distributed by power lines connecting the generating station to the main line in the home, where the 120-volt line is connected to all the electrical equipment and wall outlets in parallel. This 120-volt source of commercial electrical power is called the 60-*cycle power line,* or the *mains,* indicating that it is the main line. One side of the power line is usually connected to earth ground. The rules for ground connections in commercial electrical wiring are specified by local electrical codes.

A-c power at 120 volts is equivalent to 120-volt d-c power in heating effect. A value higher than 120 volts is not provided for home use, because of the increased danger of a fatal electric shock. Lower values than 120 volts would not be as efficient in supplying power. Higher voltage has the advantage of less I^2R loss, since the same amount of power can be produced with less current. For industrial applications, where larger amounts of power are used, the main line is often 220 to 240 volts, three-phase.

The advantage of a-c over d-c power is primarily greater efficiency in distribution from the generating station. A-c voltages can easily be stepped up by means of a transformer, with practically no losses, but a transformer cannot operate on direct current. The alternating voltage at the generating station can therefore be stepped up to values as high as 5 to 80 kv, for high-voltage distribution lines. These high-voltage lines supply large amounts of power with much less current and less I^2R loss, compared with a 120-volt line. At the home, the lower voltage required is supplied from a step-down transformer.

The frequency of 60 cps is convenient for commercial a-c power. Much lower frequencies would require transformers that are too big. In addition, too low a frequency for alternating current heating an incandescent bulb could cause the light to flicker. Too high a frequency results in excessive iron-core losses, such as hysteresis losses, in the transformers. The frequency of the a-c power mains in most European countries is 50 cps.

13·12   Motors and generators

A generator converts mechanical energy into electrical energy; a motor does the opposite, converting electricity into rotary motion. The main parts in the assembly of motors and generators are essentially the same (Fig. 13·17).

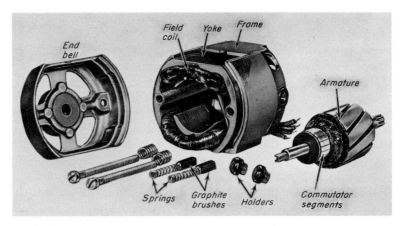

Fig. 13·17   *Main parts of a d-c motor.*

Armature. In a generator, the armature connects to the external circuit to provide the generator output voltage. Or, in a motor, the armature connects to the electrical source that drives the motor. The armature is often constructed in the form of a drum, using many conductor loops for increased output. In Fig. 13·17 the rotating armature is the *rotor* part of the assembly.

Field winding. This electromagnet provides the flux cut by the rotor. In a motor, current for the field is produced by the same source that supplies the armature. In a generator, the field current may be obtained from a separate exciter source, or from its own armature output. Residual magnetism in the iron yoke of the field allows this *self-excited generator* to start. The field coil may be connected in series with the armature, in parallel, or in a series-parallel *compound winding*. When the field winding is stationary, it is the *stator* part of the assembly.

Slip rings. In an a-c machine, two slip rings or *collector rings* enable the rotating loop to be connected to the stationary wire leads for the external circuit.

Brushes. These graphite connectors are spring-mounted to brush against the spinning rings on the rotor. The stationary external leads are connected to the brushes for connection to the rotating loop. Constant rubbing slowly wears down the brushes and they must be replaced after they are worn.

Commutator. A d-c machine has a commutator ring instead of the slip rings. As shown in Fig. 13·17, the commutator ring has segments, with one pair for each loop in the armature. Each of the commutator segments is insulated from the other by mica. The commutator converts the a-c machine to d-c operation. In a generator, the commutator segments reverse the loop connections to the brushes every half-cycle to maintain constant polarity of output voltage. For a d-c motor, the commutator segments allow the d-c source to produce torque in one direction to rotate the loop.

Brushes also are necessary with a commutator ring. The two stationary brushes contact opposite segments on the rotating commutator.

A-c induction motor. This type, for alternating current only, does not have any brushes. The stator is connected directly to the a-c source. Then alternating current in the stator winding induces current in the rotor without any physical connection between them. The magnetic field of the current induced in the rotor reacts with the stator field to produce rotation. With a single-phase a-c source, however, a starting torque must be provided. A-c induction motors are economical and rugged, without any troublesome brush arcing.

Universal motor. This type operates on either alternating or direct current because the field and armature are in series. Its construction is like a d-c motor with the rotating armature connected to a commutator and brushes. The universal motor is commonly used for small machines such as portable drills and food mixers.

Alternators. A-c generators are alternators. For large power requirements the alternator usually has a rotor field, while the armature is the stator. This method eliminates slip-ring connections with its arcing problems in the high-voltage output.

Three-phase alternating voltage. In an alternator with a rotor field, if the stator armature has three windings equally spaced around the circle, the armature will generate output voltages 120° out of phase with each other. The advantage of this three-phase a-c voltage is more efficient distribution of power. Also a-c induction motors are self-starting with a three-phase source of power. The three voltage phases of the alternator output voltage can be used either in delta or wye connections.

13·13 Nonsinusoidal a-c waveforms

The sine wave is the basic waveform for a-c variations, for several reasons. This waveform is produced by a rotary generator, as the output is proportional to the angle of rotation. The 60-cycle a-c power-line voltage is a perfect example. Because of its derivation from circular motion, any sine wave can be analyzed conveniently in angular measure, in either degrees from 0 to 360° or radians from 0 to 2π rad. In addition, electronic oscillator circuits with inductance and capacitance naturally produce sine-wave variations. Another feature of a sine wave is its basic simplicity, as the rate of change for the variations corresponds to a cosine wave, which is similar but 90° out of phase. The sine wave is the only waveform that has this characteristic of a rate of change with the same waveform as the original amplitude variations.

In many electronic applications, however, other waveshapes are important. Two examples are the sawtooth wave and square wave in Fig. 13·18. Any waveshape that is not a sine wave is called a *nonsinusoidal wave*. With nonsinusoidal waveforms, for either voltage or current, there are important differences and similarities to consider. Note the following comparisons with sine waves, which are illustrated in Fig. 13·18.

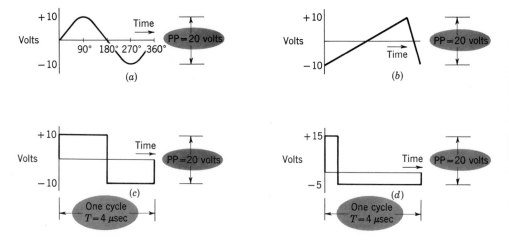

Fig. 13·18 Comparison of sine wave with nonsinusoidal a-c waveforms. (a) Sine wave. (b) Sawtooth wave. (c) Symmetrical square wave. (d) Unsymmetrical rectangular wave.

1. In all cases, the cycle is measured between two points having the same amplitude and varying in the same direction. The period is the time for one cycle. In Fig. 13·18, T for any of the waveforms is 4 μsec and the frequency is ¼ Mc.
2. Peak amplitude is measured from the zero axis to the maximum positive or negative value. However, peak-to-peak is better for measuring nonsinusoidal waveshapes because they can have unsymmetrical peaks, as in d. For all the waveforms shown here, though, the peak-to-peak (P-P) amplitude is 20 volts.
3. The RMS value of 0.707 maximum applies only to sine waves, as this factor is derived from the sine values in the angular measure used only for the sine waveform.
4. Phase angles apply only to sine waves, as angular measure is used only for sine waves. Note that the horizontal axis for time is divided into angles for the sine wave in a but there are no angles shown for the nonsinusoidal waveshapes.

The sawtooth wave in b represents a voltage that slowly increases, with a uniform or linear rate of change, to its peak value, and then drops sharply to its starting value. This waveform is also called a *ramp voltage*. Note that one complete cycle includes the slow rise and the fast drop in voltage. In this example, the period T for a complete cycle is 4 μsec. Therefore, these sawtooth cycles are repeated at the frequency of ¼ or 0.25 Mc.

The square wave in c represents a switching voltage. First, the peak voltage is instantaneously applied in positive polarity. This voltage remains on for 2 μsec, which is one half-cycle. Then the voltage is instantaneously reduced to zero and applied in reverse polarity for another 2 μsec. The complete cycle then takes 4 μsec and the frequency is ¼ Mc. The rectangular waveshape in *d* is similar but the positive and negative half-cycles are not symmetrical, neither in amplitude nor in time. However, the frequency is the same 0.25 Mc and the peak-to-peak amplitude is the same 20 volts, as in all the waveshapes.

SUMMARY

1. Alternating voltage continuously varies in magnitude and reverses in polarity. Alternating voltage applied across a load resistance produces alternating current in the circuit.
2. A complete set of values repeated periodically is one cycle of the a-c waveform. The cycle can be measured from any one point on the wave to the next successive point having the same value and varying in the same direction. One cycle includes 360° in angular measure, which is equal to 2π rad.
3. The RMS value of a sine wave is 0.707 × peak value. The peak amplitude, at 90 and 270° in the cycle, is 1.414 × RMS value. Peak-to-peak value is double the peak amplitude, or 2.828 × RMS for a symmetrical a-c waveform. The average value is 0.637 × peak value.
4. The frequency equals the number of cycles per second. One megacycle per second (Mc) equals one million cycles per second. The audio-frequency (a-f) range is 16 to 16,000 cps. Higher frequencies up to 300,000 Mc are radio frequencies (r-f).
5. The amount of time for one cycle is the period (T). The period and frequency are reciprocals: $T = 1/f$, or $f = 1/T$. The higher the frequency, the shorter is the period.
6. Wavelength (λ) is the distance a wave travels in one cycle. The higher the frequency, the shorter is the wavelength. The wavelength also depends on the velocity at which the wave travels: λ = velocity/frequency.
7. Phase angle is the angular difference in time between corresponding values in the cycles for two waveforms of the same frequency. When one sine wave has its maximum value while the other is at zero, the two waves are 90° out of phase. Two waveforms with zero phase angle between them are in phase; a 180° phase angle means opposite phase.
8. The length of a phasor indicates amplitude, while the angle of the arrow corresponds to the phase. Leading phase is shown by counterclockwise angles.
9. Sine-wave alternating voltage E applied across a load resistance R produces alternating current I in the circuit. The current has the same waveform, frequency, and phase as the applied voltage because of the resistive load. The amount of $I = E/R$.
10. The sawtooth wave and square wave are two common examples of nonsinusoidal waveforms. These amplitudes are usually measured in peak-to-peak value.
11. In motors and generators, the main parts of the assembly are the armature for the external circuit, the field to supply flux cut by the armature, slip rings for a-c machines or commutator segments for d-c machines, and brushes to contact the rotor. Either the field or the armature winding can be the rotor. A-c induction motors generally have no brushes.

SELF-EXAMINATION (*Answers at back of book.*)

Here's a chance to see how well you have learned the material in this chapter. These exercises are for your self-testing only.

Answer true or false.

1. A-c voltage varies in magnitude and reverses in polarity.
2. D-c voltage always has the same polarity.
3. Sine-wave alternating current flows in a load resistor with sine-wave voltage applied.
4. When two waves are 90° out of phase, one has its peak value when the other is at zero.
5. When two waves are in phase, they have their zero values at the same time.
6. The positive peak of a sine wave cannot occur at the same time as the negative peak.
7. The angle of 90° is the same as $\pi/2$ rad.

8. A period of 2 μsec corresponds to a lower frequency than a period of 1 μsec.
9. A wavelength of 2 ft corresponds to a lower frequency than a wavelength of 1 ft.
10. When we compare the phase between two waveforms, they must have the same frequency.
  Fill in the missing answers.
11. For the RMS voltage of 10 volts, the peak-to-peak value is _____ volts.
12. With 120 volts RMS across 100 ohms R_L, the RMS current equals _____ amp.
13. For a peak value of 100 volts, the RMS value is _____ volts.
14. The wavelength of a 1,000-kc radio wave is _____ cm.
15. The period of a 1,000-kc voltage is _____ msec.
16. The period of 1/60 sec corresponds to a frequency of _____ cps.
17. The frequency of 100 Mc corresponds to a period of _____ μsec.
18. The square wave in Fig. 13·18c has the frequency of _____ Mc.
19. The RMS voltage for the sine wave in Fig. 13·18a is _____ volts.
20. The a-c voltage across R_2 in Fig. 13·16a is _____ volts.
21. For the series a-c circuit in Fig. 13·15b, R_T is _____ ohms.
22. For the parallel a-c circuit in Fig. 13·15c, R_T is _____ ohms.
23. For the series-parallel a-c circuit in Fig. 13·16a, R_T is _____ ohms.
24. For an audio signal with T of 0.001 sec, its frequency is _____ cps.
25. For the 60-cycle a-c power-line voltage, T is _____ sec.

ESSAY QUESTIONS

1. (*a*) Define an alternating voltage. (*b*) Define an alternating current. (*c*) Why does a-c voltage applied across a load resistance produce alternating current in the circuit?
2. (*a*) State two characteristics of a sine wave of voltage. (*b*) Why does the RMS value of 0.707 × peak value apply just to sine waves?
3. Draw two cycles of an a-c sawtooth voltage waveform, with a peak-to-peak amplitude of 40 volts. Do the same for a square wave.
4. Give the angle, in degrees and radians, for each of the following: one cycle, one half-cycle, one quarter-cycle, three quarter-cycles.
5. The peak value of a sine wave is 1 volt. How much is its average value? RMS value? Effective value? Peak-to-peak value?
6. State the following ranges in cps: (*a*) audio frequencies; (*b*) radio frequencies; (*c*) standard radio broadcast band; (*d*) VHF radio band; (*e*) microwave band.
7. Make a graph with two waves, one with a frequency of 500 kc and the other 1,000 kc. Mark the horizontal axis in time and label each wave.
8. Draw the sine waves and vector diagrams to show (*a*) two waves 180° out of phase; (*b*) two waves 90° out of phase.
9. Give the voltage value for the 60-cycle a-c line voltage with an RMS value of 120 volts at each of the following times in a cycle: 0°, 30°, 45°, 90°, 180°, 270°, 360°.
10. (*a*) The phase angle of 90° equals how many radians? (*b*) For two sine waves 90° out of phase with each other, compare their amplitudes at 0°, 90°, 180°, 270°, and 360°.
11. Tabulate the sine and cosine values every 30° from 0 to 360° and draw the corresponding sine wave and cosine wave.
12. Draw a graph of the values for $(\sin \theta)^2$ plotted against θ for every 30° from 0 to 360°.
13. Referring to Fig. 13·16, prove that the circuit in *b* is the Thévenin equivalent of *a*, and the circuit in *c* is the Norton equivalent of *a*.
14. Why is the wavelength of a supersonic wave at 34.44 kc the same 1 cm as for the much higher-frequency radio wave at 30 Gc?
15. Draw the sine waves and vectors to show wave V_1 leading wave V_2 by 45°.
16. Why are amplitudes for nonsinusoidal waveforms generally measured in peak-to-peak values, rather than RMS or average value?
17. Define the following parts in the assembly of motors: (*a*) armature rotor; (*b*) field stator; (*c*) collector rings; (*d*) brushes; (*e*) commutator segments.

PROBLEMS (*Answers to selected problems at back of book.*)

1. The 60-cps power-line voltage of 120 volts is applied across a resistance of 10 ohms. (*a*) How much is the RMS current in the circuit? (*b*) What is the frequency of the current? (*c*) What is the phase angle between the current and voltage? (*d*) How much d-c applied voltage would be necessary for the same heating effect in the resistance?

2. What is the frequency for the following a-c variations? (*a*) ten cycles in 1 sec; (*b*) one cycle in ⅒ sec; (*c*) fifty cycles in 1 sec; (*d*) fifty cycles in ½ sec; (*e*) fifty cycles in 5 sec.

3. Calculate the time delay for a phase angle of 45° at the frequency of (*a*) 500 cps; (*b*) 5 Mc.

4. Calculate the period T for the following frequencies: (*a*) 500 cps; (*b*) 5 Mc; (*c*) 5 Gc.

5. Calculate the frequency for the following periods: (*a*) 0.05 sec; (*b*) 5 msec; (*c*) 5 μsec; (*d*) 5 nanosec.

6. Referring to Fig. 13·16, calculate the I^2R power dissipated in R_1, R_2, and R_L.

7. Referring to Fig. 13·18, give the positive and negative peak values for each waveform in *a*, *b*, *c*, and *d*.

8. An a-c circuit has a 5-M resistor in series with a 10-M resistor across a 200-volt source. Calculate I, V_1, V_2, P_1, and P_2.

9. The same two resistors as in Prob. 8 are in parallel. Calculate I_1, I_2, V_1, V_2, P_1, and P_2.

10. A series-parallel a-c circuit has two branches across the 60-cps 120-volt power line. One branch has 10-ohm R_1 in series with 20-ohm R_2. The other branch has 10-M R_3 in series with 20-M R_4. Find V_1, V_2, V_3, and V_4.

Review of Chapters ⑪ to ⑬

SUMMARY

1. Iron, nickel, and cobalt are magnetic materials. Magnets have a north pole and south pole at opposite ends. Opposite poles attract; like poles repel.
2. A magnet has an invisible, external magnetic field. This magnetic flux is indicated by field lines. The direction of field lines outside the magnet is from north pole to south pole.
3. A permanent magnet is made of a hard magnetic material, such as alnico, to retain its magnetism indefinitely. Iron is a soft magnetic material which can be magnetized temporarily.
4. An electromagnet has an iron core that becomes magnetized when current flows in the coil winding.
5. Magnetic units are defined in Table 11·2.
6. Continuous magnetization and demagnetization of an iron core by means of alternating current causes hysteresis losses, which increase with higher frequencies.
7. Ferrites are ceramic magnetic materials that are insulators.
8. Current in a conductor has an associated magnetic field with circular lines of force in a plane perpendicular to the wire. Their direction is counterclockwise when you look along the conductor in the direction of electron flow.
9. Motor action results from the net force of two fields that can aid or cancel. The direction of the resultant force is from the stronger field to the weaker.
10. The motion of magnetic flux cutting across a perpendicular conductor generates an induced emf. The amount of induced voltage increases with higher frequencies, more flux, and more turns of conductor.
11. Faraday's law of induced voltage is $e = N \, d\phi/dt$ volts, where N is the turns and $d\phi/dt$ is the change in flux in webers per second.
12. Lenz's law states that an induced voltage must have the polarity that opposes the change causing the induction.
13. Alternating voltage varies in magnitude and reverses in direction. An a-c voltage source produces alternating current.
14. One cycle includes the values between points having the same value and varying in the same direction. The cycle includes 360°, or 2π radians.
15. Frequency (f) equals the number of cycles per second.
16. Period (T) is time for one cycle. It equals $1/f$. When f is in cycles per second, T is in seconds.
17. Wavelength (λ) is the distance a wave travels in one cycle. $\lambda = v/f$.
18. The RMS, or effective, value of a sine wave equals 0.707 × peak value. Or, the peak value equals 1.414 × RMS value. The average value equals 0.637 × peak value.
19. Phase angle (θ) is the angular difference in time between corresponding values in the cycles for two sine waves of the same frequency.
20. Phasors can be used to indicate the amplitude and phase angle of alternating voltage or current. The length of the phasor is the amplitude while the angle is the phase.

REFERENCES (*Additional references at back of book.*)

Books

Adams, J., *Electrical Principles and Practices,* McGraw-Hill Book Company, New York.
Bishop, C., *Single and Polyphase Vectors,* The Hayden Book Companies, New York.

Croft, T., *Practical Electricity,* 4th ed., McGraw-Hill Book Company, New York.

Morecock, E. M., *Alternating-Current Circuits,* McGraw-Hill Book Company, New York.

Oppenheimer and Borchers, *Direct and Alternating Currents,* McGraw-Hill Book Company, New York.

Siskind, C. S., *Electrical Circuits,* McGraw-Hill Book Company, New York.

Timbie, W. H., *Elements of Electricity,* John Wiley & Sons, Inc., New York.

Pamphlets

Allegheny Ludlum Steel Corp., Pittsburgh, "Magnetic Materials."

Indiana Steel Products Co., Valparaiso, Ind., "Permanent-magnet Materials and Their Selection."

International Nickel Co., New York, "Magnetostriction."

REVIEW SELF-EXAMINATION *(Answers at back of book.)*

Here's another chance to check your progress. Work the exercises just as you did those at the end of each chapter and check your answers.

1. Which of the following statements is true? (*a*) Alnico is commonly used for electromagnets. (*b*) Paper cannot affect magnetic flux, because it is not a magnetic material. (*c*) Iron is generally used for permanent magnets. (*d*) Ferrites have lower permeability than air or vacuum.

2. Hysteresis losses (*a*) are caused by high-frequency alternating current in a coil with an iron core; (*b*) generally increase with direct current in a coil; (*c*) are especially important with permanent magnets that have a steady magnetic field; (*d*) cannot be produced in an iron core, because it is a conductor.

3. A magnetic flux of 25,000 lines through an area of 5 cm² results in (*a*) 5 kilolines of flux; (*b*) 5,000 maxwells of flux; (*c*) flux density of 5,000 gauss; (*d*) flux density corresponding to 25,000 amp-turns.

4. If 10 volts is applied across a relay coil with 100 turns having 2 ohms of resistance, the total force producing magnetic flux in the circuit is (*a*) 10 maxwells; (*b*) 50 gauss; (*c*) 100 oersteds; (*d*) 500 amp-turns.

5. The a-c power line voltage of 120 volts RMS has a peak value of (*a*) 100 volts; (*b*) 170 volts; (*c*) 240 volts; (*d*) 338 volts.

6. Which of the following can produce the most induced voltage? (*a*) 1-amp direct current; (*b*) 50-amp direct current; (*c*) 1-amp 60-cycle alternating current; (*d*) 1-amp 400-cycle alternating current.

7. Which of the following has the highest frequency? (*a*) $T = \frac{1}{1,000}$ sec; (*b*) $T = \frac{1}{60}$ sec; (*c*) $T = 1$ sec; (*d*) $T = 2$ sec.

8. Two waves of the same frequency have opposite phase when the phase angle between them is (*a*) 0°; (*b*) 90°; (*c*) 360°; (*d*) π rad.

9. The 120-volt 60-cycle power-line voltage is applied across a 120-ohm resistor. The current equals (*a*) 1 amp, peak value; (*b*) 120 amp, peak value; (*c*) 1 amp, RMS value; (*d*) 5 amp, RMS value.

10. When an alternating voltage reverses in polarity, the current it produces (*a*) reverses in direction; (*b*) has a steady d-c value; (*c*) has a phase angle of 180°; (*d*) alternates at 1.4 times the frequency of the applied voltage.

Chapter 14 Inductance

Inductance is the ability of a conductor to produce induced voltage when the current varies. A long wire has more inductance than a short wire, since more conductor length cut by magnetic flux produces more induced voltage. Similarly, a coil has more inductance than the equivalent length of straight wire because of the concentration of magnetic flux. Components manufactured to have a definite value of inductance are just coils of wire, therefore, called *inductors*. Figure 14·1 shows typical inductors with their schematic symbols. The construction, operation, and uses of inductors are explained in the following topics:

14·1 Induction by alternating current
14·2 Self-inductance
14·3 Self-induced voltage
14·4 Mutual inductance
14·5 Transformers
14·6 Core losses
14·7 Types of cores
14·8 Variable inductance
14·9 Inductances in series or parallel
14·10 Stray inductance
14·11 Troubles in coils

14·1 Induction by alternating current

Induced voltage is the result of flux cutting across a conductor, produced by physical motion of either the magnetic field or the conductor. When the current in a conductor varies in amplitude, however, the variations of current and its associated magnetic field are equivalent to motion of the flux. As the current increases in value, the magnetic field expands outward from the conductor. When the current decreases, the field collapses into the conductor. As the field expands and collapses with changes of current, the flux is effectively in motion. Therefore, a varying current can produce induced voltage without the need for motion of the conductor.

Figure 14·2 illustrates the changes in magnetic field associated with a sine wave of alternating current. Since the alternating current varies in amplitude and reverses in direction, its associated magnetic field has the same variations. At point *A*, the current is zero and there is no flux. At *B*, the positive direction of current provides some field lines taken here in the counterclockwise direction. Point *C* has maximum current and maximum counterclockwise flux. At *D* there is less flux than at *C*. Now the field is collapsing because of the reduced current. At *E* with zero current, there is no magnetic flux. The field can be considered as having collapsed into the wire. The next half-cycle of current allows the field to expand and collapse again, but the directions are reversed. When the flux expands at points *F* and *G*, the field lines are clockwise, corresponding to current in the negative direction. From *G* to *H* and *I*, this clockwise field collapses into the wire.

The result of an expanding and collapsing field, then, is the same as a field in motion. This moving flux cuts across the conductor that is provid-

Fig. 14·1 *Inductors and schematic symbols. (a) Air-core coil. Length 2 in. (b) Iron-core coil. Height 2 in.*

(a)

(b)

Fig. 14·2 *Magnetic field of an alternating current is effectively in motion as it expands, contracts, and reverses with the current variations.*

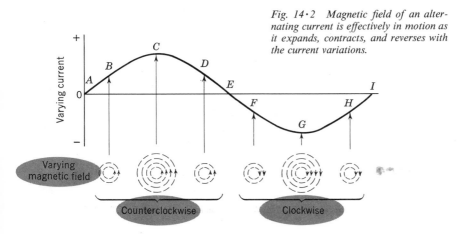

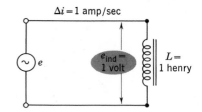

Fig. 14·3   When the current change at the rate of 1 amp per sec induces 1 volt across L, its inductance equals 1 henry.

ing the current, producing induced voltage in the wire itself. Furthermore, any other conductor in the field, whether carrying current or not, also is cut by the varying flux and has induced voltage.

It is important to note that induction by a varying current results from the change in current, not the current value itself. The current must change to provide motion of the flux. A steady direct current of a thousand amperes, as an example of a large current, cannot produce any induced voltage as long as the current value is constant. A current of 1 μa changing to 2 μa, however, does induce voltage. Also, the faster the current changes, the higher the induced voltage because, when the flux moves at a higher speed, it can induce more voltage.

Since inductance is a measure of induced voltage, the amount of inductance has an important effect in any circuit where the current changes. The inductance is an additional characteristic of the circuit besides its resistance. The characteristics of inductance are important in:

1. *A-c circuits.* Here the current is continuously changing and producing induced voltage. Lower frequencies of alternating current require more inductance to produce the same amount of induced voltage as a higher-frequency current.

2. *D-c circuits where the current changes in value.* It is not necessary for the current to reverse in direction. One example is a d-c circuit being turned on or off. When the direct current is changing between zero and its steady value, the inductance affects the circuit at the time of switching. A steady direct current that does not change in value is not affected by inductance, however, because there can be no induced voltage without a change in current.

14·2   Self-inductance

The ability of a conductor to induce voltage in itself when the current changes is its *self-inductance* or simply *inductance*. The symbol for inductance is *L*, for linkages of the magnetic flux, and its unit is the henry.[1] As illustrated in Fig. 14·3, one henry is the amount of inductance that allows one volt to be induced when the current changes at the rate of one ampere per second. The formula is

$$L = \frac{e_L}{di/dt} \tag{14·1}$$

[1] Named after Joseph Henry (1797–1878).

where e_L is in volts and di/dt is the current change in amperes per second. Again the symbol d is used for *delta* (Δ) to indicate a small change. The factor di/dt for the current variation with respect to time really specifies how fast its associated magnetic flux is cutting the conductor to produce e_L.

Example 1. The current in an inductor changes from 12 to 16 amp in 1 sec. How much is the di/dt rate of current change in amperes per second?
Answer. The di is the difference between 16 and 12, or **4 amp per sec.**

Example 2. The current in an inductor changes by 50 ma in 2 μsec. How much is the di/dt rate of current change in amperes per second?

Answer. $\qquad \dfrac{di}{dt} = \dfrac{50 \times 10^{-3}}{2 \times 10^{-6}} = 25 \times 10^3 = \mathbf{25{,}000} \ \dfrac{\mathbf{amp}}{\mathbf{sec}}$

Example 3. How much is the inductance of a coil that induces 40 volts when its current changes at the rate of 4 amp per sec?

Answer. $\qquad\qquad L = \dfrac{e_L}{di/dt} = \dfrac{40}{4} = \mathbf{10 \ henrys}$

Example 4. How much is the inductance of a coil that induces 1,000 volts when its current changes at the rate of 50 ma in 2 μsec?

Answer. $\quad L = \dfrac{e_L}{di/dt} = \dfrac{e_L \times dt}{di} = \dfrac{1 \times 10^3 \times 2 \times 10^{-6}}{50 \times 10^{-3}} = \dfrac{2 \times 10^{-3}}{50 \times 10^{-3}}$

$\qquad\qquad L = \dfrac{2}{50} = \mathbf{0.04 \ henry}$

Notice in Example 4 that the smaller inductance produces much more e_L than in Example 3. The very fast current change in Example 4 is equivalent to 25,000 amp per sec.

In terms of physical construction, the inductance of a coil depends on how it is wound.[2] Note the following factors.

1. A greater number (N) of turns increase L because more voltage can be induced. Actually L increases in proportion to N^2. Double the number of turns in the same area and length increases the inductance four times.
2. More area (A) for each turn increases L. This means a coil with larger turns has more inductance. L increases in direct proportion to A and as the square of the diameter of each turn.
3. L increases with the permeability μ of the core. For an air core μ is 1. With a magnetic core, L is increased by the μ factor as the magnetic flux is concentrated in the coil.
4. L decreases with more length for the same turns.

These physical characteristics of a coil are illustrated in Fig. 14·4. When

[2] Methods of winding coils for a specific L are described in the *A.R.R.L. Handbook* and in *Bulletin* 74 of the National Bureau of Standards.

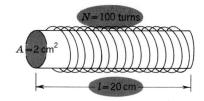

Fig. 14·4   Factors determining inductance of a coil. See text for calculating L.

the diameter is one-tenth or less of the length, the *form factor* is 0.1 or less. For this type of long coil, or solenoid, the inductance can be calculated from the formula.

$$L = \mu \times \frac{N^2 \times A}{l} \times 1.26 \times 10^{-8} \text{ henry} \qquad (14 \cdot 2)$$

where l is in centimeters and A in square centimeters. The constant factor 1.26×10^{-8} converts L to henry units.

For the coil in Fig. 14·4,

$$L = 1 \times \frac{100^2 \times 2}{20} \times 1.26 \times 10^{-8}$$

$$L = 12.6 \times 10^{-6} \text{ henry} = \mathbf{12.6 \ \mu h}$$

This value means the coil can produce a self-induced voltage of 12.6 μv when its current changes at the rate of 1 amp per sec.

Air-core coils for r-f applications have L values in millihenrys (mh) and microhenrys (μh). Note that

$$1 \text{ mh} = 1 \times 10^{-3} \text{ henry} \qquad \text{and} \qquad 1 \ \mu h = 1 \times 10^{-6} \text{ henry.}$$

For example, an r-f coil for the radio broadcast band of 540 to 1,620 kc has an inductance L of 250 μh or 0.250 mh. Iron-core inductors for the 60-cps power line and for audio frequencies have inductance values of about 1 to 25 henrys. Typical sizes for single-layer coils with an air core are given in Table 14·1. Notice that the inductance increases with more turns and wider diameter.

Table 14·1   Dimensions of air-core inductors

Diam., in.	Length, in.	Turns	Turns/in.	L, μh
½	1	8	8	0.32
1	1	8	8	1.13
1	1	16	16	4.52
1½	3	48	16	36.50

14·3   *Self-induced voltage*

The self-induced voltage e_L across an inductance L produced by a change in current di/dt can be stated as

$$e_L = L\frac{di}{dt} \qquad (14\cdot3)$$

where e_L is in volts with L in henrys and di/dt in amperes per second. This formula is just a transposed version of $L = e_L/(di/dt)$, giving the definition of inductance. Actually both versions are based on Formula (12·1): $e = N\, d\phi/dt$, which gives the voltage in terms of magnetic flux cut per second. When the magnetic flux associated with the current varies the same as i, then Formula (14·3) gives the same results for calculating induced voltage.

Example 5. How much is the self-induced voltage across a 4-henry inductance produced by a current change of 12 amp per sec.

Answer. $\qquad e_L = L\dfrac{di}{dt} = 4 \times 12 = \textbf{48 volts}$

Example 6. The current through a 200-mh L changes from 0 to 100 ma in 2 μsec. How much is e_L?

Answer. $\qquad e_L = L\dfrac{di}{dt} = 200 \times 10^{-3} \times \dfrac{100 \times 10^{-3}}{2 \times 10^{-6}}$

$\qquad e_L = \textbf{10,000 volts}$

Note the high voltage induced in the 200-mh inductance because of the fast change in current.

Lenz's law. This law states the requirement of generator action that any voltage generated by induction must oppose the motion producing the induced voltage. Otherwise, the induced voltage could increase to an unlimited amount without the need for adding any work. In terms of induced voltage produced by varying current, the change of current is equivalent to motion of the magnetic flux and must be opposed by the induced voltage. When the current increases, the induced voltage opposes the increase; when the current decreases, the induced voltage opposes the decrease. In both cases, the change is opposed by the induced voltage. Inductance, therefore, is the characteristic that opposes any change in current.

More details of applying Lenz's law to determine the polarity of e_L in a circuit are illustrated in Fig. 14·5. Note the directions carefully. In *a*, the electron flow is into the top of the coil. This current is increasing. By Lenz's law e_L must have the polarity needed to oppose the increase. The induced voltage shown with the top side negative opposes the increase in current. The reason is that this polarity of e_L can produce current in the opposite

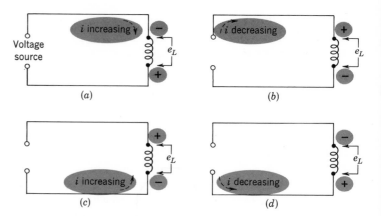

Fig. 14·5   *Determining the polarity of e_L by Lenz's law. (a) i in one direction and increasing. (b) i in same direction but decreasing. (c) i in opposite direction and increasing. (d) Same direction of i as in c but decreasing values.*

direction, from minus to plus in the external circuit with e_L as a generator. This action tends to keep the current from increasing.

In *b*, the source is still producing electron flow into the top of the coil but *i* is decreasing, because the source voltage is decreasing. By Lenz's law, e_L must have the polarity needed to oppose the decrease in current. The induced voltage shown with the top side positive now opposes the decrease. The reason is that this polarity of e_L can produce current in the same direction, tending to keep the current from decreasing.

In *c*, the voltage source reverses polarity to produce current in the opposite direction, with electron flow into the bottom of the coil. This reversed direction of current is now increasing. The polarity of e_L must oppose the increase. As shown, now the bottom of the coil is made negative by e_L, to produce current opposing the source current. Finally, in *d* the reversed current is decreasing. This decrease is opposed by the polarity shown for e_L to keep the current flowing in the same direction as the source current.

Notice that the polarity of e_L reverses for either a reversal of direction for *i*, or a reversal of change in *di* between increasing or decreasing values. When both the direction of the current and the direction of change are reversed, as in a comparison of *a* and *d*, the polarity is the same.

Sometimes the formulas for induced voltage are written with a minus sign, in order to indicate the fact that e_L opposes the change, as specified by Lenz's law. However, the negative sign is omitted here so that the actual polarity of the self-induced voltage can be determined in typical circuits.

14·4   *Mutual inductance*

When the current in an inductor changes, the varying flux can cut across any other inductor nearby, producing induced voltage in both inductors.

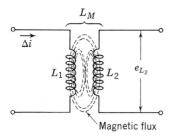

Fig. 14·6 Mutual inductance L_M between two coils L_1 and L_2 linked by magnetic flux.

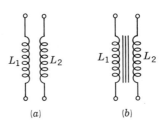

Fig. 14·7 Schematic symbols for two coils with mutual inductance. (a) Air core. (b) Iron core.

In Fig. 14·6, the coil L_1 is connected to a generator that produces varying current in the turns. The winding L_2 is not connected to L_1, but the turns are linked by the magnetic field. A varying current in L_1, therefore, induces voltage across L_1 and across L_2. If all the flux of the current in L_1 links all the turns of the coil L_2, each turn in L_2 will have the same amount of induced voltage as each turn in L_1. Furthermore, the induced voltage E_{L_2} can produce current in a load resistance connected across L_2.

When the induced voltage produces current in L_2, its varying magnetic field induces voltage in L_1. The two coils L_1 and L_2 have mutual inductance, therefore, because current in one can induce voltage in the other. The unit of mutual inductance is the henry, and the symbol is L_M. Two coils have a mutual inductance of one henry when a current change of one ampere per second in one coil induces one volt in the other coil. The schematic symbol for two coils with mutual inductance is shown in Fig. 14·7a for an air core, with an iron core in b. Iron increases the mutual inductance, since it concentrates magnetic flux. Any magnetic lines that do not link the two coils result in *leakage flux*.

Coefficient of coupling. The fraction of total flux from one coil linking another coil is the coefficient of coupling (k) between the two coils. As examples, if all the flux of L_1 in Fig. 14·6 links L_2, k equals 1, or unity coupling; if only half the flux of one coil links the other, k equals 0.5. Specifically, the coefficient of coupling is

$$K = \frac{\text{flux linkages between } L_1 \text{ and } L_2}{\text{flux produced by } L_1}$$

There are no units for k, as it is just a ratio of two values of magnetic flux. The value of k is generally stated as a decimal fraction, like 0.5, rather than per cent.

The coefficient of coupling is increased by placing the coils close together, possibly with one wound on top of the other, by placing them in parallel rather than perpendicular to each other, or by winding the coils on a common iron core. Several examples are shown in Fig. 14·8.

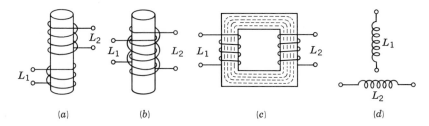

Fig. 14·8   Magnetic coupling between two coils linked by mutual induction.
(a) L_1 and L_2 wound parallel on paper or plastic form with air core; k about 0.1.
(b) L_1 wound over L_2 for tighter coupling; k about 0.3. (c) Unity coupling with
L_1 and L_2 on common iron core; k approximately 1. (d) Zero coupling between
perpendicular air-core coils; k essentially 0.

A high value of k, called *tight coupling,* allows the current in one coil to
induce more voltage in the other coil. *Loose coupling,* with a low value of k,
has the opposite effect. In the extreme case of zero coefficient of coupling,
there is no mutual inductance. Two coils may be placed perpendicular to
each other and far apart for essentially zero coupling when it is desired to
minimize interaction between the coils. Air-core coils wound on one form
have values of k equal to 0.05 to 0.3, approximately, corresponding to 5 to
30 per cent linkage. Coils on a common iron core can be considered to have
practically unity coupling, with k equal to 1.

Example 7. A coil L_1 produces 80 μwebers of magnetic flux. Of this total flux,
60 μwebers are linked with L_2. How much is k between L_1 and L_2?

Answer.
$$K = \frac{60 \ \mu\text{webers}}{80 \ \mu\text{webers}} = \textbf{0.75}$$

Example 8. A 10-henry inductance L_1 on an iron core produces 4 webers of
magnetic flux. Another coil L_2 is on the same core. How much is k between L_1
and L_2?
Answer. **Unity or 1.** All coils on a common iron core have practically perfect
coupling.

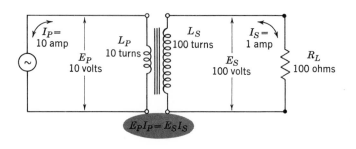

Fig. 14·9   Iron-core transformer
with 10:1 turns ratio. Primary current I_p induces secondary voltage E_s
to produce current in the secondary
load R_L.

Calculating mutual inductance. The mutual inductance increases with higher values for the primary and secondary inductances and tighter coupling:

$$L_M = k\sqrt{L_1 \times L_2} \qquad \text{henrys} \qquad (14 \cdot 4)$$

where L_1 and L_2 are the self-inductance values of the two coils, in henrys, k is the coefficient of coupling, and L_M is the mutual inductance linking L_1 and L_2. For the case illustrated in Fig. 14·8c, with L_1 having 2 henrys of self-inductance and L_2 having 8 henrys, L_M equals 4 henrys, with unity coupling. This value of L_M is calculated as follows:

$$L_M = 1\sqrt{2 \times 8} = \sqrt{16} = \textbf{4 henrys}$$

The value of 4 henrys for L_M in this example means that when the current changes at the rate of 1 amp per sec in either coil, it will induce 4 volts in the other coil.

Example 9. Two 400-mh coils L_1 and L_2 have a coefficient of coupling k equal to 0.2. Calculate L_M.

Answer. $L_M = k\sqrt{L_1 \times L_2} = 0.2\sqrt{400 \times 10^{-3} \times 400 \times 10^{-3}}$
$\qquad\qquad = 0.2 \times 400 \times 10^{-3}$
$\qquad L_M = 80 \times 10^{-3} = \textbf{80 mh}$

Example 10. If the above two coils had a mutual inductance L_M of 40 mh, how much would k be? (*Note:* transpose Formula (14·4) to find k.)

Answer. $\qquad k = \dfrac{L_M}{\sqrt{L_1 \times L_2}} = \dfrac{40 \times 10^{-3}}{\sqrt{400 \times 10^{-3} \times 400 \times 10^{-3}}}$

$\qquad k = \dfrac{40 \times 10^{-3}}{400 \times 10^{-3}} = \textbf{0.1}$

Notice that the same two coils have one-half the mutual inductance L_M, with one-half the coefficient of coupling k.

14·5 Transformers

The transformer is a common application of mutual inductance. As shown in Fig. 14·9, a transformer has the primary winding L_P connected to a voltage source that produces alternating current, while the secondary winding L_S is connected across the load resistance R_L. The purpose of the transformer is to transfer power from the primary, where the generator is connected, to the secondary, where the induced secondary voltage can produce current in the load resistance connected to L_S.

Although the primary and secondary are not connected to each other, power in the primary is coupled into the secondary by the magnetic field linking the two windings. The transformer is used to provide power for the load resistance R_L, instead of connecting R_L directly across the generator, whenever the load requires an a-c voltage higher or lower than the generator voltage. By having more or fewer turns in L_S, compared with L_P, the transformer can step up or step down the generator voltage to provide the required amount of secondary voltage. Typical transformers are shown in Figs. 14·10 and 14·11. It should be noted that a steady d-c voltage cannot be stepped up or down by a transformer, because a steady current cannot produce induced voltage.

Turns ratio. The ratio of the number of turns in the secondary to the number in the primary is the turns ratio of the transformer:

$$\text{Turns ratio} = \frac{N_s}{N_p} \qquad (14·5)$$

For example, 500 turns in the secondary and 50 turns in the primary provide a turns ratio of $^{500}\!\!/_{50}$, or $10:1$.

Voltage ratio. With unity coupling between primary and secondary, the voltage induced in each turn of the secondary is the same as the self-induced voltage of each turn in the primary. Therefore, the voltage ratio is in the same proportion as the turns ratio:

$$\frac{E_s}{E_p} = \frac{N_s}{N_p} \qquad (14·6)$$

When the secondary has more turns, the secondary voltage is higher and the primary voltage is stepped up. This principle is illustrated in Fig. 14·9 with a step-up ratio of $^{100}\!\!/_{10}$, or $10:1$. When the secondary has fewer turns, the voltage is stepped down. In either case, the ratio is in terms of the primary voltage, which may be stepped up or down in the same proportion as the turns ratio. This applies only to iron-core transformers with unity coupling. Air-core transformers for r-f circuits are generally tuned to resonance. In this case, the resonance factor is considered instead of the turns ratio.

(a)

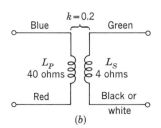

(b)

$k = 0.2$

Blue — Green

L_P — 40 ohms — L_S — 4 ohms

Red — Black or white

Fig. 14·10 (a) Air-core r-f transformer. Height 2 in. Top winding is secondary. (b) Color coding and d-c resistance of windings.

Example 11. A power transformer has 100 turns for L_p and 600 turns for L_s. What is the turns ratio? How much is the secondary voltage E_s with a primary voltage E_p of 120 volts?

Answer. The turns ratio is $^{600}\!/_{100}$ or 6:1. Therefore, E_p is stepped up by the factor 6, making E_s equal to 6 × 120, or **720 volts.**

Example 12. A power transformer has 100 turns for L_p and 5 turns for L_s. What is the turns ratio? How much is the secondary voltage E_s with a primary voltage of 120 volts?

Answer. The turns ratio is $^{5}\!/_{100}$, or 1:20. E_p is stepped down by the factor $\frac{1}{20}$, therefore making E_s equal to $^{120}\!/_{20}$, or **6 volts.**

Secondary current. By Ohm's law, the amount of secondary current equals the secondary voltage divided by the resistance in the secondary circuit. In Fig. 14·9, with a value of 100 ohms for R_L and negligible coil resistance assumed,

$$I_s = \frac{E_s}{R_L} = \frac{100 \text{ volts}}{100 \text{ ohms}} = 1 \text{ amp}$$

The power dissipated in R_L is $I_s{}^2 R_L$ or $E_s I_s$, which equals 100 watts in this example.

The power used by the secondary load resistance is supplied by the generator in the primary. With current in the secondary winding, its magnetic field opposes the varying flux of the primary current. The generator must then produce more primary current to maintain the self-induced voltage

Fig. 14·11 (a) Iron-core power transformer. Height 5 in. (b) Color coding of leads and typical windings with d-c resistance.

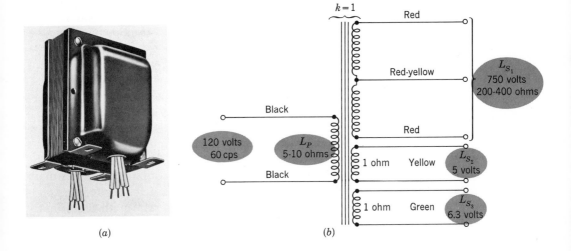

(a)   (b)

across L_p and the secondary voltage developed in L_s by mutual induction. If the secondary current doubles, for instance, because the load resistance is reduced one-half, the primary current will also double in value to provide the required power for the secondary. Therefore, the effect of the secondary-load power on the generator is the same as though R_L were in the primary, except that in the secondary the voltage for R_L is stepped up or down by the turns ratio.

Current ratio. With zero losses assumed for the transformer, the power in the secondary equals the power in the primary:

$$E_p I_p = E_s I_s \tag{14·7}$$

or

$$\frac{I_p}{I_s} = \frac{E_s}{E_p} \tag{14·8}$$

The current ratio is the inverse of the voltage ratio; that is, voltage step-up in the secondary means current step-down, and vice versa. The secondary does not generate power but only takes it from the primary. Therefore, the current step-up or step-down is in terms of the secondary current I_s, which is determined by the load resistance across the secondary voltage. These points are illustrated by the following two examples.

Example 13. A transformer with a 6:1 voltage step-up ratio has 720 volts across 7,200 ohms in the secondary. (*a*) How much is I_s? (*b*) How much is I_p?

(*a*)
$$I_s = \frac{E_s}{R_L} = \frac{720 \text{ volts}}{7{,}200 \text{ ohms}} = \textbf{0.1 amp}$$

(*b*) With a turns and voltage ratio of 6:1, the current ratio is 1:6. Therefore,

$$I_s = \tfrac{1}{6} \times I_p$$

or
$$I_p = 6 \times I_s = 6 \times 0.1 = \textbf{0.6 amp}$$

Example 14. A transformer with a 1:20 voltage step-down ratio has 6 volts across 0.6 ohm in the secondary. (*a*) How much is I_s? (*b*) How much is I_p?

(*a*)
$$I_s = \frac{E_s}{R_L} = \frac{6 \text{ volts}}{0.6 \text{ ohm}} = \textbf{10 amp}$$

(*b*)
$$I_s = 20 \times I_p$$

or
$$I_p = \tfrac{1}{20} \times I_s = \tfrac{1}{20} \times 10 = \tfrac{1}{2} = \textbf{0.5 amp}$$

Total secondary power equals primary power. Figure 14·12 illustrates a power transformer with two secondary windings L_1 and L_2. There can be one, two, or more secondary winding with unity coupling to the primary as long as all the windings are on the same iron core. Each secondary winding has induced voltage in proportion to its turns ratio with the primary winding, which is connected across the 120-volt source. The secondary winding L_1 has a turns ratio of 6:1, providing 720 volts. The 7,200-ohm

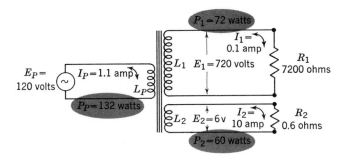

Fig. 14·12   *Power used by secondary load resistances R_1 and R_2 equals the power supplied by the primary generator.*

load resistance R_1, across L_1, allows the 720 volts to produce 0.1 amp for I_1 in this secondary circuit. The power here is 720 volts × 0.1 amp, therefore, which equals 72 watts.

The other secondary winding L_2 provides voltage step-down, with the ratio 1:20, resulting in 6 volts for R_2. The 0.6-ohm load resistance in this circuit allows 10 amp for I_2. Therefore, the power here is 6 volts × 10 amp, or 60 watts. Since the windings have separate connections, each can have its individual values of voltage and current.

All the power used in the secondary circuits is supplied by the primary, however. In this example, the total secondary power is 132 watts, equal to 72 watts for R_1 and 60 watts for R_2. The power supplied by the 120-volt source in the primary then equals 132 watts. Therefore, the primary current I_p equals the primary power P_p divided by the primary voltage E_p, or 132 watts divided by 120 volts, which equals 1.1 amp for the primary current. The same value can be calculated as the sum of 0.6 amp of primary current providing power for L_1, plus 0.5 amp of primary current for L_2, resulting in the total of 1.1 amp as the value of I_p.

Autotransformers. As illustrated in Fig. 14·13, an autotransformer consists of one continuous coil with a tapped connection such as terminal 2

Fig. 14·13   *The autotransformer. Tap at terminal 2 here at one-sixth the total turns. (a) E_p across 1 and 2 stepped up across 1 and 3. (b) E_p across 1 and 3 stepped down across 1 and 2.*

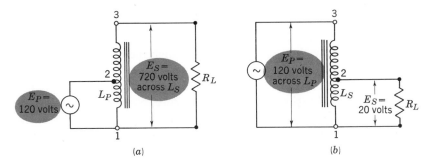

(a)   (b)

between the ends at terminals 1 and 3. In *a* the autotransformer steps up the generator voltage because E_p between 1 and 2 is connected across part of the total turns, while E_s is induced across all the turns. If the total turns across 1 and 3 equal 600, for instance, with 100 turns across 1 and 2, then primary current flowing between 1 and 2 induces the same voltage in each of the 600 turns because of the unity coupling for all turns on the iron core. With 6 times the turns for the induced secondary voltage, E_s is 6 times E_p. In *b*, the autotransformer steps down the primary voltage connected across the entire coil, since the secondary voltage is taken across less than the total turns. The winding that connects to the voltage source to supply power is the primary, while the secondary is across the load resistance R_L. The turns ratio and voltage ratio apply to the autotransformer in the same way as in a conventional transformer having an isolated secondary winding.

The autotransformer is more compact and efficient for applications where the same wire size is suitable for primary and secondary windings. The autotransformer does not, however, isolate the secondary load resistance from the primary generator.

Transformer efficiency. Efficiency is defined as the ratio of power out to power in. For example, when the power out in watts equals one-half the power in, the efficiency is ½, which equals 0.5×100 per cent, or 50 per cent. In a transformer, power out is secondary power, while power in is primary power.

Assuming zero losses in the transformer, power out equals power in and the efficiency is 100 per cent. Power transformers actually, however, have an efficiency slightly less than 100 per cent. The efficiency is approximately 80 to 90 per cent for power transformers in receivers, with a power rating of 50 to 300 watts. Transformers for higher power are more efficient because they require heavier wire, which has less resistance. In a transformer less than 100 per cent efficient, the primary supplies more than the secondary power. The primary power missing from the output is dissipated as heat in the transformer.

14·6 Core losses

The fact that the magnetic core can become warm, or even hot, shows that some of the energy supplied to the coil is used up in heat. The two main effects are eddy-current losses and hysteresis losses.

Eddy currents. In any inductance with an iron core, alternating current induces voltage in the core itself. Since it is a conductor, the iron core has current produced by the induced voltage. This current is called an *eddy current* because it flows in a circular path through the cross section of the core, as illustrated in Fig. 14·14.

The eddy currents represent wasted power dissipated as heat in the core, equal to I^2R, where R is the resistance of the core. Note in Fig. 14·14 that the eddy-current flux opposes the coil flux, requiring more current in the coil to maintain its magnetic field. The higher the frequency of the alternating current in the inductance, the greater the eddy-current loss.

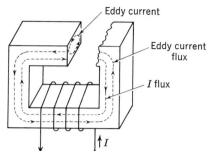

Fig. 14·14 Cross-sectional view of iron
core showing eddy currents.

Eddy currents can be induced in any conductor near a coil with alternating current, not only in its core. For instance, a coil has eddy-current
losses in a metal cover. In fact, the technique of induction heating is an
application of heat resulting from induced eddy currents.

R-f shielding. The reason why a coil may have a metal cover, usually
copper or aluminum, is to provide a shield against the varying flux of r-f
current. In this case, the shielding effect depends on using a good conductor
for the eddy currents produced by the varying flux, rather than the magnetic materials used for shielding against static magnetic flux. The shield
cover not only isolates the coil from external varying magnetic fields, but
the effect of the coil's r-f current is also minimized for external circuits. The
reason why the shield helps both ways is the same, as the induced eddy
currents have a field that opposes the field that is inducing the current. It
should be noted that the clearance between the sides of the coil and the
metal should be equal to or greater than the coil radius, to minimize the
effect of the shield in reducing the inductance.

Hysteresis losses. Another factor with a magnetic core for r-f coils is
hysteresis losses, although not so great as eddy-current losses. The hysteresis losses result from the additional power needed to reverse the magnetic
field in magnetic materials with r-f alternating current.

Air-core coils. It should be noted that air has practically no losses from
eddy currents or hysteresis. However, the inductance for small coils with
an air core is limited to low values in the microhenry range.

14·7 Types of cores

In order to minimize losses while maintaining high flux density, the core
can be made of laminated sheets insulated from each other, or insulated
powdered-iron granules and ferrite materials can be used. These core types
are illustrated in Figs. 14·15 and 14·16. The purpose is to reduce the
amount of eddy currents.

Laminated core. Figure 14·15a shows a shell-type core formed with a
group of individual laminations. Each laminated section is insulated by a
very thin coating of iron oxide and varnish. The insulating borders increase

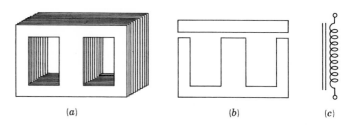

(a)   (b)   (c)

Fig. 14·15   *Laminated iron core. (a) Shell-type core.*
(b) Individual E- and I-shaped laminations. (c) Iron-
core symbol.

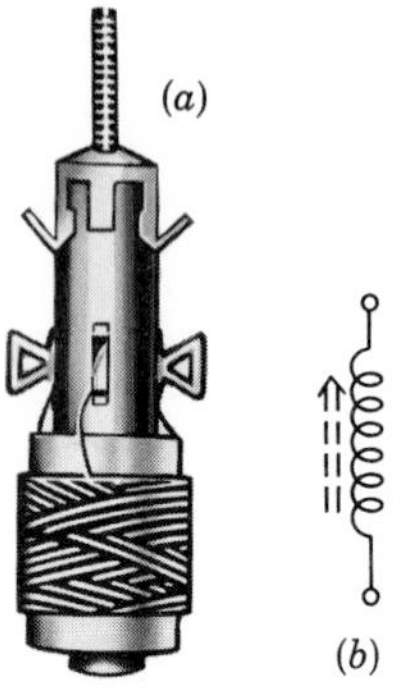

(a)

(b)

Fig. 14·16   *(a) Coil with powdered-iron slug as*
the core. Width of coil about ½ in. Screw at top ad-
justs slug for 1- to 3-mh inductance. (b) Symbol for
core of powdered iron or ferrite.

the resistance in the cross section of the core to reduce the eddy currents
but allow a low-reluctance path for high flux density around the core.
Transformers for audio frequencies and 60-cycle power are generally made
with a laminated iron core.

Powdered-iron core. To reduce eddy currents in the iron core of an inductance for radio frequencies, powdered iron is generally used. It consists
of individual insulated granules pressed into one solid form.

Ferrite core. The ferrites are ceramic materials that provide high values
of magnetic flux density but with the advantage of being an insulator.
Therefore, a ferrite core can be used in inductances for high frequencies
with minimum eddy-current losses. Figure 14·16 shows a typical inductor
with a ferrite core.

14·8   *Variable inductance*

The inductance of a coil can be varied by one of the methods illustrated
in Fig. 14·17. In *a*, more or fewer turns can be used by connection to one
of the taps, while in *b* a slider contacts the coil to vary the number of turns
used. Note that the unused turns are shorted to prevent the tapped coil
from acting as an autotransformer, since stepped-up voltage could cause
arcing across the turns. In *c* the powdered-iron slug can be moved in and
out of the coil to vary the permeability of its core. Maximum permeability
and inductance result with the slug in. The variometer in *d* illustrates an
arrangement for varying the position of one coil within the other. The total
inductance of the series-aiding coils is minimum when they are perpendicular. For any method of varying the inductance, the variable inductance
symbol in *e* can be used, although an adjustable slug is usually indicated
as in *c*.

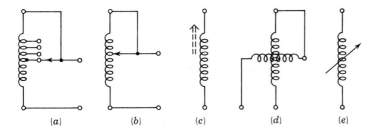

Fig. 14·17 *Methods of providing variable inductance. (a) Tapped coil. (b) Slider contact on coil. (c) Adjustable slug. (d) Variometer. (e) General symbol for variable inductance.*

A practical application of variable inductance is the *Variac* in Fig. 14·18. This unit is an autotransformer with taps to provide output voltage from zero to 140 volts, with input from the 120-volt 60-cps power line. One use is testing equipment with voltage above or below the normal line voltage. The Variac is plugged into the power line, and the equipment to be tested is plugged into the Variac. Note that the power rating of the Variac should be equal to or more than the power used by the equipment being tested.

14·9 *Inductances in series or parallel*

The total inductance of coils connected in series is the sum of the individual inductance values, as for series resistances (Fig. 14·19). Since the series coils have the same current, the total induced voltage is a result of the total number of turns. Therefore, in series,

$$L_T = L_1 + L_2 + L_3 + \cdots + \text{etc.} \qquad (14·9)$$

Fig. 14·18 *Variac rated at 300 watts. Length about 5 in.* (General Radio Corp.)

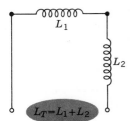

Fig. 14·19 *Inductances in series without mutual coupling.*

where L_T is in the same units of inductance as L_1, L_2, and L_3. This formula assumes no mutual induction between the coils.

Example 15. L_1 in Fig. $14 \cdot 19$ is 5 mh and L_2 is 10 mh. How much is L_T?

Answer. $L_T = 5 \text{ mh} + 10 \text{ mh} = \textbf{15 mh}$

With coils connected in parallel, the total inductance is calculated from the reciprocal formula

$$\frac{1}{L_T} = \frac{1}{L_1} + \frac{1}{L_2} + \frac{1}{L_3} + \cdots + \text{etc.} \qquad (14 \cdot 10)$$

Again, no mutual induction is assumed, as illustrated in Fig. $14 \cdot 20$.

Example 16. L_1 and L_2 in Fig. $14 \cdot 20$ are each 8 mh. How much is L_T?

Answer. $$\frac{1}{L_T} = \frac{1}{8} + \frac{1}{8} = \frac{2}{8}$$

$$L_T = \frac{8}{2} = \textbf{4 mh}$$

For the case of two series coils that have mutual inductance, the total inductance depends on the amount of coupling and on whether the coils are connected series-aiding or series-opposing. *Series-aiding* means that the common current produces the same direction of magnetic field for the

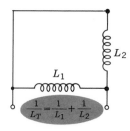

$$\frac{1}{L_T} = \frac{1}{L_1} + \frac{1}{L_2}$$

Fig. $14 \cdot 20$ *Inductances in parallel without mutual coupling.*

Fig. $14 \cdot 21$ *L_1 and L_2 in series with mutual inductance L_M. (a) Series-aiding. (b) Series-opposing.*

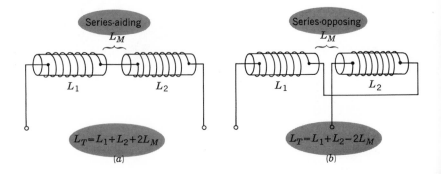

two coils. The *series-opposing* connection results in opposite fields. The coupling depends on the coil connections and direction of winding. Reversing either one reverses the field. In Fig. 14·21, two coils with the same direction of winding are connected series-aiding in *a* but series-opposing in *b*. To calculate the total inductance of two coils that are series-connected and have mutual inductance,

$$L_T = L_1 + L_2 \pm 2L_M \qquad (14 \cdot 11)$$

The mutual inductance L_M is plus, increasing the total inductance, when the coils are series-aiding, or minus when they are series-opposing to reduce the total inductance.

Formula (14·11) provides a method of determining the mutual inductance between two coils L_1 and L_2 of known inductance. First, the total inductance is measured for the series-aiding connection. Let this be L_{T_a}. Then the connections to one coil are reversed to measure the total inductance for the series-opposing coils. Let this be L_{T_o}. Then

$$L_M = \frac{L_{T_a} - L_{T_o}}{4} \qquad (14 \cdot 12)$$

When the mutual inductance is known, the coefficient of coupling k can be calculated from the fact that $L_M = k\sqrt{L_1 L_2}$.

> *Example 17.* Two series coils, each with an L of 250 μh, have a total inductance of 550 μh series-aiding and 450 μh series-opposing. (*a*) How much is the mutual inductance L_M between the two coils? (*b*) How much is the coupling coefficient k?

(*a*) $\qquad L_M = \dfrac{L_{T_a} - L_{T_o}}{4} = \dfrac{550 - 450}{4} = \dfrac{100}{4} = \textbf{25 μh}$

(*b*) $\qquad L_M = k\sqrt{L_1 L_2}$

or $\qquad k = \dfrac{L_M}{\sqrt{L_1 L_2}} = \dfrac{25}{\sqrt{250 \times 250}} = \dfrac{25}{250} = \dfrac{1}{10} = \textbf{0.1}$

14·10 Stray inductance

Although practical inductors are generally made as coils, all conductors have inductance. The amount of L is $e/(di/dt)$, as with any inductance producing induced voltage when the current changes. The inductance of any wiring not included in the conventional inductors can be considered stray inductance. In most cases, the stray inductance is very small, typical values being less than 1 μh. For high radio frequencies, though, even a small L can have an appreciable inductive effect.

One source of stray inductance is the connecting leads. A wire 0.04 in. in diameter and 4 in. long has an L of approximately 0.1 μh. At low frequencies, this inductance is negligible. However, consider the case of r-f current where i varies from 0 to 20 ma peak value in the short time of 0.025 μsec for a quarter-cycle of a 10-Mc sine wave. Then e_L equals 80 mv, which is an appreciable inductive effect. This is one reason why the connecting leads must be very short in r-f circuits.

As another example, wirewound resistors can have appreciable inductance when wound as a straight coil. This is why carbon resistors are preferred for minimum stray inductance in r-f circuits. However, noninductive wirewound resistors can also be used. These are wound in such a way that adjacent turns have current in opposite directions, so that the magnetic fields oppose each other to cancel the inductance. Another application of this technique is twisting a pair of connecting leads to reduce the inductive effect.

14·11   Troubles in coils

The most common trouble in coils is an open. As illustrated in Fig. 14·22, an ohmmeter connected across the coil reads infinite resistance for an open winding. It does not matter whether the coil has an air core or an iron core. Since the coil is open, it cannot conduct current and therefore has no inductance, because it cannot produce induced voltage. When the resistance of a coil is checked, it should be disconnected from the external circuit to eliminate any parallel paths that could affect the resistance readings.

D-c resistance of a coil. A coil has d-c resistance equal to the resistance of the wire used in the winding. The amount of resistance is less with heavier wire and fewer turns. For r-f coils with inductance values up to several millihenrys, requiring 10 to 100 turns of fine wire, the d-c resistance is 1 to 20 ohms, approximately. Inductors for 60 cps and audio frequencies with several hundred turns may have resistance values of 10 to 500 ohms, depending on the wire size.

As shown in Fig. 14·23, the d-c resistance and inductance of a coil are in series, since the same current that induces voltage in the turns must overcome the resistance of the wire. Although resistance has no function in producing induced voltage, it is useful to know the d-c coil resistance because if it is normal, usually the inductance can also be assumed to have its normal value.

Open coil. An open winding has infinite resistance, as indicated by an ohmmeter reading. With a transformer having four leads or more, check the resistance across the two leads for the primary, across the two leads for the secondary, and across any other pairs of leads for additional secondary windings. For an autotransformer with three leads, check the resistance from one lead to each of the other two. When the open is inside the winding, it is usually not practical to repair the coil and the entire unit is replaced. Sometimes, though, when the open is at the point where the internal winding joins the external terminals or leads, the connection can be soldered to repair the open.

The open in a coil is generally the result of excessive current or old age. Too much current for the wire size can burn the wire open. The entire wind-

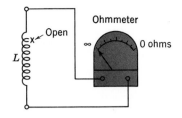

Fig. 14·22 *An open coil reads infinite resistance when its continuity is checked with an ohmmeter.*

Fig. 14·23 *The internal d-c resistance r_i is in series with the inductance of the coil.*

ing may be charred. Even without excessive current, fine wire in a coil may break open when it is old. As the wire expands with heat when current flows and contracts when the current is off, it can crystallize and become brittle, particularly where the wire bends.

Open secondary winding. When the secondary of a transformer is open, it cannot supply power to any load resistance across the open winding. Furthermore, with no current in the secondary, the primary current is also practically zero, as though the primary winding were open. The only primary current needed is the small magnetizing current to sustain the field producing induced voltage across the secondary without any load. If the transformer has several secondary windings, however, an open winding in one secondary does not affect transformer operation for the secondary circuits that are normal.

Short across the secondary winding. Excessive primary current flows, as though it were shorted, often burning out the primary winding. The reason is that the large secondary current has a strong field that opposes the flux of the self-induced voltage across the primary, making it draw more current from the generator.

Shorted turns. This condition usually cannot be checked definitely with the ohmmeter because a few shorted turns reduces the d-c resistance only slightly. When shorted turns are suspected because of reduced inductance, the best check is to substitute a new unit.

Short between primary and secondary. The resistance between separate windings is normally infinitely high. If an ohmmeter connected between primary and secondary reads relatively low resistance, it indicates a short between the primary and secondary turns. Similarly, the normal resistance from any winding to the iron core and frame is infinite; a relatively low ohmmeter reading indicates a short circuit.

SUMMARY

1. Varying current induces voltage in a conductor, since the expanding and collapsing field of the current is equivalent to flux in motion.
2. Lenz's law states that the induced voltage opposes the change in current causing the induction. For this reason an induced voltage is a back emf, or counter emf. Inductance, therefore, tends to keep the current from changing.
3. The ability of a conductor to produce induced voltage across itself when the current varies is its self-inductance, or inductance. The symbol is L and the unit of inductance is the henry.

One henry of inductance allows one volt to be induced when the current changes at the rate of 1 amp per sec. For smaller units 1 mh = 1×10^{-3} henry; 1 μh = 1×10^{-6} henry.

4. To calculate the self-induced voltage, $e_L = L \, di/dt$, with e in volts, L in henrys, and di/dt in amperes per second.

5. Mutual inductance is the ability of varying current in one conductor to induce voltage in another conductor nearby. Its symbol is L_M, measured in henrys. $L_M = k\sqrt{L_1 L_2}$, where k is the coefficient of coupling that provides the mutual inductance L_M between two coils L_1 and L_2.

6. A transformer consists of two or more windings with mutual inductance. The primary winding connects to the source voltage; the load resistance is connected across the secondary winding. A separate winding is an isolated secondary.

7. An autotransformer is a tapped coil, used to step-up or step-down voltage. There are three leads with one connection common to both the primary and secondary.

8. A transformer with an iron core has essentially unit coupling. Therefore, the voltage ratio is the same as the turns ratio: $E_s/E_p = N_s/N_p$.

9. Assuming 100 per cent efficiency for an iron-core power transformer, the power supplied to the primary equals the power used in the secondary.

10. Eddy currents are induced in the iron core of an inductance, causing wasted power that heats the core. Eddy-current losses increase with higher frequencies of alternating current. To reduce eddy currents, the iron core is laminated with insulated sections. Powdered-iron and ferrite cores also have minimum eddy-current losses. Hysteresis losses also cause wasted power.

11. Assuming no mutual coupling, series inductances are added like series resistances. For parallel inductances, the total inductance is calculated by the reciprocal formula, as for parallel resistances.

12. In addition to its inductance, a coil has d-c resistance equal to the resistance of the wire in the coil. An open coil has infinitely high resistance. Open, the coil has no inductance, because current cannot flow to produce induced voltage.

SELF-EXAMINATION (*Answers at back of book.*)

Here's a chance to find out how well you have learned the material in this chapter. These exercises are for your self-testing only.

1. Alternating current can induce voltage because alternating current has a (*a*) high peak value; (*b*) varying magnetic field; (*c*) stronger magnetic field than direct current; (*d*) constant magnetic field.

2. When current in a conductor increases, Lenz's law says that the self-induced voltage will (*a*) tend to increase the amount of current; (*b*) aid the applied voltage; (*c*) produce current opposite to the increasing current; (*d*) aid the increasing current.

3. A 5:1 voltage step-up transformer has 120 volts across the primary and 600-ohm resistance across the secondary. Assuming 100 per cent efficiency, the primary current equals (*a*) ⅕ amp; (*b*) 600 ma; (*c*) 5 amp; (*d*) 10 amp.

4. An iron-core transformer with an 8:1 step-up ratio has 120 volts applied across the primary. The voltage across the secondary equals (*a*) 15 volts; (*b*) 120 volts; (*c*) 180 volts; (*d*) 960 volts.

5. If coil length, number of turns, and area all are doubled, compared with its original value the inductance is (*a*) the same; (*b*) double; (*c*) quadrupled; (*d*) one-quarter.

6. Current changing from 4 to 6 amp in 1 sec induces 40 volts in a coil. Its inductance equals (*a*) 40 mh; (*b*) 4 henrys; (*c*) 6 henrys; (*d*) 20 henrys.

7. A laminated iron core has reduced eddy-current losses because (*a*) the laminations are stacked vertically; (*b*) the laminations are insulated from each other; (*c*) the magnetic flux is concentrated in the air gap of the core; (*d*) more wire can be used with less d-c resistance in the coil.

8. Two 250-μh coils in series without mutual coupling have a total inductance of (*a*) 125 μh; (*b*) 250 μh; (*c*) 400 μh; (*d*) 500 μh.

9. The d-c resistance of a coil made with 100 ft of gage No. 30 copper wire is approximately (*a*) less than 1 ohm; (*b*) 10.5 ohms; (*c*) 104 ohms; (*d*) more than 1 M.

10. An open coil has (*a*) infinite resistance and zero inductance; (*b*) zero resistance and high inductance; (*c*) infinite resistance and normal inductance; (*d*) zero resistance and inductance.

ESSAY QUESTIONS

1. Define 1 henry of self-inductance and 1 henry of mutual inductance.
2. State Lenz's law in terms of induced voltage produced by varying current.
3. Make a schematic diagram showing primary and secondary for an iron-core transformer with a 6:1 voltage step-up ratio: (*a*) using an autotransformer; (*b*) using a transformer with isolated secondary winding. (*c*) With 100 turns in the primary, how many turns are in the secondary for both cases?
4. Define the following: coefficient of coupling, transformer efficiency, stray inductance, and eddy-current losses.
5. Why are eddy-current losses reduced with the following cores: (*a*) laminated; (*b*) powdered-iron; (*c*) ferrite?
6. Why is a good conductor used for an r-f shield?
7. Show two methods of providing a variable inductance.
8. Derive the formula $L_M = (L_{T_a} - L_{T_o})/4$ from the fact that $L_{T_a} = L_1 + L_2 + 2L_M$ while $L_{T_o} = L_1 + L_2 - 2L_M$.
9. (*a*) Why will the primary of a power transformer have excessive current if the secondary is shorted? (*b*) Why is there no voltage across the secondary if the primary is open?
10. Describe briefly how to check a coil for an open with an ohmmeter. (*a*) What ohmmeter range should be used? (*b*) What leads will be checked on an autotransformer with one secondary and a transformer with two isolated secondary windings?

PROBLEMS (*Answers to selected problems at back of book.*)

1. Convert into henrys using powers of 10: 250 μh, 40 μh, 40 mh, 5 mh, 0.005 henry.
2. Convert the following current changes to amperes per second: (*a*) zero to 4 amp in 2 sec; (*b*) zero to 50 ma in 5 μsec; (*c*) 100 ma to 150 ma in 5 μsec; (*d*) 150 ma to 100 ma in 5 μsec.
3. Calculate the values of e_L across a 5-mh inductance for each of the current variations in question 2.
4. A coil produces a self-induced voltage of 50 mv when *i* varies at the rate of 25 ma per msec. How much is *L*?
5. A power transformer with an 8:1 turns ratio has 60 cps, 120 volts across the primary. (*a*) What is the frequency of the secondary voltage? (*b*) How much is the secondary voltage? (*c*) With a load resistance of 10,000 ohms across the secondary, how much is the secondary current? Draw the schematic diagram showing primary and secondary circuits. (*d*) How much is the primary current?
6. How much would the primary current be in a power transformer having a primary resistance of 5 ohms if it were connected by mistake to a 120-volt d-c line instead of the 120-volt a-c line?
7. For a 100-μh inductance L_1 and 200-μh inductance L_2, calculate the following: (*a*) total inductance L_T of L_1 and L_2 in series without mutual coupling; (*b*) combined inductance of L_1 and L_2 in parallel without mutual coupling; (*c*) L_T of L_1 and L_2 series-aiding, and series-opposing, with 10 μh mutual inductance; (*d*) value of the coupling factor *k*.
8. Calculate the inductance *L* for the following coils: (*a*) Air-core, 20 turns, area 3.14 cm², length 25 cm; (*b*) same coil as *a* with ferrite core having a mu of 5,000; (*c*) air core, 200 turns, area 3.14 cm², length 25 cm; (*d*) air core, 20 turns, area 3.14 cm², length 50 cm; (*e*) air core, 20 turns, diameter 4 cm, length 50 cm.
9. Calculate the resistance of the following coils (use Table 8·1): (*a*) 400 turns, each using 3 in. of No. 30 gage wire; (*b*) 40 turns, each using 3 in. of No. 10 gage wire.
10. (*a*) Calculate the period *T* for one cycle of a 10-Mc sine wave. (*b*) How much is the time for one quarter-cycle? (*c*) If *i* increases from 0 to 20 ma in this time, how much is e_L across a 0.1-μh inductance?

When alternating current flows in an inductance L, the amount of current is much less than the resistance alone would allow. This additional opposition to sine-wave alternating current, resulting from the self-induced voltage across an inductance, is its inductive reactance X_L. The X indicates reactance, which is an opposition to current and therefore is measured in ohms. The amount of X_L equals $2\pi fL$, where f is in cps and L in henrys. Note that the opposition in ohms of X_L increases for higher frequencies and more inductance. The topics explaining this important effect in sine-wave a-c circuits are:

15·1   How X_L reduces the amount of alternating current
15·2 $X_L = 2\pi fL$
15·3   Series or parallel inductive reactances
15·4   Ohm's law applied to X_L
15·5   Applications of inductive reactance
15·6   Waveshape of e_L induced by sine-wave current

15·1   How X_L reduces the amount of alternating current

Figure 15·1 illustrates how the inductive reactance of a coil reduces the current for a light bulb. The more ohms of X_L, the less current flows. When X_L reduces the current to a very low value, the bulb cannot light.

In a, there is no inductance and the a-c voltage source produces 2.4-amp current to light the bulb with full brilliance. This 2.4-amp I results from 120 volts applied across the 50-ohm R of the bulb's filament. In b, however, a coil is connected in series with the bulb. The coil has a d-c resistance of only 1 ohm, which is negligible, but the reactance of the inductance is 1,000 ohms. This X_L is a measure of the coil's reaction to sine-wave current, in producing a self-induced voltage that opposes the applied voltage and reduces the current. Now I is 120/1,000 ohms, approximately, which equals 0.12 amp. Although the d-c resistance of the coil is only 1 ohm, its X_L of 1,000 ohms limits the amount of alternating current to such a low value that the bulb cannot light. This X_L of 1,000 ohms for 60-cps current can be obtained with an inductance L of approximately 2.65 henrys.

In c, the coil is also in series with the bulb, but the applied battery voltage produces a steady value of direct current. Without any current variations, the coil cannot induce any voltage and, therefore, it has no reactance. The amount of direct current then is practically the same as though the d-c voltage source were connected directly across the bulb, and it lights with full brilliance. In this case, the coil is only a length of wire, as there is no induced voltage without current variations. The d-c resistance is the resistance of the wire in the coil.

In summary, we can make the following conclusions:

1. An inductance can have appreciable X_L in a-c circuits, to reduce the amount of current. Furthermore, the higher the frequency of the alternating current, and the greater the inductance, the higher is the X_L opposition.
2. There is no X_L for steady direct current. In this case, the coil is just a resistance equal to the resistance of the wire.

These effects have almost unlimited applications in practical circuits. Consider how useful ohms of X_L can be for different kinds of current, compared with resistance, which always has the same ohms of opposition. One example is to use X_L where it is desired to have high ohms of opposition to alternating current but little opposition for direct current. Another example is to use X_L for more opposition to a high-frequency alternating current, compared with lower frequencies.

The reason why an inductance can have X_L to reduce the amount of alternating current is the fact that self-induced voltage is produced to oppose the applied voltage. In Fig. 15·2, E_L is the voltage across L, induced

Fig. 15·1   *Illustrating the effect of inductive reactance in reducing the amount of alternating current. (a) Bulb lights with 2.4-amp alternating current. (b) Inserting X_L of 1,000 ohms reduces alternating current to 0.12 amp and the bulb cannot light. (c) With direct current, the coil has no inductive reactance and the bulb lights.*

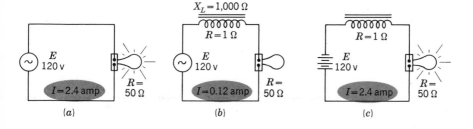

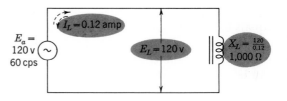

*Fig. 15·2 The inductive react-
ance X_L equals the E_L/I_L ratio
in ohms.*

by the variations in sine-wave current produced by the applied voltage E_a. The two voltages E_a and E_L are the same, as they are in parallel. However, the current I_L is the amount that allows the self-induced voltage E_L to be equal to E_a. In this example, I is 0.12 amp. This value of 60-cps current in the inductance produces E_L of 120 volts.

When we consider the E/I ratio for the ohms of opposition to the sine-wave current, this value is 120/0.12, which equals 1,000 ohms. This 1,000 ohms is what we call X_L, to indicate how much current can be produced by sine-wave voltage across an inductance.

The X_L value depends on the amount of inductance and the frequency of the alternating current. If L in Fig. 15·2 were increased, it could induce the same 120 volts for E_L with less current. Then the ratio of E_L/I_L would be greater, meaning more X_L for more inductance. Also, if the frequency were increased in Fig. 15·2, the current variations would be faster with a higher frequency. Then the same L could produce the 120-volt E_L with less current. For this condition also, the E_L/I_L ratio would be greater, because of the smaller current, indicating more X_L for a higher frequency.

15·2 $X_L = 2\pi fL$

This formula includes the effects of frequency and inductance for calculating the reactance. The frequency is in cps and L in henrys for X_L in ohms. As an example, we can calculate X_L for 2.65-henry L at the frequency of 60 cps:

$$X_L = 2\pi fL \qquad (15·1)$$
$$= 6.28 \times 60 \times 2.65$$
$$X_L = 1,000 \text{ ohms}$$

Note the following factors in the formula $X_L = 2\pi fL$:

1. The constant factor 2π equal to 6.28 indicates the circular motion from which a sine wave is derived. Therefore, this formula applies only to sine-wave a-c circuits.
2. The frequency f is a time element. Higher frequency means the current varies at a faster rate. A faster current change can produce more self-induced voltage across a given amount of inductance.
3. The inductance L indicates the physical factors of the coil that determine how much voltage it can induce for a given current change.
4. X_L is in ohms, corresponding to an E_L/I_L ratio for sine-wave a-c

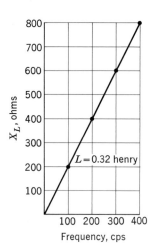

FREQUENCY, cps	$X_L = 2\pi fL,$ ohms
0	0
100	200
200	400
300	600
400	800

Fig. 15·3 Linear increase of X_L with higher frequencies. L is constant at 0.32 henry.

circuits, to determine how much current L allows for a given applied voltage.

The formula $2\pi fL$ shows that X_L is proportional to frequency. When f is doubled, for instance, X_L is doubled. This linear increase of inductive reactance with frequency is illustrated in Fig. 15·3.

The reactance formula also shows that X_L is proportional to the inductance. When the value of henrys for L is doubled, the ohms of X_L is also doubled. This linear increase of inductive reactance with frequency is illustrated in Fig. 15·4.

Example 1. How much is X_L of a 6-mh L at 41.67 kc?

Answer.
$$X_c = 2\pi fL$$
$$= 6.28 \times 41.67 \times 10^3 \times 6 \times 10^{-3}$$
$$X_L = \textbf{1,570 ohms}$$

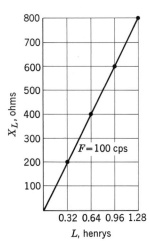

INDUCTANCE, henrys	$X_L = 2\pi fL,$ ohms
0	0
0.32	200
0.64	400
0.96	600
1.28	800

Fig. 15·4 Linear increase of X_L with higher values of inductance. Frequency is constant at 100 cps.

Example 2. Calculate X_L of (*a*) 10-henry L at 60 cps and (*b*) 5-henry L at 60 cps.

Answer.

(*a*) $$X_L = 2\pi fL = 6.28 \times 60 \times 10 = \textbf{3,768 ohms}$$

(*b*) for 5-henry L, $X_L = \frac{1}{2} \times 3,768 = \textbf{1,884 ohms}$

Example 3. Calculate X_L of a 250-μh coil at (*a*) 1 Mc and (*b*) 10 Mc.

Answer.

(*a*) $$X_L = 2\pi fL = 6.28 \times 1 \times 10^6 \times 250 \times 10^{-6} = 6.28 \times 250$$
$$X_L = \textbf{1,570 ohms}$$

(*b*) at 10 Mc, $X_L = 10 \times 1,570 = \textbf{15,700 ohms}$

The last two examples illustrate the fact that X_L is proportional to frequency and inductance. In Example 2*b*, X_L is one-half the value in *a* because the inductance is one-half. In Example 3*b*, X_L is ten times more than in *a* because the frequency is ten times higher.

Not only can X_L be calculated from f and L, but if any two factors are known, the third can be found. Very often X_L can be determined from voltage and current measurements. With the frequency known, then, L can be calculated as

$$L = \frac{X_L}{2\pi f} \tag{15·2}$$

This formula is just a transposed version of $X_L = 2\pi fL$. Use the basic units with ohms for X_L and cps for f, to calculate L in henrys.

Example 4. A coil with negligible resistance has 62.8 volts across it with 0.01 amp. How much is X_L?

Answer. $$X_L = \frac{E_L}{I_L} = \frac{62.8 \text{ volts}}{0.01 \text{ amp}} = \textbf{6,280 ohms}$$

Example 5. Calculate the L of the coil in Example 4 when the frequency is 1,000 cps.

Answer. $$L = \frac{X_L}{2\pi f} = \frac{6,280}{6.28 \times 1,000} = \frac{6,280}{6,280} = \textbf{1 henry}$$

Example 6. Calculate the inductance of a coil that has 15,700 ohms X_L at 10 Mc.

Answer. $$L = \frac{X_L}{2\pi f} = \frac{15,700}{6.28 \times 10 \times 10^6} = \frac{15,700}{62.8} \times 10^{-6}$$
$$L = 250 \times 10^{-6} = \textbf{250 μh}$$

For the third and final version of the inductive reactance formula,

$$f = \frac{X_L}{2\pi L} \tag{15·3}$$

Use the basic units of ohms for X_L and henrys for L to calculate the frequency in cps.

Example 7. At what frequency will an inductance of 1 henry have the reactance of 1,000 ohms?

Answer. $\quad f = \dfrac{X_L}{2\pi L} = \dfrac{1,000}{6.28 \times 1} = 0.159 \times 10^3 = \textbf{159 cps}$

15·3 Series or parallel inductive reactances

Since reactance is an opposition in ohms, inductive reactances in series or parallel are combined the same way as ohms of resistance. With series reactances the total reactance is the sum of the individual values, as shown in Fig. 15·5a. For example, the series reactances of 100 and 200 ohms add to equal 300 ohms of X_L across both inductances. Therefore, in series,

$$X_{L_T} = X_{L_1} + X_{L_2} + X_{L_3} + \cdots + \text{etc.} \tag{15·4}$$

For the case of parallel reactances, the combined reactance is calculated by the reciprocal formula. As shown in Fig. 15·5b, in parallel

$$\frac{1}{X_{L_T}} = \frac{1}{X_{L_1}} + \frac{1}{X_{L_2}} + \frac{1}{X_{L_3}} + \cdots + \text{etc.} \tag{15·5}$$

The combined parallel reactance will be less than the lowest branch reactance. Any short cuts for calculating parallel resistances also apply to the parallel reactances. For instance, the combined reactance of two equal reactances in parallel is one-half either reactance.

15·4 Ohm's law applied to X_L

The amount of current in an a-c circuit with just inductive reactance is equal to the applied voltage divided by X_L. Three examples are illustrated

Fig. 15·5 *Combining inductive reactances in series or in parallel.* (a) X_{L_1} and X_{L_2} in series. (b) X_{L_1} and X_{L_2} in parallel.

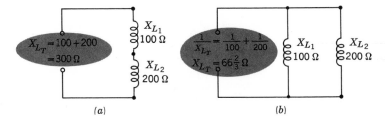

(a)　　　　　　　　　(b)

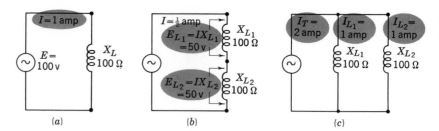

Fig. 15·6 *Circuit calculations with E, I, and ohms of X_L. (a) One reactance. (b) Two series reactances. (c) Two parallel reactances.*

in Fig. 15·6. No d-c resistance is indicated, since it is assumed to be practically zero for the coils shown. In *a*, there is just one reactance of 100 ohms. *I* equals E/X_L, or 100 volts/100 ohms, which is 1 amp.

In *b*, the total reactance is the sum of the two individual series reactances of 100 ohms each for a total of 200 ohms. The current, calculated as E/X_{L_T}, then equals 100 volts/200 ohms, which is 0.5 amp. This current is the same in both series reactances. Therefore, the voltage across each reactance equals its IX_L product. This is 0.5 amp × 100 ohms, or 50 volts across each X_L.

In *c* each parallel reactance has its individual branch current, equal to the applied voltage divided by the branch reactance. Then each branch current equals 100 volts/100 ohms, which is 1 amp. The voltage *E* is the same across both reactances, equal to the generator voltage, since they are all in parallel. The total line current of 2 amp is the sum of the two individual 1-amp branch currents. With RMS value for the applied voltage *E*, all the calculated values of currents and voltage drops in Fig. 15·6 are also RMS values.

15·5 Applications of inductive reactance

The general use of inductance is to provide minimum reactance for relatively low frequencies but more for higher frequencies. In this way, the current in an a-c circuit can be reduced for higher frequencies because of

Table 15·1 *Values of inductance for reactance of 1,000 ohms*

Inductance (approx)	Frequency	Remarks
2.7 henrys	60 cps	Power-line frequency and low audio frequency
160 mh	1,000 cps	Medium audio frequency
16 mh	10,000 cps	High audio frequency
160μh	1,000 kc (r-f)	In radio broadcast band
16 μh	10 Mc (h-f)	In short-wave radio band
1.6 μh	100 Mc (VHF)	In FM broadcast band

more X_L. There are many circuits where voltages of different frequencies are applied to produce current with different frequencies. Then, the general effect of X_L is to allow the most current for direct current and low frequencies, with less current for higher frequencies, as X_L increases. Compare this frequency factor for ohms of X_L with ohms of resistance. X_L increases with frequency, but R has the same effect in limiting direct current or alternating current of any frequency.

If 1,000 ohms is taken as a suitable value of inductive reactance for many applications, typical inductances can be calculated for different frequencies. These are listed in Table 15·1. At 60 cps, for example, the inductance is 2.7 henrys for 1,000 ohms of X_L. For this case, the inductance has practically no reactance for direct current or for very low frequencies below 60 cps. Above 60 cps, the inductive reactance is more than 1,000 ohms.

Note that the smaller inductances at the bottom of the first column still have the same X_L of 1,000 ohms as the frequency is increased. Typical r-f coils, for instance, have an inductance value in the order of 100 to 300 μh. For the very high radio-frequency (VHF) range, only several microhenrys of inductance are needed for an X_L of 1,000 ohms. It is necessary to use smaller inductance values as the frequency is increased because a coil that is too large can have excessive losses at high frequencies. With iron-core coils, particularly, the hysteresis and eddy-current losses increase with frequency.

15·6   Waveshape of e_L induced by sine-wave current

More details of inductive circuits can be analyzed by means of the waveshapes in Fig. 15·7, plotted for the calculated values in Table 15·2. The top curve shows a sine wave of current i_L flowing through a 6-mh inductance L. Since induced voltage depends on rate of change of current, rather than the absolute value of i, the curve in b shows how much the current changes. In this curve the di/dt values are plotted for the current changes every 30° of the cycle. The bottom curve shows the actual induced voltage e_L. This e_L curve is similar to the di/dt curve because e_L equals the constant factor L multiplied by di/dt.

90° phase angle. The e_L curve at the bottom of Fig. 15·7 has its zero values when the i_L curve at the top is at maximum. This comparison shows that the curves are 90° out of phase, as e_L is a cosine wave of voltage for the sine wave of current i_L. The 90° phase difference results from the fact that e_L depends on the di/dt rate of change, rather than i itself. More details of this 90° phase angle for inductance are explained in the next chapter.

Frequency. For each of the curves, the period T is 24 μsec. Therefore, the frequency is $1/T$ or $\frac{1}{24}$ μsec, which equals 41.67 kc. Each curve has the same frequency.

Ohms of X_L. The ratio of e_L/i_L actually specifies the inductive reactance, in ohms. For this comparison, we use the actual value of i_L, which has a peak value of 100 ma. The rate-of-change factor is included in the induced voltage e_L. Although the peak of e_L at 150 volts is 90° before the peak of i_L

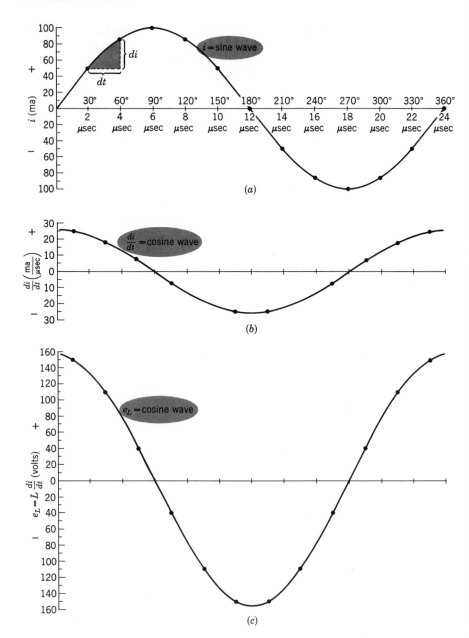

Fig. 15·7 *Waveshapes of sine-wave current i and induced voltage e_L, plotted for values in Table 15·2.*

at 100 ma, we can compare these two peak values. Then e_L/i_L is 150/0.1, which equals 1,500 ohms. This X_L is only an approximate value because e_L cannot be determined exactly for the large dt changes every 30°. If we used smaller intervals of time, the peak e_L would be 157 volts and X_L would

Table 15·2 Values for $e_L = L\dfrac{di}{dt}$ curves in Fig. 15·7

θ	Time μsec	θ	dt, μsec	di, ma	di/dt, ma per μsec	L, mh	$e_L = L\dfrac{di}{dt}$, volts
30°	2	30°	2	50	25	6	150
60°	4	30°	2	36.6	18.3	6	109.8
90°	6	30°	2	13.4	6.7	6	40.2
120°	8	30°	2	− 13.4	− 6.7	6	− 40.2
150°	10	30°	2	− 36.6	− 18.3	6	− 109.8
180°	12	30°	2	− 50	− 25	6	− 150
210°	14	30°	2	− 50	− 25	6	− 150
240°	16	30°	2	− 36.6	− 18.3	6	− 109.8
270°	18	30°	2	− 13.4	− 6.7	6	− 40.2
300°	20	30°	2	13.4	6.7	6	40.2
330°	22	30°	2	36.6	18.3	6	109.8
360°	24	30°	2	50	25	6	150

be 1,570 ohms, the same as $2\pi fL$ ohms with 6-mh L and a frequency of 41.67 kc. This is the same X_L problem as Example 1 on page 293.

The tabulated values from 0 to 90°. The numerical values in Table 15·2 are calculated as follows: The i curve is a sine wave. This means it rises to one-half its peak value in 30°, to 0.866 of the peak in 60°, and the peak value is at 90°. In the di/dt curve the changes in i are plotted. For the first 30° the di is 50 ma; the dt change is 2 μsec. Then di/dt is 25 ma per μsec. This point is plotted between 0 and 30° to indicate 25 ma per μsec is the rate of change of current for the 2-μsec interval between 0 and 30°. If smaller intervals were used, the di/dt values could be determined more accurately.

During the next 2-μsec interval from 30 to 60°, the current increases from 50 to 86.6 ma. The change of current during this time is 86.6 − 50, which equals 36.6 ma. The time is the same 2 μsec for all the intervals. Then di/dt for the next plotted point is 36.6/2, or 18.3. For the final 2-μsec change before i reaches its peak at 100 ma, the di value is 100 − 86.6, or 13.4 ma and the di/dt value is 6.7. All these values are listed in Table 15·2.

Notice that the di/dt curve in b has its peaks at the zero value of the i curve, while the peak i values correspond to zero on the di/dt curves. These conditions result because the sine wave of i has its sharpest slope at the 0 values. The rate of change is greatest when the i curve is going through the zero axis. The i curve flattens near the peaks and has zero rate of change exactly at the peak. In summary, then, the di/dt curve and the i curve are 90° out of phase with each other.

The e_L curve follows the di/dt curve exactly as $e_L = L\,di/dt$. The phase of the e_L curve is exactly the same as the di/dt curve, 90° out of phase with the i curve. For the first plotted point,

$$e_L = L\frac{di}{dt} = 6 \times 10^{-3} \times \frac{50 \times 10^{-3}}{2 \times 10^{-6}} = 150 \text{ volts}$$

The other e_L values are calculated the same way, multiplying the constant factor of 6 mh by the di/dt value for each 2-μsec interval.

90 to 180°. In this quarter-cycle, the sine wave of i decreases from its peak of 100 ma at 90° to zero at 180°. This decrease is considered a negative value for di, as the slope is negative going downward. Physically, the decrease in current means its associated magnetic flux is collapsing, compared with the expanding flux as the current increases. The opposite motion of the collapsing flux must make e_L of opposite polarity, compared with the induced voltage polarity for increasing flux. This is why the di values are negative from 90 to 180°. The di/dt values are also negative and the e_L values are negative.

180 to 270°. In this quarter-cycle the current increases in the reverse direction. If the magnetic flux is considered counterclockwise around the conductor with $+i$ values, the flux is in the reversed clockwise direction with $-i$ values. Any induced voltage produced by expanding flux in one direction will have opposite polarity from voltage induced by expanding flux in the opposite direction. This is why the di values are considered negative from 180 to 270°, compared with the positive di values from 0 to 90°. The di/dt values and the e_L values are also negative from 180 to 270°. Actually, increasing negative values and decreasing positive values are changing in the same direction, which is why e_L is negative for both the second and third quarter-cycles.

270 to 360°. In the last quarter-cycle, the negative i values are decreasing. Now the effect on polarity is like two negatives making a positive. The current and its magnetic flux have the negative direction. But the flux is collapsing, which induces opposite voltage from increasing flux. Therefore, the di values from 270 to 360° are positive, as are the di/dt values and the induced voltages e_L. Actually, the slope of the sine wave of current in the last 90° has the same positive upward direction as in the first 90°.

The same action is repeated for each cycle of sine-wave current. Then the current i_L and the induced voltage e_L are 90° out of phase because e_L depends on di/dt.

SUMMARY

1. Inductive reactance, indicated X_L, is the opposition of an inductance to the flow of sine-wave alternating current.
2. X_L is measured in ohms because it limits the current to the value $I = E/X_L$. With E in volts and X_L in ohms, I is in amperes.
3. $X_L = 2\pi f L$. With f in cps and L in henrys, X_L is in ohms. With one constant L, its X_L increases proportionately with higher frequencies. At one frequency, X_L increases proportionately with higher inductances.
4. With X_L and f known, the inductance $L = X_L/2\pi f$.
5. With X_L and L known, the frequency $f = X_L/2\pi L$.
6. The total X_L of reactances in series is the sum of the individual values, as for series resistances. Series reactances have the same current. The voltage across each inductive reactance is IX_L.
7. With parallel reactances, the total reactance is calculated by the reciprocal formula, as for parallel resistances. Each branch current is E/X_L. The total line current is the sum of the individual branch currents.
8. Table 15·3 summarizes the differences between L and X_L.

Table 15·3   Comparison of inductance and inductive reactance

INDUCTANCE	INDUCTIVE REACTANCE
Symbol is L	Symbol is X_L
Measured in henry units	Measured in ohm units
Depends on construction of coil	Depends on frequency of sine-wave current
$L = e_L/(di/dt)$, henrys	$X_L = e_L/i_L$ or $2\pi fL$, ohms

SELF-EXAMINATION (*Answers at back of book.*)

Here's a chance to find out how well you have learned the material in this chapter. These exercises are for your self-testing only.

1. Inductive reactance is measured in ohms because it (*a*) reduces the amplitude of alternating current; (*b*) increases the amplitude of alternating current; (*c*) increases the amplitude of direct current; (*d*) has a back emf opposing a steady direct current.

2. Inductive reactance applies only to sine waves because it (*a*) increases with lower frequencies; (*b*) increases with lower inductance; (*c*) depends on the factor 2π; (*d*) decreases with higher frequencies.

3. An inductance has a reactance of 10,000 ohms at 10,000 cps. At 20,000 cps, its inductive reactance equals (*a*) 500 ohms; (*b*) 2,000 ohms; (*c*) 20,000 ohms; (*d*) 32,000 ohms.

4. A 16-mh inductance has a reactance of 1,000 ohms. If two of these are connected in series without any mutual coupling, their total reactance equals (*a*) 500 ohms; (*b*) 1,000 ohms; (*c*) 1,600 ohms; (*d*) 2,000 ohms.

5. Two 5,000-ohm inductive reactances in parallel have an equivalent reactance of (*a*) 2,500 ohms; (*b*) 5,000 ohms; (*c*) 10,000 ohms; (*d*) 50,000 ohms.

6. With 10 volts applied across an inductive reactance of 100 ohms, the current equals (*a*) 10 μa; (*b*) 10 ma; (*c*) 100 ma; (*d*) 10 amp.

7. A current of 100 ma through an inductive reactance of 100 ohms produces a voltage drop equal to (*a*) 1 volt; (*b*) 6.28 volts; (*c*) 10 volts; (*d*) 100 volts.

8. The inductance required for 2,000 ohms reactance at 20 Mc equals (*a*) 10μh; (*b*) 16 μh; (*c*) 159 μh; (*d*) 320 μh.

9. A 160-μh inductance will have 5,000-ohm reactance at the frequency of (*a*) 5 kc; (*b*) 200 kc; (*c*) 1 Mc; (*d*) 5 Mc.

10. A coil has an inductive reactance of 1,000 ohms. If its inductance is doubled and the frequency is doubled, then the inductive reactance will be (*a*) 1,000 ohms; (*b*) 2,000 ohms; (*c*) 4,000 ohms; (*d*) 16,000 ohms.

ESSAY QUESTIONS

1. Explain briefly why X_L limits the amount of alternating current.
2. Give two differences and one similarity in comparing X_L and R.
3. Explain briefly why X_L increases with higher frequencies and more inductance.
4. Give two differences between inductance L and inductive reactance X_L.
5. Referring to Fig. 15·7, why are waves *a* and *b* considered to be 90° out of phase, while waves *b* and *c* have the same phase?
6. Referring to Fig. 15·3, how does this graph show a linear proportion between X_L and frequency?
7. Referring to Fig. 15·4, how does this graph show a linear proportion between X_L and L?
8. Referring to Fig. 15·7, draw three similar curves, but for a sine wave of current with a period $T = 12$ μsec for the full cycle. Use the same L of 6 mh. Compare the values of X_L obtained as $2\pi fL$ and e_L/i_L.

9. Referring to Fig. 15·3, tabulate the values of L that would be needed for each frequency listed but for an X_L of 2,000 ohms. (Do not include 0 cps.)

10. Calculate the inductance L needed for an X_L of 1,000 ohms at the following five power frequencies: 50 cps, 60 cps, 120 cps, 400 cps, and 800 cps. For 100 volts applied, make a table comparing the amount of current, X_L, and L at the five different frequencies.

PROBLEMS (*Answers to selected problems at back of book.*)

1. Calculate the X_L of a 0.5-henry inductance at 100, 200, and 1,000 cps.

2. How much is the inductance for 628 ohms reactance at 100 cps? 200 cps? 1,000 cps? 500 kc?

3. A coil with an X_L of 2,000 ohms is connected across a 10-volt a-c generator. (*a*) Draw the schematic diagram. (*b*) Calculate the current. (*c*) How much is the voltage across the coil?

4. A 20-henry coil has 10 volts applied, with a frequency of 60 cps. (*a*) Draw the schematic diagram. (*b*) How much is the inductive reactance of the coil? (*c*) Calculate the current. (*d*) What is the frequency of the current?

5. How much is the inductance of a coil with negligible resistance if the current is 0.1 amp when connected across the 60-cps 120-volt power line?

6. Referring to Fig. 15·6, how much is the inductance of L_T, L_1, and L_2 if the frequency of the source voltage E is 400 cps?

7. How much is the inductance of a coil that has a reactance of 1,000 ohms at 1,000 cps? How much will the reactance be for the same coil at 100 kc?

8. How much is the reactance of a 10-μh inductance at 100 Mc?

9. A 1,000-ohm X_{L_1} and 4,000-ohm X_{L_2} are in series across a 10-volt 60-cycle source. Draw the schematic diagram and calculate the following: total X_L, current in X_{L_1} and in X_{L_2}, voltage across X_{L_1} and across X_{L_2}, inductance of L_1 and L_2.

10. The same 1,000-ohm X_{L_1} and X_{L_2} are in parallel across the 10-volt 60-cycle source. Draw the schematic diagram and calculate the following: branch currents in X_{L_1} and in X_{L_2}, total current in the generator, voltage across X_{L_1} and across X_{L_2}, inductance of L_1 and L_2.

11. At what frequencies will X_L be 20,000 ohms for the following inductors: 2 henry, 250 mh, 800 μh, 200 μh, and 20 μh?

12. A 6-mh L_1 is in series with 8-mh L_2. The frequency is 40 kc. (*a*) How much is L_T? (*b*) Calculate X_{L_T}. (*c*) Calculate X_{L_1} and X_{L_2} to see if their sum equals X_{L_T}.

13. A 250-mh inductor with negligible resistance is connected across a 10-volt source. Tabulate the values of X_L and current in the circuit for alternating current at 20 cps, 60 cps, 100 cps, 500 cps, 5,000 cps, and 15,000 cps.

14. Do the same as in Prob. 13 for an 8-henry inductor.

Chapter ⬤**16** *Inductive circuits*

This unit describes two features of inductive circuits. One is the lagging phase angle of current in an inductive reactance. The other is the L/R time constant, which explains why a coil can produce a high-voltage arc when its circuit is opened. Finally, the practical application of using a coil as a choke to reduce the current at a specific frequency is illustrated. The topics are as follows:

16·1 Sine-wave i_L lags e_L by 90°
16·2 Inductive reactance and resistance in series
16·3 Inductive reactance and resistance in parallel
16·4 Q of a coil
16·5 L/R time constant
16·6 High voltage produced by opening the RL circuit
16·7 The general case of voltage across L
16·8 Energy in magnetic field of inductance
16·9 A-f and r-f chokes

16·1 Sine-wave i_L lags e_L by 90°

With sine-wave variations of current producing an induced voltage, the current lags its induced voltage by exactly 90°, as shown in Fig. 16·1. The inductive circuit in *a* has the current and voltage waveshapes shown in *b*. The vectors in *c* show the 90° phase angle between i_L and e_L. Therefore, we can say that i_L lags e_L by 90°. Or, e_L leads i_L by 90°. This 90° phase relation between i_L and e_L is true in any sine-wave a-c circuit, whether L is in series or parallel, and whether L is alone or combined with other components. We can always say that the voltage across any X_L is 90° out of phase with the current through it.

The 90° phase angle results because e_L depends on the rate of change

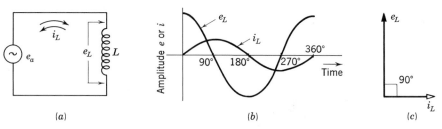

Fig. 16·1   *Current in an inductance lags 90° in time behind the voltage across the inductance. (a) Circuit. (b) Sine wave of i_L lags e_L by 90°. (c) Vector diagram.*

of i_L. As shown previously in Fig. 15·7, for a sine wave of i_L, the induced voltage is a cosine wave. The 90° difference can be measured between any two points having the same value on the i_L and e_L waves. A convenient point is the positive peak value. Note that the i_L wave does not have its positive peak until 90° after the e_L wave. Therefore, i_L lags e_L by 90°. This 90° lag is in time. The time lag is one quarter-cycle, which is one-quarter of the time for a complete cycle.

Inductive current the same in series circuit. The time delay and resultant phase angle for the current in an inductance apply only with respect to the voltage across the inductance. This condition does not change the fact that the current is the same in all parts of a series circuit. In Fig. 16·1a, the current in the generator, the connecting wires, and L must be the same because they are in series. At any instant, whatever the current value is at that time, it is the same in all the series components. The time lag is between current and voltage.

Inductive voltage the same across parallel branches. In Fig. 16·1a, the voltages across the generator and across L are the same because they are in parallel. There cannot be any lag or lead in time between these two parallel voltages. At any instant, whatever the voltage value is across the generator at that time, the voltage across L is the same. Considering the parallel voltages e_a and e_L, both are 90° out of phase with the current. In this circuit the voltage across L is determined by the applied voltage, as they must be the same. The inductive effect here is to make the current have the value that makes $L\,di/dt$ equal the parallel voltage.

The frequency is the same for i_L and e_L. Although i_L lags e_L by 90°, both waves have the same frequency. The i_L wave reaches its peak values 90° later than the e_L wave but the complete cycles of variations are repeated at the same rate. As an example, if the frequency of the sine-wave e_L in Fig. 16·1b is 100 cps, this is also the frequency for i_L. At this particular frequency of 100 cps the time delay of 90°, or ¼ cycle, equals ¹⁄₄₀₀ sec.

16·2   *Inductive reactance and resistance in series*

When a coil has series resistance, the current is limited by both X_L and R. This current I is the same in X_L and R, since they are in series. Each has

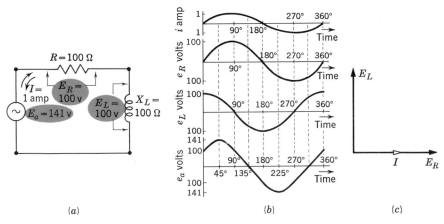

(a)   (b)   (c)

Fig. 16·2   Circuit with X_L and R in series. (a) Schematic diagram. (b) Waveforms of voltage and current. (c) Vector diagram of phase relations.

its own series voltage drop, equal to IR for the resistance and IX_L for the reactance.

Note the following points about a circuit that combines series X_L and R:

1. The current is labeled I, rather than I_L, because I flows through all the series components.
2. The current I through X_L must lag E_L by 90°, as this is the angle between current through an inductance and its self-induced voltage.
3. The current I through R and its IR voltage drop have the same phase. There is no reactance to sine-wave current in any resistance. Therefore, I and IR have the same phase angle.

An example of such a circuit is shown in Fig. 16·2. R can be either the internal resistance of the coil or an external series resistance. The I and E values may be RMS, peak, or instantaneous, as long as the same measure is applied to all. Peak values are used here for convenience in comparing the waveforms.

Since E_L is 90° out of phase with I, but E_R has the same phase as I, E_L and E_R are 90° out of phase. Specifically E_R lags E_L by 90°, just as the current I lags E_L. These phase relations are shown by the waveforms in Fig. 16·2b and the vectors in Fig. 16·3.

Combining E_R and E_L. As shown in Fig. 16·2b, when the E_R voltage wave is combined with the E_L voltage wave, the result is the voltage wave for the applied generator voltage E. The sum of E_R and E_L equals E, since the sum of series voltage drops must add to equal the applied voltage. The 100-volt peak values for E_R and for E_L total 141-volt peak value, however, instead of 200 volts, because of the 90° phase difference.

Consider some instantaneous values to see why the 100-volt peak E_R and 100-volt peak E_L cannot be added arithmetically. When E_R is at its maximum of 100 volts, for instance, E_L is at zero. The total for E then is

100 volts. Similarly, when E_L is at its maximum of 100 volts, E_R is zero and the total E then is also 100 volts. E has its maximum value of 141 volts at the time when E_L and E_R are each 70.7 volts. When series voltage drops that are out of phase are combined, therefore, they cannot be added without taking the phase difference into account.

Vector voltage triangle. Instead of combining waveforms that are out of phase, we can add them more quickly by using their equivalent vectors, as shown in Fig. 16·3. The vectors in *a* just show the 90° angle, without any addition. The method in *b* is to add the tail of one vector to the arrowhead of the other, using the angle required to show their relative phase. E_R and E_L are at right angles because they are 90° out of phase. The sum of the vectors is a resultant vector from the start of one to the end of the other. Since the E_R and E_L vectors form a right angle, the resultant vector is the hypotenuse of a right triangle, being the side opposite the 90° angle.

From the geometry of a right triangle, the Pythagorean theorem states that the hypotenuse is equal to the square root of the sum of the squares of the sides. For the voltage triangle in Fig. 16·3b, therefore, the resultant vector voltage is

$$E = \sqrt{E_R^2 + E_L^2} \qquad (16 \cdot 1)$$

where E is the vector sum of the two voltages E_R and E_L 90° out of phase. This formula is for E_R and E_L when they are in series, as then they are 90° out of phase. All values of E must be in the same units. When E is in RMS values, E_R and E_L are also.

In calculating the value of E, note that the terms E_R and E_L must each be squared before they are added to find the square root. For the example in Fig. 16·3,

$$E = \sqrt{100^2 + 100^2} = \sqrt{10,000 + 10,000} = \sqrt{20,000} = \textbf{141.4 volts}$$

Impedance triangle. A vector triangle of R and X_L in series corresponds to the voltage triangle, as shown in Fig. 16·4. It is similar to the voltage triangle in Fig. 16·3, but the common factor I cancels because the current is the same in X_L and R. The resultant of the vector addition of R and X_L is their total opposition in ohms, taking into account the 90° phase relation between IR and IX_L in a series circuit. The combined opposition

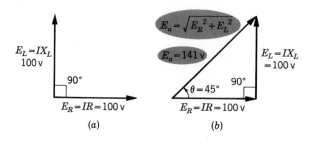

Fig. 16·3   Vector addition of two voltages 90° out of phase. (a) 90° components. (b) Vector addition.

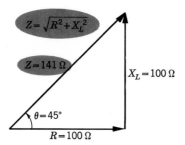

Fig. 16·4   Vector addition of R and
X_L 90° out of phase.

of resistance and reactance in an a-c circuit is called *impedance.* Its symbol
is Z, and the unit is ohms.

For the impedance triangle of a series circuit with reactance and resistance, therefore,

$$Z = \sqrt{R^2 + X_L^2} \qquad (16 \cdot 2)$$

With R and X_L in ohms, Z is also in ohms. For the example in Fig. 16·4,

$$Z = \sqrt{(100)^2 + (100)^2} = \sqrt{10,000 + 10,000} = \sqrt{20,000} = \textbf{141.4 ohms}$$

Note that the total impedance of 141 ohms divided into the applied
voltage of 141 volts results in 1 amp of current in the series circuit. The *IR*
voltage is 1 × 100, or 100 volts; the IX_L voltage is also 1 × 100, or 100 volts.
The total of the series *IR* drops of 100 volts each added vectorially equals
the applied voltage of 141 volts. Also, the applied voltage equals *IZ*, or
1 × 141, which is 141 volts.

Phase angle with series X_L. The angle between the generator voltage and
its current is the *phase angle* of the circuit. Its symbol is θ (theta). In
Fig. 16·3, the phase angle between E_a and *IR* is 45°. Since *IR* and *I* have
the same phase, the angle is also 45° between E_a and *I.*

In the corresponding impedance triangle in Fig. 16·4, the angle between
Z and R is also equal to the phase angle. Therefore, the phase angle can be
calculated from the impedance triangle of a series circuit by the formula

$$\tan \theta = \frac{X_L}{R} \qquad (16 \cdot 3)$$

The tangent (tan) is a trigonometric[1] function of any angle, equal to the
ratio of the opposite side to the adjacent side. In this impedance triangle,
X_L is the opposite side and R is the adjacent side. To calculate this phase
angle,

$$\tan \theta = \frac{X_L}{R} = \frac{100}{100} = 1$$

---

[1] Appendix E defines the trigonometric functions sine, cosine, and tangent and gives their
values.

From the table in Appendix E, the angle that has the tangent equal to 1 is 45°. Therefore, the phase angle in this example is 45°.

Example 1. If 30-ohm R and 40-ohm X_L are in series with an applied voltage E of 100 volts, find the following: Z, I, E_R, E_L, and θ. What is the phase of E_L and E_R with respect to the phase of I? Prove that the sum of the series voltage drops equals the applied voltage E.

$$Z = \sqrt{R^2 + X_L{}^2} = \sqrt{900 + 1{,}600} = \sqrt{2{,}500} = \textbf{50 ohms}$$

$$I = \frac{E}{Z} = \frac{100}{50} = \textbf{2 amp}$$

$$E_R = IR = 2 \times 30 = \textbf{60 volts}$$

$$E_L = IX_L = 2 \times 40 = \textbf{80 volts}$$

$$\tan \theta = \frac{X_L}{R} = \frac{40}{30} = \frac{4}{3} = 1.33$$

$$\theta = \textbf{53°}$$

Therefore, I lags E by 53°.

Furthermore,   **I and E_R have the same phase.**
I lags E_L by 90°.

Finally, $E = \sqrt{E_R{}^2 + E_L{}^2} = \sqrt{(60)^2 + (80)^2} = \sqrt{3{,}600 + 6{,}400}$
$= \sqrt{10{,}000} = \textbf{100 volts}$

Therefore, the sum of the voltage drops equals the applied voltage.

Series combinations of X_L and R. In a series circuit, the higher the value of X_L compared with R, the more inductive the circuit is. This means there is more voltage drop across the inductive reactance and the phase angle increases toward 90°. The series current lags the applied generator voltage. With all X_L and no R, the entire applied voltage is across X_L and θ equals 90°.

Several combinations of X_L and R in series are listed in Table 16·1 with their resultant impedance and phase angle. Note that a ratio of 10:1 or more for X_L/R means that the circuit is practically all inductive. The phase

Table 16·1   Series resistance and inductance combinations

R, ohms	X_L, ohms	Z, ohms	Phase angle θ_Z
1	10	$\sqrt{101} = 10$	84.3°
10	10	$\sqrt{200} = 14$	45°
10	1	$\sqrt{101} = 10$	5.7°

Note: θ_Z is angle of Z_T with respect to the reference I in a series circuit.

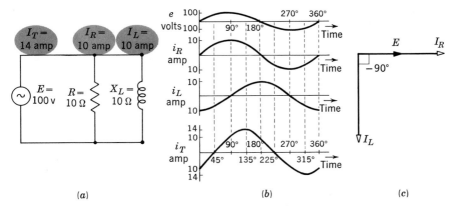

Fig. 16·5 Circuit with X_L and R in parallel. (a) Schematic diagram. (b) Waveforms of current and voltage. (c) Vector diagram of phase relations.

angle of 84.3° is only slightly less than 90° for the ratio of 10:1, and the total impedance Z is approximately equal to X_L. The voltage drop across X_L in the series circuit will be practically equal to the applied voltage, with almost none across R.

At the opposite extreme, when R is 10 times as large as X_L, the series circuit is mainly resistive. The phase angle of 5.7°, then, means the current has almost the same phase as the applied voltage, the total impedance Z is approximately equal to R, and the voltage drop across R is practically equal to the applied voltage, with almost none across X_L.

For the case when X_L and R equal each other, their resultant impedance Z is 1.41 times the value of either one. The phase angle then is 45°, halfway between 0° for resistance alone and 90° for inductive reactance alone.

16·3 Inductive reactance and resistance in parallel

For parallel circuits with X_L and R, the 90° phase angle must be considered for each of the branch currents instead of voltage drops in a series circuit. In the parallel circuit in Fig. 16·5, the voltage is the same across X_L, R, and the generator, since they are all in parallel. There cannot be any phase difference between these voltages. Each branch, however, has its individual current. For the resistive branch, $I_R = E/R$; in the inductive branch, $I_L = E/X_L$.

The resistive branch current I_R has the same phase as the generator voltage E. The inductive branch current I_L lags the parallel voltage E, however, because the current in an inductance lags the voltage across it by 90°. The total line current therefore consists of I_R and I_L, which are 90° out of phase with each other. The vector sum of I_R and I_L equals the total line current I_T.

In Fig. 16·5b, the vector sum of 10 amp for I_R and 10 amp for I_L is equal to 14 amp. The branch currents are added vectorially here because they are the factors that are 90° out of phase in a parallel circuit, corresponding to voltage drops 90° out of phase in a series circuit.

Note that the vector diagram in Fig. 16·5c has the applied voltage E of the generator as the reference phase because it is the same throughout the parallel circuit. The vector for I_L is down, as compared with up for an X_L vector. Here the parallel branch current I_L lags the parallel voltage reference E, while in a series circuit the X_L voltage leads the series current reference I. For this reason the I_L vector is shown with a negative 90° angle. The −90° means the current I_L lags the reference vector E.

The vector addition of the branch currents in a parallel circuit can be calculated by the vector triangle for currents shown in Fig. 16·6. Peak values are used for convenience in this example, but when the applied voltage is in RMS values, the calculated currents are also in RMS values. To calculate the total line current, we have

$$I_T = \sqrt{I_R^2 + I_L^2} \tag{16·4}$$

For the values in Fig. 16·6,

$$I_T = \sqrt{10^2 + 10^2} = \sqrt{100 + 100} = \sqrt{200} = \textbf{14.14 amp}$$

Impedance of X_L and R in parallel. A practical approach to the problem of calculating the total impedance of X_L and R in parallel is to calculate the total line current I_T and divide this into the applied voltage:

$$Z_T = \frac{E}{I_T} \tag{16·5}$$

For example, in Fig. 16·5, E is 100 volts and the resultant I_T, obtained as the vector sum of the resistive and reactive branch currents, is equal to 14.14 amp. Therefore,

$$Z_T = \frac{E}{I_T} = \frac{100 \text{ volts}}{14.14 \text{ amp}} = \textbf{7.07 ohms}$$

This impedance is the combined opposition in ohms across the generator, equal to the resistance of 10 ohms in parallel with the reactance of 10 ohms.

Fig. 16·6   Vector triangle of currents 90° out of phase in parallel circuit.

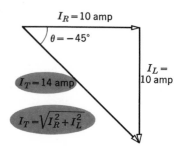

Note that the impedance for equal values of R and X_L in parallel is not one-half but equals 70.7 per cent of either one. Still, the combined value of ohms must be less than the lowest ohms value in the parallel branches.

For the general case of calculating the impedance of X_L and R in parallel, any number can be assumed for the applied voltage because in the calculations for Z in terms of the branch currents the value of E cancels. A good value to assume for E is the value of either R or X_L, whichever is the higher number. This way there are no fractions smaller than one in calculation of the branch currents.

Example 2. What is the total Z of 600-ohm R in parallel with 300-ohm X_L? With 600 volts assumed for the generator voltage,

$$I_R = \frac{600 \text{ volts}}{600 \text{ ohms}} = 1 \text{ amp}$$

$$I_L = \frac{600 \text{ volts}}{300 \text{ ohms}} = 2 \text{ amp}$$

$$I_T = \sqrt{I_R^2 + I_L^2} = \sqrt{1 + 4} = \sqrt{5}$$

$$I_T = \textbf{2.24 amp}$$

Dividing the total line current into the assumed value of 600 volts for the applied voltage gives

$$Z_T = \frac{E}{I_T} = \frac{600 \text{ volts}}{2.24 \text{ amp}} = \textbf{268 ohms}$$

The combined impedance of 600-ohm R in parallel with 300-ohm X_L is equal to 268 ohms, no matter how much the applied voltage is.

Phase angle with parallel X_L and R. In a parallel circuit, the phase angle θ is the angle between the line current I_T and the generator voltage E. The applied voltage E and the resistive branch current I_R, however, have the same phase. The phase of I_R can therefore be substituted for the phase of E. To find θ without the total line current, use the tangent formula

$$\tan \theta = \frac{-I_L}{I_R} \qquad (16 \cdot 6)$$

In Fig. $16 \cdot 6$, θ equals $-45°$ because $-I_L$ and I_R are equal.

The negative sign for $-I_L$ shows this vector points down from zero reference, opposite from X_L. Note that increasing the parallel X_L decreases the negative θ, as $-I_L$ becomes smaller, since more ohms mean less current.

Parallel combinations of X_L and R. Several combinations of X_L and R in parallel are listed in Table $16 \cdot 2$. When X_L is 10 times R, the parallel circuit is practically resistive because there is little inductive current in the line. The small value of I_L results from the high X_L. The total impedance of

*Table 16·2   Parallel resistance and inductance combinations**

R, ohms	X_L, ohms	I_R, amp	I_L, amp	I_T, amp (approx)	Z_T, ohms $= E/I_T$	Phase angle θ_I
1	10	10	1	$\sqrt{101} = 10$	1	$-5.7°$
10	10	1	1	$\sqrt{2} = 1.4$	7.07	$-45°$
10	1	1	10	$\sqrt{101} = 10$	1	$-84.3°$

*$E = 10$ volts. Note that θ_I is the angle of I_T with respect to the reference E in parallel circuits.

the parallel circuit is approximately equal to the resistance, then, since the high value of X_L in a parallel branch has little effect. The phase angle of 5.7° is practically 0° because almost all the line current is resistive.

As X_L becomes smaller, it provides more inductive current in the main line. When X_L is ¹⁄₁₀ R, practically all the line current is the I_L component. Then the parallel circuit is practically all inductive, with a total impedance practically equal to X_L. The phase angle of 84.3° is almost 90° because the line current is mostly inductive. Note that these conditions are opposite from the case of X_L and R in series. When X_L and R are equal, their branch currents are equal and the phase angle is 45°. All these phase angles are negative for parallel X_L and R.

As additional comparisons between series and parallel circuits remember that:

1. The series voltage drops E_R and E_L have individual values that are 90° out of phase. Therefore, E_R and E_L are added vectorially to equal the applied voltage E. The phase angle θ is between E and the common series current I. More series X_L allows more E_L to make the circuit more inductive with a larger positive phase angle for E with respect to I.

2. The parallel branch currents I_R and I_L have individual values that are 90° out of phase. Therefore, I_R and I_L are added vectorially to equal I_T, which is the main line current. The negative phase angle $-\theta$ is between the line current I_T and the common parallel voltage E. Less parallel X_L allows more I_L to make the circuit more inductive with a larger negative phase angle for I_T with respect to E.

16·4   Q of a coil

The ability of a coil to produce self-induced voltage is indicated by X_L, since it includes the factors of frequency and inductance. However, a coil has internal resistance, equal to the resistance of the wire in the coil. This internal r_i of the coil reduces the current, which means less ability to produce induced voltage. Combining these two factors of X_L and r_i, the quality or merit of a coil is indicated by

$$Q = \frac{X_L}{r_i} = \frac{2\pi f L}{r_i} \qquad (16·7)$$

As shown in Fig. 16·7, the internal r_i is in series with X_L. The Q is a numerical value without any units, as the ohms cancel in the ratio of reactance to resistance. As an example, a coil with r_i of 5 ohms and X_L of 500 ohms has a Q of 100. The Q of coils may range in value from less than 10 for a low-Q coil, up to 1,000. R-f coils generally have a Q of about 30 to 300.

At low frequencies, r_i is just the d-c resistance of the wire in the coil. However, for r-f coils the losses increase with higher frequencies and the effective r_i increases. The increased resistance results from eddy currents and other losses. Because of these losses, the Q of a coil does not increase without limit as X_L increases for higher frequencies. Generally, the Q can increase by the factor of about 2 for higher frequencies, within the range for which the coil is designed. The highest Q for r-f coils generally results with an inductance value that provides X_L of about 1,000 ohms at the operating frequency.

More fundamentally, Q can be defined as the ratio of reactive power in the inductance to the real power dissipated in the resistance. Then

$$Q = \frac{P_L}{P_{r_i}} = \frac{I^2 X_L}{I^2 r_i} = \frac{X_L}{r_i} = \frac{2\pi f L}{r_i}$$

which is the same as Formula (16·7).

Skin effect. This effect indicates the tendency of r-f current to flow at the surface of a conductor, at very high frequencies, with little current in the solid core at the center. The skin effect results from the fact that current in the center of the wire encounters slightly more inductance because of the magnetic flux concentrated in the metal, compared with the edges where part of the flux is in air. Because of skin effect, conductors for VHF currents are often made of hollow tubing. The skin effect increases the effective resistance, as a smaller cross-sectional area is used for the current path in the conductor.

A-c effective resistance. When the power and current supplied to a coil are measured for r-f applied voltage, the $I^2 R$ loss corresponds to a much higher resistance than the d-c resistance measured with an ohmmeter. This higher resistance which can be calculated as watts/I^2, is the a-c effective

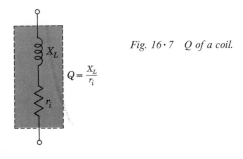

Fig. 16·7   Q of a coil.

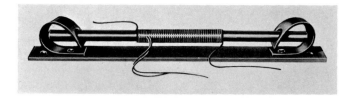

*Fig. 16·8 Miniature ferrite coil antenna for radio receiver. Length
3¾ in.; inductance 700 µh.* (J. W. Miller Co.)

resistance R_e. Although a result of high-frequency alternating current, R_e
is not a reactance. R_e is a resistive component because it draws in-phase
current from the a-c voltage source.

The factors that make R_e of a coil more than its d-c resistance include
skin effect, eddy currents, and hysteresis losses. Air-core coils have low
losses but are limited to small values of inductance. For a magnetic core
in r-f coils, a powdered-iron or ferrite slug is generally used. In a powdered-
iron slug, the granules of iron are insulated from each other to reduce eddy
currents. Ferrite materials have small eddy-current losses as they are insulators, although magnetic. A ferrite core is easily saturated, however, so
that its use is limited to coils with low values of current. A common application is the ferrite-core antenna coil in Fig. 16·8. To reduce R_e for small r-f
coils, stranded wire can be made with separate strands insulated from each
other and braided so that each strand is as much on the outer surface as all
the other strands. This is called *litzendraht* or *litz wire*.

As an example of the total effect of a-c losses, assume an air-core r-f coil
of 50-µh inductance has a resistance of 1 ohm with the d-c measurement of
the battery in an ohmmeter. However, in an a-c circuit with 2-Mc current,
the effective coil resistance R_e can increase to 12 ohms. The increased
resistance reduces the Q of the coil.

Actually, the Q can be used to determine the effective a-c resistance.
Since Q is X_L/R_e, then R_e equals X_L/Q. For this 50-µh L at 2 Mc its X_L,
equal to $2\pi fL$, is 628 ohms. The Q of the coil can be measured on a Q-meter,
which operates on the principle of resonance. Let the measured Q be 50.
Then $R_e = {}^{628}\!/_{50}$, equal to 12.6 ohms.

Example 3. An air-core coil with turns of 2 in. diameter in a single layer has
X_L of 700 ohms and R_e of 2 ohms. Calculate Q.

Answer.
$$Q = \frac{X_L}{R_e} = \frac{700}{2} = \textbf{350}$$

Example 4. A 200-µh coil has a Q of 40 at 0.5 Mc. Find R_e.

Answer. $R_e = \dfrac{X_L}{Q} = \dfrac{2\pi fL}{Q} = \dfrac{2\pi \times 0.5 \times 10^6 \times 200 \times 10^{-6}}{40} = \dfrac{628}{40}$

$R_e = \textbf{15.7 ohms}$

16·5 L/R time constant

The formula for inductive reactance is derived on the basis of sine-wave alternating current. Therefore, calculating X_L does not indicate the effect of inductance in a circuit where the current variations are nonsinusoidal. One example is the change of current in a d-c circuit when the switch is closed or opened, as illustrated in Fig. 16·9. When S is closed, the current changes as I increases from zero to 1 amp. Eventually, I will have the steady value of 1 amp, equal to the battery voltage of 10 volts divided by the circuit resistance of 10 ohms. While the current is building up from zero to 1 amp, however, I is changing and the inductance opposes the change. The action of the RL circuit during this time is its *transient response,* meaning a temporary condition existing only until the *steady-state* current of 1 amp is reached. Similarly, when S is opened, the transient response of the RL circuit opposes the decay of current toward the steady-state value of zero.

The transient response is measured in terms of the ratio L/R, which is the time constant of an inductive circuit. To calculate the time constant

$$T = \frac{L}{R} \text{ sec} \qquad (16\cdot8)$$

where T is the time constant and L the inductance in henrys. R is the ohms of resistance in series with L, being either the coil resistance, an external resistance, or both in series. In Fig. 16·9,

$$T = \frac{L}{R} = \frac{1}{10} = 0.1 \text{ sec}$$

Specifically, the time constant is a measure of how long it takes the current to change by 63.2 per cent or approximately 63 per cent. In Fig. 16·9, the current increases from zero to 0.63 amp, which is 63 per cent of the

Fig. 16·9 *Transient response of RL circuit. When switch is closed current builds up from zero to steady-state value of 1 amp.*

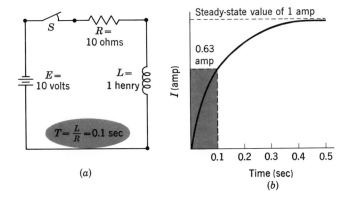

(a)

(b)

steady-state value, in the period of 0.1 sec, which is the time constant. In the period of 5 time constants, the current is practically equal to its steady-state value, equal to 1 amp here.

If the switch is opened now, so that the current can decay to zero, I will decrease to 36.8 per cent, or approximately 37 per cent of the steady-state value in 1 time constant. For the example in Fig. 16·9, I will decay from 1 to 0.37 amp in 1 time constant. With the switch open, however, note that the time constant is shorter because of the high series resistance of the open switch. The current decays practically to zero in 5 time constants.

The reason why L/R equals time can be illustrated as follows: Since induced voltage $E = L(di/dt)$, by transposing terms, L has the dimensions of $E \times T/I$. Dividing L by R results in $E \times T/IR$. As the IR and E factors cancel, T remains to indicate the dimension of time for the ratio L/R.

Notice that the current changes by 63 per cent in one time constant, for either an increase or a decrease. On the rise, I builds up from zero to 0.63 amp in one L/R time unit. On the decay, in one L/R unit the I drops by 0.63 amp, from 1 amp to 0.37 amp. In both cases the current change is 0.63 amp in one time constant.

Example 5. What is the time constant of a 20-henry coil having 100 ohms of series resistance?

Answer.
$$T = \frac{L}{R} = \frac{20 \text{ henrys}}{100 \text{ ohms}} = \textbf{0.2 sec}$$

Example 6. An applied d-c voltage of 10 volts will produce the steady-state current of 100 ma in the 100-ohm coil of Example 5. How much is the current after 0.2 sec? After 1 sec?

Answer. Since 0.2 sec is 1 time constant, I then is 63 per cent of 100 ma, which equals **63 ma**. After 5 time constants, or 1 sec, the current will reach its steady-state value of **100 ma** and remain at this value as long as the applied voltage stays at 10 volts.

Example 7. If a 1-M resistance is added in series with the coil of Example 5, how much will the time constant be for the higher-resistance RL circuit?

Answer. $T = \dfrac{L}{R} = \dfrac{20 \text{ henrys}}{1,000,100 \text{ ohms}} = 20 \times 10^{-6} \text{ sec (approx)} = \textbf{20 } \boldsymbol{\mu}\textbf{sec}$

The L/R time constant becomes longer with larger values of inductance. More series resistance, however, makes the time constant shorter. A shorter time constant allows the current in the inductance to increase more rapidly when voltage is applied to produce current. Similarly, the current can decay to zero more quickly with a shorter time constant when the applied voltage is removed. With a faster change in current, either increasing or decreasing, the inductance can produce a larger self-induced voltage. The shorter time constant with more series resistance results from the fact that the circuit is less inductive, allowing less opposition to changes in current.

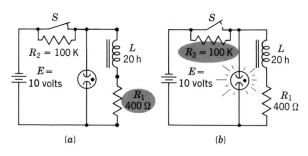

Fig. 16·10 *Demonstration of high voltage produced by opening RL circuit. (a) With switch closed, applied E of 10 volts cannot light 90-volt neon bulb. (b) Short time constant when S is opened produces large self-induced voltage that lights bulb.*

16·6 High voltage produced by opening the RL circuit

When an inductive circuit is opened, the time constant for current decay to zero is very short, since L/R becomes smaller with the high resistance of the open circuit. The current then drops quickly to zero, producing a high value of self-induced voltage across the coil. This high voltage can be much greater than the applied voltage. There is no gain in energy, though, because the high voltage exists only for a short time while the current is decreasing rapidly. After the current has reached zero, there is no voltage across L.

The high value of self-induced voltage produced by the rapidly collapsing field when an RL circuit is opened can be demonstrated by a neon bulb connected in the circuit, as shown in Fig. 16·10. The neon bulb requires 90 volts for ionization when it glows. When the switch is closed in a, current from the battery stores energy in the magnetic field of the coil. The current rises at a rate determined by the L/R time constant, where R is the comparatively low resistance of the coil. The emf of 10 volts across the coil, equal to the applied voltage, cannot ionize the neon bulb. When the switch is opened in b, however, the high resistance of R_2 is now in series with L. With very high R, the result is a very short time constant for current decay. This rapid change in current induces a high voltage across L. Then the neon bulb becomes ionized, and it lights for an instant. The instantaneous voltage across L can be more than 90 volts because of the fast change in current as it drops to zero.

Applications. There are many uses of the high voltage generated by opening an inductive circuit. One example is the high voltage produced for the ignition system in an automobile. Here the circuit of the battery in series with a high-inductance spark coil is opened by the breaker points of the distributor, to produce the high-voltage spark needed for each cylinder. Several thousand volts can easily be produced by opening an inductive circuit very rapidly. Another important application is the high voltage of about 15 kv for the anode of the picture tube in television receivers.

16·7 The general case of voltage across L

The voltage across any inductance in any circuit is always equal to $L \, di/dt$. This formula gives the instantaneous values of e_L, based on the self-induced voltage produced by a change in magnetic flux.

A sine waveform of current i produces a cosine waveform for the induced voltage e_L, equal to $L\,di/dt$. This means e_L has the same waveform as i but they are 90° out of phase. The amount of e_L can be calculated as IX_L in sine-wave a-c circuits. Since X_L is $2\pi fL$ the factors that determine the induced voltage are included in the frequency and inductance. Usually, it is more convenient to work with X_L in sine-wave a-c circuits.

However, with a nonsinusoidal waveform of current, the concept of reactance cannot be used. X_L applies only to sine waves. Then e_L must be calculated as $L\,di/dt$.

An example is illustrated in Fig. 16·11a for sawtooth current. This waveform is often used in the deflection circuits for the picture tube in television receivers. The sawtooth rise is a uniform or linear increase of current from zero to 90 ma in this example. The sharp drop in current is from 90 ma to zero. Note that the rise is relatively slow, as it takes 90 μsec. This is nine times longer than the sharp drop in 10 μsec. The complete period of one cycle of this sawtooth wave is 100 μsec, equal to the rise of i to the peak value and its drop back to the starting value.

The increase of current has a constant slope, as i increases 90 ma in 90 μsec, or 10 ma for every 10 μsec of time. Then di/dt is constant at 10 ma per 10 μsec for the entire rise time of the sawtooth waveform. This is why the e_L waveform has a constant value of voltage during the linear rise of i.

The drop in i is also linear but much faster. During this time, the slope is 90 ma per 10 μsec for di/dt.

In determining the polarity of e_L in Fig. 16·11b, apply Lenz's law to indicate that e_L opposes the change in current. With electron flow into the top of L, then, e_L is negative to oppose an increase of current. This polarity opposes the direction of electron flow shown for the current i produced by the source. For the rise time, then, the induced voltage here is labeled $-e_L$. During the drop of current, the induced voltage has opposite polarity, which is labeled $+e_L$. These voltage polarities are for the top of L with respect to chassis ground.

Fig. 16·11 Waveshape of e_L equal to $L\,di/dt$ for sawtooth waveform of i.
(a) Sawtooth current i. (b) Rectangular induced voltage e_L.

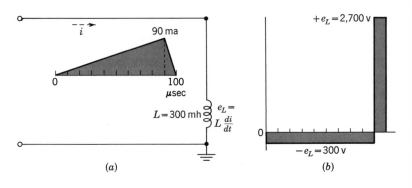

The calculations for the values of induced voltage across the 300-mh L are as follows:

For the sawtooth rise:

$$-e_L = L\frac{di}{dt} = 300 \times 10^{-3} \times \frac{10 \times 10^{-3}}{10 \times 10^{-6}} = \textbf{300 volts}$$

For the sawtooth drop:

$$+e_L = L\frac{di}{dt} = 300 \times 10^{-3} \times \frac{90 \times 10^{-3}}{10 \times 10^{-6}} = \textbf{2,700 volts}$$

The decrease in current produces nine times more voltage because the sharp drop in i is nine times faster than the relatively slow rise.

Remember that the di/dt factor can be very large, even with small currents, when the time is short. For instance, a current change of 1 ma in 1 μsec is equivalent to a di/dt value of 1,000 amp per sec.

16·8 Energy in magnetic field of inductance

Magnetic flux associated with current in an inductance has electrical energy supplied by the voltage source producing the current. The energy is stored in the field, since it can do the work of producing induced voltage when the flux moves. The amount of electrical energy stored is

$$\text{Energy} = \frac{1}{2}LI^2 \qquad\qquad (16\cdot9)$$

The factor of ½ gives the average result of I in producing energy. With L in henrys and I in amperes, the energy is in watt-seconds, or *joules.* For a 10-henry L with 3-amp I, the electrical energy stored in the magnetic field equals

$$\text{Energy} = \frac{1}{2}LI^2 = \frac{10 \times 9}{2} = 45 \text{ watt-sec, or joules}$$

This 45 joules of energy is supplied by the voltage source that produces 3 amp in the inductance. When the circuit is opened, the magnetic field collapses. The energy in the collapsing magnetic field is returned to the circuit in the form of induced voltage, which tends to keep the current flowing. The entire 45 joules is available for the work of inducing voltage, since no energy is dissipated by the magnetic field. With resistance in the circuit, however, the I^2R loss with induced current dissipates all the energy after a period of time.

16·9 A-f and r-f chokes

We have considered RL circuits with sine waves, nonsinusoidal waveforms, and the transient response in a d-c circuit. These examples really include all the main types of inductive circuits. Let us return to the idea of

Fig. 16·12   *An inductance with X_L at least $10 \times R$ is used as a choke. Practically all the applied voltage is across the choke.*

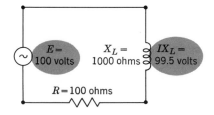

E = 100 volts $X_L =$ 1000 ohms $IX_L =$ 99.5 volts

R = 100 ohms

(a)

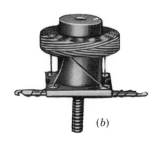

(b)

Fig. 16·13   *Typical chokes. (a) 60-cps choke with 8-henry inductance, 350-ohm resistance, and current rating of 100 ma. Physical size, 4 in. wide. (b) R-f choke of 5 mh with 50-ohm resistance and 50-ma rating. Physical size, 1 in. wide.*

sine-wave current now, in order to analyze a very useful application of inductive reactance.

Considering *RL* circuits with sine-wave current, the inductance has the useful characteristic of providing more ohms of reactance at higher frequencies. Resistance has the same amount of opposition at all frequencies. These characteristics can be applied to an *RL* circuit where it is desired that *L* have practically all the voltage drop in the series circuit, with very little of the applied voltage developed across *R*. This circuit is illustrated in Fig. 16·12. The inductance here is used as a *choke*. Therefore, a choke is an inductance in series with an external resistance to prevent a-c signal voltage of the generator from developing any appreciable voltage across the resistance.

The dividing line in calculations for an inductance used as a choke can be taken as the condition when X_L is 10 or more times as large as the series *R*. Then the series *RL* circuit is primarily inductive. Practically all

Table 16·3   *Typical chokes for reactance of 10,000 ohms**

F	L	Remarks
100 cps	16 henrys	Low audio frequency
1,000 cps	1.6 henrys	Medium audio frequency
10 kc	0.16 henry	High audio frequency
1,000 kc	1.6 mh	Radio frequency
100 Mc	16 μh	Very high radio frequency

* For X_L 10 times series. *R* of 1,000 ohms.

the voltage drop of the a-c generator is across L, with little across R. In addition, this case results in a phase angle of practically 90°.

Typical values of a choke for audio or radio frequencies can be calculated if we assume a series resistance of 1,000 ohms. Then X_L must be at least 10,000 ohms. As listed in Table 16·3, at 100 cps a choke has the relatively large inductance of 16 henrys to provide 10,000 ohms of inductive reactance. Higher frequencies allow a smaller value of L for a choke with the same reactance. For the radio frequency of 1 Mc, the required inductance is 1.6 mh; at 100 Mc, in the VHF range, the choke is only 16 μh. The same inductance at a higher frequency will have more reactance, which makes the inductance more effective as a choke. Some typical chokes are shown in Fig. 16·13.

Choosing a choke for a circuit. As an example of using these calculations, suppose that we have the problem of determining what kind of a coil to use as a choke for the following application. L is to be an r-f choke in series with an external R of 3,000 ohms, with a current of 90 ma and frequency of 2 Mc. Then X_L must be at least $10 \times 3,000$ or 30,000 ohms. At 2 Mc,

$$L = \frac{X_L}{2\pi f} = \frac{30,000}{2\pi \times 2 \times 10^6} = \frac{30,000}{12.56 \times 10^6} = \frac{30}{12.56} \times 10^{-3}$$
$$L = 2.4 \times 10^{-3} = 2.4 \text{ mh (approx)}$$

A typical commercial size easily available is 2.5 mh, with a current rating of 115 ma and internal resistance of 40 ohms, similar to the r-f choke in Fig. 16·13b. Note that the higher current rating is suitable and the internal resistance is negligible compared with the external R. The inductance a little higher than the calculated value will provide more X_L, which is better for a choke.

SUMMARY

1. In a sine-wave a-c circuit, the current through an inductance lags 90° behind the voltage across the inductance because $e_L = L\, di/dt$. This fundamental fact is the basis of all the following relations.
2. Therefore, inductive reactance X_L is a vector quantity 90° out of phase with R. The vector combination of X_L and R is their impedance Z.
3. These three types of opposition to current are compared in Table 16·4.

Table 16·4 Comparison of resistance, inductive reactance, and impedance

R	$X_L = 2\pi fL$	$Z = \sqrt{R^2 + X_L^2}$
Ohms unit	Ohms unit	Ohms unit
IR voltage same phase as I	IX_L voltage leads I by 90°	IZ is applied voltage
Same for all frequencies	Increases at higher frequencies	Increases at higher frequencies because X_L increases

Table 16·5   *Series and parallel RL circuits*

X_L AND R IN SERIES	X_L AND R IN PARALLEL
I the same in X_L and R	E the same across X_L and R
$E_{applied} = \sqrt{E_R^2 + E_L^2}$	$I_T = \sqrt{I_R^2 + I_L^2}$
$Z = \sqrt{R^2 + X_L^2}$	$Z = \dfrac{E}{I_T}$
V_L leads V_R by 90°	I_L lags I_R by 90°
$\tan \theta = \dfrac{X_L}{R}$; θ increases as more X_L makes circuit inductive	$\tan \theta = \dfrac{-I_L}{I_R}$; negative θ decreases as more X_L means less I_L

4. The phase angle θ is the angle between the applied voltage and its current. Numerically this is the angle whose tangent equals X_L/R with R and X_L in series.
5. The opposite characteristics for series and parallel circuits with X_L and R are summarized in Table 16·5.
6. The Q of a coil is X_L/r_i, where r_i is its internal resistance.
7. The transient response of an RL circuit with nonsinusoidal current is indicated in terms of the time constant $T = L/R$. With L in henrys and R in ohms, T is the time in seconds for the current to change by 63 per cent.
8. At the instant an RL circuit is opened, high voltage is generated by the inductance because of the short time constant and fast current decay.
9. A choke is an inductance with reactance greater than the series resistance by a factor of 10 or more, for the purpose of providing practically all the a-c applied voltage across L with little voltage across R.
10. In sine-wave circuits calculate e_L as IX_L. Then e_L has a phase angle 90° different from the current. When the current is not a sine wave, figure $e_L = L\,di/dt$. Then the waveshape of e_L is different from the waveshape of current.

SELF-EXAMINATION (*Answers at back of book.*)

Here's a chance to find out how well you have learned the material in this chapter. These exercises are for your self-testing only.
1. In a sine-wave a-c circuit with inductive reactance, the (*a*) phase angle of the circuit is always 90°; (*b*) voltage across the inductance must be 90° out of phase with the applied voltage; (*c*) current through the inductance lags its induced voltage by 90°; (*d*) current through the inductance and voltage across it are 180° out of phase.
2. In a sine-wave a-c circuit with X_L and R in series, the (*a*) voltages across R and X_L are in phase; (*b*) voltages across R and X_L are 180° out of phase; (*c*) voltage across R lags the voltage across X_L by 90°; (*d*) voltage across R leads the voltage across X_L by 90°.
3. In a sine-wave a-c circuit with 40-ohm R in series with 30-ohm X_L, the total impedance Z equals (*a*) 30 ohms; (*b*) 40 ohms; (*c*) 50 ohms; (*d*) 70 ohms.
4. In a sine-wave a-c circuit with 90-ohm R in series with 90-ohm X_L, phase angle θ equals (*a*) 0°; (*b*) 30°; (*c*) 45°; (*d*) 90°.
5. A 250-μh inductance is used as a choke at 10 Mc. At 12 Mc the choke (*a*) does not have enough inductance; (*b*) has more reactance; (*c*) has less reactance; (*d*) needs more turns.
6. The combined impedance of 1,000-ohm R in parallel with 1,000-ohm X_L equals (*a*) 500 ohms; (*b*) 707 ohms; (*c*) 1,000 ohms; (*d*) 2,000 ohms.
7. A coil with 1,000 ohms X_L at 3 Mc and 10 ohms internal resistance has a Q of (*a*) 3; (*b*) 10; (*c*) 100; (*d*) 1,000.

8. A 250-μh inductance is in series with 50-ohm resistance. The time constant of the circuit equals (*a*) 25 μsec; (*b*) 5 μsec; (*c*) 2 sec; (*d*) 25 sec.
9. An arc across the switch opening an *RL* circuit is a result of the (*a*) long time constant; (*b*) large self-induced voltage across the inductance; (*c*) surge of voltage caused by *IR* drop across the resistance; (*d*) low resistance of the open switch.
10. In a sine-wave a-c circuit with a resistive branch and inductive branch in parallel, the (*a*) voltage across the inductance leads the voltage across the resistance by 90°; (*b*) resistive branch current is 90° out of phase with the inductive branch current; (*c*) resistive and inductive branch currents have the same phase; (*d*) resistive and inductive branch currents are 180° out of phase.

ESSAY QUESTIONS

1. What characteristic of the current in an inductance determines the amount of induced voltage? State briefly why.
2. Draw a schematic diagram showing an inductance connected across a sine-wave voltage source and indicate the current and voltage that are 90° out of phase.
3. Why does the voltage across a resistance have the same phase as the current through the resistance?
4. (*a*) Draw the sine waveforms for two voltages 90° out of phase, each with a peak value of 100 volts. (*b*) Explain why their vector sum equals 141 volts and not 200 volts. (*c*) When will the sum of two 100-volt drops in series equal 200 volts?
5. (*a*) Define the phase angle of a sine-wave a-c circuit. (*b*) State the formula for the phase angle in a circuit with X_L and R in series.
6. Define the following: Q of a coil, a-c effective resistance, r-f choke, and sawtooth current.
7. Referring to Fig. 16·2, why do the waveshapes shown in *b* all have the same frequency?
8. Describe how to check the trouble of an open choke with an ohmmeter.
9. Redraw the circuit and graph in Fig. 16·9 with values for 20-henry L and 400-ohm R.
10. Why is the R_e of a coil considered resistance rather than reactance?

PROBLEMS (*Answers to selected problems at back of book.*)

1. Draw the schematic diagram of a circuit with X_L and R in series across a 100-volt source. Calculate Z, I, IR, IX_L, and θ, approximately, for the following values: (*a*) 100-ohm R, 1-ohm X_L; (*b*) 1-ohm R, 100-ohm X_L; (*c*) 50-ohm R, 50-ohm X_L.
2. Draw the schematic diagram of a circuit with X_L and R in parallel across a 100-volt source. Calculate I_R, I_{X_L}, I_T, and Z, approximately, for the following values: (*a*) 100-ohm R, 1-ohm X_L; (*b*) 1-ohm R, 100-ohm X_L; (*c*) 50-ohm R, 50-ohm X_L.
3. A coil has an inductance of 1 henry and 100-ohm internal resistance. (*a*) Draw the equivalent circuit of the coil showing its internal resistance in series with its inductance. (*b*) How much is the coil's inductive reactance at 60 cps? (*c*) How much is the total impedance of the coil at 60 cps? (*d*) How much current will flow when the coil is connected across a 100-volt source with a frequency of 400 cps?
4. A 10-henry inductance is in series with 10 ohms of resistance, a switch, and a 10-volt battery. (*a*) How much is the time constant for current build-up when the switch is closed? (*b*) How much is the current in the circuit 1 sec after the switch is closed? (*c*) How much is the current in the circuit 5 sec after the switch is closed?
5. Calculate the inductance required for a choke in series with a resistance of 10,000 ohms when the frequency of the current is 5 kc. 5 Mc. 50 Mc. Do the same for the case where the series resistance is 100 ohms.
6. How much is the impedance Z of a coil that allows 0.3 amp current when connected across a 120-volt 60-cycle source? How much is the X_L of the coil if its resistance is 5 ohms? (*Hint:* $X_L{}^2 = Z^2 - R^2$.)

7. Referring to Fig. 16·11, (*a*) calculate the energy stored in the magnetic field of the 300-mh L at the current peak of 90 ma. (*b*) Calculate the value of $+e_L$ if i drops from 90 to 0 ma in 5 μsec.

8. A 350-μh L has a Q of 35 at 1.5 Mc. Calculate the effective a-c resistance R_e.

9. How much L is required to produce e_L equal to 6 kv when i_L drops from 300 ma to zero in 8 μsec?

10. Referring to Fig. 16·10, if R_1 is increased to 2,000 ohms calculate the time constant of the circuit with the switch closed.

11. A 100-ohm R is in series with L across a 141-volt 60-cps generator. E_R is 100 volts. Find L.

12. A 1-M R is in series with 100-μh L across a 10-volt 20-Mc generator. Find X_L.

13. A 400-ohm R and 400-ohm X_L are in series across a 100-volt 400-cps source. Find Z, I, V_L, V_R, and θ.

14. The same R and X_L of question 13 are in parallel. Find I_R, I_L, I_T, Z, and θ.

15. The frequency is raised to 800 cps for the parallel circuit in Prob. 14. Compare I_R, I_L, and θ for the two frequencies of 400 cps and 800 cps.

16. The current shown below flows through a 20-mh inductance. Show the corresponding waveform of induced voltage e_L with values.

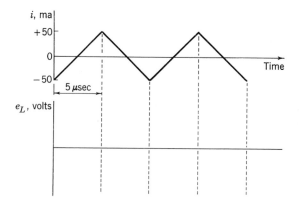

Review of chapters ● 14 ● *to* ● 16 ●

SUMMARY

1. The ability of a conductor to produce induced voltage across itself when the current changes is its self-inductance or inductance. The symbol is L, and the unit is the henry. One henry allows one volt to be induced when the current changes at the rate of 1 amp per sec.
2. The polarity of the induced voltage always opposes the change in current that is causing the induced voltage. This is Lenz's law.
3. Mutual inductance is the ability of varying current in one coil to induce voltage in another coil nearby, without any connection between them. Its symbol is L_M and the unit is the henry also.
4. A transformer consists of two or more windings with mutual inductance. The primary connects to the source voltage, the secondary to the load. With an iron core, the voltage ratio between primary and secondary equals the turns ratio.
5. Efficiency of a transformer equals the ratio of power output from the secondary to power input to the primary, $\times$ 100 per cent.
6. Eddy currents are induced in the iron core of an inductance, causing I^2R losses that increase with higher frequencies. Laminated-iron, powdered-iron, or ferrite cores have minimum eddy-current losses. Hysteresis also increases the losses.
7. Series inductances without mutual coupling add like series resistances; with parallel inductances, the combined inductance is calculated by the reciprocal formula.
8. Inductive reactance X_L equals $2\pi f L$ ohms, where f is in cycles per second and L in henrys. X_L increases with more inductance and higher frequencies.
9. A common application of X_L is an a-f or r-f choke, which has high reactance for one group of frequencies but less reactance for lower frequencies.
10. X_L is a vector quantity that has its current lagging 90° behind its induced voltage. In series circuits, R and X_L are added vectorially because their voltage drops are 90° out of phase; in parallel circuits, the resistive and inductive branch currents are 90° out of phase.
11. Impedance Z, in ohms, is the total opposition of an a-c circuit with resistance and reactance. For series circuits, $Z = \sqrt{R^2 + X_L{}^2}$ and $I = E/Z$. For parallel circuits, $I_T = \sqrt{I_R{}^2 + I_L{}^2}$ and $Z = E/I_T$.
12. The Q of a coil is X_L/R.
13. The time constant of an inductive circuit equals L/R. With L in henrys and R in ohms, the time constant is in seconds. This is the time for the current to change by 63 per cent.
14. The voltage across L is always equal to $L\, di/dt$ for any waveshape of current.

REFERENCES (*Additional references at back of book.*)

Brookes, A. M. P., *Basic Electric Circuits,* Pergamon Press, New York.

Dawes, C. L., *Industrial Electricity, Vol. 1, Direct Currents,* 3d ed., McGraw-Hill Book Company, New York.

De France, J. J., *Direct Current Fundamentals,* Prentice-Hall, Inc., Englewood Cliffs, N.J.

Gillie, A. C., *Electrical Principles of Electronics,* McGraw-Hill Book Company, New York.

Slurzberg, M., and W. Osterheld, *Essentials of Electricity—Electronics,* 3d ed., McGraw-Hill Book Company, New York.

REVIEW SELF-EXAMINATION (*Answers at back of book.*)

Here's another chance to check your progress. Work the exercises just as you did those at the end of each chapter and check your answers.

1. A battery connected across an inductance in series with a switch (*a*) can produce induced voltage as the current decreases when the switch is opened; (*b*) cannot produce induced voltage because the current has one polarity; (*c*) must supply at least 500 volts to produce any induced voltage; (*d*) produces more induced voltage when the switch is closed than when it is opened.

2. Alternating current in an inductance produces maximum induced voltage when the current has its (*a*) maximum value; (*b*) maximum change in magnetic flux; (*c*) minimum change in magnetic flux; (*d*) RMS value of 0.707 × peak.

3. An iron-core transformer connected to the 120-volt 60-cycle power line has a turns ratio of 20:1. The voltage across the secondary equals (*a*) 20 volts; (*b*) 60 volts; (*c*) 120 volts; (*d*) 2,400 volts.

4. Two 250-mh chokes in series have a total inductance of (*a*) 60 mh; (*b*) 125 mh; (*c*) 250 mh; (*d*) 500 mh.

5. Which of the following will have minimum eddy-current losses? (*a*) iron core; (*b*) laminated iron core; (*c*) powdered-iron core; (*d*) air core.

6. Which of the following will have maximum inductive reactance? (*a*) 2-henry inductance at 60 cps; (*b*) 2-mh inductance at 60 kc; (*c*) 5-mh inductance at 60 kc; (*d*) 5-mh inductance at 100 kc.

7. A 100-ohm R is in series with 100 ohms of X_L. The total impedance Z equals (*a*) 70.7 ohms; (*b*) 100 ohms; (*c*) 141 ohms; (*d*) 200 ohms.

8. A 100-ohm R is in parallel with 100 ohms of X_L. The total impedance Z equals (*a*) 70.7 ohms; (*b*) 100 ohms; (*c*) 141 ohms; (*d*) 200 ohms.

9. If two waves have the frequency of 1,000 cps and one is at the maximum value when the other is at zero, the phase angle between them is (*a*) 0°; (*b*) 90°; (*c*) 180°; (*d*) 360°.

10. If an ohmmeter check on a 50-μh choke reads 0, the coil is probably (*a*) open; (*b*) defective; (*c*) normal; (*d*) partially open.

Chapter ⬤17 Capacitance

Just as inductance is an important characteristic for circuits with alternating current in a coil of wire, capacitance is a similar but opposite characteristic that is important with alternating voltage across an insulator or dielectric. This unit explains what capacitance is and how it stores an electric charge. The commercial types of capacitors are described with their standard color coding. Typical troubles are given, showing how the capacitor can break down and how to check capacitors with an ohmmeter. The topics are as follows:

17·1   How charge is stored in the dielectric
17·2   Electric field between charges
17·3   Charging and discharging a capacitor
17·4   The farad unit of capacitance
17·5   Typical capacitors
17·6   Capacitor color coding
17·7   Parallel capacitances
17·8   Series capacitances
17·9   Stray capacitive and inductive effects
17·10 Troubles in capacitors

17·1   How charge is stored in the dielectric

It is possible for dielectric materials such as air, mica, or paper to hold an electric charge because free electrons cannot flow through an insulator. However, the charge must be applied by some source. In Fig. 17·1, the battery can charge the capacitor shown. With the dielectric contacting the two conductors connected to the potential difference E, electrons from the voltage source accumulate on the side of the capacitor connected to the negative terminal of E. The opposite side of the capacitor connected to the

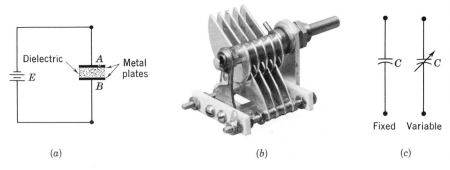

Fig. 17·1 Capacitance stores charge in the dielectric between two conductors. (a) Structure. (b) Air-dielectric capacitor. Length 2 in. (c) Schematic symbols for fixed and variable capacitances.

positive terminal of E loses electrons. As a result, the excess of electrons
produces a negative charge on one side of the capacitor, while the opposite
side has a positive charge. As an example, if 6.25×10^{18} electrons are
accumulated, the negative charge equals 1 coul. The charge on only one
plate need be considered, as the number of electrons accumulated on one
plate is exactly the same as the number taken from the opposite plate.

What the voltage source does is simply redistribute some electrons from
one side of the capacitor to the other side. This process is charging the
capacitor. The charging continues until the potential difference across the
capacitor is equal to the applied voltage. Without any series resistance, the
charging is instantaneous. Practically, however, there is always some series
resistance. The charging current is transient, as it flows only until the
capacitor is charged to the applied voltage. Then there is no current in the
circuit.

The result is a device for storing charge in the dielectric. Storage means
that the charge remains even after the voltage source is disconnected. The
measure of how much charge can be stored is the capacitance C. More
charge stored for a given amount of applied voltage means more capacitance. Components made to supply a specified amount of capacitance are
called *capacitors*, or often by their old name *condensers*.

Electrically, then, capacitance is the ability to store charge. Physically,
a capacitance consists simply of two conductors separated by an insulator.
As an example, Fig. 17· 1b shows a capacitor using air for the dielectric
between the metal plates. There are many types with different dielectric
materials but the schematic symbols shown in c apply to all capacitors.

17·2   Electric field between charges

The ability of a capacitor to store charge results from the force between
static charges on opposite sides of the dielectric. We cannot see the force
of attraction or repulsion between charges, just as the force of gravity is

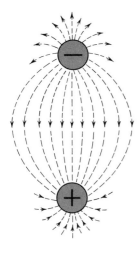

Fig. 17·2 Electrostatic field between unlike charges.

invisible, but the force is evident in the work it can do. In order to illustrate this electric force, it is common practice to map a field of lines of force, as in Fig. 17·2. The lines of force for static changes form an *electrostatic* field, *electric* field, or *dielectric* field. The total lines can be considered dielectric flux, corresponding to magnetic flux of magnetic lines of force in the field of an electrical current. In general, a magnetic field is associated with moving charges or current, while an electric field is associated with potential difference or voltage, resulting from static charges at rest.

The direction of electric lines of force in Fig. 17·2 shows the force on an electron in the field: attraction to the positive charge and repulsion from the negative charge. The amount of force is given by Coulomb's law of the force between electrostatic charges:

$$F = 9 \times 10^9 \times \frac{q_1 q_2}{d^2} \qquad (17 \cdot 1)$$

where q_1 and q_2 are the two charges in coulomb units. The force F is in newtons in the mks[1] system of units, and the distance d between charges is in meters. The constant factor 9×10^9 converts the values to mks units for a dielectric of air or vacuum.

The polarity need not be considered in calculations, as opposite charges have a force of attraction while similar charges repel. As an example, we can calculate the force between 20-μcoul charges, with a dielectric thickness of 1×10^{-4} m as the distance, in air or vacuum. Then

$$F = 9 \times 10^9 \times \frac{q_1 \times q_2}{d^2} = 9 \times 10^9 \frac{20 \times 10^{-6} \times 20 \times 10^{-6}}{(1 \times 10^{-4})^2}$$

$$= \frac{9 \times 400 \times 10^{-3}}{1 \times 10^{-8}} = 3,600 \times 10^5$$

$$F = \mathbf{3.6 \times 10^8 \ newtons}$$

[1] See Appendix D, Physics Units, for description of the mks system.

17·3   Charging and discharging a capacitor

These are the two main effects with capacitors. Applied voltage puts charge in the capacitor. The accumulation of charge results in a buildup of potential difference across the capacitor plates. When the capacitor voltage equals the applied voltage, there is no more charging. The charge remains in the capacitor, with or without the applied voltage connected. However, the capacitor discharges when a conducting path is provided between the plates, without any applied voltage. Actually, it is only necessary that the capacitor voltage be more than the applied voltage. Then the capacitor can serve as voltage source, temporarily, to produce discharge current in the discharge path. The capacitor discharge continues until the capacitor voltage drops to zero or is equal to the applied voltage.

Applying the charge. In Fig. 17·3a, the capacitor is neutral with no charge because it has not been connected to any source of applied voltage and there is no electrostatic field in the dielectric. Closing the switch in Fig. 17·3b, however, allows the negative battery terminal to repel free electrons in the conductor to plate A. At the same time, the positive terminal attracts free electrons from plate B. The side of the dielectric at plate A accumulates electrons because they cannot flow through the insulator, while plate B has an equal surplus of protons.

Remember that the opposite charges have an associated potential difference, which is the voltage across the capacitor. The charging process continues until the capacitor voltage equals the battery voltage, equal to 10 volts in this example. Then no further charging is possible because the applied voltage cannot make free electrons flow in the conductors. Note that the potential difference across the charged capacitor is 10 volts between plates A and B. There is no potential difference from each plate to its battery terminal, however, which is the reason why the capacitor stops charging.

Storing the charge. The negative and positive charges on opposite plates have an electrostatic field through the dielectric, shown by the dotted field lines in Fig. 17·3b and c. Note that the capacitor concentrates the electric

Fig. 17·3   *Storing charge in capacitance. (a) Capacitor with no charge. (b) Battery charges capacitor to the applied voltage. (c) Stored charge remains in capacitor providing 10 volts without the battery. (d) Discharging the capacitor.*

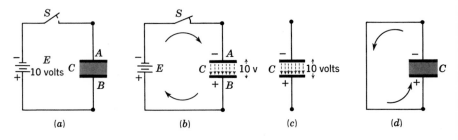

(a)   (b)   (c)   (d)

field in the dielectric between the two plates, instead of having the lines of force spread out in all directions. This action is similar to an iron core concentrating magnetic flux in a coil.

It is the action of lines of force in the electrostatic field through the dielectric that results in storage of the charge. The field can distort the dielectric molecular structure so that it is no longer neutral. In the dielectric, its structure becomes strained by the field, with the result that the insulator has the charge supplied by the voltage source. Since the insulator cannot conduct, the charge remains on the capacitor even after the battery voltage is removed, as illustrated in Fig. 17·3c.

Discharging. The action of neutralizing the charge by connecting a conducting path across the dielectric is discharging the capacitor. As shown in Fig. 17·3d, the wire between plates A and B is a low-resistance path for discharge current. With the stored charge in the dielectric providing the potential difference, 10 volts is available to produce discharge current. The negative plate repels electrons, which are attracted to the positive plate through the wire, until the positive and negative charges are neutralized. Then there is no net charge, the capacitor is completely discharged, the voltage across it equals zero, and there is no discharge current. Now the capacitor is in the same uncharged condition as in Fig. 17·3c. It can be charged again, however, by a source of applied voltage.

Nature of the capacitance. A capacitor has the ability to store the amount of charge necessary to provide a potential difference equal to the charging voltage. If 100 volts were applied in Fig. 17·3, the capacitor would charge to 100 volts. The capacitor charges to the applied voltage because, when the capacitor voltage is less, it takes on more charge. As soon as the capacitor voltage equals the applied voltage, no more charging current can flow. Note that any charge or discharge current flows through the conducting wires to the plates but not through the dielectric.

17·4 The farad unit of capacitance

With more charging voltage, the electrostatic field is stronger and more charge is stored in the dielectric. The amount of charge Q stored in the capacitance is therefore proportional to the applied voltage E. Also, a larger capacitance can store more charge. These relations are summarized by the formula

$$Q = CE \qquad \text{coul} \qquad (17·2)$$

where Q is the charge stored in the dielectric and E is the applied voltage producing the electrostatic field through the dielectric. C is a physical constant, indicating the capacitance in terms of how much charge can be stored for a given amount of charging voltage. When one coulomb is stored in the dielectric with a potential difference of one volt, the capacitance is one *farad*.[2]

[2] Named after Michael Faraday (1791–1867).

Practical capacitors have sizes in the order of millionths of a farad, or smaller. Therefore, the common units are

$$1 \text{ microfarad} = 1 \text{ } \mu f = 1 \times 10^{-6} \text{ farad}$$
$$1 \text{ micromicrofarad} = 1 \text{ } \mu\mu f = 1 \times 10^{-12} \text{ farad}$$
or
$$1 \text{ picofarad} = 1 \text{ pf} = 1 \times 10^{-12} \text{ farad}$$

The pf and $\mu\mu f$ units are the same but the use of picofarads has recently become standard to eliminate confusion with microfarads.

Example 1. How much charge is stored in a 2-μf capacitor with 50 volts across it?

Answer. $Q = CE = 2 \times 10^{-6} \times 50 = \mathbf{100 \times 10^{-6} \text{ coul}}$

Example 2. How much charge is stored in a 40-μf capacitor with 50 volts across it?

Answer. $Q = CE = 40 \times 10^{-6} \times 50 = \mathbf{2{,}000 \times 10^{-6} \text{ coul}}$

Note that the larger capacitor stores more charge for the same voltage, in accordance with the definition of capacitance as the ability to store charge.

The formula $Q = CE$ can be transposed to

$$C = \frac{Q}{E} \tag{17·3}$$

or

$$E = \frac{Q}{C} \tag{17·4}$$

For all three formulas, the basic units are volts for E, coulombs for Q, and farads for C. The formula $C = Q/E$ actually defines one farad of capacitance as one coulomb of charge stored for one volt potential difference.

Example 3. A constant current of 2 μa charges a capacitor for 20 sec. How much charge is stored in the capacitor?

Answer. $Q = I \times t = 2 \times 10^{-6} \times 20 = \mathbf{40 \text{ } \mu coul}$

Example 4. The voltage across the charged capacitor in Example 3 is 20 volts. Calculate C.

Answer. $C = \dfrac{Q}{E} = \dfrac{40 \times 10^{-6}}{20} = 2 \times 10^{-6} = \mathbf{2 \text{ } \mu f}$

Example 5. A constant current of 5 ma charges a 10-μf capacitor for 1 sec. How much is the voltage across the capacitor?
Answer. To find the stored charge first,

$$Q = I \times t = 5 \times 10^{-3} \times 1 = 5 \times 10^{-3} \text{ coul}$$

Also, $E = \dfrac{Q}{C} = \dfrac{5 \times 10^{-3}}{10 \times 10^{-6}} = \dfrac{5}{10} \times 10^{3} = \mathbf{500 \text{ volts}}$

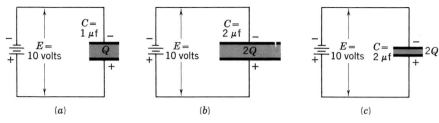

Fig. 17·4 Increasing stored charge and capacitance by increasing plate area and decreasing distance between plates. (a) Capacitance of 1 µf. (b) 2-µf capacitance with twice the plate area and same distance. (c) 2-µf capacitance with one-half the distance and same plate area.

Larger plate area increases capacitance. As illustrated in Fig. 17·4, when the area of each plate is doubled, the capacitance in *b* stores twice the charge of *a*. The potential difference in both cases is still 10 volts. This voltage produces a given strength of electric field. A larger plate area, however, means that more of the dielectric surface can contact each plate, allowing more lines of force through the dielectric between the plates and less flux leakage outside the dielectric. Then the field can store more charge in the dielectric. The result of larger plate area is more charge stored for the same applied voltage, therefore, which means the capacitance is larger.

Thinner dielectric increases capacitance. As illustrated in Fig. 17·4c when the distance between plates is reduced one-half, the capacitance stores twice the charge of Fig. 17·4a. The potential difference is still 10 volts, but its electrostatic field has greater flux density in the thinner dielectric. Then the field between opposite plates can store more charge in the dielectric. With less distance between the plates, the stored charge is greater for the same applied voltage, therefore, which means the capacitance is larger.

Dielectric constant (k). This indicates the ability of an insulator to concentrate dielectric flux. Its numerical value is specified as the ratio of dielectric flux in the insulator compared with the flux in air or vacuum. The dielectric constant of air or vacuum is 1, since it is the reference. Mica, for example, has an average dielectric constant of 6, meaning it can provide a density of electrostatic flux 6 times as great as that of air or vacuum for the same applied voltage and equal physical size. Insulators generally have a value of k greater than 1, as listed in Table 17·1. Higher values of dielectric constant k allow greater values of capacitance.

Dielectric strength. Table 17·1 also lists breakdown-voltage ratings for typical dielectrics. Dielectric strength is the ability of a dielectric to withstand a potential difference without arcing across the insulator. This voltage rating is important because rupture of the insulator provides a conducting path through the dielectric. Then it cannot store charge, because the capacitor is shorted. Since the breakdown voltage increases with greater thickness, capacitors for higher voltage ratings have more distance between the plates. This distance reduces the capacitance, however, all other factors remaining the same.

Table 17·1   Dielectric materials*

Material	Dielectric constant k	Dielectric strength, volts per mil
Air or vacuum	1	20
Ceramics	80–1,200	600–1,250
Glass	8	335–2,000
Mica	3–8	600–1,500
Oil	2–5	375
Paper	2–6	1,250

* Exact values depend on specific composition of different types.

The physical factors for a parallel-plate capacitor can be summarized by the formula

$$C = k \times \frac{A}{d} \times 22.4 \times 10^{-14} \qquad \text{farad} \qquad (17·5)$$

A is the area of either plate (in.^{2}) and d is the distance (in.) between plates. k is the dielectric constant, as listed in Table 17·1, which equals 1 for air or vacuum. The constant factor 22.4×10^{-14} converts C to farad units.

Example 6. Calculate the capacitance between two plates each 4 in.^{2}, separated by 0.02 in., with air the dielectric.

Answer. $C = k \times \dfrac{A}{d} \times 22.4 \times 10^{-14} = 1 \times \dfrac{4}{0.02} \times 22.4 \times 10^{-14}$

$= \dfrac{89.6}{0.02} \times 10^{-14} = \dfrac{89.6}{2} \times 10^{-12}$

$C = 44.8 \times 10^{-12} = \textbf{44.8 pf}$

Note the small capacitance with a relatively large plate area of 4 in.^{2}. If the dielectric used is paper with a dielectric constant of 6, C will be 6 × 44.8 or 268.8 pf.

Table 17·2   Types of capacitors

Dielectric	Construction	Capacitance	Breakdown, volts
Air	Meshed plates	10–400 pf	400 (0.02-in. air gap)
Ceramic	Tubular Disk	0.5–1,600 pf 0.002–0.1 μf	500–20,000
Electrolytic	Aluminum Tantalum	5–1,000 μf 0.01–300 μf	10–450 6–50
Mica	Stacked sheets	10–5,000 pf	500–20,000
Paper	Rolled foil	0.001–1 μf	200–1,600

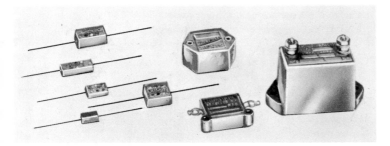

Fig. 17·5   Mica capacitors. (Aerovox Corp.)

17·5   Typical capacitors

Commercial capacitors are generally classified according to the dielectric. Most common are air, mica, paper, and ceramic capacitors, plus the electrolytic type. Electrolytic capacitors use a molecular-thin oxide film as the dielectric, resulting in large capacitance values in little space. These types are compared in Table 17·2 and shown in Figs. 17·5 to 17·9. There is no required polarity, since either side can be the more positive plate, except for electrolytic capacitors. These are marked to indicate which side must be positive to maintain the internal electrolytic action that produces the dielectric required to form the capacitance.

Mica capacitors. Thin mica sheets are stacked between tinfoil sections for the conducting plates to provide the required capacitance. Alternate strips of tinfoil are connected together and brought out as one terminal for one set of plates, while the opposite terminal connects to the other set of plates. The entire unit is generally in a molded Bakelite case. Mica capacitors are often used for small capacitance values of 50 to 500 pf; their length is ¾ in. or less with about ⅛ in. thickness. Typical mica capacitors are shown in Fig. 17·5.

Paper capacitors. In this construction, two rolls of tinfoil conductor separated by a tissue-paper insulator are rolled into a compact cylinder. Each outside lead connects to its roll of tinfoil as a plate. The entire cylinder is generally placed in a cardboard container coated with wax or encased in plastic. Paper capacitors are often used for medium capacitance values of 0.001 to 1.0 µf approximately. The physical size for 0.05 µf is typically 1½ in. long with ½ in. diameter. Paper capacitors are shown in Fig. 17·6.

A black band at one end of a paper capacitor indicates the lead connected to the outside foil. This lead should be used for the ground or low-potential side of the circuit to take advantage of shielding by the outside foil. There is no required polarity, however, since the capacitance is the same no matter which side is grounded. It should also be noted that in the schematic symbol for C the curved line indicates the low-potential side of the capacitor.

Many capacitors of foil construction use a polystyrene plastic film in-

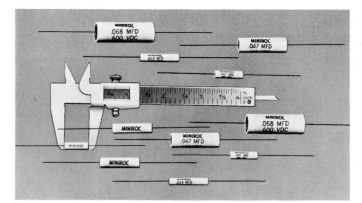

Fig. 17·6 Tubular paper capacitors. (Sprague Electric Co.)

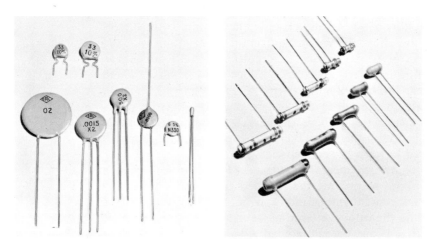

Fig. 17·7 Ceramic capacitors. Disk type at left; tubular type at right. Shown actual size, approximately. (Centralab Div., Globe-Union Inc.)

stead of tissue. Two types are Teflon[3] and Mylar[3] plastic film. These feature very high insulation resistance, of over 1,000 M, low losses, and longer service life without voltage breakdown, compared with paper capacitors. The plastic capacitors are available in sizes of 0.001 to 1.0 μf, like paper capacitors.

Ceramic capacitors. The ceramic dielectric materials are made from earth fired under extreme heat. By use of titanium dioxide, or several types of silicates, very high values of dielectric constant can be obtained. In the disk form, silver is fired onto both sides of the ceramic, to form the conductor plates. With a k value of 1,200, the disk ceramics feature capacitance values up to 0.01 μf in much less space than a paper capacitor. For tubular ceramics, the hollow ceramic tube has a silver coating on the in-

[3] Du Pont trademarks.

side and outside surfaces. With values of 1 to 500 pf, these capacitors have the same applications as mica capacitors but are smaller. Typical ceramic capacitors are shown in Fig. 17·7.

Temperature coefficient. Ceramic capacitors are often used for temperature compensation, to increase or decrease capacitance with a rise in temperature. The temperature coefficient is given in parts per million per degree centigrade (per °C), with a reference of 25°C. As an example, a negative 750 ppm unit is stated as N750. This means that a 10° rise in temperature decreases C by 750×10 or 7,500 parts per million. A positive temperature coefficient of the same value would be stated as P750. Units that do not change in capacitance are labeled NPO.

Variable capacitors. Figure 17·1*b* shows a variable air capacitor. In this construction, the fixed metal plates connected together form the *stator*. The movable plates connected together on the shaft form the *rotor*. Capacitance is varied by rotating the shaft to make the rotor plates mesh with the stator plates. They do not touch, however, since air is the dielectric. Full mesh is maximum capacitance. Moving the rotor completely out of mesh provides minimum capacitance.

A common application is the tuning capacitor in radio receivers. When you tune to different stations, the capacitance varies as the rotor moves in or out of mesh. Combined with an inductance, the variable capacitance then tunes the receiver to a different frequency for each station. Usually two or three capacitor sections are *ganged* on one common shaft.

Electrolytic capacitors. These capacitors are commonly used in capacitance values of 5 to 1000 μf because electrolytics provide the most capacitance in the smallest space with least cost. Figure 17·8 shows a typical

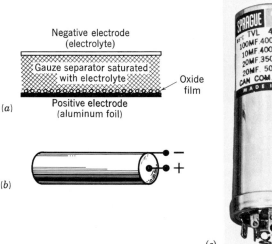

(a)

Negative electrode
(electrolyte)

Gauze separator saturated
with electrolyte

Oxide
film

Positive electrode
(aluminum foil)

(b)

(c)

Fig. 17·8 *Construction of dry electrolytic capacitor. (a) Internal electrodes. (b) Foil rolled into cartridge. (c) Typical capacitor with multiple sections. Height about 3 in.*

electrolytic. The construction consists of two metal electrodes, usually aluminum, in an electrolyte of borax, phosphate, or carbonate. Between the two aluminum strips, absorbent gauze soaks up electrolyte to provide the required electrolysis. When d-c voltage is applied to form the capacitance during manufacture, the electrolytic action accumulates a molecular-thin layer of aluminum oxide at the junction between the positive aluminum electrode and the electrolyte. Since the oxide film is an insulator, there is capacitance between the positive aluminum electrode and the electrolyte in the gauze separator. The negative aluminum electrode simply provides a connection to the electrolyte.

With the extremely thin dielectric film, very large capacitance values can be obtained. The area is increased by means of long strips of aluminum foil and gauze, which are rolled into a compact cylinder having very high capacitance. For example, an electrolytic capacitor the same size as a 0.1-μf paper capacitor, but rated at 10-volt breakdown, may have 1,000 μf capacitance. Higher voltage ratings up to 450 volts are often used in typical capacitance values of 8 to 80 μf.

Electrolytic capacitors must be connected so that the applied voltage maintains the positive electrode more positive than the negative terminal. Otherwise, the insulating oxide film is not formed and there is no capacitance. If the electrolytic is connected in opposite polarity, the reversed electrolysis forms gas and the capacitor becomes hot and may explode.

The disadvantage of electrolytics, in addition to the required polarization, is their relatively high leakage current, since the oxide film is not a perfect insulator. This leakage current through the dielectric is about 0.1 to 0.5 ma per μf of capacitance.

Nonpolarized electrolytic capacitors are also available for applications in a-c circuits without any d-c polarizing voltage. One use is for a-c motors. A nonpolar electrolytic actually contains two capacitors, connected internally in series-opposing polarity. The net capacitance is reduced one-half.

Tantalum capacitors. These are a new type of electrolytic, using tantalum instead of aluminum. Niobium is also used. They feature larger capacitance in a smaller size, longer shelf life, and less leakage current. Although the voltage ratings are lower than for aluminum electrolytics, tantalum capacitors are commonly used for low-voltage applications in transistor circuits. Typical capacitors are shown in Fig. 17·9.

Capacitance tolerance. Ceramic disk capacitors for general applications usually have a tolerance of ±20 per cent. Paper capacitors usually have a tolerance of ±10 per cent. For closer tolerances, mica or ceramic tubular capacitors are used. These have standard tolerance values of ±2 to 20 per cent. Silver-plated mica capacitors are available with a tolerance of ±1 per cent. The tolerance may be less on the minus side to make sure there is enough capacitance, particularly with electrolytic capacitors, which have a wide tolerance. For instance, a 20-μf electrolytic with a tolerance of −10 per cent, +100 per cent may have a capacitance of 18 to 40 μf.

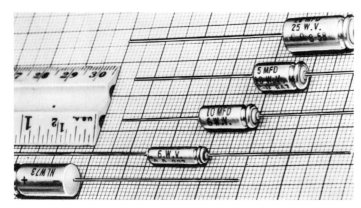

Fig. 17·9 Low-voltage miniature electrolytic capacitors for transistor circuits. (Cornell-Dubilier Electronics.)

Voltage rating of capacitors. This rating specifies the maximum potential difference that can be applied across the plates without puncturing the dielectric. Usually the voltage rating is for temperatures up to about 60°C. Higher temperatures result in a lower voltage rating. Voltage ratings for general-purpose paper, mica, and ceramic capacitors are typically 500 volts. Oil-filled capacitors are generally available in ratings of 600 to 7,500 volts. Electrolytic capacitors are commonly used in 25-, 150-, and 450-volt ratings. Now 6-volt and 10-volt electrolytic capacitors are often used in transistor circuits.

For applications where the lower voltage rating is permissible, more capacitance can be obtained in a smaller physical size. These are d-c voltage ratings. The breakdown rating is much lower for a-c voltage because of the internal heat produced by continuous charge and discharge.

The potential difference across the capacitor depends upon the applied voltage and is not necessarily equal to the voltage rating. A voltage rating higher than the potential difference applied across the capacitor provides a safety factor for long life in service. With electrolytic capacitors, however, the actual capacitor voltage should be close to the rated voltage to produce the oxide film that provides the specified capacitance.

17·6 Capacitor color coding

Mica and tubular ceramic capacitors are color-coded to indicate their capacitance value. Since coding is necessary only for very small sizes, the color-coded capacitance value is always in pf units. The colors used are the same as for resistor coding, from black for 0 up to white for 9.

Mica capacitors generally use the six-dot system shown in Fig. 17·10. Read the top row first from left to right, and then the bottom row, in reverse order right to left. White for the first dot indicates the new EIA coding, but the capacitance value is read from the next three dots. As an example, if the colors are red, green, and brown for dots 2, 3, and 4, the capacitance is

250 pf. If the first dot is silver, it indicates a paper capacitor, but the capacitance is still read from dots 2, 3, and 4. Dot 5 specifies tolerance, while dot 6 gives the EIA class. There are seven classes from A to G specifying temperature coefficient, leakage resistance, and additional variable factors. Appendix G has more detailed information on the tolerance and class coding. Also listed are discontinued codes found on capacitors in old equipment.

For tubular ceramic capacitors, the system shown in Fig. 17·11 is used with color dots or bands. The wide color band specifying temperature coefficient indicates the left end, which is the side connected to the inner electrode. Capacitance is read from the next three colors, in either dots or stripes. For instance, brown, black, and brown for bands or dots 2, 3, and 4 means 100 pf. Gray and white are used as decimal multipliers for very small values, with gray for 0.01 and white for 0.1. For instance, green, black, and white in dots 2, 3, and 4 means 50×0.1, or 5 pf. The color codes for tolerance and temperature coefficient of ceramic capacitors are listed in Appendix G.

In reading the color-coded capacitance value, keep in mind that mica capacitors generally range from 10 to 5,000 pf. The small tubular ceramic capacitors are usually 0.5 to 1,000 pf. With paper and ceramic disk capacitors, the capacitance and voltage rating is generally printed on the case. Where no voltage rating is specified, it is usually about 400 to 600 volts. Electrolytic capacitors always have the capacitance and voltage rating printed on the case.

17·7 Parallel capacitances

Connecting capacitances in parallel is equivalent to adding the plate areas. Therefore, the total capacitance is the sum of the individual capacitances. As illustrated in Fig. 17·12,

$$C_t = C_1 + C_2 + \cdots + \text{etc.} \qquad (17·6)$$

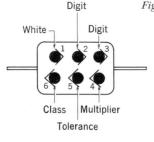

Digit

White

Digit

Class | Multiplier

Tolerance

Fig. 17·10   Six-dot color code for mica capacitors.

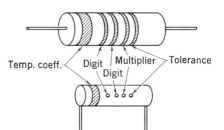

Fig. 17·11   Color code for ceramic tubular capacitors.

Temp. coeff.   Digit Multiplier Tolerance
Digit

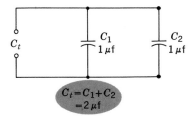

$$C_t = C_1 + C_2$$
$$= 2\,\mu f$$

Fig. 17·12   Capacitances in parallel.

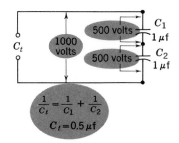

$$\frac{1}{C_t} = \frac{1}{C_1} + \frac{1}{C_2}$$
$$C_t = 0.5\,\mu f$$

Fig. 17·13   Capacitances in series.

A 10-μf capacitor in parallel with a 5-μf capacitor, for example, provides 15-μf capacitance for the parallel combination. The voltage is the same across the parallel capacitors. Note that adding parallel capacitances is opposite to the case of inductances in parallel.

17·8   Series capacitances

Connecting capacitances in series is equivalent to increasing the thickness of the dielectric. Therefore, the combined capacitance is less than the smallest individual value. As shown in Fig. 17·13 the combined equivalent capacitance is calculated by the reciprocal formula

$$\frac{1}{C_t} = \frac{1}{C_1} + \frac{1}{C_2} + \cdots + \text{etc.} \tag{17·7}$$

Any of the short-cut calculations for the reciprocal formula apply. For example, the combined capacitance of two equal capacitances of 10 μf in series is 5 μf.

Capacitors are used in series to provide a higher voltage breakdown rating for the combination. For instance, each of three equal capacitances in series has one-third the applied voltage as its potential difference.

With unequal capacitances in series, the voltage across each is inversely proportional to its capacitance, as illustrated in Fig. 17·14. The smaller capacitance has the larger proportion of the applied voltage. The reason is

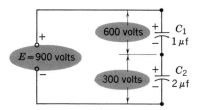

Fig. 17·14   With series capacitances the smaller capacitance has more voltage for the same charge.

that the series capacitances all have the same charge because they are in one current path. With equal charge, a smaller capacitance has a greater potential difference.

We can consider the amount of charge in the series capacitors in Fig. 17·14. Let the charging current be 600 μa flowing for 1 sec. The charge Q equals $I \times t$, then, or 600 μcoul. Both C_1 and C_2 have Q equal to 600 μcoul, as they are in the same series path for charging current. With the same charge in C_1 and C_2, they have different voltages because of different capacitance values. For each capacitor $E = Q/C$. The voltage E_1 across C_1 then is 600 μcoul/1 μf, which equals 600 volts. For C_2, its voltage E_2 is 600 μcoul/2 μf, which equals 300 volts.

The charging current is the same in all parts of the series path, including the junction between C_1 and C_2, even though this point is separated from the source voltage by two insulators. At the junction, the current is the resultant of electrons repelled by the negative plate of C_2 and attracted by the positive plate of C_1. The amount of current is how much would be produced by one capacitance of ⅔ μf, which is the equivalent capacitance of C_1 and C_2 in series.

17·9 Stray capacitive and inductive effects

These two important characteristics can be evident in all circuits with all types of components. A capacitor has a small amount of inductance in the conductors. A coil has some capacitance between windings. A resistor has a small amount of inductance and capacitance. After all, a capacitance physically is simply an insulator between two points having a difference of potential. An inductance is basically just a conductor carrying current. Actually, though, these stray effects are usually quite small, compared with the concentrated or lumped values of capacitors or inductors. Typical values of stray capacitance may be 1 to 10 pf, while stray inductance is usually a fraction of 1 μh. For very high radio frequencies, however, when small values of L and C must be used, the stray effects become important.

Stray circuit capacitance. The wiring and the components in a circuit have capacitance to the metal chassis. This stray capacitance C_s is typically 5 to 10 pf. To reduce C_s, the wiring should be short, with the leads and components placed high off the chassis. Sometimes, for very high frequencies, the stray capacitance is included as part of the circuit design and changing the placement of components or wiring affects the circuit operation. Such critical *lead dress* is usually specified in the manufacturer's service notes.

Leakage resistance of a capacitor. Consider a capacitor charged by a d-c voltage source. After the charging voltage is removed, a perfect capacitor would keep its charge indefinitely. After a long period of time, however, the charge will be neutralized by a small leakage current through the dielectric and across the insulated case between terminals, because there is no perfect insulator. For paper, ceramic, and mica capacitors, though, the leakage current is very slight or, inversely, the leakage resistance is very high. As shown in Fig. 17·15, the leakage resistance R_l is indicated by a high resist-

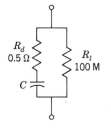

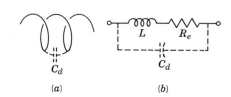

Fig. 17·15 *Equivalent cir-*
cuit of a capacitor.

Fig. 17·16 *Equivalent circuit of an r-f coil.*

ance in parallel with the capacitance *C*. For paper, ceramic, or mica capacitors R_l is 100 M or more. However, electrolytic capacitors may have a leakage resistance as low as 0.5 M.

Absorption losses in capacitors. With a-c voltage applied to a capacitor, the continuous charge, discharge, and reverse charging action cannot be followed instantaneously in the dielectric. This corresponds to hysteresis losses in magnetic materials. With high-frequency charging voltage for a capacitor, there may be a difference between the amount of a-c voltage applied and the a-c voltage stored in the dielectric. The difference can be considered *absorption loss* in the dielectric. With higher frequencies, the losses increase. In Fig. 17 · 15, the small value of 0.5 ohm for R_d indicates a typical value for paper capacitors. For ceramic and mica capacitors, the dielectric losses are even smaller. These losses need not be considered for electrolytic capacitors because they are generally not used for radio frequencies.

Power factor of a capacitor. The quality of a capacitor in terms of minimum loss is often indicated by its power factor, which states the fraction of input power dissipated as heat loss in the capacitor. The lower the numerical value of the power factor, the better is the quality of the capacitor. Since the losses are in the dielectric, the power factor of the capacitor is essentially the power factor of the dielectric, independent of capacitance value or voltage rating. At radio frequencies, approximate values of power factor are 0.000 for air or vacuum, 0.0004 for mica, about 0.01 for paper, and 0.0001 to 0.03 for ceramics.

The reciprocal of the power factor can be considered the *Q* of the capacitor, similar to the idea of *Q* of a coil. For instance, a power factor of 0.001 corresponds to a *Q* of 1,000. Higher *Q* therefore means better quality for the capacitor.

Inductance of a capacitor. Capacitors with a coiled construction, particularly paper and electrolytic capacitors, have some internal inductance. The larger the capacitor, the greater is its series inductance. Mica and ceramic capacitors have very little inductance, however, which is why they are generally used for radio frequencies.

For use above audio frequencies, the rolled-foil type of capacitor must have a noninductive construction. This means the start and finish of the foil winding must not be the terminals of the capacitor. Instead, the foil windings are offset. Then one terminal can contact all layers of one foil at one edge, while the opposite edge of the other foil contacts the second terminal. Most rolled-foil capacitors, including the paper and mylar types, are constructed this way.

Distributed capacitance of a coil. As illustrated in Fig. 17·16, a coil has distributed capacitance C_d between turns. Note that each turn is a conductor separated from the next turn by an insulator, which is the definition of capacitance. Furthermore, the potential of each turn is different from the next, providing part of the total voltage as a potential difference to charge C_d. The result then is the equivalent circuit shown for an r-f coil. L is the inductance and r_e its internal effective a-c resistance in series with L, while the total distributed capacitance C_d for all the turns is across the entire coil. Special methods of winding for minimum C_d include *space-wound* coils, where the turns are spaced far apart; the honeycomb or *universal* winding, with the turns crossing each other at right angles; and the *bank winding*, with separate sections called *pies*. These windings are for r-f coils. In audio and power transformers, a grounded conductor shield, called a *Faraday screen,* is often placed between windings to reduce capacitive coupling.

Reactive effects in resistors. As illustrated by the high-frequency equivalent circuit in Fig. 17·17 a resistor can include a small amount of inductance and capacitance. For carbon-composition resistors, their inductance is usually negligible. However, approximately 0.5 pf of capacitance across the ends may have an effect, particularly with large resistances used for high radio frequencies. Wirewound resistors definitely have enough inductance to be evident at radio frequencies. However, special resistors are available with double windings in a noninductive method based on cancellation of opposing magnetic fields.

17·10   Troubles in capacitors

Capacitors can become open or shorted. In either case, the capacitor is useless because it cannot store charge. A leaky capacitor is equivalent to

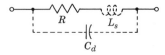

Fig. 17·17   High-frequency equivalent circuit of a resistor.

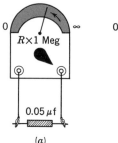
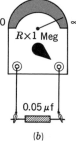

Fig. 17·18   Checking a capacitor with ohmmeter of a VTVM. (a) Capacitor action as needle is moved by charging current. (b) Leakage-resistance reading after capacitor has charged.

a partial short, where the dielectric gradually loses its insulating properties under the stress of applied voltage, lowering its resistance. A good capacitor has very high resistance of the order of megohms; a shorted capacitor has zero ohms resistance, or continuity; the resistance of a leaky capacitor is lower than normal.

Checking capacitors with an ohmmeter. A capacitor usually can be checked with an ohmmeter. The highest ohms range, such as $R \times 1$ M, is preferable. Also, disconnect one side of the capacitor from the circuit to eliminate any parallel resistance paths that can lower the resistance. Keep your fingers off the connections, since the body resistance lowers the reading.

As illustrated in Fig. 17·18, the ohmmeter leads are connected across the capacitor. For a good capacitor, the meter pointer moves quickly toward the low-resistance side of the scale and then slowly recedes toward infinity. The reading when the pointer stops moving is the insulation resistance of the capacitor, which is normally very high. For paper, mica, and ceramic capacitors, the resistance can be 500 to 1,000 M, or more, which is practically infinite resistance. Electrolytic capacitors, however, have a lower normal resistance of the order of 0.5 M or more. In all cases discharge the capacitor before checking with the ohmmeter.

When the ohmmeter is initially connected, its battery charges the capacitor. This charging current is the reason the meter pointer moves away from infinity, since more current through the ohmmeter means less resistance. Maximum current flows at the first instant of charge. Then the charging current decreases as the capacitor voltage increases toward the applied voltage; therefore, the needle pointer slowly moves toward infinite resistance. Finally the capacitor is completely charged to the ohmmeter battery voltage, the charging current is zero, and the ohmmeter reads just the small leakage current through the dielectric. This charging effect, called *capacitor action,* shows that the capacitor can store charge, indicating a normal capacitor.

Troubles in a capacitor are indicated as follows:

1. If an ohmmeter reading immediately goes practically to zero and stays there, the capacitor is shorted.
2. If the capacitor shows charging, but the final resistance reading is appreciably less than normal, the capacitor is leaky. Such capacitors are particularly troublesome in high-resistance circuits. When checking electrolytics, reverse the ohmmeter leads and take the higher of the two readings.
3. If the capacitor shows no charging action but just reads very high resistance, it may be open. Some precautions must be remembered, however, since very high resistance is a normal condition for capacitors. Reverse the ohmmeter leads to discharge the capacitor, and check it again. In addition, remember that capacitance values of 100 pf or less normally have very little charging current for the low battery voltage of the ohmmeter.

Shorted capacitors. In normal service, capacitors can become shorted because the dielectric deteriorates with age, usually over a period of years, under the stress of charging voltage, especially with higher temperatures. This effect is more common with paper and electrolytic capacitors. The capacitor may become leaky gradually, indicating a partial short, or the dielectric may be punctured, causing a short circuit.

Open capacitors. In addition to the possibility of an open connection in any type of capacitor, electrolytics develop high resistance in the electrolyte with age, particularly at high temperatures. After service of a year or two, when the electrolyte dries up, the capacitor is partially open. Much of the capacitor action is gone, and the capacitor should be replaced.

Shelf life. Except for electrolytics, capacitors do not deteriorate with age while stored, since there is no applied voltage. Electrolytic capacitors, however, like dry cells, should be used fresh from manufacture.

SUMMARY

1. A capacitor consists of two conductors separated by a dielectric insulator. Its ability to store charge is the capacitance C. Applying voltage to store charge is charging the capacitor; shorting the two conductors of the capacitor to neutralize the charge is discharging the capacitor.
2. The unit of capacitance is the farad. One farad of capacitance stores one coulomb of charge with one volt applied. Practical capacitors have much smaller capacitance values, from 1 pf to 1,000 μf. One pf is 1×10^{-12} farad; one μf is 1×10^{-6} farad.
3. $Q = CE$, where Q is the charge in coulombs, C the capacitance in farads, and E the potential difference across the capacitor in volts.
4. Capacitance increases with larger plate area.
5. Capacitance increases with less distance between the plates.
6. The ratio of charge stored in different insulators to the charge stored in air is the dielectric constant k of the material. Air or vacuum has a dielectric constant of 1.
7. The most common types of commercial capacitors are air, paper, mica, ceramic, and electrolytic. Electrolytics are the only capacitors with polarity. The different types are compared in Table 17·2.
8. Mica and tubular ceramic capacitors are color-coded by the systems shown in Figs. 17·10 and 17·11.
9. For parallel capacitors,

$$C_t = C_1 + C_2 + C_3 + \cdots + \text{etc.}$$

Connecting capacitors in parallel increases the combined capacitance.

10. For series capacitors,

$$\frac{1}{C_t} = \frac{1}{C_1} + \frac{1}{C_2} + \frac{1}{C_3} + \cdots + \text{etc.}$$

Connecting capacitors in series decreases the combined capacitance.

11. When checked with an ohmmeter, a good capacitor shows charging current, and then the ohmmeter reading steadies at the insulation resistance. All types except electrolytics normally have a very high insulation resistance of 500 to 1,000 M. Electrolytics have more leakage current, with a typical resistance of 0.5 M.
12. The main comparisons between the opposite characteristics of capacitance and inductance are summarized in Table 17·3.

Table 17·3   Comparison of capacitance and inductance

CAPACITANCE	INDUCTANCE
Symbol is C	Symbol is L
Farad unit	Henry unit
Stores charge Q	Conducts current I
Needs dielectric as insulator	Needs wire conductor
More plate area allows more C	More turns allow more L
Dielectric with higher k concentrates electric field for more C	Core with higher μ concentrates magnetic field for more L
$1/C_T = 1/C_1 + 1/C_2$ in series	$L_T = L_1 + L_2$ in series
$C_T = C_1 + C_2$ in parallel	$1/L_T = 1/L_1 + 1/L_2$ in parallel

SELF-EXAMINATION (*Answers at back of book.*)

Here's a chance to find out how well you have learned the material in this chapter. These exercises are for your self-testing only.

1. A capacitor consists of two (*a*) conductors separated by an insulator; (*b*) insulators separated by a conductor; (*c*) conductors alone; (*d*) insulators alone.
2. A capacitance of 0.02 μf equals (*a*) 0.02×10^{-12} farad; (*b*) 0.02×10^{-6} farad; (*c*) 0.02×10^6 farad; (*d*) 200×10^{-12} farad.
3. A 10-μf capacitance charged to 10 volts has a stored charge equal to (*a*) 10×10^{-6} coul; (*b*) 100×10^{-6} coul; (*c*) 10 coul; (*d*) 100 coul.
4. Capacitance increases with (*a*) larger plate area and greater distance between plates; (*b*) smaller plate area and less distance between plates; (*c*) larger plate area and less distance between plates; (*d*) higher values of applied voltage.
5. Which of the following statements is correct? (*a*) Air capacitors have a black band to indicate the outside foil. (*b*) Mica capacitors are available in capacitance values of 1 to 10 μf. (*c*) Electrolytic capacitors must be connected in the correct polarity. (*d*) Ceramic capacitors must be connected in the correct polarity.
6. Voltage applied across a ceramic dielectric produces an electrostatic field 100 times greater than in air. The dielectric constant k of the ceramic equals (*a*) 33⅓; (*b*) 50; (*c*) 100; (*d*) 10,000.
7. A six-dot mica capacitor color-coded white, red, green, brown, red, and yellow has the capacitance value of (*a*) 25 pf; (*b*) 124 pf; (*c*) 250 pf; (*d*) 925 pf.
8. The combination of two 0.02-μf 500-volt capacitors in series has capacitance and breakdown rating of (*a*) 0.01 μf, 500 volts; (*b*) 0.01 μf, 1,000 volts; (*c*) 0.02 μf, 500 volts; (*d*) 0.04 μf, 500 volts.
9. The combination of two 0.02-μf 500-volt capacitors in parallel has capacitance and breakdown rating of (*a*) 0.01 μf, 1,000 volts; (*b*) 0.02 μf, 500 volts; (*c*) 0.04 μf, 500 volts; (*d*) 0.04 μf, 1,000 volts.
10. For a good 0.05-μf paper capacitor, the ohmmeter reading should (*a*) go quickly to 100 ohms, approximately, and remain there; (*b*) show low resistance momentarily and back off to a very high resistance; (*c*) show high resistance momentarily and then a very low resistance; (*d*) not move at all.

ESSAY QUESTIONS

1. Define capacitance with respect to physical structure and electrical function. Explain how a two-wire conductor has capacitance.

2. (*a*) What is meant by a dielectric material? (*b*) Name five common dielectric materials. (*c*) Define dielectric flux.

3. Explain briefly how to charge a capacitor. How is a charged capacitor discharged?

4. Define one farad of capacitance. Convert the following into farads using powers of 10: 50 pf, 0.001 μf, 0.047 μf, 0.01 μf, 10 μf.

5. State the effect on capacitance of (*a*) larger plate area; (*b*) thinner dielectric. (*c*) Higher value of dielectric constant.

6. Give one reason for your choice of the type of capacitor to be used in the following applications: (*a*) 80-μf capacitance for a circuit where one side is positive and the applied voltage never exceeds 150 volts; (*b*) 1.5-pf capacitance for an r-f circuit where the required voltage rating is less than 500 volts; (*c*) 0.05-μf capacitance for an audio circuit where the required voltage rating is less than 500 volts.

7. (*a*) Give the capacitance value of six-dot mica capacitors color-coded as follows: (1) Black, red, green, brown, black, black. (2) White, green, black, black, green, brown. (3) White, gray, red, brown, silver, black. (*b*) Give the capacitance value of the tubular ceramic capacitors color-coded as follows: (4) Black, brown, black, black, brown. (5) Brown, gray, black, gray, black.

8. Draw a diagram showing the least number of 400-volt 2-μf capacitors needed for a combination rated at 800 volts with 2-μf total capacitance.

9. Given two identical uncharged capacitors. First one is charged to 500 volts. Then this charged capacitor is connected across the uncharged capacitor. Why will the voltage across both capacitors then be 250 volts?

10. Describe briefly how you would check a 0.05-μf capacitor with an ohmmeter. State the ohmmeter indications for the case of the capacitor being good, shorted, or open.

11. Define the following: (*a*) stray circuit capacitance, (*b*) distributed capacitance of a coil; (*c*) leakage resistance of a capacitor; (*d*) power factor and Q of a capacitor.

12. Give one similarity and two differences in comparing the electric field in a capacitor and the magnetic field in a coil.

PROBLEMS (*Answers to selected problems at back of book.*)

1. How much charge in coulombs is in a 4-μf capacitor charged to 100 volts?

2. A 4-μf capacitor has 400 μcoul of charge. How much voltage is across the capacitor? How much is the voltage across an 8-μf capacitor with the same 400-μcoul charge?

3. A 2-μf capacitor is charged by a constant 3-μa charging current for 4 sec. How much charge is stored in the capacitor? How much is the voltage across the capacitor?

4. A 1-μf capacitor C_1 and 10-μf capacitor C_2 are in series with a constant 2-ma charging current. After 5 sec, how much charge is in C_1 and in C_2? How much is the voltage across C_1 and across C_2?

5. Calculate the capacitance of the following (note 144 in.$^2 = 1$ ft^2): (*a*) plates 8 ft^2, separated by ¼ in. with air dielectric; (*b*) air capacitor with plates 3 in.^{2}, separated by 0.03 in., with 8 sections in parallel; (*c*) mica capacitor ($k = 5$) with thickness of 0.01 in., plates 1 in.^{2}, and five sections in parallel; (*d*) rolled paper capacitor ($k = 4$) with thickness of 0.001 in., and foil 2 in. wide by 12 ft long.

6. How much capacitance stores 6,000 μcoul of charge with 150 volts applied? The charge of how many electrons is stored? What type of capacitor is this most likely to be?

7. With 100 volts across a capacitor, it stores 100 μcoul of charge. Then the applied voltage is doubled to 200 volts. How much is the voltage across the capacitor? How much charge is stored? How much is its capacitance?

8. Referring to the parallel capacitors in Fig. 17·12, calculate the charge Q_1 in C_1 and Q_2 in C_2 with E of 500 volts. How much is the total charge Q_t in both capacitors? Calculate the total capacitance C_t as Q_t/E.

9. Calculate the force in newtons between charges of 80 μcoul and 20 μcoul separated by 0.04 m in air.

18

When a capacitor charges and discharges with varying voltage applied, alternating current can flow. Although there cannot be any current through the dielectric of the capacitor, its charge and discharge produces current in the circuit connected to the capacitor plates. This ability of a capacitor to allow alternating current to flow with sine-wave voltage applied is specified by the capacitive reactance X_C. The amount of X_C is $1/(2\pi f C)$, with f in cps and C in farads for X_C in ohms. The reactance of X_C is in ohm units, like X_L, but their effects are opposite in terms of frequency. While X_L is directly proportional to f, X_C is inversely proportional to f. Because of this reciprocal relation in $X_C = 1/(2\pi f C)$, the ohms of X_C decrease for higher frequencies and more capacitance. With fewer ohms of opposition for X_C, the amount of current increases. The topics explaining these effects of X_C in sine-wave a-c circuits are:

18·1   How alternating voltage produces alternating current in a capacitive circuit
18·2 $X_C = 1/(2\pi f C)$
18·3   Series or parallel capacitive reactances
18·4   Ohm's law for capacitive reactance
18·5   Applications of capacitive reactance
18·6   Charge and discharge current produced by sine-wave voltage

18·1   *How alternating voltage produces alternating current in a capacitive circuit*

The fact that current flows with a-c voltage applied is demonstrated in Fig. 18·1, where the bulb lights in *a* and *b* because of the capacitor charge and discharge current. There is no current through the dielectric, which is an insulator. While the capacitor is being charged by increasing applied

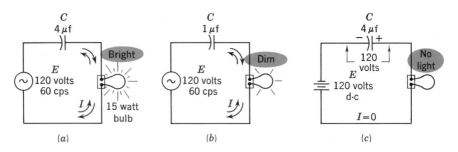

Fig. 18·1 Current in a capacitive circuit. (a) 4-μf capacitor allows enough 60-cps current to light bulb brightly. (b) Less current with smaller capacitor causes dim light. (c) Bulb cannot light with d-c voltage applied.

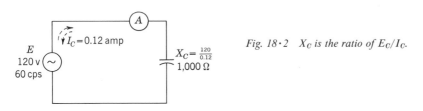

Fig. 18·2 X_C is the ratio of E_C/I_C.

voltage, however, the charging current flows in one direction in the conductors to the plates. While the capacitor is discharging, when the applied voltage decreases, the discharge current flows in the reverse direction. With alternating voltage applied, the capacitor alternately charges and discharges. First the capacitor is charged in one polarity, and then it discharges; next the capacitor is charged in the opposite polarity, and then it discharges again. The cycles of charge and discharge current provide alternating current in the circuit, at the same frequency as the applied voltage. This is the current that lights the bulb.

In Fig. 18·1a, the 4-μf capacitor provides enough alternating current to light the bulb brightly. In Fig. 18·1b, the 1-μf capacitor has less charge and discharge current because of the smaller capacitance, and the light is not so bright. Therefore, the smaller capacitor has more opposition to alternating current as less current flows with the same applied voltage; that is, it has more reactance for less capacitance.

In Fig. 18·1c, the steady d-c voltage will charge the capacitor to 120 volts. Because the applied voltage does not change, though, the capacitor will just stay charged. Since the potential difference of 120 volts across the charged capacitor is a voltage drop opposing the applied voltage, no current can flow. Therefore, the bulb cannot light. The bulb may flicker on for an instant as charging current flows when voltage is applied, but this current is only temporary until the capacitor is charged. Then the capacitor has the applied voltage of 120 volts, but there is zero voltage across the bulb. As a result, the capacitor is said to *block* direct current or voltage. In other words, after the capacitor has been charged by a steady d-c voltage, there is no current in the d-c circuit. All the applied d-c voltage is across the charged capacitor with zero voltage across any series resistance.

In summary, then, this demonstration shows the following points:

1. Alternating current flows in a capacitive circuit with a-c voltage applied.
2. A smaller capacitance allows less current, which means more X_C with more ohms of opposition.
3. Lower frequencies for the applied voltage result in less current and more X_C. With a steady d-c voltage source, which corresponds to a frequency of zero, the opposition of the capacitor is infinite and there is no current. In this case the capacitor is effectively an open circuit.

These effects have almost unlimited applications in practical circuits because X_C depends on frequency. A very common use of a capacitor is to provide little opposition, allowing a large current, for a-c voltage but to block any d-c voltage. Another example is to use X_C for less opposition to a high-frequency alternating current, compared with lower frequencies.

The reason why a capacitor allows current to flow in an a-c circuit is the alternate charge and discharge. If we insert an ammeter in the circuit, as shown in Fig. 18·2, the a-c meter will read the amount of charge and discharge current. In this example I_C is 0.12 amp. This current is the same in the voltage source, the connecting leads, and the plates of the capacitor. However, there is no current in the dielectric between the plates of the capacitor.

When we consider the ratio of E_C/I_C for the ohms of opposition to the sine-wave current, this value is 120/0.12, which equals 1,000 ohms. This 1,000 ohms is what we call X_C, to indicate how much current can be produced by sine-wave voltage applied to a capacitor.

The X_C value depends on the amount of capacitance and the frequency of the applied voltage. If C in Fig. 18·2 were increased, it could take on more charge for more charging current and then produce more discharge current. Then X_C is less for more capacitance. Also, if the frequency were increased in Fig. 18·2, the capacitor could charge and discharge faster to produce more current. This action also means E_C/I_C would be less, with more current for the same applied voltage. Then X_C is less for higher frequencies.

18·2 $X_C = 1/(2\pi fC)$

This formula includes the effects of frequency and capacitance for calculating the ohms of reactance. The frequency is in cps and C in farads for X_C in ohms. As an example, we can calculate X_C for 2.65-μf C at 60 cps:

$$X_C = \frac{1}{2\pi fC} \qquad (18·1)$$

$$= \frac{1}{2\pi \times 60 \times 2.65 \times 10^{-6}}$$

$$= \frac{0.159 \times 10^6}{60 \times 2.65} = \frac{159,000}{159}$$

$$X_C = \textbf{1,000 ohms}$$

The constant factor 2π equal to 6.28 indicates the circular motion from which a sine wave is derived. Therefore, the formula applies only to sine-wave circuits. To simplify calculations of X_C, the constant reciprocal $\frac{1}{6.28}$ can be taken as 0.159, approximately. Then

$$X_C = \frac{0.159}{fC} \tag{18·2}$$

Remember that C must be in farads for X_C in ohms. Although C values are usually μf (10^{-6}) or pf (10^{-12}), substitute the value of C in farads with the required negative power of 10.

Example 1. How much is X_C for (*a*) 0.1-μf C at 1,000 cps? (*b*) 1-μf C at the same frequency?

Answer.

(*a*) $$X_C = \frac{0.159}{fC} = \frac{0.159 \times 10^6}{0.1 \times 1,000} = \frac{0.159 \times 10^3}{0.1}$$

$$X_C = \textbf{1,590 ohms}$$

(*b*) At the same frequency, with ten times more C, X_C is $1,590/10$, which equals **159 ohms.**

Note that X_C in (*b*) is one-tenth the X_C in (*a*) because C is ten times larger.

Example 2. How much is X_C of 100-pf C at (*a*) 1 Mc? (*b*) 10 Mc?

Answer.

(*a*) $$X_C = \frac{0.159}{fC} = \frac{0.159}{1 \times 10^6 \times 100 \times 10^{-12}} = \frac{0.159 \times 10^6}{100}$$

$$X_C = \textbf{1,590 ohms}$$

(*b*) At ten times the frequency, X_C is $1,590/10$, which equals **159 ohms.**

Note that X_C in (*b*) is one-tenth the X_C in (*a*) because f is ten times larger.

In comparing the values in the two examples, notice that because of the higher frequencies in Example 2, the smaller capacitor of 100 pf has the same reactance at 1 Mc as the 0.1-μf capacitor at 1 kc. The reason is that reducing C by the factor of $\frac{1}{1,000}$ is exactly canceled by increasing f by the factor of 1,000.

Example 3. How much is X_C of a 240-pf C at 41.67 kc?

Answer.

$$X_C = \frac{0.159}{fC} = \frac{0.159}{41.67 \times 10^3 \times 240 \times 10^{-12}} = \frac{0.159 \times 10^9}{41.67 \times 240}$$

$$X_C = \textbf{15,900 ohms}$$

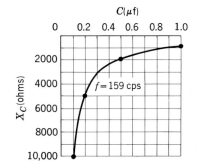

X_C Increases with Smaller C	
$X_C^* = 1/(2\pi f C)$, ohms	C, µf
1,000	1.0
2,000	0.5
5,000	0.2
10,000	0.1

*$f = 159$ cps

Fig. 18·3 *Capacitive reactance X_C decreases with higher values of C.*

Fig. 18·4 *Capacitive reactance X_C decreases with higher frequencies.*

X_C Increases with Lower Frequencies	
$X_C^* = 1/(2\pi f C)$, ohms	f, Mc
1,000	1.0
2,000	0.5
5,000	0.2
10,000	0.1

*$C = 159$ pf

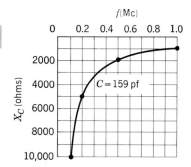

X_C is inversely proportional to capacitance. This statement means that X_C increases as the capacitance is reduced. In Fig. 18·3, when C is reduced by the factor of ⅒, from 1.0 to 0.1 µf, X_C increases 10 times from 1,000 to 10,000 ohms; decreasing C one-half, from 0.2 to 0.1 µf, doubles X_C from 5,000 to 10,000 ohms.

This inverse relation between C and X_C is illustrated by the graph in Fig. 18·3. Note that values of X_C increase downward on the graph, indicating negative reactance that is opposite from inductive reactance. With C increasing to the right, the decreasing values of X_C approach the zero axis of the graph.

X_C is inversely proportional to frequency. Figure 18·4 illustrates the inverse relation between X_C and f. With f increasing to the right in the graph from 0.1 to 1 Mc, the negative value of X_C of the 159-pf capacitor decreases from 10,000 to 1,000 ohms as the X_C curve comes closer to the zero axis. The graphs are nonlinear because of the inverse relation between X_C and f or C. At one end, the curves approach infinitely high reactance for zero capacitance or zero frequency. At the other end, the curves approach zero reactance for infinitely high capacitance or frequency.

In some applications, it is necessary to find the value of capacitance required for a desired value of X_C, at a specific frequency. For this case the reactance formula can be transposed:

$$C = \frac{0.159}{f X_C} \qquad \text{farads} \qquad (18·3)$$

Example 4. What capacitance is needed to have 100-ohm X_C at 1 Mc?

$$C = \frac{0.159}{fX_C} = \frac{0.159}{1 \times 10^6 \times 100} = \frac{0.159 \times 10^{-6}}{1 \times 100} = 0.00159 \times 10^{-6} \text{ farad}$$
$$= \textbf{0.00159 } \boldsymbol{\mu}\textbf{f}$$

Or, to find the frequency at which a given capacitance has a specified X_C, the reactance formula can be transposed:

$$f = \frac{0.159}{CX_C} \qquad \text{cps} \qquad (18 \cdot 4)$$

Example 5. At what frequency will a 0.1-μf capacitor have X_C equal to 1,000 ohms?

$$f = \frac{0.159}{CX_C} = \frac{0.159}{0.1 \times 10^{-6} \times 1,000} = \frac{0.159}{0.1 \times 10^{-6} \times 10^3}$$
$$= 0.159 \times 10^4 = \textbf{1,590 cps}$$

18·3 Series or parallel capacitive reactances

Because capacitive reactance is an opposition in ohms, series or parallel reactances are combined in the same way as resistances. As shown in Fig. 18·5a, series reactances of 100 and 200 ohms add to equal 300 ohms of X_{C_T} across both:

$$X_{C_T} = X_{C_1} + X_{C_2} + \cdots + \text{etc.} \qquad \text{in series} \qquad (18 \cdot 5)$$

For parallel reactances, the combined reactance is calculated by the reciprocal formula, as shown in Fig. 18·5b.

$$\frac{1}{X_{C_T}} = \frac{1}{X_{C_1}} + \frac{1}{X_{C_2}} + \cdots + \text{etc.} \qquad \text{in parallel} \qquad (18 \cdot 6)$$

Fig. 18·5 Reactances combine like resistances. (a) Addition of series reactances. (b) Two reactances in parallel equal their product over their sum.

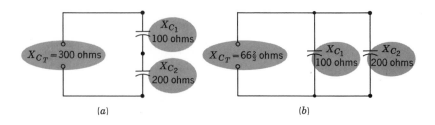

(a)   (b)

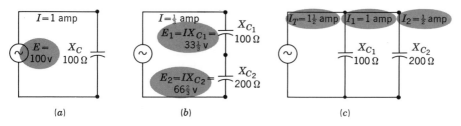

Fig. 18·6 Circuit calculations with X_C. (a) $I = E/X_C$. (b) Sum of series voltage drops equals the applied voltage. (c) Sum of parallel branch currents equals total line current.

In Fig. 18·5b the parallel combination of 100 and 200 equals 66⅔ ohms for X_{C_T}. The combined parallel reactance is smaller than the lowest branch reactance. Any short cuts for combining parallel resistances also apply to parallel reactances.

Combining reactances is opposite to the way capacitances are combined. The two procedures are equivalent, however, because capacitive reactance is inversely proportional to capacitance. The general case is that ohms of opposition add in series but combine by the reciprocal formula in parallel. This rule applies to resistances, to a combination of inductive reactances alone, or to capacitive reactances alone.

18·4 Ohm's law for capacitive reactance

The current in an a-c circuit with X_C alone is equal to the applied voltage divided by the ohms of X_C. Three examples with X_C are illustrated in Fig. 18·6. In a, there is just one reactance of 100 ohms. The current I equals E/X_C, or 100 volts/100 ohms, which is 1 amp.

For the series circuit in b the total reactance, equal to the sum of the series reactances, is 300 ohms. Then the current is 100 volts/300 ohms, which equals ⅓ amp. Also, the voltage across each reactance is equal to its IX_C product. The sum of these series voltage drops equals the applied voltage.

For the parallel circuit in c, each parallel reactance has its individual branch current, equal to the applied voltage divided by the branch reactance. The voltage E is the same across both reactances, equal to the generator voltage, since they are all in parallel. Also, the total line current of 1½ amp is equal to the sum of the individual branch currents of 1 and ½ amp each. With the applied voltage E in RMS value, all the calculated currents and voltage drops in Fig. 18·6 are also RMS values.

18·5 Applications of capacitive reactance

The general use of X_C is to block direct current but provide low reactance for alternating current. In this way, a varying a-c component can be separated from a steady direct current. Furthermore, a capacitor can have less reactance for alternating current of high frequencies, compared with lower

Table 18·1 Capacitance values for reactance of 1,000 ohms

C (approx)	Frequency	Remarks
2.7 µf	60 cps	Power-line frequency and low audio frequency
0.16 µf	1,000 cps	Medium audio frequency
0.016 µf	10,000 cps	High audio frequency
160 pf	1,000 kc (r-f)	In AM radio broadcast band
16 pf	10 Mc (h-f)	In short-wave radio band
1.6 pf	100 Mc (VHF)	In FM radio broadcast band

frequencies. Note the following differences in ohms of R, X_L, and X_C. Ohms of R remain the same for d-c circuits or a-c circuits. Ohms of reactance, however, either X_L or X_C, depend on the frequency. The effects of X_L and X_C are opposite, as X_L increases with frequency but X_C decreases with frequency.

If 1,000 ohms is taken as the desired value of X_C, capacitor values can be calculated for different frequencies, as listed in Table 18·1. The capacitance values indicate typical capacitor sizes for different frequency applications. Capacitors of 2 to 100 µf can be considered for low reactance at the power-line frequency of 60 cps. For the a-f range, typical capacitors may be 0.001 to 1.0 µf. In r-f applications, the required capacitance may be 1 to 1,000 pf.

18·6 Charge and discharge current produced by sine-wave voltage

In Fig. 18·7 sine-wave voltage applied across a capacitor produces alternating charge and discharge current. The action is considered for each quarter-cycle. Note that the voltage e_C across the capacitor is the same as the applied voltage e_a at all times because they are in parallel. The values of current i, however, depend on the charge and discharge of C. When e_a is increasing, it charges C to keep e_C at the same voltage as e_a; when e_a is decreasing, C discharges to maintain e_C at the same voltage as e_a. When e_a is not changing, there is no charge or discharge current.

During the first quarter-cycle in Fig. 18·7a, e_a is positive and increasing, charging C in the polarity shown. The electron flow is from the negative terminal of the source voltage, producing charging current in the direction indicated by the arrow for i. Next, when the applied voltage decreases during the second quarter-cycle e_C also decreases by discharging. The discharge current is from the negative plate of C, through the source, and back to the positive plate. Note that the discharge current in b has the opposite direction from the charge current in a.

For the third quarter-cycle in c the applied voltage e_a increases again but in the negative direction. Now C charges again but in reversed polarity. Here the charging current is in the opposite direction from the charge cur-

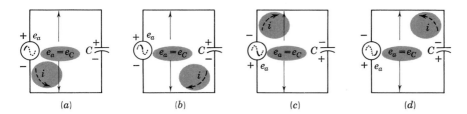

Fig. 18·7 *Capacitive charge and discharge current. (a) e_a increasing positive charges C. (b) C discharges as e_a decreases. (c) e_a increases negative to charge C in opposite polarity. (d) C discharges as reversed e_a decreases.*

rent in *a* but the same direction as the discharge current in *b*. Finally, the negative applied voltage decreases during the final quarter-cycle in *d*. As a result, C discharges. This discharge current is opposite to the charge current in *c* but in the same direction as the charge current in *a*.

For the sine wave of applied voltage, therefore, the capacitor provides a cycle of alternating charge and discharge current. Notice that capacitive current flows, for either charge or discharge, whenever the voltage changes, for either an increase or decrease. Also, *i* and *e* have the same frequency.

Calculating the values of i_C. The greater the voltage change, the greater is the amount of capacitive current. Furthermore, a larger capacitor can allow more charge current when the applied voltage increases and produce more discharge current. Because of these factors the amount of capacitive current can be calculated as

$$i_C = C \frac{de}{dt} \tag{18·7}$$

where *i* is in amperes, with C in farads and *de/dt* in volts per second. As an example, suppose that the voltage across a 240-pf capacitor changes by 25 volts in 1 μsec. The amount of capacitive current then is

$$i_C = C \frac{de}{dt} = 240 \times 10^{-12} \times \frac{25}{1 \times 10^{-6}}$$

$$= 240 \times 25 \times 10^{-6} = 6{,}000 \times 10^{-6}$$

$$i_C = 6 \times 10^{-3} \text{ amp} = \mathbf{6 \text{ ma}}$$

Notice how Formula (18·7) is similar to the capacitor charge formula $Q = CE$. When the voltage changes, this *de/dt* factor produces a change in the charge Q. When the charge moves, this *dq/dt* change is the current i_C. Therefore, *dq/dt* or $i_C = de/dt$.

Furthermore the formula for capacitive current $i_C = C \, de/dt$ corresponds to the formula for induced voltage $e_L = L \, di/dt$. In both cases there must be a change to have an effect. For inductance, e_L is induced when the current changes. For capacitance, i_C results when the voltage changes.

These formulas give the fundamental definitions for the amount of reactive effect for inductance or capacitance. Just as one henry is defined as the amount of inductance that produces one volt e_L when the current changes at the rate of 1 amp per sec, one farad can also be defined as the amount of capacitance that produces one amp i_C when the voltage changes at the rate of 1 volt per sec.

By means of Formula (18·7), then, i_C can be calculated to find the instantaneous value of charge or discharge current when the voltage changes across a capacitor.

Example 6. Calculate the instantaneous value of charging current i_C produced by a 6-μf C when its potential difference is increased by 50 volts in 1 sec.

Answer.
$$i_C = C\frac{de}{dt} = 6 \times 10^{-6} \times \frac{50}{1}$$

$$i_C = \textbf{300 μa}$$

Fig. 18·8   Waveshapes of sine-wave voltage with charge and discharge current i_C, plotted for values in Table 18·2.

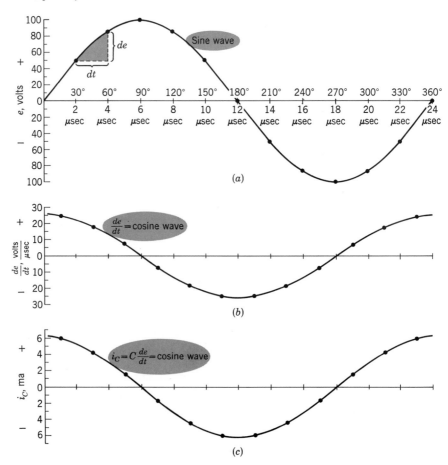

Table 18·2   Values for $i_C = C\dfrac{de}{dt}$ curves in Fig. 18·8

Time		dt		de,	de/dt,	C,	$i_C = C\,de/dt$, ma
θ	μsec	θ	μsec	volts	volts per μsec	pf	
30°	2	30°	2	50	25	240	6
60°	4	30°	2	36.6	18.3	240	4.4
90°	6	30°	2	13.4	6.7	240	1.6
120°	8	30°	2	− 13.4	− 6.7	240	− 1.6
150°	10	30°	2	− 36.6	− 18.3	240	− 4.4
180°	12	30°	2	− 50	− 25	240	− 6
210°	14	30°	2	− 50	− 25	240	− 6
240°	16	30°	2	− 36.6	− 18.3	240	− 4.4
270°	18	30°	2	− 13.4	− 6.7	240	− 1.6
300°	20	30°	2	13.4	6.7	240	1.6
330°	22	30°	2	36.6	18.3	240	4.4
360°	24	30°	2	50	25	240	6

Example 7. Calculate i_C for the same C as in Example 6 where its potential difference is *decreased* by 50 volts in 1 sec.

Answer. For the same C de/dt, i_C is the same **300 μa** answer. However, this 300 μa is discharge current, which flows in the opposite direction from i_C on charge. If desired, the i_C for discharge current can be considered negative, or − 300 μa.

Example 8. Calculate i_C produced by a 250-pf capacitor for a change of 50 volts in 1 μsec.

Answer. $i_C = C\dfrac{de}{dt} = 250 \times 10^{-12} \times \dfrac{50}{1 \times 10^{-6}} = 12{,}500 \times 10^{-6}$

$i_C = \textbf{12,500 μa}$

Notice that more i_C is produced here although C is smaller than in Example 6, because de/dt is a much faster voltage change.

Waveshapes of e_C and i_C. More details of capacitive circuits can be analyzed by means of the waveshapes in Fig. 18·8, plotted for the calculated values in Table 18·2. The top curve shows a sine wave of voltage e_C across a 240-pf capacitance C. Since the capacitive current i_C depends on the rate of change of voltage, rather than the absolute value of e, the curve in b shows how much the voltage changes. In this curve, the de/dt values are plotted for every 30° of the cycle. The bottom curve shows the actual capacitive current i_C. This i_C curve is similar to the de/dt curve because i_C equals the constant factor C multiplied by de/dt. All three curves are similar to the three curves shown in Fig. 15·7 for inductive circuits, but with the voltage and current curves interchanged. Both examples illustrate the effects of the rate of change in a sine wave.

90° phase angle. The i_C curve at the bottom in Fig. 18·8 has its zero values when the e_C curve at the top is at maximum. This comparison shows that the curves are 90° out of phase, as i_C is a cosine wave of current for the sine wave of voltage e_C. The 90° phase difference results from the fact that i_C depends on the *de/dt* rate of change, rather than *e* itself. More details of this 90° phase angle for capacitance are explained in the next chapter.

For each of the curves, the period T is 24 μsec. Therefore, the frequency is $1/T$ or ½₄ μsec, which equals 41.67 kc. Each curve has the same frequency, although there is 90° phase difference between i and e.

Ohms of X_C. The ratio of e_C/i_C actually specifies the capacitive reactance, in ohms. For this comparison, we use the actual value of e_C, which has the peak of 100 volts. The rate-of-change factor is included in i_C. Although the peak of i_C at 6 ma is 90° ahead of the peak of e_C at 100 volts, we can compare these two peak values. Then e_C/i_C is 100/0.006, which equals 16,667 ohms. This X_C is only an approximate value because i_C cannot be determined exactly for the large *dt* changes every 30°. If we used smaller intervals of time, the peak i_C would be 6.28 ma and X_C would be 15,900 ohms, the same as $2\pi fL$ ohms with a 240-pf C and frequency of 41.67 kc. This is the same X_C problem as Example 3 on page 352.

SUMMARY

1. Capacitive reactance, indicated by X_C, is the opposition of a capacitance to the flow of sine-wave alternating current.
2. X_C is measured in ohms because it limits the current to the value E/X_C. With E in volts and X_C in ohms, I is in amperes.
3. $X_C = 1/(2\pi fC)$. With f in cycles per second and C in farads, X_C is in ohms.
4. For one value of capacitance, X_C decreases with higher frequencies.
5. At one frequency, X_C decreases with higher values of capacitance.
6. With X_C and f known, the capacitance $C = 1/(2\pi fX_C)$.
7. With X_C and C known, the frequency $f = 1/(2\pi CX_C)$.
8. The total X_C of capacitive reactances in series equals the sum of the individual values, as for series resistances. The series reactances have the same current. The voltage across each series reactance is IX_C.
9. With parallel capacitive reactances, the combined reactance is calculated by the reciprocal formula, as for parallel resistances. Each branch current is E/X_C. The total line current is the sum of the individual branch currents.
10. Table 18·3 summarizes the differences between C and X_C.
11. Table 18·4 compares the opposite types of reactance X_L and X_C.

Table 18·3   Comparison of capacitance and capacitive reactance

CAPACITANCE	CAPACITIVE REACTANCE
Symbol is C	Symbol is X_C
Measured in farad units	Measured in ohm units
Depends on construction of capacitor	Depends on frequency of sine-wave voltage
$C = i_C/(de/dt)$ farads	$X_C = e_C/i_C$ or $1/(2\pi fC)$ ohms

Table 18·4   Comparison of inductive and capacitive reactances

X_L, OHMS	X_C, OHMS
Increases with more inductance	Decreases with more capacitance
Increases for higher frequencies	Decreases for higher frequencies
Allows more current for lower frequencies; passes direct current	Allows less current for lower frequencies; blocks direct current

SELF-EXAMINATION (*Answers at back of book.*)

Here's a chance to find out how well you have learned the material in this chapter. These exercises are for your self-testing only.

1. Alternating current can flow in a capacitive circuit with a-c voltage applied because (*a*) of the high peak value; (*b*) varying voltage produces charge and discharge current; (*c*) charging current flows when the voltage decreases; (*d*) discharge current flows when the voltage increases.
2. With higher frequencies, the amount of capacitive reactance (*a*) increases; (*b*) stays the same; (*c*) decreases; (*d*) increases only when the voltage increases.
3. At one frequency, larger capacitance results in (*a*) more reactance; (*b*) the same reactance; (*c*) less reactance; (*d*) less reactance if the voltage amplitude decreases.
4. The capacitive reactance of a 0.1-μf capacitor at 1,000 cps equals (*a*) 1,000 ohms; (*b*) 1,600 ohms; (*c*) 2,000 ohms; (*d*) 3,200 ohms.
5. Two 1,000-ohm X_C values in series have a total reactance of (*a*) 500 ohms; (*b*) 1,000 ohms; (*c*) 1,414 ohms; (*d*) 2,000 ohms.
6. Two 1,000-ohm X_C values in parallel have a combined reactance of (*a*) 500 ohms; (*b*) 707 ohms; (*c*) 1,000 ohms; (*d*) 2,000 ohms.
7. With 50 volts RMS applied across 100-ohm X_C, the RMS current in the circuit equals (*a*) 0.5 amp; (*b*) 0.637 amp; (*c*) 0.707 amp; (*d*) 1.414 amp.
8. With steady d-c voltage from a battery applied to a capacitance, after it charges to the battery voltage, the current in the circuit (*a*) depends on the current rating of the battery; (*b*) is greater for larger values of capacitance; (*c*) is smaller for larger values of capacitance; (*d*) is zero for any capacitance value.
9. The capacitance needed for 1,000-ohm reactance at 2 Mc is (*a*) 2 pf; (*b*) 80 pf; (*c*) 1,000 pf; (*d*) 2,000 pf.
10. A 0.2-μf capacitance will have a reactance of 1,000 ohms at the frequency of (*a*) 800 cps; (*b*) 1 kc; (*c*) 1 Mc; (*d*) 8 Mc.

ESSAY QUESTIONS

1. Why is capacitive reactance measured in ohms? State two differences between capacitance and capacitive reactance.
2. Referring to Fig. 18·1, explain briefly why the bulb lights in *a* but not in *c*.
3. Explain briefly what is meant by two factors being inversely proportional. How does this apply to X_C and C? X_C and f?
4. In comparing X_L with X_C give two differences and one similarity.
5. In comparing X_C and R, give two differences and one similarity.
6. Referring to Fig. 18·8, why are waves *a* and *b* considered to be 90° out of phase, while waves *b* and *c* have the same phase?
7. Referring to Fig. 18·3, how does this graph show an inverse relation between X_C and C?
8. Referring to Fig. 18·4, how does this graph show an inverse relation between X_C and f?
9. Referring to Fig. 18·8, draw three similar curves but for a sine wave of voltage with a period $T = 12$ μsec for the full cycle. Use the same C of 240 pf. Compare the value of X_C obtained as $1/(2\pi f C)$ and e_C/i_C.

10. (a) What is the relation between charge q and current i? (b) How is this comparison similar to the relation between $Q = CE$ and $i = C\, de/dt$?

PROBLEMS (Answers to selected problems at back of book.)

1. Referring to Fig. 18·4, give the values of C needed for 2,000-ohm X_C at the four frequencies listed.
2. What size capacitance is needed for 100-ohm reactance at 100 kc?
3. A capacitor with X_C of 2,000 ohms is connected across 10-volt 1,000-cps source. (a) Draw the schematic diagram. (b) How much is the current in the circuit? (c) What is the frequency of the current?
4. How much is the capacitance of a capacitor that draws 0.1 amp from the 60-cps 120-volt power line?
5. A 1,000-ohm X_{C_1} and a 4,000-ohm X_{C_2} are in series across a 10-volt source. (a) Draw the schematic diagram. (b) Calculate the current in the series circuit. (c) How much is the voltage across X_{C_1}? (d) How much is the voltage across X_{C_2}?
6. The 1,000-ohm X_{C_1} and 4,000-ohm X_{C_2} in question 5 are in parallel across the 10-volt source. (a) Draw the schematic diagram. (b) Calculate the branch current in X_{C_1}. (c) Calculate the branch current in X_{C_2}. (d) Calculate the total line current. (e) How much is the voltage across both reactances?
7. At what frequency will a 0.01-μf capacitor have a reactance of 10,000 ohms?
8. Four capacitive reactances of 100, 200, 300, and 400 ohms each are connected in series across a 40-volt source. (a) Draw the schematic diagram. (b) How much is the total X_{C_T}? (c) Calculate I. (d) Calculate the voltages across each capacitance. (e) If the frequency of the applied voltage is 1,600 kc, calculate the required value of each capacitance.
9. Three equal capacitive reactances of 600 ohms each are in parallel. (a) How much is the equivalent combined reactance? (b) If the frequency of the applied voltage is 800 kc, how much is the capacitance of each capacitor and how much is the equivalent combined capacitance of the three in parallel?
10. A 2-μf C is in series with a 4-μf C. The frequency is 5 kc. (a) How much is C_T? (b) Calculate X_{C_T}. (c) Calculate X_{C_1} and X_{C_2} to see if their sum equals X_{C_T}.
11. A capacitor across the 120-volt 60-cycle a-c power line allows 0.4-amp current. Calculate X_C and C. What size C is needed to double the current?
12. A 0.01-μf capacitor is connected across a 10-volt source. Tabulate the values of X_C and current in the circuit at 0 cps (for steady d-c voltage), and a-c voltage at 20 cps, 60 cps, 100 cps, 500 cps, 5 kc, 10 kc, and 455 kc.
13. At what frequencies will X_C be 20,000 ohms for the following capacitors: 2 μf, 0.1 μf, 0.05 μf, 0.002 μf, 250 pf, 100 pf, 47 pf?
14. What size C is needed to have X_C the same as the X_L of a 6-mh L at 100 kc?

Chapter 19 Capacitive circuits

This unit describes two features of capacitive circuits. One is the leading phase angle of the capacitor charge and discharge current; the other is the RC time constant. Finally, the practical application of a coupling capacitor shows how it is used to pass a-c voltage while blocking d-c voltage. The topics are as follows:

19·1 Sine-wave e_C lags i_C by 90°
19·2 Capacitive reactance and resistance in series
19·3 Capacitive reactance and resistance in parallel
19·4 Capacitive voltage dividers
19·5 RC time constant
19·6 Energy in electrostatic field of capacitance
19·7 R-f and a-f coupling capacitors
19·8 Comparison of reactance and time constant

19·1 Sine-wave e_C lags i_C by 90°

For a sine wave of applied voltage, the capacitor provides a cycle of alternating charge and discharge current, as shown in Fig. 19·1a. In b the waveshape of this charge and discharge current i_C is compared with the voltage e_C.

Note that the instantaneous value of i_C is zero when e_C is at its maximum value. At either its positive or negative peak, e_C is not changing. For one instant at both peaks, therefore, the voltage must have a static value before changing its direction. Then e is not changing and C is not charging or discharging. The result is zero current at this time.

Also note that i_C is maximum when e_C is zero. When e_C crosses the zero axis, i_C has its maximum value because then the voltage is changing most rapidly. With C having no charge and e increasing rapidly in either

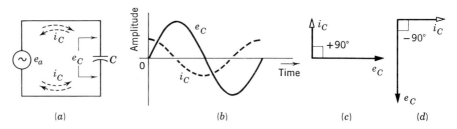

Fig. 19·1 i_C leads e_C by 90°. (a) Circuit of sine-wave voltage e_a applied across C. (b) Waveshapes of i_C at peak values 90° ahead of e_C. (c) Vector diagram of i_C leading e_C by counterclockwise angle of 90°. (d) Vector diagram with i_C as reference to show e_C lagging i_C by clockwise angle of −90°.

polarity, there must be maximum charging current to keep C charged to the same voltage as e.

Therefore, i_C and e_C are 90° out of phase, since the maximum value of one corresponds to the zero value of the other; i_C leads e_C because i_C has its maximum value a quarter-cycle before the time that e_C reaches its peak. The vectors in Fig. 19·1c show i_C leading e_C by the counterclockwise angle of 90°. Here e_C is the horizontal vector for the reference angle of 0°. In Fig. 19·1d, however, the current i_C is the horizontal vector for reference. Since i_C must be 90° leading, e_C is shown lagging by the clockwise angle of −90°. In series circuits, the current i_C is the reference and then the voltage e_C can be considered to lag i_C by 90°. In parallel circuits, the voltage e_C is the reference and then the current i_C can be considered to lead e_C by 90°.

The 90° phase angle results because i_C depends on the rate of change of e_C. As shown previously in Fig. 18·8, for a sine wave of e_C, the capacitive charge and discharge current is a cosine wave. This 90° phase between e_C and i_C is true in any sine-wave a-c circuit, whether C is in series or parallel and whether C is alone or combined with other components. We can always say that for any X_C its current and voltage are 90° out of phase.

Capacitive current the same in series circuit. The leading phase angle of capacitive current is only with respect to the voltage across the capacitor, which does not change the fact that the current is the same in all parts of a series circuit. In Fig. 19·1a, for instance, the current in the generator, the connecting wires, and both plates of the capacitor must be the same because they are all in the same series path. At any instant, whatever the current value is at that time, it is the same in all the series components. However, there is no current through the dielectric. Note that the 90° lead in time is between current and voltage.

Capacitive voltage the same across parallel branches. In Fig. 19·1a, the voltage is the same across the generator and C because they are in parallel. There cannot be any lag or lead in time between these two parallel voltages. At any instant, whatever the voltage value is across the generator at that time, the voltage across C is the same. With respect to the series current, however, both e_a and e_C are 90° out of phase with i_C.

The frequency is the same for e_C and i_C. Although e_C lags i_C by 90°, both waves have the same frequency. For example, if the frequency of the sine-wave e_C in Fig. 19·1b is 100 cps, this is also the frequency of i_C.

19·2 Capacitive reactance and resistance in series

When resistance is in series with capacitive reactance (Fig. 19·2), both determine the current. I is the same in X_C and R, since they are in series. Each has its own series voltage drop, equal to IR for the resistance and IX_C for the reactance. If the capacitive reactance alone is considered, its voltage drop lags the series current I by 90°. The IR voltage has the same phase as I, however, because resistance provides no phase shift. Therefore, resistance and capacitive reactance combined in series must be added vectorially because they are 90° out of phase with each other.

Vector addition of E_C and E_R. In Fig. 19·2b, the current vector is shown horizontal, as the reference phase, because I is the same throughout the series circuit. The resistive voltage drop IR has the same phase as I. The capacitor voltage IX_C must be 90° clockwise from I and IR, as the capac-itive voltage lags.

Note that the IX_C vector is downward, exactly opposite from an IX_L vector, because of the opposite phase angle. The vector voltages E_R and E_C, being 90° out of phase, still form a right triangle, however. Therefore

$$E_a = \sqrt{E_R^2 + E_C^2} \tag{19·1}$$

This formula applies just to series circuits because then E_C is 90° out of phase with E_R. All values of E must be in the same units.

In calculating the value of E, first square E_R and square E_C, then add and take the square root. For the example in Fig. 19·2,

$$E_a = \sqrt{(100)^2 + (100)^2} = \sqrt{10,000 + 10,000}$$
$$= \sqrt{20,000} = \textbf{141 volts}$$

Fig. 19·2 X_C and R in series. (a) Circuit. (b) Vector triangle of voltages showing E_C lagging E_R by $-90°$. (c) Similar impedance triangle showing X_C lagging R by $-90°$.

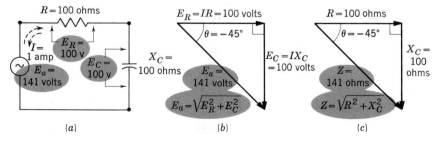

The two vector voltages total 141 volts instead of 200 volts because the 90° phase means the peak value of one occurs when the other is at zero.

Vector addition of X_C and R. The voltage triangle in Fig. 19·2b corresponds to the impedance triangle in Fig. 19·2c because the common factor I can be canceled with the same current in X_C and R. Their vector sum is the combined impedance

$$Z = \sqrt{R^2 + X_C^2} \qquad (19\cdot2)$$

With R and X_C in ohms, Z is also in ohms. For the example in Fig. 19·2c,

$$Z = \sqrt{(100^2) + (100)^2}$$
$$= \sqrt{10,000 + 10,000}$$
$$Z = \sqrt{20,000} = \textbf{141 ohms}$$

Note that the total impedance of 141 ohms divided into the applied voltage of 141 volts allows the current of 1 amp in the series circuit. The IR voltage drop is 1 × 100, or 100 volts; the IX_C voltage drop is also 1 × 100, or 100 volts. The vector sum of the two series voltage drops of 100 volts each equals the applied voltage of 141 volts. Also, the applied voltage equals IZ, or 1 × 141, which is 141 volts.

Phase angle with series X_C. As with inductive reactance, θ is the phase angle between the generator voltage and its series current. As shown in Fig. 19·2b and c, θ can be calculated from the voltage or impedance triangle.

With series X_C, the phase angle is negative, clockwise from the zero reference angle of I, because the X_C voltage lags its current. To indicate the negative phase angle, therefore, X_C has a negative sign, indicating this vector points downward from the horizontal reference, instead of upward as with series inductive reactance. To calculate the phase angle with series X_C and R, then,

$$\tan \theta = \frac{-X_C}{R} \qquad (19\cdot3)$$

Using the tangent formula for the circuit in Fig. 19·2c,

$$\tan \theta = \frac{-X_C}{R} = \frac{-100}{100} = -1$$

then $\qquad \theta = -45°$

The negative sign means the angle is clockwise from zero, to indicate the leading capacitive current in a circuit with series X_C.

Series combinations of X_C and R. In a series circuit, the higher the value of X_C compared with R, the more capacitive is the circuit. There is more

Table 19·1   Series resistance and capacitive reactance combinations

R, ohms	X_C, ohms	Z, ohms (approx)	Phase angle θ_Z
1	10	$\sqrt{101} = 10$	$-84.3°$
10	10	$\sqrt{200} = 14$	$-45°$
10	1	$\sqrt{101} = 10$	$-5.7°$

Note: θ_Z is angle of Z_T with respect to the reference I in series circuits.

voltage drop across the capacitive reactance, and the phase angle increases toward $-90°$. The series X_C always makes the current lead the applied voltage. With all X_C and no R, the entire applied voltage is across X_C and θ equals $-90°$.

Several combinations of X_C and R in series are listed in Table 19·1, with their resultant impedance values and phase angle. Note that a ratio of 10:1 or more for X_C/R means the circuit is practically all capacitive. The phase angle of $-84.3°$ is almost $-90°$, and the total impedance Z is approximately equal to X_C. The voltage drop across X_C in the series circuit is then practically equal to the applied voltage, with almost none across R.

At the opposite extreme, when R is 10 times more than X_C, the series circuit is mainly resistive. The phase angle of $-5.7°$ then means the current has almost the same phase as the applied voltage; Z is approximately equal to R, and the voltage drop across R is practically equal to the applied voltage with almost none across X_C.

For the case when X_C and R equal each other, the resultant impedance Z is 1.41 times either one. The phase angle then is $-45°$, halfway between $0°$ for resistance alone and $-90°$ for capacitive reactance alone.

19·3   Capacitive reactance and resistance in parallel

Now the 90° phase angle for X_C must be with respect to branch currents, instead of voltage drops in a series circuit. In the parallel circuit in Fig. 19·3a, the voltage is the same across X_C, R, and the generator, since they are all in parallel. There cannot be any phase difference between the parallel voltages. Each branch, however, has its individual current. For the resistive branch, I_R is E/R; in the capacitive branch, $I_C = E/X_C$. These current vectors are shown in Fig. 19·3b.

Note that the vector diagram has the generator voltage E as the reference phase because it is the same throughout the circuit. The resistive branch current I_R has the same phase as E, but the capacitive branch current I_C leads E by 90°. The vector for I_C is up, compared with down for an X_C vector, because the parallel branch current I_C leads the reference E, while in a series circuit the X_C voltage lags the series current as the reference. The total line current therefore consists of I_R and I_C 90° out of phase with each other. The vector sum of I_R and I_C equals I_T:

$$I_T = \sqrt{I_R^2 + I_C^2} \qquad (19·4)$$

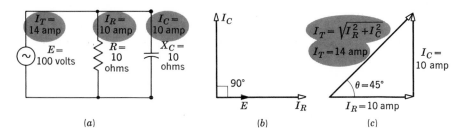

Fig. 19·3 X_C and R in parallel. (a) Circuit. (b) Current vectors
showing I_C leading E by 90°. (c) Vector triangle of branch currents
I_C and I_R to calculate total line current I_T.

In Fig. 19·3c, the vector sum of 10 amp for I_R and 10 amp for I_C equals
14.14 amp. The branch currents are added vectorially since they are the
factors 90° out of phase in a parallel circuit, corresponding to the voltage
drops 90° out of phase in a series circuit.

Impedance of X_C and R in parallel. As usual, the impedance of a parallel
circuit equals the applied voltage divided by the total line current:
$Z = E/I_T$. In Fig. 19·3, for example,

$$Z = \frac{E}{I_T} = \frac{100 \text{ volts}}{14.14 \text{ amp}} = 7.07 \text{ ohms}$$

which is the opposition in ohms across the generator, equal to the resistance of 10 ohms in parallel with the reactance of 10 ohms. Notice that the
impedance of equal values of R and X_C is not one-half but equals 70.7 per
cent of either one.

Phase angle in parallel circuits. In Fig. 19·3c, the phase angle θ is 45°
because R and X_C are equal, resulting in equal branch currents. The phase
angle is between the total current I_T and the generator voltage E. However, the phase of E is the same as I_R. Therefore, θ is between I_T and I_R.

Using the tangent formula to find θ from the current triangle in
Fig. 19·3c gives

$$\tan \theta = \frac{I_C}{I_R} \qquad (19 \cdot 5)$$

The phase angle is positive because the I_C vector is upward, leading E
by 90°. This direction is opposite from the lagging vector of series X_C. The
effect of X_C is no different, however. Only the reference is changed for the
phase angle. Note that the vector triangle of branch currents for parallel
circuits gives θ as the angle of I_T with respect to the generator voltage E,
but the vector triangle of voltages for a series circuit gives θ as the angle
of E with respect to the generator current I.

Parallel combinations of X_C and R. In Table 19·2, when X_C is 10 times R,
the parallel circuit is practically resistive because there is little leading

capacitive current in the main line. The small value of I_C results from the high reactance of shunt X_C. Then the total impedance of the parallel circuit is approximately equal to the resistance, since the high value of X_C in a parallel branch has little effect. The phase angle of 5.7° is practically 0° because almost all the line current is resistive. As X_C becomes smaller, it provides more leading capacitive current in the main line. When X_C is $\frac{1}{10}$ R, practically all the line current is the I_C component. Then the parallel circuit is practically all capacitive, with a total impedance practically equal to X_C. The phase angle of 84.3° is almost 90° because the line current is mostly capacitive. Note that these conditions are opposite to the case of X_C and R in series. With X_C and R equal, their branch currents are equal and the phase angle is 45°.

As additional comparisons between series and parallel circuits remember that:

1. The series voltage drops E_R and E_C have individual values that are 90° out of phase. Therefore, E_R and E_C are added vectorially to equal the applied voltage E. The negative phase angle $-\theta$ is between E and the common series current I. More series X_C allows more E_C to make the circuit more capacitive, with a larger negative phase angle for E with respect to I.
2. The parallel branch currents I_R and I_C have individual values that are 90° out of phase. Therefore, I_R and I_L are added vectorially to equal I_T, which is the main line current. The positive phase angle θ is between the line current I_T and the common parallel voltage E. Less parallel X_C allows more I_C to make the circuit more capacitive, with a larger positive phase angle for I_T with respect to E.

19·4   Capacitive voltage dividers

When capacitors are connected in series across a voltage source, the series capacitors serve as a voltage divider. Each capacitor has part of the applied voltage, and the sum of all the series voltage drops equals the source voltage. The amount of voltage across each is inversely proportional to its capacitance. For instance, with 2 μf in series with 1 μf, the smaller capacitor has double the voltage of the larger capacitor. Assuming 120 volts applied, one-third of this, or 40 volts, is across the 2-μf capacitor, with two-thirds, or 80 volts, across the 1-μf capacitor. The two series volt-

Table 19·2   Parallel resistance and capacitive reactance combinations*

R, ohms	Xc, ohms	IR, amp	Ic, amp	IT, amp (approx)	ZT, ohms (approx)	Phase angle θT
1	10	10	1	$\sqrt{101} = 10$	1	5.7°
10	10	1	1	$\sqrt{2} = 1.4$	7.07	45°
10	1	1	10	$\sqrt{101} = 10$	1	84.3°

* $E = 10$ volts. Note that θ_I is angle of I_T with respect to the reference E in parallel circuits.

age drops of 40 and 80 volts each add to equal the applied voltage of 120 volts. The addition is just the sum of the two voltages. It is only when voltages are out of phase with each other that the vector addition becomes necessary.

A-c divider. With sine-wave alternating current, the voltage division between series capacitors can be calculated on the basis of reactance. In Fig. 19·4a, the total reactance is 120 ohms across the 120-volt source. The current in the series circuit then is 1 amp. This current is the same for X_{C_1} and X_{C_2} in series. Therefore, the IX_C voltage across C_1 is 40 volts, with 80 volts across C_2. The voltage division is proportional to the series reactances, as it is to series resistances. However, reactance is inversely proportional to capacitance. As a result, the smaller capacitance has more reactance and a greater part of the applied voltage.

D-c divider. In Fig. 19·4b, both C_1 and C_2 will be charged by the battery. The voltage across the series combination of C_1 and C_2 must equal E. When charging current flows, electrons repelled from the negative battery terminal accumulate on the negative plate of C_1, repelling electrons from its positive plate. These electrons flow through the conductor to the negative plate of C_2. With the positive battery terminal attracting electrons, the charging current from the positive plate of C_2 returns to the positive side of the d-c source. Then C_1 and C_2 become charged in the polarity shown.

C_1 and C_2 are in the same series path for charging current. Therefore, both have the same amount of charge at all times. With the series combination charged to the applied voltage, C_1 and C_2 each have the same charge. However, the potential difference provided by the equal charges is inversely proportional to capacitance. The reason is that $Q = CE$, or $E = Q/C$. Therefore, the 1-μf capacitor has double the voltage of the 2-μf capacitor, with the same charge in both.

If you measure with a d-c voltmeter across C_1, the meter reads 40 volts. Across C_2 the d-c voltage is 80 volts. The measurement from the negative side of C_1 to the positive side of C_2 is the same as the applied battery voltage of 120 volts. If the meter is connected from the positive side of C_1 to the negative plate of C_2, however, the voltage is zero. These plates have the

Fig. 19·4   *Series capacitors divide the applied voltage inversely proportional to their capacitances. (a) A-c divider. (b) D-c divider.*

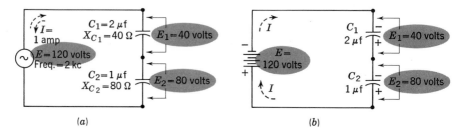

(a)   (b)

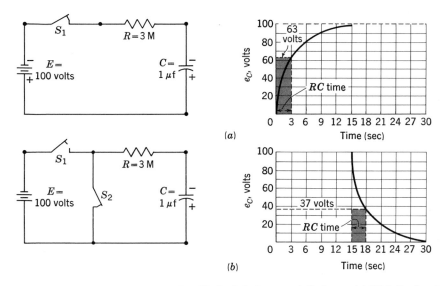

Fig. 19·5 *RC charge and discharge. (a) With S_1 closed and S_2 open, C charges through R to 63 per cent of E in 1 time constant of 3 sec. (b) With S_1 open and S_2 closed, C discharges through R to 37 per cent of its initial voltage in 1 time constant of 3 sec.*

same potential because they are joined by a conductor of zero resistance. The polarity marking at the junction between C_1 and C_2 indicates the voltage at this point with respect to the opposite plate for each capacitor. This junction is positive compared with the opposite plate of C_1 with a surplus of electrons, but the same point is negative compared with the opposite plate of C_2, which has a deficiency of electrons.

19·5 RC time constant

Since the formula for capacitive reactance is based on sine-wave voltage and current, X_C values do not apply exactly in circuits where the voltage variations are not sinusoidal. One example is the sudden change in applied voltage when a switch is closed or opened. In Fig. 19·5, for example, when the switch S_1 is closed in *a*, the applied voltage rises instantaneously from zero to 100 volts; in *b*, when S_1 is opened, the applied voltage drops from 100 volts to zero. The reaction to such an instantaneous increase or decrease in applied voltage is the *transient response* of the *RC* circuit.

Formula to calculate the time constant. The transient response is measured in terms of the product $R \times C$, which is the time constant of a capacitive circuit. To calculate the time constant,

$$T = R \times C \qquad \text{sec} \qquad (19 \cdot 6)$$

where R is in ohms and C in farads. Since the units for RC circuits are often megohms and microfarads, it is also convenient to specify the time constant as

$$T \text{ (sec)} = R \text{ (megohms)} \times C \text{ (microfarads)} \qquad (19 \cdot 7)$$

In Fig. $19 \cdot 5$, for example, with R equal to 3 M and $C = 1$ μf, T is 3 sec. Here the 1×10^6 factor of R cancels the 1×10^{-6} factor of C. The resistance R must be in series with C. This RC product is then the time constant, for either charge or discharge.

The reason why the RC product corresponds to time can be illustrated as follows: $C = Q/E$. The charge Q is the product of $I \times T$. The factor E is IR. Therefore, RC is equivalent to $(R \times Q)/E$, or $(R \times IT)/(IR)$. Since I and R cancel, T remains to indicate the dimension of time.

The time constant indicates the rate of charge or discharge. On charge, RC specifies the time it takes C to charge to 63 per cent of the charging voltage; on discharge, RC specifies the time it takes C to discharge 63 per cent of the way down to the value equal to 37 per cent of the initial voltage across C at the start of discharge. In Fig. $19 \cdot 5a$, for example, the time constant on charge is 3 sec. Therefore, in 3 sec, C charges to 63 per cent of the 100 volts applied, reaching 63 volts in RC time. After 5 time constants, which is 15 sec here, C is practically completely charged to the full 100 volts applied. If C discharges now, after being charged to 100 volts, C will discharge down to 37 volts in 3 sec. After 5 time constants, C discharges down to zero.

A shorter time constant allows the capacitor to charge or discharge faster. If the RC product in Fig. $19 \cdot 5$ is 1 sec, C will charge to 63 volts in 1 sec, instead of 3 sec, and reach the full applied voltage of 100 volts in 5 sec instead of 15 sec. Charging to the same voltage in less time means a faster charge. On discharge also, the shorter time constant will allow C to discharge from 100 volts to 37 volts in 1 sec instead of 3 sec, and down to zero in 5 sec instead of 15 sec. For the opposite case, a longer time constant means slower charge or discharge of the capacitor.

RC applications. Several examples are given here to illustrate how the time constant can be applied to RC circuits.

Example 1. What is the time constant of 0.01-μf capacitor in series with a 1-M resistance?

$$T = R \times C = 1 \text{ M} \times 0.01 \text{ } \mu\text{f} = \textbf{0.01 sec}$$

This is the time constant for charging or discharging, assuming the series resistance is the same for charge or discharge.

Example 2. With a d-c voltage of 300 volts applied, how much is the voltage across C in Example 1 after 0.01 sec of charging? After 0.05 sec?

Since 0.01 sec is 1 time constant, the voltage across C then is 63 per cent of

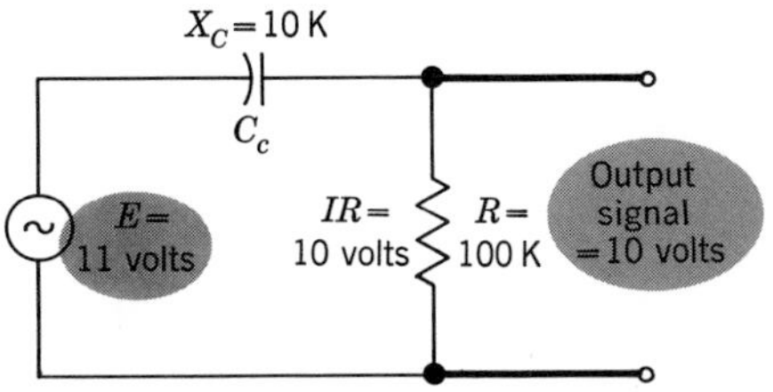

Fig. 19·6 *RC coupling circuit. Low value of X_C allows practically all the applied voltage to be developed across R with almost none across C.*

300 volts, which equals **189 volts.** After 5 time constants, or 0.05 sec, C will be charged practically to the applied voltage of **300 volts.**

Example 3. If the capacitor in Example 2 is allowed to charge to 300 volts and then discharged, how much is the capacitor voltage 0.01 sec after the start of discharge? The series resistance is the same on discharge as on charge.

In 1 time constant C discharges to 37 per cent of its initial voltage or 0.37×300 volts, which equals **111 volts.**

Example 4. If the capacitor in Example 2 is made to discharge after being charged to 200 volts, how much will the voltage across C be 0.01 sec later? The series resistance is the same on discharge as on charge.

In 1 time constant C discharges to 37 per cent of its initial voltage, or 0.37×200, which equals **74 volts.**

This example shows that the capacitor can charge or discharge from any voltage value, not just after one RC or five RC.

Example 5. If a 1-M resistance is added in series with the capacitor in Example 1, how much will the time constant be?

Now the series resistance is 2 M. Therefore, RC is 2×0.01, or **0.02 sec.**

The RC time constant becomes longer with larger values of R and C. More capacitance means that the capacitor can store more charge. Therefore, it takes longer to store the charge needed to provide a potential difference equal to 63 per cent of the applied voltage. More resistance reduces the charging current, requiring more time for charging the capacitor.

It should be noted that the RC time constant specifies just a rate. The actual amount of voltage across C depends upon the applied voltage as well as upon the RC time constant. The capacitor takes on charge whenever its voltage is less than the applied voltage. The charging continues at the RC rate until either the capacitor is completely charged or the applied voltage decreases. The capacitor discharges whenever its voltage is more than the applied voltage. The discharge continues at the RC rate until either the capacitor is completely discharged or the applied voltage increases.

To summarize these two important principles:

1. C charges when the net charging voltage is more than e_C.
2. C discharges when e_C is more than the net charging voltage.

Charge and discharge curves. In Fig. 19·5a, the RC charge curve has the rise shown because the charging is fastest at the start, then tapers off as *C* takes on additional charge at a slower rate, owing to the fact that as *C* charges, its potential difference increases. Then the difference in voltage between *E* and e_C is reduced. Less potential difference reduces the current that puts the charge in *C*. The more *C* charges, the more slowly it takes on additional charge.

Similarly, on discharge, *C* loses its charge fastest at the start, and then the discharge tapers off as *C* loses charge at a slower rate. At first, e_C has its highest value and can produce maximum discharge current. With the discharge continuing, e_C goes down and there is less discharge current. The more *C* discharges, the more slowly it can lose the remainder of its charge. This type of variation is called an *exponential* curve.[1]

Capacitance opposes voltage changes across itself. This ability corresponds to the ability of inductance to oppose a change of current. In terms of an *RC* circuit, when the applied voltage increases, the voltage across the capacitance cannot increase until the charging current has stored enough charge in *C*. The increase in applied voltage is present across the resistance in series with *C* until the capacitor has charged to the higher applied voltage. When the applied voltage decreases, the voltage across the capacitor cannot go down immediately, because the series resistance limits the discharge current. As a result, the voltage across the capacitance in an *RC* circuit cannot follow instantaneously the changes in applied voltage. Therefore, the capacitance is able to oppose changes in voltage across itself. The instantaneous variations in *E* are present across the series resistance, however, since the series voltage drops must add to equal the applied voltage at all times.

19·6 Energy in electrostatic field of capacitance

The electrostatic field of the charge stored in the dielectric has electrical energy supplied by the voltage source that charges *C*. This energy is stored in the dielectric. The proof is the fact that the capacitance can produce discharge current when the voltage source is removed. The electrical energy stored is

$$\text{Energy} = \mathcal{E} = \tfrac{1}{2}CE^2 \qquad \text{joules} \qquad (19·8)$$

where *C* is the capacitance in farads and *E* is the voltage across the capacitor. For example, a 1-μf capacitor charged to 400 volts has stored energy equal to

$$\mathcal{E} = \tfrac{1}{2}CE^2 = \frac{1 \times 10^{-6} \times (400)^2}{2} = \frac{1 \times 10^{-6} \times 16 \times 10^4}{2}$$

$$\mathcal{E} = 8 \times 10^{-2} = \textbf{0.08 watt-second, or joule}$$

This 0.08 joule of energy is supplied by the voltage source that charges

[1] Universal curves that can be used for any *RC* circuit or *RL* circuit are shown in Appendix F.

the capacitor to 400 volts. When the charging circuit is opened, the stored energy remains as charge in the dielectric. With a closed path provided for discharge, the entire 0.08 joule is available to produce discharge current. As the capacitor discharges, the energy is used in producing discharge current. When the capacitor is completely discharged, the stored energy is zero.

The stored energy is the reason why a charged capacitor can produce an electric shock, even when not connected into a circuit. When you touch the two leads of the charged capacitor, its voltage produces discharge current through your body. Stored energy greater than 1 joule can be dangerous with a capacitor charged to a voltage high enough to produce an electric shock.

19·7   R-f and a-f coupling capacitors

In Fig. 19·6, C_c is used in the application of a coupling capacitor. Its low reactance allows practically all the a-c signal voltage of the generator to be developed across R. Very little of the a-c voltage is across C_c. The coupling capacitor is used for this application because at lower frequencies it provides more reactance, resulting in less a-c voltage coupled across R and more across C_c. For d-c voltage, all the voltage is across C with none across R, since the capacitor blocks direct current. As a result, the output signal voltage across R includes the desired frequencies but not direct current or very low frequencies.

The dividing line for C_c to be a coupling capacitor at a specific frequency can be taken as the condition when X_{C_c} is one-tenth or less of the series R. Then the series RC circuit is primarily resistive. Practically all the voltage drop of the a-c generator is across R, with little across C. In addition, this case results in a phase angle of practically $0°$.

Typical values of a coupling capacitor for audio or radio frequencies can be calculated if we assume a series resistance of 160,000 ohms. Then X_C must be 16,000 ohms or less. Typical values for C_c are listed in Table 19·3. At 100 cps, a coupling capacitor must be 0.1 μf to provide 16,000 ohms of reactance. Higher frequencies allow a smaller value of C_c for a coupling capacitor having the same reactance. At 100 Mc in the VHF range, for instance, the required capacitance is only 0.1 pf. It should be noted that the

*Table 19·3   Coupling capacitors with reactance of 16,000 ohms**

f	C_c	Remarks
100 cps	0.1 μf	Low audio frequencies
1,000 cps	0.01 μf	Medium audio frequencies
10 kc	0.001 μf	High audio frequencies
1,000 kc	10 pf	Radio frequencies
100 Mc	0.1 pf	Very high frequencies

* For X_C one-tenth of series R of 160,000 ohms.

Table 19·4   RC circuits

SINE-WAVE VOLTAGE APPLIED	NONSINUSOIDAL VOLTAGE APPLIED
Examples are 60-cps power line, a-f signal voltage, and r-f signal voltage	Examples are d-c circuit opened or closed by a switch, and a-c circuit with rectangular or square-wave voltage
Capacitive reactance $X_C = 1/(2\pi fC)$	Time constant $T = RC$
Large C results in small X_c	Large C results in long time constant
$I_C = E_C/X_C$	$i_C = C\, de/dt$
X_C can cause phase shift between E_C and I_C	Waveshape can change between i_C and e_C

C_c values are calculated for each frequency as a lower limit. At higher frequencies, the same size C_c will have less reactance than $\frac{1}{10}R$, which improves the coupling.

Choosing a coupling capacitor for a circuit. As an example of using these calculations, suppose that we have the problem of determining C_c for a transistorized audio amplifier. This application also illustrates the relatively large capacitance needed with low series resistance. C is to be a coupling capacitor for audio frequencies of 50 cps and up, with a series R of 4,000 ohms. Then the required value of X_C is 4,000/10 or 400 ohms. At 50 cps,

$$C = \frac{0.159}{f \times X_C} = \frac{0.159}{50 \times 400} = \frac{159,000 \times 10^{-6}}{20 \times 10^3}$$
$$C = 7.95 \times 10^{-6} = 7.95\ \mu f$$

A typical commercial size of low-voltage electrolytic readily available is 10 μf. The slightly higher capacitance value is better for coupling. The voltage rating can be 3 to 10 volts, depending on the circuit, with a typical transistor supply voltage of 9 volts. Although electrolytic capacitors have relatively high leakage current, they can be used for coupling capacitors in this application because of the low series resistance. It should be noted that coupling capacitors with low series resistance in transistor circuits are much larger than the values in Table 19·3, which are calculated for a typical high series resistance in vacuum-tube amplifier circuits. In both cases, though, the coupling capacitor has the capacitance needed for X_C one-tenth the series R, at the lowest frequency.

19·8   Comparison of reactance and time constant

The formula for capacitive reactance includes the factor of time in terms of frequency in $1/(2\pi fC)$. Therefore, capacitive reactance and time constant are both a measure of the reaction of capacitance to a change in voltage. The X_C formula is a special case but a very important one that applies just to sine waves. The RC time constant can be applied to any waveshape.

If we consider the application of a coupling capacitor, for instance, the condition that its X_C value be one-tenth or less of its series R at the desired frequency is equivalent to having an RC time constant that is long compared with the time of one cycle. In terms of X_C, it has little a-c voltage drop, then, with practically all the a-c applied voltage across the series R. For the time constant of the coupling circuit, when the RC product is long compared with the period of one cycle at the desired frequency, C_c cannot take on much charge, allowing practically all the a-c applied voltage to be developed as an IR drop across the series resistance by the charge and discharge current. These comparisons are summarized in Table 19·4.

For the general case, the capacitive charge and discharge current i_C is always equal to $C\,de/dt$. A sine wave of voltage variations for e_C produces a cosine wave of current i. This means e_C and i_C have the same waveform but they are 90° out of phase. It is usually more convenient to use X_C for calculations in sine-wave circuits. Since X_C is $1/(2\pi fC)$, the factors that determine the amount of charge and discharge current are included in f and C. Then I_C equals E_C/X_C. Or, if I_C is known, E_C is equal to $I_C \times X_C$.

With a nonsinusoidal waveform of voltage e_C, the concept of reactance cannot be used. X_C applies only to sine waves. Then i_C must be determined as $C\,de/dt$. An example is illustrated in Fig. 19·7 to show the change of waveform here, instead of the change of phase angle in sine-wave circuits. Note that the sawtooth waveform of voltage e_C corresponds to a rectangular waveform of current. The linear rise of the sawtooth wave produces a constant amount of charging current i_C because the rate of change is constant for the charging voltage. When the capacitor discharges, e_C drops sharply. Then discharge current is in the opposite direction from charge current and has a much larger value because of the faster rate of change.

An interesting feature of these capacitive waveshapes is the fact that they are the same as the inductive waveshapes shown before in Fig. 16·11, but with the current and voltage waveshapes interchanged. This comparison follows from the fact that both i_C and e_L depend on rate of change.

Fig. 19·7   Waveshape of i_C equal to $C\,de/dt$ for sawtooth waveform of e. (a) Sawtooth voltage. (b) Rectangular current.

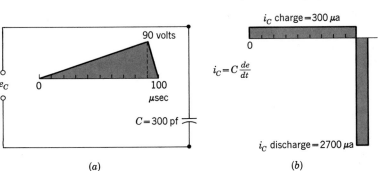

i_C charge $= 300\ \mu a$

$i_C = C\dfrac{de}{dt}$

90 volts

e_C 0   100 μsec

$C = 300$ pf

i_C discharge $= 2700\ \mu a$

(a)   (b)

SUMMARY

1. In a sine-wave a-c circuit, the voltage across a capacitance lags its charge and discharge current by 90°.
2. Therefore, capacitive reactance X_C is a vector quantity out of phase with its series resistance by $-90°$ because $i_C = C\, de/dt$. This fundamental fact is the basis of all the following relations.
3. The vector combination of X_C and R in series is their impedance Z. These three types of opposition to current are compared in Table 19·5.
4. The opposite characteristics for series and parallel circuits with X_C and R are summarized in Table 19·6.
5. Two or more capacitors in series across a voltage source E serve as a voltage divider. E is divided among the individual capacitors inversely proportional to the capacitance of each. The smallest capacitance has the largest part of the applied voltage.
6. A coupling capacitor has X_C less than its series resistance by the factor of $\frac{1}{10}$ or less, for the purpose of providing practically all the a-c applied voltage across R with little across C.
7. The transient response of an RC circuit with nonsinusoidal voltage is indicated by the time constant, which equals the RC product. With C in farads and R in ohms, T is the time in seconds for the voltage across C to change by 63 per cent.
8. The energy stored as charge in a capacitance is $\mathcal{E} = \frac{1}{2}CE^2$. With C in farads and E in volts, the energy is in joules.

SELF-EXAMINATION (*Answers at back of book.*)

Here's a chance to find out how well you have learned the material in this chapter. These exercises are for your self-testing only.

1. In a capacitive circuit (*a*) a decrease in applied voltage makes a capacitor charge; (*b*) a steady value of applied voltage causes discharge; (*c*) an increase in applied voltage makes a capacitor discharge; (*d*) an increase in applied voltage makes a capacitor charge.
2. In a sine-wave a-c circuit with X_C and R in series, the (*a*) phase angle of the circuit is $-90°$ with high series resistance; (*b*) voltage across the capacitance must be 90° out of phase with its charge and discharge current; (*c*) voltage across the capacitance has the same phase as its charge and discharge current; (*d*) charge and discharge current to the capacitor must be 90° out of phase with the applied voltage.
3. A 250-pf C is in series with a 1-M R across a 100-volt battery. The voltage equals 63 volts across (*a*) C after 250 μsec; (*b*) R after 250 μsec; (*c*) C after 1,250 μsec; (*d*) R after 1,250 μsec.
4. In a sine-wave a-c circuit with a resistive branch and capacitive branch in parallel, the (*a*) voltage across the capacitance lags the voltage across the resistance by 90°; (*b*) resistive branch current is 90° out of phase with the capacitive branch current; (*c*) resistive and capacitive branch currents have the same phase; (*d*) resistive and capacitive branch currents are 180° out of phase.
5. In a sine-wave a-c circuit with 90-ohm R in series with 90-ohm X_C, the phase angle θ equals (*a*) $-90°$; (*b*) $-45°$; (*c*) $0°$; (*d*) $90°$.
6. The combined impedance of 1,000-ohm R in parallel with 1,000-ohm X_C equals (*a*) 500 ohms; (*b*) 707 ohms; (*c*) 1,000 ohms; (*d*) 2,000 ohms.

Table 19·5   Comparison of resistance, capacitive reactance, and impedance

R	$X_C = \dfrac{1}{2\pi fC}$	$Z = \sqrt{R^2 + X_C^2}$
Ohms unit	Ohms unit	Ohms unit
IR voltage same phase as I	IX_C voltage lags I_C by 90°	IZ is applied voltage
Same for all frequencies	Decreases at higher frequencies	Decreases as X_C decreases

Table 19·6   Series and parallel RC circuits

X_C AND R IN SERIES	X_C AND R IN PARALLEL
I the same in X_C and R	E the same across X_C and R
$E_{\text{applied}} = \sqrt{E_R^2 + E_C^2}$	$I_T = \sqrt{I_R^2 + I_C^2}$
$Z = \sqrt{R^2 + X_C^2}$	$Z = \dfrac{E}{I_T}$
V_C lags V_R by $90°$	I_C leads I_R by $90°$
$\tan \theta = \dfrac{-X_C}{R}$	$\tan \theta = \dfrac{I_C}{I_R}$

7. With 100 volts applied across two series capacitors of 5 μf each, the voltage across each capacitor will be (*a*) 5 volts; (*b*) 33⅓ volts; (*c*) 50 volts; (*d*) 66⅔ volts.
8. In a sine-wave a-c circuit with X_C and R in series, the (*a*) voltages across R and X_C are in phase; (*b*) voltages across R and X_C are 180° out of phase; (*c*) voltage across R leads the voltage across X_C by 90°; (*d*) voltage across R lags the voltage across X_C by 90°.
9. A 1-μf capacitor charged to 2,000 volts has stored energy equal to (*a*) 1 joule; (*b*) 2 joules; (*c*) 4 joules; (*d*) 2,000 joules.
10. A 0.01-μf capacitance in series with R is used as a coupling capacitor C_c for 1,000 cps. At 10,000 cps, (*a*) C_c has too much reactance to be good for coupling. (*b*) C_c has less reactance, which improves the coupling. (*c*) C_c has the same reactance and coupling. (*d*) The voltage across R is reduced by one-tenth.

ESSAY QUESTIONS

1. (*a*) Why does a capacitor charge when the applied voltage increases? (*b*) Why does the capacitor discharge when the applied voltage decreases?
2. A sine wave of voltage E is applied across a capacitor C. (*a*) Draw the schematic diagram. (*b*) Draw the sine waves of voltage E and current I out of phase by 90°. (*c*) Draw a vector diagram showing the phase angle of $-90°$ between E and I.
3. Why will a circuit with R and X_c in series be less capacitive as the frequency of the applied voltage is increased?
4. Define the following: coupling capacitor, sawtooth voltage, watt-second, joule, time constant.
5. Give three comparisons between RC circuits with sine-wave voltage applied and nonsinusoidal voltage applied.
6. Give five differences between RC circuits and RL circuits.
7. Compare the functions of a coupling capacitor with a choke coil, with two differences in their operation.
8. State two troubles possible in coupling capacitors and describe briefly how you would check with an ohmmeter.

PROBLEMS (*Answers to selected problems at back of book.*)

1. A 40-ohm R is in series with 30-ohm X_C across a 100-volt sine-wave a-c source of applied voltage E. (*a*) Draw the schematic diagram. (*b*) Calculate the total impedance Z. (*c*) Calculate the current I. (*d*) Calculate the voltages across R and across C. (*e*) What is the phase angle θ of the circuit? (*f*) Compare the phase of the current in R and in X_C.
2. A 40-ohm R and 30-ohm X_C are in parallel across a 100-volt sine-wave a-c source of applied voltage. (*a*) Draw the schematic diagram. (*b*) Calculate each branch current. (*c*) How much is the total line current? (*d*) Calculate the combined impedance Z. (*e*) What is the phase angle of the circuit? (*f*) Compare the phase of the voltage across R and across X_C.

3. Draw the schematic diagram of a capacitor in series with 1-M resistance across a 10-volt a-c source E. What size C is needed for equal voltages across R and X_C at the frequency of 100 cps? 100 kc?

4. Draw the schematic diagram of two capacitors C_1 and C_2 in series across 10,000 volts. C_1 is 900 pf and has 9,000 volts across it. (a) How much is the voltage across C_2? (b) How much is the capacitance of C_2?

5. In Fig. 19·2a, how much is C for the X_C value of 100 ohms at the frequency of 60 cps? 1,000 cps? 1 Mc?

6. Calculate the time constant of the following combinations: (a) R is 1 M; C is 0.001 μf. (b) R is 1,000 ohms; C is 1 μf. (c) R is 250 k; C is 0.05 μf. (d) R is 10 k; C is 100 pf.

7. A 100-volt E is in series with 2-M resistance and 2-μf C. (a) How much time is required for e_C to be 63 volts? (b) How much is e_C after 40 sec?

8. The C in Prob. 7 is allowed to charge for 4 sec, and then made to discharge for 8 sec. How much is e_C?

9. A 100-volt E is applied in series with a 1-M resistance and 4-μf C that has already been charged to 63 volts. How much is e_C after 4 sec?

10. How much energy in joules is stored in a 500-pf capacitor charged to 10 kv? A 1-μf capacitor charged to 5 kv? A 40-μf capacitor charged to 400 volts?

11. How much C is required to limit the stored energy to 1 joule with 300 volts E?

12. A 1,500-ohm R is in series with 0.01-μf C across a 30-volt source with frequency of 8 kc. Calculate X_C, Z, θ, I, V_R, and V_C.

13. The same R and C as in Prob. 12 are in parallel. Calculate I_C, I_R, I_T, Z, θ, V_R, and V_C.

14. A 0.05-μf capacitor is in series with 50,000-ohm R and a 10-volt source. Tabulate the values of X_C, I, E_R, and E_C at 0 cps (for steady d-c voltage), 20 cps, 60 cps, 100 cps, 500 cps, 5,000 cps, and 15,000 cps.

15. For the waveshape of capacitor voltage e_C below, show the corresponding charge and discharge current i_C, with values for 200-pf capacitance. Compare these waveshapes with Prob. 16 in Chap. 16.

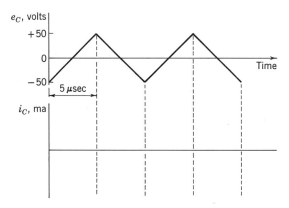

Review of chapters ⬤**17** *to* ⬤**19**

SUMMARY

1. A capacitor, or condenser, consists of two conductors separated by an insulator, which is a dielectric material. With voltage applied to the conductors, charge is stored in the dielectric. One coulomb of charge stored with one volt applied corresponds to one farad of capacitance C. The common units of capacitance are microfarads (10^{-6}) or picofarads (10^{-12}).
2. Capacitance increases with plate area and larger values of dielectric constant but decreases with the distance between plates.
3. The most common types of capacitors are air, paper, mica, ceramic, and electrolytic. Electrolytics must be connected in the correct polarity. The color coding for mica and ceramic tubular capacitors is illustrated in Figs. $17 \cdot 10$ and $17 \cdot 11$.
4. The total capacitance of parallel capacitors is the sum of the individual values; the combined capacitance of series capacitors is found by the reciprocal formula. These rules are opposite from the formulas for resistors and inductors in series or parallel.
5. In checking with an ohmmeter, a good capacitor shows charging current and then the ohmmeter reads a very high value of ohms equal to the insulation resistance. A shorted capacitor reads zero ohms; an open capacitor does not show any charging current.
6. $X_C = 1/(2\pi f C)$ ohms, with f in cycles per sec and C in farads. The higher the frequency and the greater the capacitance, the smaller X_C is.
7. A common application of X_C is in a-f or r-f coupling capacitors, which have low reactance for one group of frequencies but more reactance for lower frequencies. This is just the opposite of an inductance used as a choke.
8. X_C is a vector quantity where the voltage across the capacitor lags 90° behind its charge and discharge current. This phase angle of X_C is exactly opposite from the phase angle for X_L.
9. In series circuits R and X_C are added vectorially because their voltage drops are 90° out of phase. Therefore, the total impedance Z equals $\sqrt{R^2 + X_C^2}$; the current $I = E/Z$.
10. For parallel circuits, the resistive and capacitive branch currents are added vectorially: $I_T = \sqrt{I_R^2 + I_C^2}$; the impedance $Z = E/I_T$.
11. The time constant of a capacitive circuit equals $R \times C$. With R in ohms and C in farads, the RC product is the time in seconds for the voltage across C to change by 63 per cent. On charge, the capacitor charges to 63 per cent of the applied voltage; on discharge, the capacitor discharges down to 37 per cent of its initial voltage.
12. Capacitive charge or discharge current i_C is always equal to $C\, de/dt$ for any waveshape of capacitor voltage.

REFERENCES (*Additional references at back of book.*)

Gillie, A. C., *Electrical Principles of Electronics,* McGraw-Hill Book Company, New York.
Jackson, H. W., *Introduction to Electric Circuits,* Prentice-Hall, Inc., Englewood Cliffs, N.J.
Schure, A., *RC and RL Time Constant,* John F. Rider, Publisher, Inc., New York.
Slurzberg, M., and W. Osterheld, *Essentials of Electricity for Radio and Television,* 3d ed., McGraw-Hill Book Company, New York.

REVIEW SELF-EXAMINATION (*Answers at back of book.*)

Here's another chance to check your progress. Work the exercises just as you did those at the end of each chapter and check your answers.

Answer true or false.

1. A capacitor can store charge because it has a dielectric between two conductors.
2. With 100 volts applied, a 0.01-μf capacitor stores 1 μcoul of charge.

3. The smaller the capacitance, the higher the potential difference across it for a given amount of charge stored in the capacitor.

4. A 250-pf capacitance equals 250×10^{-12} farad.

5. The thinner the dielectric, the more the capacitance and the lower is the voltage breakdown rating for a capacitor.

6. Larger plate area increases the capacitance.

7. Capacitors in series provide less capacitance but a higher voltage breakdown rating for the combination.

8. Capacitors in parallel increase the total capacitance with the same voltage rating.

9. Two 0.01-μf capacitors in parallel have a total capacitance of 0.005 μf.

10. A good 0.01-μf paper capacitor will show charging current and read 500 M or more on an ohmmeter.

11. If the capacitance is doubled, the reactance is one-half.

12. If the frequency is doubled, the reactance is one-half.

13. The reactance of a 0.1-μf capacitor at 60 cps equals approximately 60 ohms.

14. In a series circuit, the voltage across C lags 90° behind the current.

15. The phase angle of a series circuit can be any angle between 0 and 90°, depending on the ratio of X_C to R.

16. In a parallel circuit, the voltage across C lags 90° behind its capacitive branch current.

17. In a parallel circuit of two resistances with 1 amp in each branch, the total line current equals 1.414 amp.

18. A 1,000-ohm X_C in parallel with a 1,000-ohm R has a combined impedance of 707 ohms.

19. A 1,000 ohm X_C in series with a 1,000-ohm R has a total impedance of 1,414 ohms.

20. Neglecting its sign, the phase angle is 45° for both circuits in questions 18 and 19.

21. X_L and X_C are opposite reactances.

22. The total impedance of 1-M R in series with 5-ohm X_C is approximately 1 M with a phase angle of 0°.

23. The combined impedance of 5-ohm R in shunt with 1-M X_C is approximately 5 ohms with a phase angle of 0°.

24. X_L and X_C change with frequency, but L and C do not depend on the frequency.

25. A long RC time constant corresponds to a large C and R.

26. When the RC time constant for discharge is calculated, R must be the resistance in the path for discharge current.

27. Resistance and impedance are both measured in ohms.

28. X_L and X_C are both measured in ohms.

29. Z can change with frequency because it includes reactance.

30. With 100 volts applied, a 1-μf capacitor in series with a 1-M resistor will charge to 63 volts in 1 sec.

31. A 1-μf capacitor charged to 2,000 volts has stored energy equal to 1 joule.

32. If a capacitor charged to 100 volts is discharged, after RC time of discharge, the voltage across the capacitor equals 37 volts.

33. When the applied voltage increases, charging current can flow as the capacitor takes on additional charge.

34. When the applied voltage decreases, a charged capacitor can discharge because it has a higher potential difference than the source.

35. Capacitors in series have the same charge and discharge current.

36. Capacitors in parallel have the same voltage.

37. The vector combination of 30-ohm R in series with 40-ohm X_C equals 70 ohms of impedance.

38. A six-dot mica capacitor color-coded white, green, black, black, red, and yellow has the capacitance value of 500 pf.

39. Capacitive current can be considered leading current in a series circuit.

40. In a series circuit, the higher the value of X_c, the greater is its voltage drop compared with the IR drop.

Chapter **20** *Alternating-current circuits*

This unit shows how to analyze sine-wave a-c circuits that combine R, X_L, and X_C. There are two aspects to consider: how much current flows and what is the phase angle? These questions are answered for both series and parallel circuits. Finally, the idea of how a-c power can differ from d-c power is explained, and the types of a-c meters are described, including the wattmeter. The topics are:

20·1   A-c circuits with resistance but no reactance
20·2   Circuits with inductive reactance alone
20·3   Circuits with capacitive reactance alone
20·4   Opposite reactances cancel
20·5   Series reactance and resistance
20·6   Parallel reactance and resistance
20·7   Series-parallel reactance and resistance
20·8   Real power
20·9   A-c meters
20·10 Wattmeters
20·11 Summary of types of ohms in a-c circuits
20·12 Summary of types of vectors in a-c circuits

20·1   A-c circuits with resistance but no reactance

Combinations of series and parallel resistances are shown in Fig. 20·1. In both *a* and *b*, all voltages and currents throughout the resistive circuit are in the same phase as the applied voltage because there is no reactance to cause a lead or lag in either current or voltage.

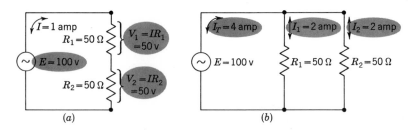

Fig. 20·1   *A-c circuits with resistance but no reactance. (a) Series resistances. (b) Parallel resistances.*

For the circuit in Fig. 20·1*a*, with two 50-ohm resistances in series across the 100-volt source, the calculations are as follows:

$$R_T = R_1 + R_2 = 50 + 50 = 100 \text{ ohms}$$
$$I = E/R_T = {}^{100}\!/_{100} = 1 \text{ amp}$$
$$V_1 = IR_1 = 1 \times 50 = 50 \text{ volts}$$
$$V_2 = IR_2 = 1 \times 50 = 50 \text{ volts}$$

Note that the series resistances R_1 and R_2 serve as a voltage divider, as in d-c circuits, each having one-half the applied voltage because each is one-half the total series resistance. The voltage drops V_1 and V_2 are both in phase with the series current I, which is the common reference, and I is in phase with the applied voltage E.

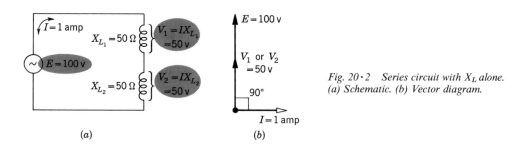

Fig. 20·2   *Series circuit with X_L alone. (a) Schematic. (b) Vector diagram.*

Fig. 20·3   *Parallel circuit with X_L alone. (a) Schematic. (b) Vector diagram.*

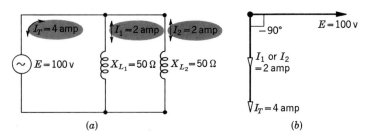

For the circuit in Fig. 20·1b, with two 50-ohm resistances in parallel across the 100-volt source, the calculations are:

$$I_1 = E/R_1 = {}^{100}\!/_{50} = 2 \text{ amp}$$
$$I_2 = E/R_2 = {}^{100}\!/_{50} = 2 \text{ amp}$$
$$I_T = I_1 + I_2 = 2 + 2 = 4 \text{ amp}$$

With a total current of 4 amp in the main line from the 100-volt source, the combined parallel resistance is 25 ohms, for the two 50-ohm branches. Each branch current has the same phase as the applied voltage, which is the reference because it is common to both branches.

20·2   Circuits with inductive reactance alone

The circuits with X_L in Figs. 20·2 and 20·3 correspond to the series and parallel circuits in Fig. 20·1, with the ohms of X_L equal to the R values. Since the applied voltage is the same, the values of current correspond, since ohms of X_L are just as effective as ohms of R in limiting the current or producing a voltage drop. Although X_L is a vector quantity with a 90° phase angle, all the ohms of opposition are the same kind of reactance in this example. Therefore, without any R or X_C, the series ohms can be combined directly. Similarly, the parallel I_L currents can be added.

For the series circuit in Fig. 20·2a, the calculations are:

$$X_{L_T} = X_{L_1} + X_{L_2} = 50 + 50 = 100 \text{ ohms}$$
$$I = E/X_{L_T} = {}^{100}\!/_{100} = 1 \text{ amp}$$
$$V_1 = IX_{L_1} = 1 \times 50 = 50 \text{ volts}$$
$$V_2 = IX_{L_2} = 1 \times 50 = 50 \text{ volts}$$

Note that the two series voltage drops of 50 volts each add to equal the total applied voltage of 100 volts.

With regard to the phase angle for the inductive reactance, the voltage across any X_L always leads the current through it by 90°. In Fig. 20·2b, I is the reference vector because it is common to all the series components. Therefore, the voltage vectors for V_1 or V_2 across either reactance, or E across both reactances, are shown leading I by 90°.

For the parallel circuit in Fig. 20·3a the calculations are:

$$I_1 = E/X_{L_1} = {}^{100}\!/_{50} = 2 \text{ amp}$$
$$I_2 = E/X_{L_2} = {}^{100}\!/_{50} = 2 \text{ amp}$$
$$I_T = I_1 + I_2 = 2 + 2 = 4 \text{ amp}$$

These two branch currents can be added because they both have the same phase, which is 90° lagging the voltage reference vector as shown in b.

Since the voltage E is common to the branches, this voltage is also across X_{L_1} and X_{L_2}. For this reason, E is the reference vector for parallel circuits. Note that there is no fundamental change between Fig. 20·2b which shows each X_L voltage leading its current by 90° and Fig. 20·3b showing each X_L current lagging its voltage by −90°. The phase angle between the inductive current and voltage is still the same 90°.

20·3 Circuits with capacitive reactance alone

Again, reactances are shown in Figs. 20·4 and 20·5 with X_C values of 50 ohms, the same as before. Since there is no R or X_L, the series ohms of X_C can be combined directly. Also the parallel I_C currents can be added.

For the series circuit in Fig. 20·4a, the calculations for V_1 and V_2 are the same as before. These two series voltage drops of 50 volts each add to equal the total applied voltage.

With regard to the phase angle for the capacitive reactance, the voltage across any X_C always lags its capacitive charge and discharge current I by 90°. For the series circuit in Fig. 20·4, I is the reference vector. It leads by 90° V_1 across X_{C_1}, V_2 across X_{C_2}, and E across both reactances. Or, we can say that each voltage lags I by −90°.

For the parallel circuit in Fig. 20·5, E is the reference vector. The calculations for I_1 and I_2 are the same as before. However, now each of the capacitive branch currents or the total line current leads E by 90°.

20·4 Opposite reactances cancel

In a circuit with both X_L and X_C, the opposite phase angles enable one to cancel the effect of the other. For X_L and X_C in series, the net reactance is the difference between the two series reactances, resulting in less reactance than either one. In parallel circuits, the I_L and I_C branch currents

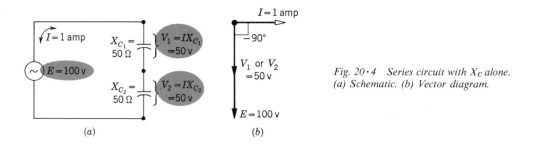

(a)

(b)

Fig. 20·4   Series circuit with X_C alone. (a) Schematic. (b) Vector diagram.

Fig. 20·5   Parallel circuit with X_C alone. (a) Schematic. (b) Vector diagram.

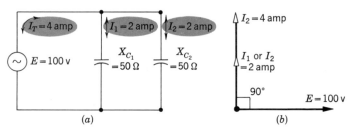

(a)

(b)

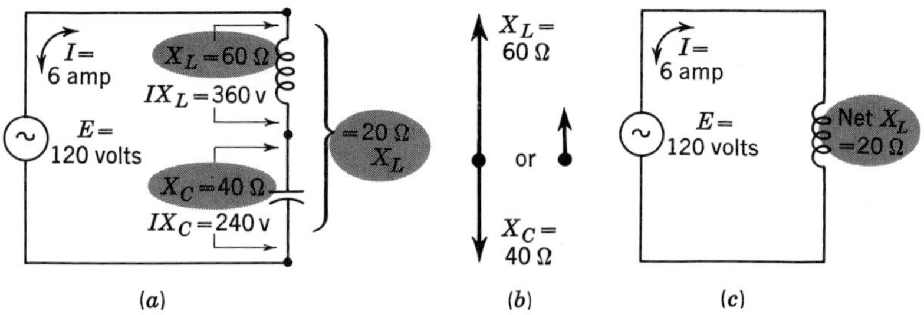

Fig. 20·6 With X_L and X_C in series, their ohms of reactance cancel. (a) Series circuit. (b) Vectors for X_L and X_C with net resultant vector equal to the difference between 60-ohm X_L and 40-ohm X_C reactances. (c) Equivalent circuit with net reactance of 20-ohm X_L.

cancel. The net line current then is the difference between the two branch currents, resulting in less total line current than either branch current.

X_L and X_C in series. For the example in Fig. 20·6, the series combination of 60-ohm X_L and 40-ohm X_C in *a* and *b* is equivalent to the net reactance of 20-ohm X_L shown in *c*. Then with 20 ohms as the net reactance across the 120-volt source, the current is 6 amp. This current lags the applied voltage E by 90° because the net reactance is inductive.

For the two series reactances in *a*, the current is the same through both X_L and X_C. Therefore, the IX_L drop is 6 amp × 60 ohms, or 360 volts, and the IX_C drop is 6 amp × 40 ohms, or 240 volts.

Note that each individual reactive voltage drop can be more than the applied voltage. The sum of the series voltage drops still is 120 volts, however, equal to the applied voltage. This results because the IX_L and IX_C voltages are opposite. The IX_L voltage leads the series current by 90°; the IX_C voltage lags the same current by 90°. Therefore, IX_L and IX_C are 180° out of phase with each other, which means they are of opposite polarity and cancel. Then the total voltage across the two in series is 360 volts minus 240 volts, which equals the applied voltage of 120 volts.

If the values in Fig. 20·6 were reversed, with X_C of 60 ohms and X_L of 40 ohms, the net reactance would be 20-ohm X_C. The current would be 6 amp again but with a leading phase angle of −90° for the capacitive current. The IX_C voltage would then be larger at 360 volts, with an IX_L value of 240 volts, but the difference still equals the applied voltage of 120 volts.

X_L and X_C in parallel. In Fig. 20·7, the 60-ohm X_L and 40-ohm X_C are in parallel across the 120-volt source. Then the 60-ohm X_L branch current I_L is 2 amp, and the 40-ohm X_C branch current I_C is 3 amp. The X_C branch has more current because its reactance is less than X_L.

In terms of phase angle, I_L lags the parallel voltage E by 90°, while I_C leads the same voltage by 90°. Therefore, the opposite reactive branch currents are 180° out of phase with each other and cancel. The net line cur-

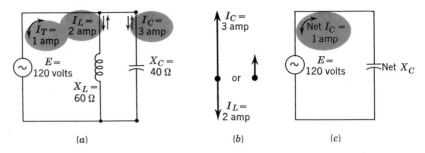

(a)   (b)   (c)

Fig. 20·7   With X_L and X_C in parallel, their branch currents cancel. (a) Parallel circuit. (b) Vectors for branch currents I_C and I_L with net resultant vector equal to the difference between 3-amp I_C and 2-amp I_L. (c) Equivalent circuit with net line current of 1-amp I_C.

rent then is the difference between 3 amp for I_C and 2 amp for I_L, which equals the net value of 1 amp. This resultant current leads E by 90° because it is capacitive current.

If the values in Fig. 20·7 were reversed, with X_C of 60 ohms and X_L of 40 ohms, I_L would be larger. I_L then equals 3 amp, with I_C of 2 amp. The net line current is 1 amp again but inductive. Then the net inductive line current lags E by 90°.

20·5   Series reactance and resistance

In this case, the resistive and reactive effects must be combined vectorially. For series circuits, the ohms of opposition are added to find Z. First add all the series resistances for one total R. Also combine all the series reactances, adding the same kind but subtracting opposites. The result is one net reactance, indicated X, which may be either capacitive or inductive, depending on which kind of reactance is larger. Then the total R and net X can be added vectorially to find the ohms of opposition for the entire series circuit.

Magnitude of Z. After the total R and net reactance X are found, they can be combined vectorially by the formula

$$Z = \sqrt{R^2 + X^2} \tag{20·1}$$

The circuit's total impedance Z is the vector sum of the series resistance and reactance. The sign of X does not matter in calculating the magnitude of Z. With either a positive value for X_L or negative value for X_C, the square is a positive value for both cases. An example is illustrated in Fig. 20·8. Here the net series reactance in b is 30-ohm X_C, equal to 60-ohm X_L subtracted from 90-ohm X_C shown in a. The net 30-ohm X_C in b is in series with 40-ohm R. Therefore,

$$Z = \sqrt{R^2 + X^2} = \sqrt{(40)^2 + (30)^2} = \sqrt{1,600 + 900} = \sqrt{2,500}$$
$$Z = \textbf{50 ohms}$$

$I = E/Z.$ The current is 100 volts/50 ohms in this example, or 2 amp.

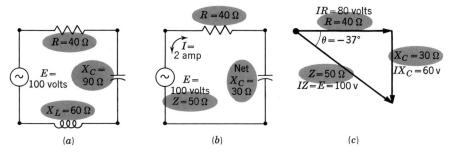

Fig. 20·8 Impedance Z of series circuit with R, X_L, and X_C. (a) R, X_L, and X_C in series. (b) Equivalent circuit with net reactance. (c) Vector diagram showing phase angle.

Series voltage drops. All the series components have the same 2-amp current. Therefore, the IR drop is 80 volts, the IX_C drop is 180 volts, and the IX_L drop is 120 volts. Since IX_C and IX_L are voltages of opposite polarity, the net reactive voltage is 180 volts minus 120 volts, which equals 60 volts. The vector sum of IR at 80 volts and the net reactive voltage IX of 60 volts equals the applied voltage E of 100 volts.

Phase angle of Z. The phase angle of the series circuit is the angle whose tangent equals X/R. X is the net reactance of -30 ohms for X_C and R is 40 ohms. Then θ is $-37°$, approximately. The negative angle for Z indicates lagging capacitive reactance for the series circuit. If the values of X_L and X_C were reversed, the phase angle would be $+37°$, instead of $-37°$, because of the net X_L. However, the magnitude of Z would still be the same.

More series components. How to combine any number of series resistances and reactances can be illustrated by Fig. 20·9. Here the total series R of 40 ohms is the sum of 30 ohms for R_1 and 10 ohms for R_2. Note that the order of connection does not matter, since the current is the same in all series components.

The total series X_C is 90 ohms, equal to the sum of 70 ohms for X_{C_1} and 20 ohms for X_{C_2}. Similarly, the total series X_L is 60 ohms, equal to the sum of 30 ohms for X_{L_1} and 30 ohms for X_{L_2}.

The net reactance X equals 30 ohms, which is 90 ohms of X_C minus 60 ohms of X_L. Since X_C is larger than X_L, the net reactance is capacitive. The circuit in Fig. 20·9 is equivalent to Fig. 20·8, therefore, since 40-ohm R is in series with a net X_C of 30 ohms.

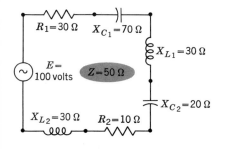

Fig. 20·9 Series a-c circuit with more components than Fig. 20·8, but the same values of Z, I, and θ.

20·6   Parallel reactance and resistance

With parallel circuits, the branch currents for resistance and reactance are added vectorially. Then the total line current is found by the formula

$$I_T = \sqrt{I_R^2 + I_X^2} \tag{20·2}$$

Calculating I_T. As an example, Fig. 20·10a shows a circuit with three branches. Since the voltage across all the parallel branches is the applied E of 100 volts, the individual branch currents are

$$I_R = \frac{E}{R} = \frac{100 \text{ volts}}{25 \text{ ohms}} = 4 \text{ amp}$$

$$I_L = \frac{E}{X_L} = \frac{100 \text{ volts}}{25 \text{ ohms}} = 4 \text{ amp}$$

$$I_C = \frac{E}{X_C} = \frac{100 \text{ volts}}{100 \text{ ohms}} = 1 \text{ amp}$$

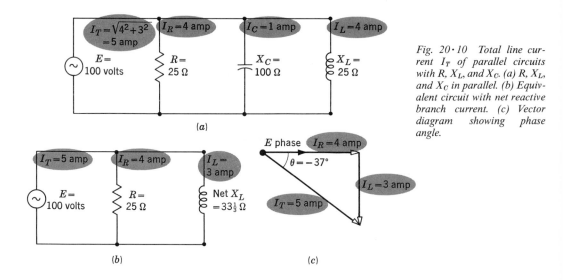

Fig. 20·10   Total line current I_T of parallel circuits with R, X_L, and X_C. (a) R, X_L, and X_C in parallel. (b) Equivalent circuit with net reactive branch current. (c) Vector diagram showing phase angle.

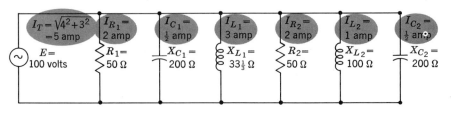

Fig. 20·11   Parallel a-c circuit with more components than Fig. 20·10, but the same values of I_T, Z, and θ.

The net reactive branch current I_X is 3 amp, then, equal to the difference between the 4-amp I_L and 1-amp I_C, as shown in *b*. To calculate I_T as the vector sum of I_R and I_X, therefore,

$$I_T = \sqrt{I_R^2 + I_X^2} = \sqrt{4^2 + 3^2} = \sqrt{16 + 9} = \sqrt{25}$$
$$I_T = 5 \text{ amp}$$

The vector diagram for I_T is shown in *c*. Note that the sign of I_X does not matter in calculating I_T, as the square of I will always be a positive number.

$\mathbf{Z_T = E/I_T}$. This gives the total impedance of a parallel circuit. In this example, Z_T is 100 volts/5 amp, which equals 20 ohms. This value is the equivalent impedance of all three branches in parallel across the source E.

Phase angle. The phase angle of the parallel circuit is found from the branch currents, with θ the angle whose tangent equals I_X/I_R. For this example, I_X is the net inductive current of 3-amp I_L. Also, I_R is 4 amp. These vectors are shown in Fig. 20·10*c*. Then θ is a negative angle with the tangent of ¾ or 0.75. This phase angle is $-37°$, approximately. The negative angle for current indicates lagging inductive current. The value of $-37°$ is the phase angle of I_T with respect to the voltage reference E.

When Z_T is calculated as E/I_T for a parallel circuit, the phase angle of Z_T is the same value as for I_T but with opposite sign. In this example, Z_T is 20 ohms with a phase angle of $+37°$, for I_T of 5 amp with an angle of $-37°$. We can consider that Z_T has the phase of E with respect to I_T.

More parallel branches. Figure 20·11 illustrates how any number of parallel resistances and reactances can be combined. The total resistive branch current I_R of 4 amp is the sum of 2 amp each for the R_1 branch and the R_2 branch. Note that the order of connection does not matter, since the parallel branch currents add in the main line. Effectively, two 50-ohm resistances in parallel are equivalent to one 25-ohm resistance.

Similarly, the total inductive branch current I_L is 4 amp, equal to 3 amp for I_{L_1} and 1 amp for I_{L_2}. Also, the total capacitive branch current I_C is 1 amp, equal to ½ amp each for I_{C_1} and I_{C_2}.

The net reactive branch current I_X is 3 amp, then, equal to 4-amp I_L minus 1-amp I_C. Since I_L is larger, the net current is inductive. The circuit in Fig. 20·11 is equivalent to Fig. 20·9, therefore, with both having 4-amp resistive current I_R and 3-amp net inductive current I_L adding vectorially to total 5 amp I_T in the main line.

20·7 Series-parallel reactance and resistance

Figure 20·12 shows how a series-parallel circuit can be reduced to a series circuit with just one reactance and one resistance. The method is straightforward as long as resistance and reactance are not combined in one bank or string, as in Fig. 20·12.

Working backward toward the generator from the outside branch in Fig. 20·12*a*, we have X_{L_1} and X_{L_2} of 100 ohms each in series, which totals

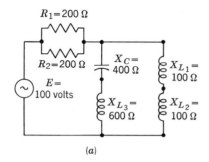

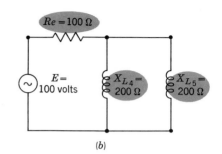

(a)

(b)

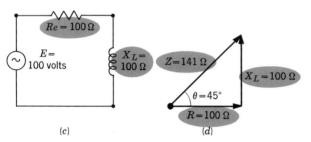

(c)

(d)

Fig. 20·12   Reducing series-parallel circuit with R, X_L, and X_C to series circuit with one R and one X. (a) Actual circuit. (b) Simplified arrangement. (c) Equivalent series circuit. (d) Vector diagram for equivalent circuit.

200 ohms. This string in *a* is equivalent to X_{L_5} in *b*. In the other branch, the net reactance of X_{L_3} and X_C is equal to 600 ohms minus 400 ohms. This is equivalent to the 200 ohms of X_{L_4} in *b*. The bank of X_{L_4} with X_{L_5} of 200 ohms each in parallel equals 100 ohms. In *c*, this 100-ohm X_L is in series with the 100-ohm R_e. Therefore, the equivalent R_e of 100 ohms is in series with the equivalent X_L of 100 ohms, as in *c*.

The vector diagram for the equivalent circuit in *d* shows the total impedance *Z* of 141 ohms for 100-ohm *R* in series with 100-ohm X_L. With 141-ohm impedance across the applied *E* of 100 volts, the current in the generator is 0.7 amp. The phase angle θ is 45° for this circuit.[1]

20·8   Real power

In an a-c circuit with reactance, the current *I* supplied by the generator either leads or lags the generator voltage *E*. Then the product *EI* is not the real power produced by the generator, since the voltage may have a high value while the current is near zero, or vice versa. The real power, however, can always be calculated as I^2R, where *R* is the total resistive component of the circuit, because current and voltage have the same phase in a resistance. To find the corresponding value of power as *EI*, this product must be multiplied by the cosine of the phase angle θ. Then

$$\text{Real power} = I^2R \qquad (20 \cdot 3)$$

or

$$\text{Real power} = EI \cos \theta \qquad (20 \cdot 4)$$

[1] More complicated a-c circuits with series-parallel impedances are analyzed with complex numbers, as explained in Chap. 21.

where E and I are in RMS values, to calculate the real power. Multiplying EI by the cosine of the phase angle provides the resistive component for real power equal to I^2R.

For example, the a-c circuit in Fig. 20·13 has 2 amp through 100-ohm R in series with the X_L of 173 ohms. Therefore,

$$\text{Real power} = I^2R = 4 \times 100 = \textbf{400 watts}$$

Furthermore, in this circuit the phase angle is 60° with a cosine of 0.5. The applied voltage E is 400 volts. Therefore,

$$\text{Real power} = EI \cos \theta = 400 \times 2 \times 0.5 = \textbf{400 watts}$$

In both examples, the real power is the same 400 watts because this is the amount of power supplied by the generator and dissipated in the resistance. Either formula can be used for calculating the real power, depending on which is more convenient.

Power factor. Because it includes the resistive component, $\cos \theta$ is the power factor of the circuit, converting the EI product to real power. For series circuits,

$$\text{Power factor} = \cos \theta = \frac{R}{Z} \qquad (20\cdot5)$$

or for parallel circuits

$$\text{Power factor} = \cos \theta = \frac{I_R}{I_T} \qquad (20\cdot6)$$

In Fig. 20·13, as an example of a series circuit,

$$\text{Power factor} = \cos \theta = \frac{R}{Z} = \frac{100 \text{ ohms}}{200 \text{ ohms}} = 0.5$$

For the parallel circuit in Fig. 20·10,

$$\text{Power factor} = \cos \theta = \frac{I_R}{I_T} = \frac{4 \text{ amp}}{5 \text{ amp}} = 0.8$$

The power factor is not an angular measure but a numerical ratio, with a value between 0 and 1, equal to the cosine of the phase angle. With all resistance and zero reactance, R and Z are the same for a series circuit, or I_R and I_T are the same for a parallel circuit, and the ratio is 1. Therefore, unity power factor means a resistive circuit. At the opposite extreme, all reactance with zero resistance makes the power factor zero, meaning that the circuit is all reactive.

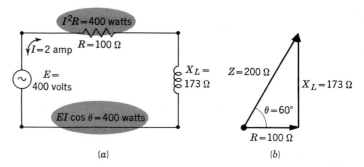

Fig. 20·13   *Real power in series circuit. (a) Schematic diagram.*
(b) Vectors showing phase angle.

Volt-amperes of apparent power. There is no real power dissipated in capacitive or inductive reactance having zero resistance. Although a reactance draws current from the a-c source, E and I are 90° out of phase, with one at zero while the other is maximum. The current in X_L stores energy in the electromagnetic field of the inductance; in a capacitance the charge stores energy in the dielectric field. For both cases, the stored energy can be returned to the circuit, however, so that no power is dissipated in a pure reactance. The product of $E \times I$ where they are 90° out of phase then is considered *apparent power, wattless power,* or *reactive volt-amperes.* The unit is volt-amperes instead of watts, since the watt unit is reserved for real power.

20·9   A-c meters

The D'Arsonval moving-coil type of meter movement will not read if used in an a-c circuit because the average value of an alternating current is zero. Since the two opposite polarities cancel, an alternating current cannot deflect the meter movement either upscale or downscale. An a-c meter must produce deflection of the meter pointer upscale regardless of polarity. This deflection is accomplished by one of the following three methods for a-c meters.

1. Thermal type. In this method, the heating effect of the current, which is independent of polarity, is used to provide meter deflection. Two examples are the thermocouple type and the hot-wire meter.

2. Electromagnetic type. In this method, the relative magnetic polarity is maintained constant although the current reverses. Examples are the iron-vane meter, dynamometer, and wattmeter.

3. Rectifier type. The rectifier changes the a-c input to d-c output for the meter, which is usually a D'Arsonval movement. This type is the most common for a-c voltmeters generally used for audio and radio frequencies.

All a-c meters have scales calibrated in RMS values, unless noted otherwise on the meter.

A thermocouple consists of two dissimilar metals, shorted at one end but open at the opposite side. Heat at the shorted junction produces a small d-c voltage across the open ends, which are connected to a d-c meter movement. In the hot-wire meter, current heats a wire to make it expand and this motion is converted into meter deflection. Both types are used as a-c meters for radio frequencies.

The iron-vane meter and dynamometer have very low sensitivity, compared with a D'Arsonval movement. They are used in power circuits, for either direct current or alternating current.

The rectifier type of a-c voltmeter can use copper oxide, selenium, germanium, or a vacuum tube for the rectifier. A separate scale for a range of 10 volts or less is generally necessary because of nonlinear rectification at low amplitudes. It should also be noted that the rectifier arrangement is not suitable for measuring current, because a current meter must have very low resistance. For this reason a-c/d-c multimeters generally measure a-c voltages as well as d-c voltages, but not alternating current.

A-c meters, other than the rectifier type, generally have a nonlinear scale that is crowded at the low end. This crowding of the scale readings results from the fact that the deflection is proportional to the square of the current.

20·10   Wattmeters

The wattmeter uses fixed coils to indicate current in the circuit, while the movable coil indicates voltage (Fig. 20·14). The deflection then is proportional to power. Either d-c power or real a-c power can be read directly by the wattmeter.

In Fig. 20·14*a*, the coils L_{I_1} and L_{I_2} in series are the stationary coils serving as an ammeter to measure current. The two I terminals are connected in one side of the line in series with the load. The movable coil L_E and its multiplier resistance R_M are used as a voltmeter, with the E terminals connected across the line in parallel with the load. Then the current in the fixed coils is proportional to I, while the current in the movable coil is proportional to E. As a result, the deflection is proportional to the EI product, which is power.

Fig. 20·14   Wattmeter. (a) Schematic of voltage and current coils. (b) 0-500-wattmeter. (W. M. Welch Mfg. Co.)

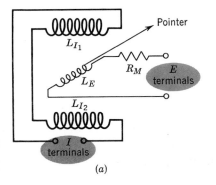

(a)   (b)

Table 20·1   Types of ohms in a-c circuits

	Resistance R, ohms	Inductive reactance X_L, ohms	Capacitive reactance X_C, ohms	Impedance Z, ohms
Definition	In-phase opposition to alternating or direct current	90° leading opposition to alternating current	90° lagging opposition to alternating current	Vector combination of resistance and reactance $Z = \sqrt{R^2 + X^2}$
Effect of frequency	Same for all frequencies	Increases with higher frequencies	Decreases with higher frequencies	X_L component increases, but X_C decreases
Phase angle θ	0°	I_L lags E_L by 90°	E_C lags I_C by 90°	$\tan \theta = \dfrac{X}{R}$ in series, or $\dfrac{I_X}{I_R}$ in parallel

Furthermore, it is the *EI* product for each instant of time that produces deflection. For instance, if the *E* value is high when the *I* value is low, for a phase angle close to 90°, there will be little deflection. The meter deflection is proportional to the watts of real power, therefore, regardless of the power factor in a-c circuits.

20·11   Summary of types of ohms in a-c circuits

The differences in R, X_L, X_C, and Z are listed in Table 20·1, but the following general features should also be noted. Ohms of opposition limit the amount of current in d-c circuits or a-c circuits. Resistance R is the same for either case. However, a-c circuits can have ohms of reactance because of the variations in alternating current or voltage. X_L is the reactance of an inductance with sine-wave changes in current. X_C is the reactance of a capacitor with sine-wave changes in voltage. Both X_L and X_C are measured in ohms, like R, but reactance has a 90° phase angle, while the phase angle for resistance is 0°. A circuit with steady direct current cannot have any reactance.

Ohms of X_L or X_C are opposite, as X_L has a phase angle of $+90°$, while X_C has the angle of $-90°$. Any individual X_L or X_C always has a phase angle of exactly 90°.

Ohms of impedance Z result from the vector combination of resistance and reactance. In fact, Z can be considered the general form of any ohms of opposition in a-c circuits. Note that Z can have any phase angle, depending on the relative amounts of R and X that are added vectorially to result in Z. When Z consists mostly of R with little reactance, the phase angle of Z is close to 0°. If the resistance and reactance are equal the phase angle of Z is 45°. Whether the angle is positive or negative depends on whether the net reactance is inductive or capacitive. When Z consists mainly of X with little R, the phase angle of Z is close to 90°.

20·12 Summary of types of vectors in a-c circuits

The vectors for ohms, volts, and amperes are shown in Fig. 20·15. Note the following similarities and differences:

In series circuits, ohms and voltage drops have similar vectors because I is common to all the components.

R, V_R, and I_R always have the same angle because there is no phase shift in a resistance.

X_L or X_C are 90° vectors in opposite directions. X_L or V_L always has the angle of $+90°$ with an upward vector. X_C or V_C always has the angle of $-90°$ with a downward vector.

The vector of a parallel branch current is opposite from its reactance. Therefore, I_C is upward at $+90°$, opposite from X_C downward at $-90°$. Also, I_L is downward at $-90°$ opposite from X_L upward at $+90°$. In short, I_C or I_L are opposite from each other, and the vectors for branch currents are both opposite from their corresponding reactance.

The vectors for reactance or their reactive branch currents are always exactly 90°, forming a right angle with a resistive vector.

The vector resultant for ohms of reactance and resistance is the impedance Z. The phase angle θ for Z can be any angle between 0 and 90°. In a series circuit, θ for Z is the same as θ for E with respect to the common current I.

Fig. 20·15 *Summary of vector relations in a-c circuits. (a) X_L and R in series (b) X_C and R in series. (c) Parallel branches with I_C and I_R. (d) Parallel branches with I_L and I_R.*

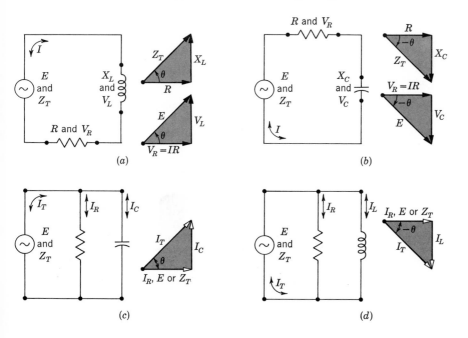

The vector resultant of branch currents is the total line current I_T. The phase angle of I_T with respect to the common applied voltage E can be any angle between 0 and 90°. In a parallel circuit, θ for I_T is the same value but of opposite sign from θ for Z, which is the impedance of the combined parallel branches.

Such vector combinations are necessary in sine-wave a-c circuits in order to take into account the effect of reactance. The vectors can be analyzed either graphically, as in Fig. 20·15, or by the shorter technique of complex numbers, which correspond to the vectors. How to use complex numbers in the analysis of a-c circuits is explained in the next chapter.

SUMMARY

1. In a-c circuits with resistance alone, the circuit is analyzed the same way as for d-c circuits, generally with RMS a-c values. Without any reactance, the phase angle is zero.
2. When capacitive reactances alone are combined, the X_C values are added in series and combined by the reciprocal formula in parallel, just like ohms of resistance. Similarly, ohms of X_L alone can be added in series or combined by the reciprocal formula in parallel.
3. Since X_C and X_L are opposite reactances, they cancel each other. In series, the ohms of X_C and X_L cancel. In parallel, the capacitive and inductive branch currents I_C and I_L cancel.
4. In a-c circuits with R, X_L, and X_C, the circuit can be reduced to one equivalent resistance and one net reactance. In series, the total R and net X are added vectorially, by Formula (20·1). The phase angle of the series R and X equals the angle whose tangent is X/R. In parallel, the total resistive branch current and net reactive branch current are added vectorially, by Formula (20·2). The phase angle of the parallel R and X equals the angle whose tangent is I_X/I_R.
5. R, X_L, X_C, and Z in a-c circuits all are ohms of opposition. The differences with respect to frequency and phase angle are summarized in Table 20·1.
6. The vector relations for resistance and reactance are summarized in Fig. 20·15.
7. In a-c circuits with reactance, the real power in watts equals I^2R, or $EI\cos\theta$, where θ is the phase angle. The real power is the power dissipated as heat in resistance. $\cos\theta$ is the power factor of the circuit.
8. The scales of a-c meters are calibrated to read RMS values.
9. The wattmeter uses a movable coil to indicate voltage, while the fixed coils measure current.

SELF-EXAMINATION (*Answers at back of book.*)

Here's a chance to find out how well you have learned the material in this chapter. These exercises are for your self-testing only.

1. In an a-c circuit with resistance but no reactance (*a*) two 1,000-ohm resistances in series total 1,414 ohms; (*b*) two 1,000-ohm resistances in series total 2,000 ohms; (*c*) two 1,000-ohm resistances in parallel total 707 ohms; (*d*) 1,000-ohm R in series with 400-ohm R totals 600 ohms.
2. An a-c circuit has 100-ohm X_{C_1}, 50-ohm X_{C_2}, 40-ohm X_{L_1} and 30-ohm X_{L_2}, all in series. The net reactance equals (*a*) 80-ohm X_L; (*b*) 200-ohm X_L; (*c*) 80-ohm X_C; (*d*) 220-ohm X_C.
3. An a-c circuit has 40-ohm R, 90-ohm X_L, and 60-ohm X_C, all in series. The impedance Z equals (*a*) 50 ohms; (*b*) 70.7 ohms; (*c*) 110 ohms; (*d*) 190 ohms.
4. An a-c circuit has 100-ohm R, 100-ohm X_L, and 100-ohm X_C, all in series. The impedance Z of the series combination is equal to (*a*) 33⅓ ohms; (*b*) 70.7 ohms; (*c*) 100 ohms; (*d*) 300 ohms.
5. An a-c circuit has 100-ohm R, 300-ohm-X_L, and 200-ohm X_C, all in series. The phase angle θ of the circuit equals (*a*) 0°; (*b*) 37°; (*c*) 45°; (*d*) 90°.
6. The power factor of an a-c circuit equals (*a*) cosine of the phase angle; (*b*) tangent of the phase angle; (*c*) zero for a resistive circuit; (*d*) unity for a reactive circuit.

7. Which vectors in the following combinations are *not* in opposite directions? (*a*) X_L and X_C; (*b*) X_L and I_C; (*c*) I_L and I_C; (*d*) X_C and I_C.
8. In Fig. 20·8*a*, the voltage drop across X_L equals (*a*) 60 volts; (*b*) 66⅔ volts; (*c*) 120 volts; (*d*) 200 volts.
9. In Fig. 20·10*a*, the combined impedance of the parallel circuit equals (*a*) 5 ohms; (*b*) 12.5 ohms; (*c*) 20 ohms; (*d*) 100 ohms.
10. The wattmeter (*a*) has voltage and current coils to measure real power; (*b*) has three connections, two of which are used at a time; (*c*) measures apparent power because the current is the same in the voltage and current coils; (*d*) can measure d-c power but not 60-cps a-c power.

ESSAY QUESTIONS

1. Why can series or parallel resistances be combined in a-c circuits the same way as in d-c circuits?
2. (*a*) Why do X_L and X_C reactances in series cancel each other? (*b*) With X_L and X_C reactances in parallel, why do their branch currents cancel?
3. Give one difference in electrical characteristics comparing R and X_C, R and X_L, R and Z, X_C and C, X_L and L.
4. Give three types of a-c meters.
5. Make a diagram showing a resistance R_1 in series with the load resistance R_L, with a wattmeter connected to measure the power in R_L.
6. What is the difference between volt-amperes and watts?
7. Make a vector diagram for the circuit in Fig. 20·8*a*, showing the phase of the voltage drops IR, IX_C, and IX_L with respect to the reference phase of the current I.
8. Explain briefly why the two opposite vectors at $+90°$ for X_L and $-90°$ for I_L both follow the principle that any self-induced voltage leads the current through the coil by $90°$.
9. Explain briefly why vectors for inductance are opposite from vectors for capacitance.
10. Why is a reactance vector always at exactly $90°$ but an impedance vector can be less than $90°$?
11. Why must the impedance of a series circuit be more than either its reactance or resistance?
12. When resistance is increased in a series impedance, Z increases but θ decreases. Explain why.

PROBLEMS (*Answers to selected problems at back of book.*)

1. Refer to Fig. 20·1*a*. (*a*) Calculate the total real power supplied by the source. (*b*) Why is the phase angle zero? (*c*) What is the power factor of the circuit?
2. In a series a-c circuit, 2 amp flows through 20-ohm R, 40-ohm X_L, and 60-ohm X_C. (*a*) Make a schematic diagram of the series circuit. (*b*) Calculate the voltage drop across each series component. (*c*) How much is the applied voltage? (*d*) Calculate the power factor of the circuit. (*e*) What is the phase angle θ?
3. A parallel circuit has the following five branches: three resistances of 30 ohms each; X_L of 600 ohms; X_C of 400 ohms. (*a*) Make a schematic diagram of the circuit. (*b*) What is the total impedance of the circuit? (*c*) What is the phase angle θ? (*d*) If 100 volts is applied, how much is the total line current?
4. Referring to Fig. 20·8, assume that the frequency is doubled from 500 to 1,000 cps. Find X_L, X_C, Z, I, and θ for this higher frequency. Also, calculate L and C.
5. A series circuit has 300-ohm R, 500-ohm X_{C_1}, 300-ohm X_{C_2}, 800-ohm X_{L_1}, and 400-ohm X_{L_2} all in series with an applied voltage E of 400 volts. (*a*) Draw the schematic diagram with all components. (*b*) Draw the equivalent circuit reduced to one resistance and one reactance. (*c*) Calculate I and the phase angle θ.
6. Do the same as Prob. 5 for a circuit with the same components in parallel across E.
7. A series circuit has 600-ohm R, 10-μh inductance L, and 4-μf capacitance C all in series with the 60-cycle 120-volt power line as applied voltage. (*a*) Find the reactance of L and of C. (*b*) Calculate the current I in the circuit and the phase angle θ.

8. Do the same as in Prob. 7 for the same circuit, but the 120-volt source has the frequency of 10 Mc.

9. (*a*) Referring to the series circuit Fig. 20·6, what is the phase angle between the IX_L voltage of 360 volts and IX_C voltage of 240 volts? (*b*) Draw the two sine waves for these voltages, showing their relative amplitudes and phase corresponding to the vector diagram in *b*. Also show the resultant sine wave of voltage across the net X_L.

10. Do the same as in Prob. 9 for the currents in the parallel circuit of Fig. 20·7.

11. A wattmeter measures 5 amp in the series coil and 120 volts across the voltage coil. (*a*) Calculate the real power in watts. (*b*) How much resistance dissipates this amount of I^2R power?

12. How much resistance must be inserted in series with a 1.9-henry inductance to limit the current to 0.1 amp from the 120-volt 60-cps power line?

13. How much resistance must be inserted in series with a 10-μf capacitance to provide a phase angle of $-45°$? The source is the 120-volt 60-cps power line.

14. With same R as in Prob. 13 what value of C is necessary for the angle of $-45°$ at the frequency of 2 Mc?

15. How much capacitance, in μf units must be inserted in series with 200-ohm R for a current of 0.3 amp, from the 120-volt 60-cps power line?

21

Complex numbers form a numerical system that includes the phase angle of a quantity, with its magnitude. Therefore, complex numbers are useful in a-c circuits, when the reactance of X_L or X_C makes it necessary to consider phase. Any type of a-c circuit can be analyzed with complex numbers, but they are especially convenient for converting a parallel circuit to an equivalent series circuit and for solving series-parallel circuits that have both resistance and reactance in one or more branches. Actually, the use of complex numbers is the best way to analyze complex a-c circuits with resistance and reactance. The topics here are:

21·1   Positive and negative numbers
21·2   The *j* operator
21·3   Definition of a complex number
21·4   How complex numbers are applied to a-c circuits
21·5   Impedance in complex form
21·6   Operations with complex numbers
21·7   Magnitude and angle of a complex number
21·8   Polar form of complex numbers
21·9   Converting polar to rectangular form
21·10 Complex numbers in series a-c circuits
21·11 Complex numbers in parallel a-c circuits
21·12 Complex numbers in series-parallel circuits

21·1   *Positive and negative numbers*

Our common use of numbers as either positive or negative represents only two special cases. In their more general form, numbers have both quantity and phase angle. In Fig. 21·1, positive and negative numbers are shown as corresponding to the phase angles of 0 and 180°, respectively. As

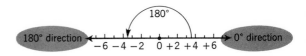

Fig. 21·1   *Positive and negative numbers.*

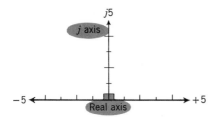

Fig. 21·2   *j axis at 90° from real axis.*

examples, the numbers 2, 4, and 6 represent units along the horizontal or *x* axis, extending toward the right along the line of zero phase angle. Therefore, positive numbers really represent units having the phase angle of 0°. Or, this phase angle corresponds to the factor of +1. To indicate 6 units with zero phase angle, then, 6 is multiplied by +1 as a factor for the positive number of 6. The + sign is often omitted, as it is assumed unless indicated otherwise.

In the opposite direction, negative numbers correspond to 180°. Or, this phase angle corresponds to the factor of −1. Actually, −6 represents the same quantity as 6 but rotated through the phase angle of 180°. The angle of rotation is the *operator* for the number.

21·2   The j operator

The operator for a number can be any angle between 0 and 360°. Since the angle of 90° is important in a-c circuits, the factor *j* is used to indicate 90°. See Fig. 21·2. Here, the number 5 means 5 units at 0°, the number −5 is at 180°, while *j*5 indicates the 90° angle. The *j* is usually written before the number. Any quantity at right angles to the zero axis, therefore, 90° counterclockwise, is on the +*j* axis.

In mathematics, numbers on the horizontal axis are real numbers, including positive and negative values. Numbers on the *j* axis are called *imaginary numbers,* only because they are not on the real axis. Also, the factor *i* is used in place of *j*. In electricity, however, *j* is used to avoid confusion with *i* as the symbol for current. Furthermore, there is nothing imaginary about electrical quantities on the *j* axis. An electrical shock from *j*500 volts is just as dangerous as 500 volts positive or negative.

More features of the *j* operator are shown in Fig. 21·3. The angle of 180° corresponds to the *j* operation of 90° repeated twice. This angular rotation is indicated by the factor j^2. Note that the *j* operation multiplies itself, instead of adding. Since j^2 means 180°, which corresponds to the factor of −1, we can say that j^2 is the same as −1. In short, the operator j^2 for a

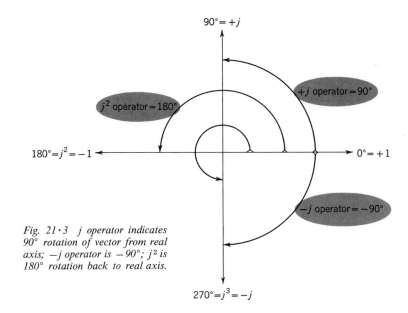

90° = +*j*

+*j* operator = 90°

*j*² operator = 180°

180° = *j*² = −1

0° = +1

−*j* operator = −90°

Fig. 21·3 *j operator indicates
90° rotation of vector from real
axis; −j operator is −90°; j² is
180° rotation back to real axis.*

270° = *j*³ = −*j*

number means multiply by −1. For instance, *j*²8 is −8. Furthermore, the angle of 270° is the same as −90°, which corresponds to the operator −*j*. These characteristics of the *j* operator are summarized as follows:

$$0° = 1 \text{ as a factor}$$
$$90° = j \text{ as a factor}$$
$$180° = j^2 \text{ as a factor} = -1$$
$$270° = j^3 = j^2 \times j = -1 \times j = -j$$
$$360° = \text{same as } 0°$$

As examples, the number 4 or −4 represents 4 units on the real, horizontal axis; *j*4 means 4 units with a leading phase angle of 90°; −*j*4 means 4 units with a lagging phase angle of −90°.

21·3 Definition of a complex number

The combination of a real and imaginary term is a complex number. Usually, the real number is written first. As an example, (3 + *j*4) is a complex number including 3 units on the real axis added to 4 units 90° out of phase on the *j* axis. The name *complex number* just means that its terms must be added vectorially.

The vectors for several complex numbers are shown in Fig. 21·4. Note that the +*j* vector is 90° up; the −*j* vector is down for −90°. The vectors are shown with the end of one joined to the start of the next, to be ready for vector addition. Graphically, the sum is the hypotenuse of the right triangle formed by the two vectors. Since a number like 3 + *j*4 specifies the vectors

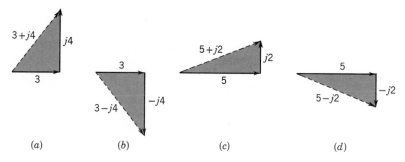

Fig. 21·4 Vectors corresponding to real terms and j terms, in rectangular coordinates.

in rectangular coordinates, this system is the *rectangular form* of complex numbers.

Be careful to distinguish a number like $j2$ where 2 is a coefficient, from j^2 where 2 is the exponent. The number $j2$ means 2 units up on the j axis of 90°. However, j^2 is the operator of -1, which is on the real axis in the negative direction. Another comparison to note is between $j3$ and j^3. The number $j3$ is 3 units up on the j axis, while j^3 is the same as the $-j$ operator, which is down on the $-90°$ axis.

Also note that either the real term or j term can be the larger of the two. When the j term is larger, the angle is more than 45°; when the j term is smaller, the angle is less than 45°. If the j term and real term are equal, the angle is 45°.

21·4 How complex numbers are applied to a-c circuits

The applications are just a question of using a real term for 0°, $+j$ for 90°, and $-j$ for $-90°$, to denote the phase angles. Specifically, Fig. 21·5 illustrates the following rules:

0° or a real number without any j operator is used for resistance R. For instance, 8 ohms of R is stated just as 8.

90° or $+j$ is used for inductive reactance X_L. For instance, 4 ohms X_L is $j4$ ohms. This rule always applies to X_L, whether it is in series or parallel with R. The reason is the fact that X_L represents voltage across an inductance, which always leads the current through the inductance by 90° ($+j$).

Fig. 21·5 Rectangular form of complex numbers for impedances.

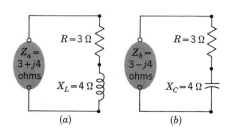

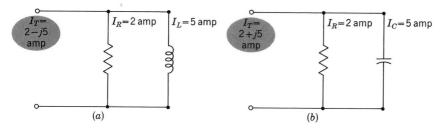

Fig. 21·6 *Rectangular form of complex numbers for branch currents.*

−90° or −j is used for capacitive reactance X_C. For instance, 4 ohms X_C is $-j4$ ohms. This rule always applies to X_C, whether it is in series or parallel with R. The reason is the fact that X_C represents voltage across a capacitor which always lags the charge and discharge current of the capacitor by 90° $(-j)$.

With reactive branch currents, the sign for j is reversed, compared with reactive ohms, because of the opposite phase angle. As shown in Fig. 21·6a and b, $-j$ is used for inductive branch current and $+j$ for capacitive branch current.

21·5 *Impedance in complex form*

The rectangular form of complex numbers is a convenient way to state the impedance of series resistance and reactance. In Fig. 21·5a the impedance is $3 + j4$, as Z_a is the vector sum of 3 ohms R in series with 4 ohms X_L. Similarly, Z_b is $3 - j4$ for 3 ohms R in series with 4 ohms X_C. The minus sign results from adding the negative term for $-j$. More examples are:

For 4-k R and 2-k X_L in series, $Z_T = 4{,}000 + j2{,}000$
For 3-k R and 9-k X_C in series, $Z_T = 3{,}000 - j9{,}000$
For zero R and 7 ohms X_L in series, $Z_T = 0 + j7$
For 12 ohms R and zero reactance in series, $Z_T = 12 + j0$

Note the general form of stating $Z = R \pm jX$. If one term is zero, substitute 0 for this term, in order to keep Z in its general form. This procedure is not required but there is usually less confusion when the same form is used for all types of Z.

The advantage of this method is that multiple impedances written as complex numbers can then be calculated as follows:

$$Z_T = Z_1 + Z_2 + Z_3 + \text{etc.} \qquad \text{for series impedances}$$

$$\frac{1}{Z_T} = \frac{1}{Z_1} + \frac{1}{Z_2} + \frac{1}{Z_3} + \text{etc.} \qquad \text{for parallel impedances}$$

or $$Z_T = \frac{Z_1 \times Z_2}{Z_1 + Z_2} \qquad \text{for two impedances in parallel}$$

Examples are shown in Fig. 21·7. The circuit in *a* is just a series combination of resistances and reactances. Combining the real terms and *j* terms separately, $Z_T = 12 + j4$. The parallel circuit in *b* shows that X_L is $+j$ and X_C is $-j$ even though they are in parallel branches.

So far, these types of circuits can be analyzed with or without complex numbers. For the series-parallel circuit in Fig. 21·7c, however, the notation of complex numbers is necessary to state the complex impedance Z_T, consisting of branches with reactance and resistance in one or more of the branches. Z_T is just stated here in its form as a complex impedance. In order to calculate Z_T, some of the rules described in the next section must be used for combining complex numbers.

21·6 *Operations with complex numbers*

Real numbers and *j* terms cannot be combined directly because they are 90° out of phase. The following rules apply:

For addition or subtraction. Add or subtract the real and *j* terms separately:

$$(9 + j5) + (3 + j2) = 9 + 3 + j5 + j2 = \mathbf{12 + j7}$$
$$(9 + j5) + (3 - j2) = 9 + 3 + j5 - j2 = \mathbf{12 + j3}$$
$$(9 + j5) + (3 - j8) = 9 + 3 + j5 - j8 = \mathbf{12 - j3}$$

The answer should be in the form of $R \pm jX$, where R is the algebraic sum of all the real or resistive terms and X is the algebraic sum of all the imaginary or reactive terms.

To multiply or divide a j term by a real number. Just multiply or divide the numbers. The answer is still a *j* term. Note the algebraic signs in the following examples. If both factors have the same sign, either $+$ or $-$, the answer is $+$; if one factor is negative the answer is negative.

$$4 \times j3 = \mathbf{j12} \qquad\qquad j12 \div 4 = \mathbf{j3}$$
$$j5 \times 6 = \mathbf{j30} \qquad\qquad j30 \div 6 = \mathbf{j5}$$
$$j5 \times (-6) = \mathbf{-j30} \qquad\qquad j30 \div (-6) = \mathbf{-j5}$$
$$-j5 \times 6 = \mathbf{-j30} \qquad\qquad -j30 \div 6 = \mathbf{-j5}$$
$$-j5 \times (-6) = \mathbf{j30} \qquad\qquad -j30 \div (-6) = \mathbf{j5}$$

To multiply or divide a real number by a real number. Just multiply or divide the real numbers, as in arithmetic, without any regard to *j* operation. The answer is still a real number.

To multiply a j term by a j term. Multiply the numbers and the *j* coefficients to produce a j^2 term. The answer is a real term because j^2 is -1, which is on the real axis. Multiplying two *j* terms shifts the number 90° from the *j* axis to the real axis of 180°. As examples:

$$j4 \times j3 = j^2 12 = (-1)(12) = \mathbf{-12}$$

$$j4 \times (-j3) = -j^2 12 = -(-1)(12) = \mathbf{12}$$

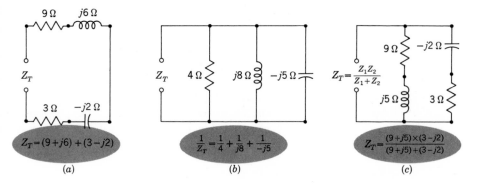

Fig. 21·7 X_L is a $+j$ term and X_C is a $-j$ term, whether in series or parallel. (a) Series circuit. (b) Parallel branches. (c) Complex branch impedances Z_1 and Z_2 in parallel.

To divide a j term by a j term. Divide the numbers and the j coefficients to produce a real number, as the j factors cancel. For instance:

$$j12 \div j4 = 3 \qquad -j12 \div j4 = -3$$
$$j30 \div j5 = 6 \qquad j30 \div -j6 = -5$$
$$j15 \div j3 = 5 \qquad -j15 \div -j3 = 5$$

To multiply complex numbers. Follow the rules of algebra for multiplying two factors, each having two terms:

$$(9 + j5) \times (3 - j2) = 27 + j15 - j18 - j^2 10$$
$$= 27 - j3 + 10$$
$$= 37 - j3$$

Note that $-j^2 10$ equals $+10$ because j^2 is -1 and $-j^2$ is $+1$.

To divide complex numbers. This process becomes more involved because division of a real number by an imaginary number is not possible. Therefore, the denominator must first be converted to a real number without any j term.

Converting the denominator to a real number without any j term is called *rationalization* of the fraction. To do this, multiply both numerator and denominator by the conjugate of the denominator. Conjugate complex numbers have equal terms but opposite signs for the j term. For instance, $(1 + j2)$ has the conjugate $(1 - j2)$. This conversion is permissible because the value of a fraction is not changed when both numerator and denominator are multiplied by the same factor. An example of division with rationalization of the denominator follows:

$$\frac{4 - j1}{1 + j2} = \frac{4 - j1}{1 + j2} \times \frac{(1 - j2)}{(1 - j2)}$$
$$= \frac{4 - j8 - j1 + j^2 2}{1 - j^2 4} = \frac{4 - j9 - 2}{1 + 4}$$
$$= \frac{2 - j9}{5} = 0.4 - j1.8$$

Note that the product of a complex number and its conjugate always equals the sum of the squares of the numbers in each term. As another example, the product of $(2 + j3)$ and its conjugate $(2 - j3)$ must be $4 + 9$, which equals 13. Simple numerical examples of division and multiplication are given here because when the required calculations become too long it is easier to divide and multiply complex numbers in polar form, as explained in Sec. 21·8.

21·7   Magnitude and angle of a complex number

In electrical terms the complex impedance $(4 + j3)$ means 4 ohms resistance and 3 ohms inductive reactance with a leading phase angle of 90°. See Fig. 21·8a. The magnitude of the combined Z is the resultant, equal to $\sqrt{16 + 9} = \sqrt{25} = 5$ ohms. Finding the square root of the sum of the squares is vector addition of two terms. The phase angle of the resultant Z is the angle whose tangent is ¾ or 0.75. This angle equals 37°. Therefore, $4 + j3 = 5\underline{/37°}$.

When calculating the tangent ratio note the j term is the numerator and the real term is the denominator because the tangent of the phase angle is the ratio of the opposite side to the adjacent side. With a negative j term, the tangent is negative, which means a negative phase angle.

Note the following definitions: $(4 + j3)$ is the complex number in rectangular coordinates. The real term is 4. The imaginary term is $j3$. The resultant 5 is the magnitude, absolute value, or modulus of the complex number. Its phase angle or argument is 37°. The resultant value by itself

Fig. 21·8   Magnitude and angle of a complex number. (a) Rectangular form. (b) Polar form.

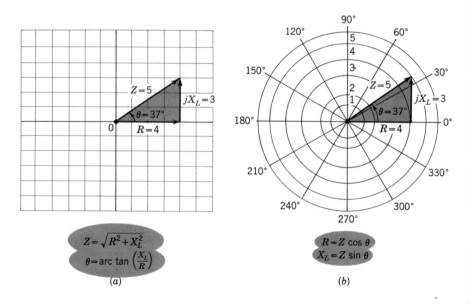

can be written as $|5|$, with vertical lines to indicate it is the magnitude without the phase angle. As additional examples:

$$2 + j4 = \sqrt{4 + 16} \text{ (arctan 2)} \qquad = 4.47\underline{/63°}$$
$$4 + j2 = \sqrt{16 + 4} \text{ (arctan 0.5)} \qquad = 4.47\underline{/27°}$$
$$8 + j6 = \sqrt{64 + 36} \text{ (arctan 0.75)} \quad = 10\underline{/37°}$$
$$4 + j4 = \sqrt{16 + 16} \text{ (arctan 1)} \qquad = 5.66\underline{/45°}$$
$$4 - j4 = \sqrt{16 + 16} \text{ (arctan } -1) \qquad = 5.66\underline{/-45°}$$
$$8 - j6 = \sqrt{64 + 36} \text{ (arctan } -0.75) = 10\underline{/-37°}$$

Note that arctan 2, as an example, means the angle with a tangent equal to 2. This can also be indicated as $\tan^{-1} 2$. In either case, the angle is specified as having 2 for its tangent, and the angle is $63°$.

21·8   *Polar form of complex numbers*

Calculating the magnitude and phase angle of a complex number is actually converting to an angular form in polar coordinates. As shown in Fig. 21·8, the rectangular form $4 + j3$ is equal to $5\underline{/37°}$ in polar form. In polar coordinates, the distance out from the center is the magnitude of the vector Z. Its phase angle θ is counterclockwise from the $0°$ axis.

To convert any complex number to polar form:

1. Find the magnitude by vector addition of the j term and real term.
2. Find the angle whose tangent is the j term divided by the real term.

$$2 + j4 = 4.47\underline{/63°} \qquad 4 + j4 = 5.66\underline{/45°}$$
$$4 + j2 = 4.47\underline{/27°} \qquad 4 - j4 = 5.66\underline{/-45°}$$
$$8 + j6 = 10\underline{/37°} \qquad 8 - j6 = 10\underline{/-37°}$$

These examples are the same as given before for finding the magnitude and phase angle of a complex number.

The magnitude in polar form must be more than either term in rectangular form, but less than the arithmetic sum of the two terms. For instance, in $8 + j6 = 10\underline{/37°}$ the magnitude of 10 is more than 8 or 6 but less than their sum of 14.

Applied to a-c circuits with resistance for the real term and reactance for the j term, then, the polar form of a complex number states the resultant impedance and its phase angle. Note the following cases for an impedance where either the resistance or reactance is reduced to zero.

$$5 + j0 = 5\underline{/0°} \qquad 0 + j5 = 5\underline{/90°} \qquad 0 - j5 = 5\underline{/-90°}$$

The polar form is much more convenient for multiplying or dividing complex numbers. The reason why is that multiplication in polar form is reduced to addition of the angles, and the angles are just subtracted for division in polar form. The following rules apply:

For multiplication. Multiply the magnitudes but add the angles algebraically:

$$24\underline{/40°} \times 2\underline{/30°} = 48\underline{/+70°}$$
$$24\underline{/40°} \times -2\underline{/30°} = -48\underline{/+70°}$$
$$12\underline{/-20°} \times 3\underline{/-50°} = 36\underline{/-70°}$$
$$12\underline{/-20°} \times 4\underline{/5°} = 48\underline{/-15°}$$

When you multiply by a real number, just multiply the magnitudes:

$$4 \times 2\underline{/30°} = 8\underline{/30°} \qquad -4 \times 2\underline{/30°} = -8\underline{/30°}$$
$$4 \times 2\underline{/-30°} = 8\underline{/-30°} \qquad -4 \times -2\underline{/30°} = 8\underline{/30°}$$

This rule follows from the fact that a real number has an angle of 0°. When you add 0° to any angle, the sum equals the same angle.

For division. Divide the magnitudes but subtract the angles algebraically:

$$24\underline{/40°} \div 2\underline{/30°} = 12\underline{/40° - 30°} \quad = 12\underline{/10°}$$
$$12\underline{/20°} \div 3\underline{/50°} = 4\underline{/20° - 50°} \quad = 4\underline{/-30°}$$
$$12\underline{/-20°} \div 4\underline{/50°} = 3\underline{/-20° - 50°} \quad = 3\underline{/-70°}$$

To divide by a real number, just divide the magnitudes:

$$12\underline{/30°} \div 2 = 6\underline{/30°}$$
$$12\underline{/-30°} \div 2 = 6\underline{/-30°}$$

This rule is also a special case that follows from the fact that a real number has a phase angle of 0°. When you subtract 0° from any angle the remainder equals the same angle.

For the opposite case, however, when you divide a real number by a complex number the angle of the denominator changes its sign in the answer in the numerator. This rule still follows the procedure of subtracting angles for division, since a real number has a phase angle of 0°. As examples:

$$\frac{10}{5\underline{/30°}} = \frac{10\underline{/0°}}{5\underline{/30°}} \quad = 2\underline{/0° - 30°} = 2\underline{/-30°}$$

$$\frac{10}{5\underline{/-30°}} = \frac{10\underline{/0°}}{5\underline{/-30°}} = 2\underline{/0° - (-30°)} = 2\underline{/+30°}$$

21·9 *Converting polar to rectangular form*

Complex numbers in polar form are convenient for multiplication and division, but they cannot be added or subtracted. The reason is that changing the angle corresponds to the operation of multiplying or dividing.

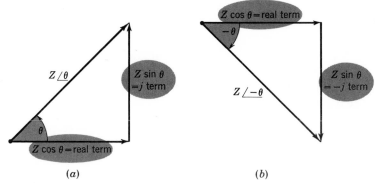

Fig. 21·9   *Converting polar form of Z /θ to rectangular form of R ± jX. (a) Positive angle θ in first quadrant has +j term. (b) Negative angle −θ in fourth quadrant has −j term.*

When complex numbers in polar form are to be added or subtracted, therefore, they must be converted back into rectangular form.

Consider the impedance Z/θ in polar form. Its value is the hypotenuse of a right triangle with sides formed by the real term and j term in rectangular coordinates. See Fig. 21·9. Therefore, the polar form can be converted to rectangular form by finding the horizontal and vertical sides of the right triangle. Specifically:

$$\text{Real term} = Z \cos \theta$$
$$j \text{ term} = Z \sin \theta$$

In Fig. 21·9a, Z in polar form is $5/37°$. The sine of 37° is 0.6 and its cosine is 0.8.

To convert to rectangular form:

$$\text{Real term} = Z \cos \theta = 5 \times 0.8 = 4$$
$$j \text{ term} = Z \sin \theta = 5 \times 0.6 = 3$$

Therefore, $5/37° = 4 + j3.$

This example is the same as the illustration in Fig. 21·8.

In Fig. 21·9b, the values are the same but the j term is negative when θ is negative. The negative angle has a negative j term because the opposite side is in the fourth quadrant, where the sine is negative. However, the real term is still positive because the cosine is positive. These rules apply for angles in the first or fourth quadrant, from 0 to 90° or 0 to −90°. As examples:

$$14.14/45° = 10 + j10 \qquad 100/30° = 86.6 + j50$$
$$14.14/-45° = 10 - j10 \qquad 100/-30° = 86.6 - j50$$
$$14.14/90° = 0 + j10 \qquad 100/60° = 50 + j86.6$$
$$14.14/-90° = 0 - j10 \qquad 100/-60° = 50 - j86.6$$

When going from one form to the other, keep in mind whether the angle is smaller or greater than 45° and if the *j* term is smaller or larger than the real term. For angles between 0 and 45°, the opposite side, which is the *j* term, must be smaller than the real term. For angles between 45 and 90° the *j* term must be larger than the real term.

To summarize how complex numbers are used in a-c circuits in rectangular and polar form:

1. For addition or subtraction, complex numbers must be in rectangular form. This procedure applies to the addition of impedances in a series circuit. If the series impedances are in rectangular form, just combine all the real terms and *j* terms separately. If the series impedances are in polar form they must be converted to rectangular form to be added.

2. For multiplication and division, complex numbers are generally used in polar form because the calculations are faster. If the complex number is in rectangular form, convert to polar form. With the complex number available in both forms, then you can quickly add or subtract in rectangular form and multiply or divide in polar form. Sample problems showing how to apply these methods in the analysis of a-c circuits are illustrated in the following sections.

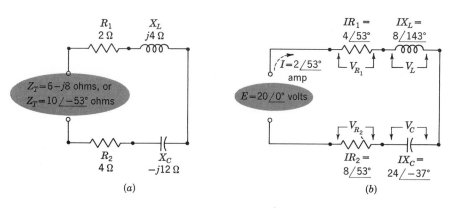

Fig. 21·10 Complex numbers applied to series a-c circuits. See text for analysis. (a) Circuit with series impedances. (b) Current and voltages. (c) Vector diagram to show phase angles.

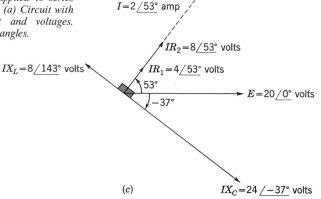

21·10   Complex numbers in series a-c circuits

Refer to the diagram in Fig. 21·10. Although a circuit like this with only series resistances and reactances can be solved just by vectors, the complex numbers show more details of the phase angles. The total Z_T in a is the sum of the impedances in rectangular form:

$$Z_T = 2 + j4 + 4 - j12 = 6 - j8$$

The total series impedance then is $6 - j8$. Actually, it amounts to adding all the series resistances for the real term and finding the algebraic sum of all the series reactances for the j term.

If we want Z_T in polar form

$$Z_T = 6 - j8 = \sqrt{36 + 64}\ \underline{/\arctan \frac{-8}{6}}$$
$$= \sqrt{100}\ \underline{/\arctan - 1.33}$$
$$Z_T = 10\underline{/-53°}\text{ ohms.}$$

The angle of $-53°$ for Z_T means this is the phase angle of the circuit. Or, the applied voltage and the current are $53°$ out of phase.

The reason for calculating the polar form is to divide Z_T into the applied voltage E to calculate the current I. See Fig. 21·10b. Note that the E of 20 volts is a real number without any j term. Therefore, the applied voltage is $20\underline{/0°}$. This angle of $0°$ for E makes it the reference phase for the following calculations. To calculate the current:

$$I = \frac{E}{Z_T} = \frac{20\underline{/0°}}{10\underline{/-53°}} = 2\underline{/0° - (-53°)}$$
$$I = 2\underline{/53°}\text{ amp}$$

Note that Z_T has the negative angle of $-53°$ but the sign changes to $+53°$ for I because of the division into a quantity with the angle of $0°$. In general, the reciprocal of an angle in polar form is the same angle with opposite sign. The fact that I has the angle of $+53°$ means it leads E. The positive angle for I shows the series circuit is capacitive, with leading current. This angle is more than $45°$ because the net reactance is more than the total resistance, resulting in a tangent function greater than 1.

To calculate the voltage drops around the circuit, each resistance or reactance can be multiplied by I:

$$V_{R_1} = IR_1 = 2\underline{/53°} \times 2\underline{/0°} = 4\underline{/53°}\text{ volts}$$
$$V_L = IX_L = 2\underline{/53°} \times 4\underline{/90°} = 8\underline{/143°}\text{ volts}$$
$$V_C = IX_C = 2\underline{/53°} \times 12\underline{/-90°} = 24\underline{/-37°}\text{ volts}$$
$$V_{R_2} = IR_2 = 2\underline{/53°} \times 4\underline{/0°} = 8\underline{/53°}\text{ volts}$$

The vectors for these voltages are in Fig. $21 \cdot 10c$ to show the phase angles, using the applied voltage E as the zero reference phase. The angle of 53° for V_{R_1} and V_{R_2} shows that the voltage across a resistance has the same phase as the current. These voltages lead E by 53° because of the leading current.

For V_C, its angle of $-37°$ means it lags the generator voltage E by this much. However, this voltage across X_C still lags the current by 90°, which is the difference between 53 and $-37°$.

The angle of 143° for V_L, in the second quadrant, is still 90° leading the current at 53°, as $143° - 53° = 90°$. With respect to the generator voltage E, though, the phase angle of V_2 is 143°.

If we want to add the voltage drops around the circuit to see if they equal the applied voltage, each value of V must be converted to rectangular form. Then each real component with 0° phase has the same phase as E and these values can be added. In rectangular form, then

$$
\begin{aligned}
V_{R_1} &= 4\underline{/53°} &&= 2.408 + j3.196 \text{ volts} \\
V_L &= 8\underline{/143°} &&= -6.392 + j4.816 \text{ volts} \\
V_C &= 24\underline{/-37°} &&= 19.176 - j14.448 \text{ volts} \\
V_{R_2} &= 8\underline{/53°} &&= 4.816 + j6.392 \text{ volts} \\
&&& \text{Total} = 20.008 - j0.044 \text{ volts} \\
&&& E = 20\underline{/0°} \text{ volts (approx)}
\end{aligned}
$$

Note that for $8\underline{/143°}$ in the second quadrant, the cosine is negative for a negative real term but the sine is positive for a positive j term.

$20 \cdot 11$ Complex numbers in parallel a-c circuits

A useful application here is converting a parallel circuit to an equivalent series circuit. See Fig. $21 \cdot 11$, with 10-ohm X_L in parallel with 10-ohm R. In complex notation, R is $10 + j0$ while X_L is $0 + j10$. Their combined parallel impedance Z_T equals the product over the sum. Or

$$
Z_T = \frac{(10 + j0) \times (0 + j10)}{(10 + j0) + (0 + j10)} = \frac{10 \times j10}{10 + j10} = \frac{j100}{10 + j10}
$$

Converting to polar form for division,

$$
Z_T = \frac{j100}{10 + j10} = \frac{100\underline{/90°}}{14.14\underline{/45°}} = 7.07\underline{/45°} \text{ ohms}
$$

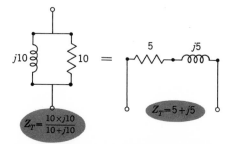

Fig. $21 \cdot 11$ *Complex numbers applied to parallel a-c circuit to convert parallel bank to equivalent series impedance.*

Converting the Z_T of $7.07\underline{/45°}$ into rectangular form to see its resistive and reactive components,

$$\text{Real term} = 7.07 \cos 45° = 7.07 \times 0.707 = 5$$
$$j \text{ term} = 7.07 \sin 45° = 7.07 \times 0.707 = 5$$

Therefore, $\qquad Z_T = 7.07\underline{/45°}$ in polar form

or $\qquad Z_T = 5 + j5$ in rectangular form

The rectangular form of Z_T means that 5-ohm R in series with 5-ohm X_L is the equivalent of 10-ohm R in parallel with 10-ohm X_L, as shown in Fig. 21·11.

In parallel circuits, it is usually easier to add branch currents than to combine reciprocal impedances. For this reason, branch conductance (G) is often used instead of branch resistance, where $G = 1/R$. Similarly, reciprocal terms can be defined for complex impedances. The two main types are *admittance Y*, which is the reciprocal of impedance, and *susceptance B*, which is the reciprocal of reactance. These characteristics can be summarized as follows:

$$\text{Conductance} = G = \frac{1}{R} \qquad \text{mhos}$$

$$\text{Susceptance} = B = \frac{1}{\pm X} \qquad \text{mhos}$$

$$\text{Admittance} = Y = \frac{1}{Z} \qquad \text{mhos}$$

The phase angle for B or Y is the same as current. Therefore, the sign is opposite from the angle of X or Z because of the reciprocal relation. Then an inductive branch has susceptance $-jB$, while a capacitive branch has susceptance $+jB$. With parallel branches of conductance and susceptance the total admittance $Y_T = G \pm jB$. For the two branches in Fig. 21·11, $Y_T = 0.1 - j0.1$ mho in rectangular form. In polar form

$$Y_T = 0.14\underline{/-45°} \text{ mho}$$

This numerical value is the same as I_T with 1 volt applied across Z_T of $7.07\underline{/45°}$ ohms.

21·12 Complex numbers in series-parallel circuits

A common application is a circuit with two branches Z_1 and Z_2, where each is a complex impedance with both reactance and resistance. See Fig. 21·12. A circuit like this can be solved only graphically or by complex numbers. Actually, using complex numbers is the shortest method. The procedure here is to find Z_T as the product divided by the sum for Z_1 and

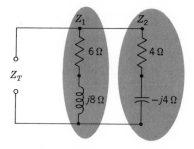

Fig. 21·12 *Finding Z_T for two complex impedances, Z_1 and Z_2 in parallel. See text for solution.*

Z_2. A good way to start is to state each branch impedance in both rectangular and polar forms. Then Z_1 and Z_2 are ready for addition, multiplication, and division. The solution of this circuit follows:

$$Z_1 = 6 + j8 = 10\underline{/53°}$$
$$Z_2 = 4 - j4 = 5.66\underline{/45°}$$

The combined impedance

$$Z_T = \frac{Z_1 \times Z_2}{Z_1 + Z_2}$$

Use the polar form of Z_1 and Z_2 to multiply but add in rectangular form:

$$Z_T = \frac{10\underline{/53°} \times 5.66\underline{/-45°}}{6 + j8 + 4 - j4} = \frac{56.6\underline{/8°}}{10 + j4}$$

Converting the denominator to polar form for easier division,

$$10 + j4 = 10.8\underline{/22°}$$

Therefore,
$$Z_T = \frac{56.6\underline{/8°}}{10.8\underline{/22°}}$$
$$Z_T = 5.24 \text{ ohms}\underline{/-14°}$$

The resistive component of Z_T is $5.24 \times \cos -14° = 5.08$ ohms. The $-j$ component is $5.24 \times \sin -14° = 1.27$ ohms. In rectangular form, then,

$$Z_T = 5.08 - j1.27$$

Therefore, this series-parallel circuit combination is equivalent to 5.08 ohms resistance in series with 1.27 ohms capacitive reactance. This problem can also be done in rectangular form by rationalizing the fraction for Z_T.

Another example is shown in Fig. 21·13. Because this circuit has more

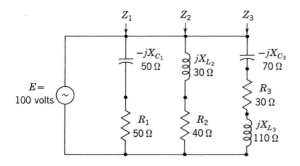

Fig. 21·13 Finding Z_T for three complex impedances in parallel. See text for solution by means of complex branch currents.

than two complex impedances in parallel, the method of branch currents is used. There will be several conversions between rectangular and polar form, since addition must be in rectangular form, but division is easier in polar form. The sequence of calculations is:

1. Convert each branch impedance to polar form. This is necessary for dividing into the applied voltage E to calculate the individual branch currents. If E is not given, any convenient value can be assumed. Note that E has a phase angle of $0°$ because it is the reference.

2. Convert the individual branch currents from polar to rectangular form so that they can be added for the total line current. This step is necessary because the resistive and reactive components of the branch currents must be added separately.

3. Convert the total line current from rectangular to polar form for dividing into the applied voltage to calculate the total impedance.

4. The total impedance can remain in polar form with its magnitude and phase angle, or can be converted to rectangular form for its resistive and reactive components. These are the steps in the following calculations to solve the circuit in Fig. 21·13.

Branch impedances:

$$Z_1 = 50 - j50 = 70.7\underline{/-45°}$$
$$Z_2 = 40 + j30 = 50\underline{/+37°}$$
$$Z_3 = 30 + j40 = 50\underline{/+53°}$$

Branch currents:

$$I_1 = \frac{E}{Z_1} = \frac{100}{70.7\underline{/-45°}} = 1.414 \text{ amp}\underline{/+45°} = 1 + j1$$

$$I_2 = \frac{E}{Z_2} = \frac{100}{50\underline{/37°}} = 2.00 \text{ amp}\underline{/-37°} = 1.6 - j1.2$$

$$I_3 = \frac{E}{Z_3} = \frac{100}{50\underline{/53°}} = 2.00 \text{ amp}\underline{/-53°} = 1.2 - j1.6$$

In rectangular form,

$$I_T = I_1 + I_2 + I_3$$
$$= 1 + 1.6 + 1.2 + j1 - j1.2 - j1.6$$
$$I_T = 3.8 - j1.8$$

In polar form,

$$I_T = 4.2 \text{ amp} \underline{/-25.4°}$$

In polar form,

$$Z_T = \frac{E}{I_T}$$

$$Z_T = \frac{100}{4.2\underline{/-25.4°}}$$

$$Z_T = 23.8 \text{ ohms}\underline{/+25.4°}$$

In rectangular form,

$$Z_T = 21.4 + j10.2$$

Therefore, the complex a-c circuit in Fig. 21·13 is equivalent to the combination of 21.4 ohms R in series with 10.2 ohms X_L. This problem can also be done by combining Z_1 and Z_2 as $Z_1 Z_2/(Z_1 + Z_2)$ and then combining this value with Z_3 in parallel to find the total Z_T of the three branches.

SUMMARY

1. In complex numbers, resistance R is a real term and reactance is a j term. Thus 8-ohm R is 8; 8-ohm X_L is $j8$; 8-ohm X_C is $-j8$. The general form of a complex impedance with series resistance and reactance then is $Z = R \pm jX$, in rectangular form.
2. The same notation can be used for series voltages where $V = V_R \pm jV_X$.
3. For branch currents $I_T = I_R \pm jI_X$, but the reactive branch currents have signs opposite from impedances. Thus capacitive branch current is jI_C, while inductive branch current is $-jI_L$.
4. To convert from rectangular to polar form: $R \pm jX = Z\underline{/\theta}$. The magnitude of Z is $\sqrt{R^2 + X^2}$. Also, θ is the angle with $\tan = X/R$.
5. To convert from polar to rectangular form, $Z\underline{/\theta} = R \pm jX$, where R is $Z \cos \theta$ and the j term is $Z \sin \theta$. A positive angle has a positive j term; a negative angle has a negative j term. Also, the angle is more than 45° for a j term larger than the real term; the angle is less than 45° for a j term smaller than the real term.
6. The rectangular form must be used for addition or subtraction of complex numbers.
7. The polar form is usually more convenient in multiplying and dividing complex numbers. For multiplication, multiply the magnitudes and add the angles; for division, divide the magnitudes and subtract the angles.
8. To find the total impedance Z_T of a series circuit, add all the resistances for the real term and find the algebraic sum of the reactances for the j term. The result is $Z_T = R \pm jX$. Then convert Z_T to polar form for dividing into the applied voltage to calculate the current.
9. To find the total impedance Z_T of two complex branch impedances Z_1 and Z_2 in parallel, Z_T can be calculated as $Z_1 Z_2/(Z_1 + Z_2)$. Then divide Z_T in polar form into the applied voltage to calculate the main-line current.

SELF-EXAMINATION (*Answers at back of book.*)

Here's a chance to see how well you have learned the material in this chapter. These exercises are for your self-testing only.

Match the values in the column at the left with those at the right.

1. $24 + j5 + 16 + j10$
2. $24 - j5 + 16 - j10$
3. $j12 \times 4$
4. $j12 \times j4$
5. $j12 \div j3$
6. $(j2 + 4) \times (j2 - 4)$
7. 1,200-ohm R + 800-ohm X_C
8. 5-amp I_R + 7-amp I_C
9. 90-volt V_R + 60-volt V_L
10. $14\underline{/28°} \times 2\underline{/22°}$
11. $14\underline{/28°} \div 2\underline{/22°}$
12. $15\underline{/42°} \times 3\underline{/0°}$
13. $6\underline{/-75°} \times 4\underline{/30°}$
14. $50\underline{/45°} \div 5\underline{/-45°}$
15. $60\underline{/-80°} \div 5\underline{/5°}$
16. Admittance Y

(a) $28\underline{/50°}$
(b) $7\underline{/6°}$
(c) $12\underline{/-85°}$
(d) $40 + j15$
(e) $90 + j60$ volts
(f) $45\underline{/42°}$
(g) $24\underline{/-45°}$
(h) 4
(i) $10\underline{/90°}$
(j) -48
(k) $5 + j7$ amp
(l) 20
(m) $40 - j15$
(n) $j48$
(o) $1,200 - j800$ ohms
(p) $1/Z$

PROBLEMS (*Answers to selected problems at back of book.*)

1. State Z in rectangular form for the following series circuits: (a) 4-ohm R and 3-ohm X_C; (b) 4-ohm R and 3-ohm X_L; (c) 3-ohm R and 6-ohm X_L; (d) 3-ohm R and 3-ohm X_C.
2. Draw the schematic diagram for the impedances in question 1.
3. Convert the following impedances to polar form: (a) $4 - j3$; (b) $4 + j3$; (c) $3 + j$; (d) $3 - j3$.
4. Convert the following impedances to rectangular form: (a) $5\underline{/-27°}$; (b) $5\underline{/27°}$; (c) $6.71\underline{/63.4°}$; (d) $4.24\underline{/-45°}$.
5. Find the total Z_T in rectangular form for the following three series impedances: $12\underline{/10°}$, $25\underline{/15°}$, and $34\underline{/26°}$.
6. Multiply the following, in polar form: (a) $45\underline{/24°} \times 10\underline{/54°}$; (b) $45\underline{/-24°} \times 10\underline{/54°}$; (c) $18\underline{/-64°} \times 4\underline{/14°}$; (d) $18\underline{/-64°} \times 4\underline{/-14°}$.
7. Divide the following, in polar form: (a) $45\underline{/24°} \div 10\underline{/10°}$; (b) $45\underline{/24°} \div 10\underline{/-10°}$; (c) $500\underline{/-72°} \div 5\underline{/12°}$; (d) $500\underline{/-72°} \div 5\underline{/-12°}$.
8. Match the four vector diagrams in Fig. 21·4a, b, c, and d, with the four circuits in Figs. 21·5 and 21·6.
9. Find Z_T in polar form for the series circuit in Fig. 21·7a.
10. Find Z_T in polar form for the series-parallel circuit in Fig. 21·7c.
11. Solve the circuit in Fig. 21·12 to find Z_T in rectangular form by rationalization. (*Note:* This answer will be more exact because whole numbers are used.)
12. Solve the circuit in Fig. 21·12 to find Z_T in polar form, using the method of branch currents. (Assume an applied voltage of 100 volts.)
13. Solve the circuit in Fig. 21·13 to find Z_T in polar form, without using branch currents. (Find the impedance of two branches in parallel; then combine this impedance with the third branch impedance.)
14. Solve the series a-c circuit in Fig. 20·8 in the previous chapter by the use of complex numbers. Find $Z\underline{/\theta}$, $I\underline{/\theta}$, and each $V\underline{/\theta}$. Prove the sum of the complex voltage drops around the circuit equals the applied voltage E. Make a vector diagram showing all phase angles with respect to E.
15. The following components are in series: $L = 100$ μh, $C = 20$ pf, $R = 2,000$ ohms. At the frequency of 2 Mc calculate X_L, X_C, Z_T, I, θ, V_R, V_L, and V_C. $E = 60$ volts.
16. Solve the same circuit as in question 15, for the frequency of 4 Mc. Give three effects of the higher frequency.

Chapter **22** Resonance

This unit explains how X_L and X_C can be combined to favor one particular frequency, the resonant frequency to which the LC circuit is tuned. The main application of resonance is in r-f circuits for tuning to an a-c signal of the desired frequency. All examples of tuning in radio and television receivers, transmitters and electronics equipment in general are applications of resonance. The topics are:

22·1   The resonance effect
22·2   Series resonance
22·3   Parallel resonance
22·4   Calculating the resonant frequency
22·5 Q magnification factor of resonant circuit
22·6   Bandwidth of resonant circuit
22·7   Tuning
22·8   Mistuning
22·9   Analysis of parallel-resonant circuits
22·10 Choosing L and C for a resonant circuit

22·1   The resonance effect

Inductive reactance increases as the frequency is increased but capacitive reactance decreases with higher frequencies. Because of these opposite characteristics, for any LC combination there must be a frequency at which the X_L equals the X_C, as one increases while the other decreases. This case of equal and opposite reactances in an a-c circuit is called *resonance*, and the a-c circuit is then a *resonant circuit*. The resonant condition is one of the most important applications of a-c circuits, as the effect of one particular frequency is intensified or magnified when the inductive and capacitive reactances balance each other. Any LC circuit can be resonant. It all depends on the frequency. At the resonant frequency, an LC combination provides the resonance effect. Off the resonant frequency, either below or above, the LC combination is just another a-c circuit.

The frequency at which the opposite reactances are equal is the *resonant frequency*. This frequency can be calculated as $f_r = 1/(2\pi\sqrt{LC})$ where L is the inductance in henrys, C the capacitance in farads, and f_r is the resonant frequency, in cps, that makes $X_L = X_C$. In general, we can say that large values of L and C provide a relatively low resonant frequency. Smaller values of L and C allow higher values for f_r. The resonance effect is most useful for radio frequencies, where the required values of microhenrys for L and picofarads for C are easily obtained.

The most common application of resonance in r-f circuits is called *tuning*. In this use, the LC circuit provides maximum voltage output at the resonant frequency, compared with the amount of output at any other frequency either below or above resonance. This idea is illustrated in Fig. 22·1a where the LC circuit resonant at 1,000 kc magnifies the effect of this particular frequency. The result is maximum output at 1,000 kc, compared with lower or higher frequencies. For the wavemeter in b, note that the capacitance C can be varied to provide resonance at different frequencies. The wavemeter can be tuned to any one frequency in a range depending on the LC combination.

All examples of tuning in radio and television are applications of resonance. When you tune a radio to one station, the LC circuits are tuned to resonance for that particular carrier frequency. Also, when you tune a television receiver to a particular channel, the LC circuits are tuned to resonance for that station. There are almost unlimited uses for resonance in a-c circuits.

22·2   Series resonance

In the series a-c circuit in Fig. 22·2a, when the frequency of the applied voltage is 1,000 kc, the reactance of the 239-μh inductance equals 1,500

Fig. 22·1   (a) Circuit resonant at 1,000 kc to provide maximum output at this resonant frequency. (b) Wavemeter as an example of tuning a resonant LC circuit. (James Millen Mfg. Co., Inc.)

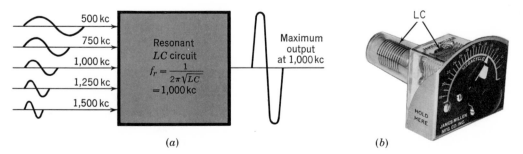

(a)   (b)

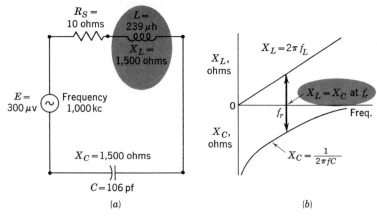

(a)

(b)

Fig. 22·2   Series resonance. (a) Schematic diagram of series R, L, and C, with X_C equal to X_L at 1,000 kc. R_S is coil resistance. (b) X_C and X_L are equal and opposite at the resonant frequency f_r.

ohms. At the same frequency, the reactance of the 106-pf capacitance also is 1,500 ohms. Therefore, this LC combination is resonant at 1,000 kc, which is f_r, because the inductive reactance and capacitive reactance are equal at this frequency.

In a series a-c circuit, inductive reactance leads by 90°, compared with the zero reference angle of the resistance, while capacitive reactance lags by 90°. Therefore, X_L and X_C are 180° out of phase, and the opposite react-ances cancel each other completely when they are equal. Figure 22·2b shows X_L and X_C equal, resulting in a net reactance of zero ohms. The only opposition to current then is the coil resistance, R_S, which is the limit on how low the series resistance in the circuit can be. With zero reactance and just the low value of series resistance, the generator voltage produces the greatest amount of current in the series LC circuit at the resonant fre-quency. The series resistance should be as small as possible for a sharp increase in current at resonance.

Fig. 22·3   Graphs showing maximum current at f_r compared with frequencies below and above resonance, for the series circuit in Fig. 22·2. (a) Amplitude of individual cycles of alternating current. (b) Response curve showing amount of current below and above resonance. Current values in Table 22·1.

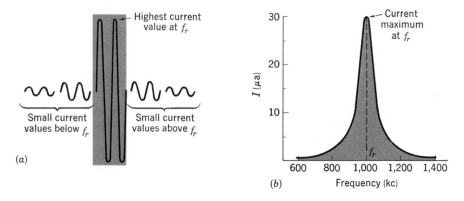

Maximum current at series resonance. The main characteristic of series resonance is the resonant rise of current to its maximum value of E/R at the resonant frequency. For the circuit in Fig. $22 \cdot 2a$, the maximum current at series resonance is 30 μa, equal to 300 $\mu v/10$ ohms. At any other frequency either below or above the resonant frequency, there is less current in the circuit.

This resonant rise of current to 30 μa at 1,000 kc is illustrated in Fig. $22 \cdot 3$. In a, the amount of current is shown as the amplitude of individual cycles of the alternating current produced in the circuit by the a-c generator voltage. Whether the amplitude of one a-c cycle is considered in terms of peak, RMS, or average value, the amount of current is greatest at the resonant frequency. In b, the current amplitudes are plotted on a graph for frequencies at and near the resonant frequency, producing a typical *response curve* for a series-resonant circuit. The response curve in b can be considered as an outline of the increasing and decreasing amplitudes for the individual cycles shown in a.

The response curve of the series-resonant circuit shows that the current is small below resonance, rises to its maximum value at the resonant frequency, and then drops off to small values also above resonance. To prove this fact, Table $22 \cdot 1$ lists the calculated values of impedance and current in the circuit of Fig. $22 \cdot 2$, at the resonant frequency of 1,000 kc, and at two frequencies below and two frequencies above resonance.

Below resonance, at 600 kc, X_C is more than X_L and there is appreciable net reactance, which limits the current to a relatively low value. At the higher frequency of 800 kc, X_C decreases and X_L increases, making the two reactances closer to the same value. The net reactance is then smaller, allowing more current. At the resonant frequency, X_L and X_C are equal, the net reactance is zero, and the current has its maximum value equal to E/R. Above resonance at 1,200 and 1,400 kc, X_L is greater than X_C, providing net reactance that limits the current to much smaller values than at resonance.

Table $22 \cdot 1$ Series-resonance calculations for the circuit in Fig. $22 \cdot 2$*

Frequency, kc	$X_L = 2\pi fL$, ohms	$X_C = \dfrac{1}{2\pi fC}$, ohms	Net reactance, ohms		Z_T, ohms†	$I = \dfrac{E}{Z_T}$, μa†	$E_L = IX_L$, μv	$E_C = IX_C$, μv
			$X_C - X_L$	$X_L - X_C$				
600	900	2,500	1,600		1,600	0.19	171	475
800	1,200	1,875	675		675	0.44	528	825
1,000	1,500	1,500	0	0	10 (resistive)	30 (resistive)	45,000	45,000
1,200	1,800	1,250		550	550	0.55	990	688
1,400	2,100	1,070		1,030	1,030	0.29	609	310

* $L = 239$ μh, $C = 106$ pf, $E = 300$ μv, $R = 10$ ohms.
† Z_T and I calculated approximately without R when its resistance is very small compared with the net X_L or X_C.

In summary, below the resonant frequency, although X_L is small, X_C has high values that limit the amount of current; above the resonant frequency, X_C is small, but X_L has high values that limit the current; at the resonant frequency, X_L equals X_C and they cancel to allow maximum current.

Minimum impedance at series resonance. Since the reactances cancel at the resonant frequency, the impedance of the series circuit is minimum, equal to just the low value of series resistance. This minimum impedance at resonance is resistive, resulting in zero phase angle. At resonance, therefore, the resonant current is in phase with the generator voltage.

Resonant rise in voltage across series *L* or *C*. The maximum current in a series *LC* circuit at resonance is useful because it produces maximum voltage across either X_L or X_C at the resonant frequency. As a result, the series-resonant circuit can select one frequency by providing much more voltage output at the resonant frequency, compared with frequencies above and below resonance. Figure 22·4 illustrates the resonant rise in voltage across the capacitance in a series a-c circuit. At the resonant frequency of 1,000 kc, the voltage across *C* rises to the value of 45,000 μv, while the input voltage is only 300 μv.

In Table 22·1, the voltage across *C* is calculated as IX_C and across *L* as IX_L. Below the resonant frequency, X_C has a higher value than at resonance, but the current is small. Similarly, above the resonant frequency, X_L is higher than at resonance, but the current has a low value because of the inductive reactance. At resonance, although X_L and X_C cancel each other to allow maximum current, each reactance by itself has an appreci-

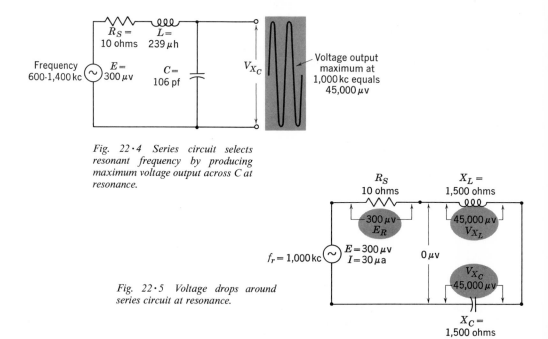

Fig. 22·4 Series circuit selects resonant frequency by producing maximum voltage output across C at resonance.

Fig. 22·5 Voltage drops around series circuit at resonance.

able value. Since the current is the same in all parts of a series circuit, the maximum current at resonance produces maximum voltage IX_C across C and IX_L across L at the resonant frequency.

Although the voltage across X_C and X_L is reactive, it is an actual voltage that can be measured. In Fig. 22·5, the voltage drops around the series-resonant circuit are 45,000 μv across C, 45,000 μv across L, and 300 μv across R_s. The voltage across the resistance is equal to the generator voltage and has the same phase. Across the series combination of both L and C, the voltage is zero because the two series voltage drops are equal and opposite. In order to use the resonant rise of voltage, therefore, the output must be connected across either L or C alone. We can consider the E_{X_L} and E_{X_C} voltages as similar to the idea of two batteries connected in series opposition. Together, the net resultant is zero for the equal and opposite voltages, but each battery still has its own potential difference.

In summary, for a series-resonant circuit the main characteristics are:

1. The current I is maximum at the resonant frequency f_r.
2. I is in phase with the generator voltage, or the phase angle of the circuit is 0°. However, the individual voltage drops E_L and E_C are still 90° out of phase with I.
3. The voltage is maximum across either L or C alone, as E_L is IX_L while E_C is IX_C.
4. The impedance is minimum at f_r, equal only to the low value of R_s which is generally the internal resistance of the coil.

22·3   Parallel resonance

With L and C in parallel as shown in Fig. 22·6, when X_L equals X_C, the reactive branch currents are equal and opposite at resonance. Then they cancel each other to produce minimum current in the main line. Since the line current is minimum, the impedance is maximum. These relations are based on R_s being very small compared with X_L at resonance. In this case, the branch currents are practically equal when X_L and X_C are equal.

Minimum line current at parallel resonance.   To show how the current in the main line dips to its minimum value when the parallel LC circuit is resonant, Table 22·2 lists the values of branch currents and the total line current for the circuit in Fig. 22·6. With L and C the same as in the series circuit of Fig. 22·2, X_L and X_C have the same values at the same frequencies. Since L, C, and the generator are in parallel, the voltage applied across the branches equals the generator voltage of 300 μv. Therefore, each reactive branch current is calculated as 300 μv divided by the reactance of the branch.

The values in the top row of Table 22·2 are obtained as follows: at 600 kc the capacitive branch current equals 300 μv/2,500 ohms or 0.12 μa. The inductive branch current at this frequency is 300 μv/900 ohms, or 0.33 μa. Since this is a parallel a-c circuit, the capacitive current leads by 90° while the inductive current lags by 90°, compared with the reference angle of the

Table 22·2   Parallel-resonance calculations for the circuit in Fig. 22·6*

Frequency, kc	$X_C = \dfrac{1}{2\pi fC}$, ohms	$X_L = 2\pi fL$, ohms	$I_C = \dfrac{E}{X_C}$, μa	$I_L = \dfrac{E}{X_L}$, μa†	Net reactive line current, μa		I_T, μa†	$Z_T = \dfrac{E}{I_T}$, ohms†
					$I_L - I_C$	$I_C - I_L$		
600	2,500	900	0.12	0.33	0.21		0.21	1,400
800	1,875	1,200	0.16	0.25	0.09		0.09	3,333
1,000	1,500	1,500	0.20	0.20	0	0	0.00133 (resistive)	225,000‡ (resistive)
1,200	1,250	1,800	0.24	0.17		0.08	0.08	3,800
1,400	1,070	2,100	0.28	0.14		0.14	0.14	2,143

$f_r \rightarrow$

* $L = 239$ µh, $C = 106$ pf, $E = 300$ µv.

† I_L, I_T, and Z_T calculated approximately without R when its resistive component of the line current is very small compared with I_L.

‡ At resonance, Z_T calculated by Eq. (22·8).

generator voltage, which is applied across the parallel branches. Therefore, the opposite currents are 180° out of phase, canceling each other in the main line. The net current in the line, then, is the difference between 0.33 and 0.12, which equals 0.21 µa.

Following this procedure, the calculations show that as the frequency is increased toward resonance, the capacitive branch current increases because of the lower value of X_C, while the inductive branch current decreases with higher values of X_L. As a result, there is less net line current as the two branch currents become more nearly equal. At the resonant frequency of 1,000 kc, both reactances are 1,500 ohms and the reactive branch currents are both 0.20 µa, canceling each other completely. Above the resonant frequency, there is more current in the capacitive branch than in the inductive branch and the net line current increases above its minimum value at resonance, as illustrated in Fig. 22·6b.

The in-phase current due to R_s in the inductive branch can be ignored off resonance because it is so small compared with the reactive line current. At the resonant frequency when the reactive currents cancel, however, the resistive component is the entire line current. Its value at resonance equals 0.00133 µa in this example. This small resistive current is the minimum value of the line current at parallel resonance.

Maximum line impedance at parallel resonance. The minimum line current resulting from parallel resonance is useful because it corresponds to maximum impedance in the line across the generator. Therefore, an impedance that has a high value for just one frequency but low impedance for other frequencies, either below or above resonance, can be obtained by using a parallel LC circuit resonant at the desired frequency. This is another method of selecting one frequency by resonance. The response curve in Fig. 22·6c shows how the impedance rises to maximum for a parallel resonance.

Referring to Table 22·2, the total impedance of the parallel a-c circuit is calculated as the generator voltage divided by the total line current. At 600 kc, as an example, Z_T equals 300 μv/0.21 μa, or 1,400 ohms. At 800 kc, the impedance is higher because there is less line current. At the resonant frequency of 1,000 kc, the line current is at its minimum value of 0.00133 μa. Then impedance is maximum, equal to 300 μv/0.00133 μa, or 225,000 ohms. Above 1,000 kc, the line current increases, and the impedance decreases from its maximum value.

The idea of how the line current can have a very low value even though the reactive branch currents are appreciable is illustrated in Fig. 22·7. In *a* the resistive component of the total line current is shown as though it were a separate branch drawing an amount of resistive current from the generator in the main line equal to the current resulting from the coil resistance. Each reactive branch current has its value equal to the generator voltage divided by the reactance. Since they are equal and of opposite phase, however, in any part of the circuit where both reactive currents are present, the net amount of electron flow in one direction at any instant of time corresponds to zero current. The graph in *b* shows how equal and opposite currents for I_L and I_C cancel.

If a meter is inserted in series with the main line to indicate total line current I_T, it dips sharply to the minimum value of line current at the reso-

Fig. 22·6 Parallel resonance. (a) Schematic diagram of L and C in parallel branches. (b) Response curve showing line current minimum at the resonant frequency. (c) Response curve showing impedance of parallel-resonant circuit across the line maximum at the resonant frequency.

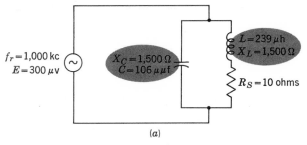

$f_r = 1,000$ kc
$E = 300 \mu$v

$X_C = 1,500 \Omega$
$C = 106 \mu\mu$f

$L = 239 \mu$h
$X_L = 1,500 \Omega$

$R_S = 10$ ohms

(a)

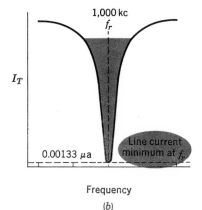

1,000 kc
f_r

I_T

0.00133 μa

Line current minimum at f_r

Frequency

(b)

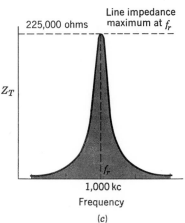

Line impedance maximum at f_r

225,000 ohms

Z_T

f_r

1,000 kc

Frequency

(c)

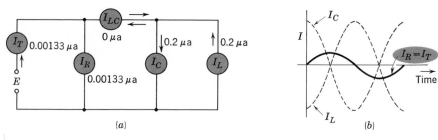

Fig. 22·7 Distribution of currents in parallel-resonant circuit. (a) Circuit. (b) Graph of equal and opposite reactive currents.

nant frequency. With minimum current in the line, the impedance across the line is maximum at the resonant frequency. The maximum impedance at parallel resonance corresponds to a high value of resistance, without reactance, since the line current is then resistive with zero phase angle.

In summary, for a parallel-resonant circuit, the main characteristics are:

1. The line current I_T is minimum at the resonant frequency f_r, as the individual branch currents I_L and I_C cancel.
2. I_T is in phase with the generator voltage E, or the phase angle of the circuit is $0°$. However, the individual branch currents I_L and I_C are still $90°$ out of phase with E.
3. The impedance equal to E/I_T is maximum at f_r because of the minimum I_T.

22·4   Calculating the resonant frequency

For any LC circuit, series or parallel, the frequency that makes the inductive reactance and capacitive reactance equal is $1/(2\pi\sqrt{LC})$. This formula is derived as follows:

$$X_L = X_C \qquad \text{or} \qquad 2\pi f L = \frac{1}{2\pi f C}$$

Using f_r to indicate the resonant frequency, we have

$$2\pi f_r L = \frac{1}{2\pi f_r C}$$

Transposing the factor f_r gives

$$2\pi L (f_r)^2 = \frac{1}{2\pi C}$$

Transposing the factor $2\pi L$ gives

$$f_r^2 = \frac{1}{(2\pi)^2 LC}$$

The square root of both sides is then

$$f_r = \frac{1}{2\pi\sqrt{LC}} \qquad (22\cdot1)$$

With units of henrys for L and farads for C, the resonant frequency f_r is in cycles per second. Since $1/2\pi$ is a numerical value equal to ⅙.₂₈, or 0.159, a more convenient form for calculations is

$$f_r = \frac{0.159}{\sqrt{LC}} \qquad \text{cps} \qquad (22\cdot2)$$

For example, to find the resonant frequency of the LC combination in Fig. 22·2, the values of 239×10^{-6} henry and 106×10^{-12} farad are substituted for L and C:

$$f_r = \frac{0.159}{\sqrt{239 \times 10^{-6} \times 106 \times 10^{-12}}} = \frac{0.159}{\sqrt{253 \times 10^{-16}}}$$

Taking the square root of the denominator,

$$f_r = \frac{0.159}{15.9 \times 10^{-8}} = \frac{0.159}{0.159 \times 10^{-6}} = \frac{0.159 \times 10^6}{0.159}$$

$$= 1 \times 10^6 \text{ cps} = 1 \text{ Mc} = 1,000 \text{ kc}$$

The f_r is inversely proportional to L or C. It is important to note that higher values of L or C result in lower values of f_r. Also, an LC circuit can be resonant at any frequency from a few cycles per second to many megacycles, depending upon the inductance and capacitance values. As examples, an LC combination with the relatively large values of 8-henry inductance and 20-μf capacitance is resonant at the low audio frequency of 12.6 cps; a small inductance of 2 μh will resonate with the small capacitance of 3 pf at the high radio frequency of 64.9 Mc. These examples are solved in the next two problems for more practice with the resonant frequency formula. Such calculations are often used in practical applications of tuned circuits. Probably the most important feature of any LC combination is its resonant frequency.

Example 1. Calculate the resonant frequency for 8-henry L and 20-μf C.

Answer.
$$f_r = \frac{1}{2\pi\sqrt{LC}} = \frac{0.159}{\sqrt{8 \times 20 \times 10^{-6}}}$$

$$= \frac{0.159 \times 10^3}{\sqrt{160}} = \frac{159}{12.65}$$

$$f_r = \textbf{12.6 cps}$$

Example 2. Calculate the resonant frequency for 2-μh L and 3-pf C.

Answer.
$$f_r = \frac{1}{2\pi\sqrt{LC}} = \frac{0.159}{\sqrt{2 \times 10^{-6} \times 3 \times 10^{-12}}}$$

$$= \frac{0.159}{\sqrt{6 \times 10^{-18}}} = \frac{0.159 \times 10^9}{\sqrt{6}} = \frac{159 \times 10^6}{\sqrt{6}}$$

$$f_r = \frac{159}{2.45} \times 10^6 = \textbf{64.9 Mc}$$

LC product determines f_r. There are any number of LC combinations that can be resonant at one frequency. Table $22 \cdot 3$ lists five possible combinations of L and C resonant at 1,000 kc. The resonant frequency is the same because when either L or C is decreased by the factor of 10 or 2, the other is increased by the same factor, resulting in a constant value for the LC product. The reactance at resonance changes with different combinations of L and C, but in all five cases X_L and X_C are equal to each other at 1,000 kc. This is the resonant frequency determined by the LC product in the formula $f_r = 1/(2\pi\sqrt{LC})$.

Measuring L or C by resonance. Of the three factors L, C, and f_r in the resonant-frequency formula, any one can be calculated when the other two are known. The resonant frequency of the LC combination can be found experimentally by determining the frequency that produces the resonant response in an LC combination. With a known value of either L or C, and the resonant frequency determined, the third factor can be calculated. This method is commonly used for measuring inductance or capacitance. To find C,

$$f_r = \frac{1}{2\pi\sqrt{LC}}$$

Squaring both sides to eliminate the radical gives

$$f_r^2 = \frac{1}{(2\pi)^2 LC}$$

Transposing C and f_r^2 gives

$$C = \frac{1}{(2\pi)^2 f_r^2 L} = \frac{1}{4\pi^2 f_r^2 L} = \frac{0.0254}{f_r^2 L} \tag{22·3}$$

Table $22 \cdot 3$ *LC combinations resonant at 1,000 kc*

L, μh	C, pf	LC product	X_L, ohms at 1,000 kc	X_C, ohms at 1,000 kc
23.9	1,060	25,334	150	150
119.5	212	25,334	750	750
239	106	25,334	1,500	1,500
478	53	25,334	3,000	3,000
2,390	10.6	25,334	15,000	15,000

With f_r in cycles per second, the units are farads for C and henrys for L. The constant factor 0.0254 in the numerator is the reciprocal of 39.44 for $4\pi^2$ in the denominator. These numbers remain the same for any values of f_r, L, and C.

Similarly, the formula can be transposed to find L. Then

$$L = \frac{1}{(2\pi)^2 f_r^2 C} = \frac{1}{4\pi^2 f_r^2 C} = \frac{0.0254}{f_r^2 C} \qquad (22\cdot4)$$

Example 3. What value of C resonates with 239-µh L at 1 Mc?

Answer.

$$C = \frac{0.0254}{f_r^2 L} = \frac{0.0254}{(1 \times 10^6)^2 \times 239 \times 10^{-6}} = \frac{0.0254}{1 \times 10^{12} \times 239 \times 10^{-6}}$$

$$= \frac{0.0254}{239 \times 10^6} = \frac{0.0254}{239} \times 10^{-6} = \frac{25,400}{239} \times 10^{-12}$$

$$C = 106 \times 10^{-12} \text{ farad} = \textbf{106 pf}$$

Example 4. What value of L resonates with 106-pf C at 1,000 kc?

Answer. $$L = \frac{0.0254}{f_r^2 C} = \frac{0.0254}{1 \times 10^{12} \times 106 \times 10^{-12}} = \frac{0.0254}{106}$$

$$L = \frac{25,400}{106} \times 10^{-6} = 239 \times 10^{-6} \text{ henry} = \textbf{239 µh}$$

These values are from the LC circuit illustrated in Fig. 22·2 for series resonance and Fig. 22·6 for parallel resonance.

22·5   Q magnification factor of resonant circuit

The quality, or figure of merit, of the resonant circuit, in sharpness of resonance, is indicated by the factor Q. In general, the higher the ratio of the reactance at resonance to the series resistance, the higher is the Q and the sharper the resonance effect.

Q of series circuit. In a series-resonant circuit

$$Q = \frac{X_L}{R_s} \qquad (22\cdot5)$$

where Q is the figure of merit, X_L is the inductive reactance at the resonant frequency, and R_s is the resistance in series with X_L. In the series-resonant circuit in Fig. 22·2,

$$Q = \frac{1,500 \text{ ohms}}{10 \text{ ohms}} = 150$$

Q is a numerical factor without any units, since it is a ratio of reactance to resistance and the ohms cancel. Since the series resistance limits the amount of current at resonance, the lower the resistance, the sharper is the increase to maximum current at the resonant frequency, and the higher the Q. Also, a higher value of inductive reactance at resonance allows the maximum current to produce a higher value of voltage output.

The Q has the same value if calculated with X_C instead of X_L, since they are equal at resonance. The Q of the circuit is generally considered in terms of X_L, however, because usually the coil has the series resistance of the circuit. In this case, the Q of the coil and the Q of the series-resonant circuit are the same. If extra resistance is added, the Q of the circuit will be less than the Q of the coil. The highest possible Q for the circuit is the Q of the coil.

The value of 150 can be considered as a high Q. For circuits resonant at radio frequencies, typical values of Q are 50 to 250, approximately. Less than 10 is a low value of Q; more than 300 is a very high Q.

Higher L/C ratio can provide higher Q. As shown in Table 22·3, different LC combinations can be resonant at the same frequency. However, the amount of reactance at resonance is different. More X_L can be obtained with a higher L and smaller C for resonance, although X_L and X_C must be equal at the resonant frequency. Therefore, both X_L and X_C are higher with a higher L/C ratio for resonance.

More X_L can allow a higher Q if the a-c resistance does not increase as much as the reactance. With typical r-f coils, an approximate rule is that maximum Q can be obtained when X_L is about 1,000 ohms.

Q rise in voltage across series L or C. The Q of the resonant circuit can be considered a magnification factor that determines how much the voltage across L or C is increased by the resonant rise of current in a series circuit. Specifically, the voltage output at series resonance is Q times the generator voltage:

$$E_{X_L} = E_{X_C} = Q \times E_{\text{gen}} \qquad (22\cdot6)$$

In Fig. 22·4, for example, the generator voltage is 300 μv and Q is 150. The resonant rise of voltage across L or C then equals 300 μv $\times$ 150, or 45,000 μv. Note that this is the same value calculated in Table 22·2 for E_{X_C} or E_{X_L} at resonance.

How to measure Q in a series-resonant circuit. The fundamental nature of Q for a series-resonant circuit can be seen from the fact that the Q can be determined experimentally by measuring the Q rise in voltage across either L or C and comparing this voltage with the generator voltage E. As a formula,

$$Q = \frac{E_{\text{out}}}{E_{\text{in}}} \qquad (22\cdot7)$$

where E_{out} is the a-c voltage measured across the coil or capacitor and E_{in} is the generator voltage. Referring to Fig. 22·5, suppose that you measure with an a-c voltmeter across L or C and this voltage equals 45,000 μv, at the resonant frequency. Also, measure the generator input of 300 μv. Then

$$Q = \frac{E_{\text{out}}}{E_{\text{in}}} = \frac{45,000\ \mu v}{300\ \mu v} = \mathbf{150}$$

This method is better than the X_L/R formula for determining Q because R is the a-c resistance of the coil, which is not so easily measured. Remember that the coil's a-c resistance can be more than double the d-c resistance measured with an ohmmeter. In fact, measuring Q with Formula (22·7) makes it possible to calculate the a-c resistance. These points are illustrated in the following examples.

Example 5. A series circuit resonant at 0.4 Mc develops 100 mv across a 250-μh L, with 2 mv input. Calculate Q.

Answer.
$$Q = \frac{E_{\text{out}}}{E_{\text{in}}} = \frac{100\ mv}{2\ mv} = \mathbf{50}$$

Example 6. How much is the a-c resistance of the coil in the preceding example?

Answer. The Q of the coil is 50. Also, at the resonant frequency f_r,
$$X_L = 2\pi f L = 2\pi \times 0.4 \times 10^6 \times 250 \times 10^{-6} = 2\pi \times 100$$
$$X_L = 628\ \text{ohms}$$

Also,
$$Q = \frac{X_L}{R} \quad \text{or} \quad R = \frac{X_L}{Q}$$

Then,
$$R = \frac{X_L}{Q} = \frac{628\ \text{ohms}}{50} = \mathbf{12.56\ ohms}$$

Q of parallel circuit. In a parallel-resonant circuit, where R_S is very small compared with X_L, the Q also equals X_L/R_S. Note that R_S is still the resistance of the coil in series with X_L. See Fig. 22·8. The Q of the coil determines the Q of the parallel circuit here because it is less than the Q of the capacitive branch. Capacitors used in tuned circuits generally have very high Q because of their low losses. In Fig. 22·8, the Q is 1,500 ohms/10 ohms, or 150, the same as the series-resonant circuit with the same values.

This example assumes that the generator resistance is very high and

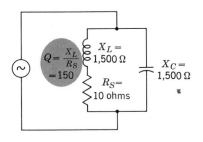

Fig. 22·8 *Q of a parallel-resonant circuit in terms of X_L and its series resistance R_S.*

there is no other resistance branch shunting the tuned circuit. Then the Q of the parallel-resonant circuit is the same as the Q of the coil. Actually, shunt resistance can lower the Q of a parallel-resonant circuit, as analyzed in Sec. 22·9.

Q rise in impedance across parallel-resonant circuit. For parallel resonance, the Q magnification factor determines by how much the impedance across the parallel LC circuit is increased because of the minimum line current. Specifically, the impedance across the parallel-resonant circuit is Q times the inductive reactance at the resonant frequency:

$$Z_T = Q \times X_L \qquad (22·8)$$

Referring back to the parallel-resonant circuit in Fig. 22·6, as an example, X_L is 1,500 ohms and Q is 150. The result is a rise of impedance to the maximum value of $150 \times 1,500$ ohms, or 225,000 ohms, at the resonant frequency. Since the line current equals E/Z_T, the minimum value of line current then is 300 μv/225,000 ohms, which equals 0.00133 μa.

Note that the minimum line current at f_r is $1/Q$ of either branch current. In Fig. 22·7, I_L or I_C is 0.2 μa and Q is 150. Therefore, I_T is 0.2/150, or 0.00133 μa, which is the same answer as E/Z_T.

How to measure Z_T of a parallel-resonant circuit. Formula (22·8) is also useful in its transposed version as $Q = Z_T/X_L$. We can measure Z_T by the method illustrated in Fig. 22·9. Then Q can be calculated.

To measure Z_T, first tune the LC circuit to resonance. Then adjust R_1 to the resistance that makes its a-c voltage equal to the a-c voltage across the tuned circuit. With equal voltages, Z_T must be the same as R_1. For the example here, which corresponds to the parallel resonance shown in Figs. 22·6 and 22·8, Z_T is 225,000 ohms. Therefore, Q is 150, equal to Z_T/X_T or 225,000/1,500.

Example 7. In Fig. 22·9, assume that with 4 volts a-c input signal, V_{R_1} is 2 volts when R_1 is 225 K. Determine Z_T and Q.

Answer. Z_T is **225 K,** the same as R_1, because they divide E equally. The amount of input voltage does not matter, as the voltage division determines the relative proportions between R_1 and Z_T. With 225 K for Z_T and 1.5 K for X_L, the Q is $225/_{1.5}$, which equals **150,** the same as before.

Example 8. A parallel LC circuit tuned to 200 kc with 350-μh L has a measured Z_T of 17,600 ohms. Calculate Q.

Answer. First, calculate X_L at f_r.

$$X_L = 2\pi f L = 2\pi \times 200 \times 10^3 \times 350 \times 10^{-6}$$
$$X_L = 440$$

Then,
$$Q = \frac{Z_T}{X_L} = \frac{17,600}{440} = \mathbf{40}$$

22·6 Bandwidth of resonant circuit

When we say an *LC* circuit is resonant at one frequency, this is true for the maximum resonance effect. However, other frequencies close to f_r also are effective. For series resonance, frequencies just below and above f_r produce increased current, but a little less than the value at resonance. Similarly, for parallel resonance, frequencies close to f_r can provide a high impedance, although a little less than the maximum Z_T. Therefore, any resonant frequency has an associated band of frequencies that provide resonance effects. How wide the band is depends on the Q of the resonant circuit. Actually, it is practically impossible to have an *LC* circuit with a resonant effect at only one frequency. The width of the resonant band of frequencies centered around f_r is called the *bandwidth* of the tuned circuit.

Measurement of bandwidth. The group of frequencies with a response 70.7 per cent of maximum, or more, is generally considered the bandwidth of the tuned circuit, as shown in Fig. 22·10b. The resonant response here is increasing current for the series circuit in *a*. Therefore, the bandwidth is measured between the two frequencies, f_1 and f_2, producing 70.7 per cent of the maximum current at f_r. For a parallel circuit, the resonant response is increasing impedance Z_T. Then the bandwidth is measured between the two frequencies allowing 70.7 per cent of the maximum Z_T at f_r.

The bandwidth indicated on the response curve in Fig. 22·10b equals

Fig. 22·9 *Adjust R_1 to make E_{R_1} equal E_{LC}. Then $Z_T = R_1$.*

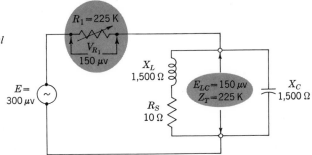

Fig. 22·10 *Bandwidth of tuned LC circuit. (a) Series circuit with input of 0 to 100 kc. (b) Response curve of resonant rise in current with bandwidth Δf equal to 20 kc between f_1 and f_2.*

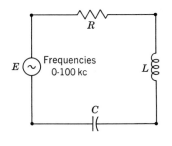

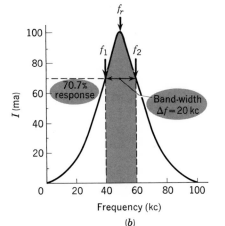

(a)

(b)

20 kc. This value is the difference between f_2 at 60 kc and f_1 at 40 kc, both with 70.7 per cent response. Compared with the maximum current of 100 ma for f_r at 50 kc, f_1 below resonance and f_2 above resonance each allow a rise to 70.7 ma. All frequencies in this band 20 kc wide allow 70.7 ma, or more, as the resonant response in this example.

Bandwidth equals f_r/Q. Sharp resonance with high Q means narrow bandwidth. Or the lower the Q, the broader is the resonant response and the greater the bandwidth. Also, the higher the resonant frequency, the greater is the range of frequency values included in the bandwidth for a given sharpness of resonance. Therefore, the bandwidth of a resonant circuit equals

$$f_2 - f_1 = \Delta f = \frac{f_r}{Q} \qquad (22 \cdot 9)$$

where Δf is the total bandwidth, in the same units as the resonant frequency f_r. For example, a series circuit resonant at 800 kc with a Q of 100 has a bandwidth of $800/100$, or 8 kc. This means I is 70.7 per cent or more of maximum for all frequencies in the band 8 kc wide centered around 800 kc, from 796 to 804 kc. With a parallel-resonant circuit having a Q higher than 10, Formula (22·9) can be used for calculating the bandwidth of frequencies which provide 70.7 per cent or more of the maximum Z_T.

The effect on bandwidth for different values of Q is illustrated in Fig. 22·11. Note that higher values of Q for the same resonant frequency

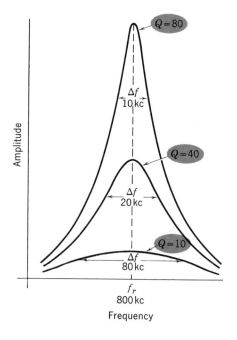

Fig. 22·11 Higher Q provides sharper resonant response. Amplitude is current in series-resonant circuit or impedance of parallel-resonant circuit. Bandwidth at half-power frequencies indicated by Δf.

result in narrower bandwidth and sharper slope for the sides or *skirts* of the response curve, in addition to greater amplitude.

The edge frequencies f_1 and f_2 are separated from f_r by one-half of the total bandwidth. For the top curve in Fig. 22·11 as an example, with a Q of 80, Δf is 10 kc centered around 800 kc for f_r. Then

$$f_2 = f_r + \frac{\Delta f}{2} = 800 + 5 = 805 \text{ kc}$$

$$f_1 = f_r - \frac{\Delta f}{2} = 800 - 5 = 795 \text{ kc}$$

Example 9. An LC circuit resonant at 2,000 kc has a Q of 100. Find the total bandwidth Δf and the edge frequencies f_1 and f_2.

Answer.
$$\Delta f = \frac{f_r}{Q} = \frac{2,000 \text{ kc}}{100} = 20 \text{ kc}$$
$$f_1 = f_r - \Delta f/2 = 2,000 - 10 = 1,990 \text{ kc}$$
$$f_2 = f_r + \Delta f/2 = 2,000 + 10 = 2,010 \text{ kc}$$

Example 10. Do the same as in Example 9 for f_r equal to 6,000 kc and the same Q of 100.

Answer.
$$f = \frac{f_r}{Q} = \frac{6,000 \text{ kc}}{100} = 60 \text{ kc}$$
$$f_1 = 6,000 - 30 = 5,970 \text{ kc}$$
$$f_2 = 6,000 + 30 = 6,030 \text{ kc}$$

Notice that Δf is three times as wide for the same Q because f_r is three times higher.

Half-power points. It is simply for convenience in calculations that the bandwidth is defined between the two frequencies having 70.7 per cent response. At each of these frequencies, the net capacitive or inductive reactance equals the resistance. Then the total impedance of series reactance and resistance is 1.4 times greater than R. With this much more impedance, the current is reduced to $1/1.414$, or 0.707, of its maximum value. Furthermore, the relative current or voltage value of 70.7 per cent corresponds to 50 per cent in power, since power is I^2R or E^2/R and the square of 0.707 equals 0.50. Therefore, the bandwidth between frequencies having 70.7 per cent response in current or voltage is also the bandwidth in terms of half-power points.

Measuring bandwidth to calculate Q. The half-power frequencies f_1 and f_2 can be determined experimentally. For series resonance, find the two frequencies at which the current is 70.7 per cent of maximum I. Or, for parallel resonance, find the two frequencies that make the impedance 70.7 per cent of the maximum Z_T. The following method uses the technique

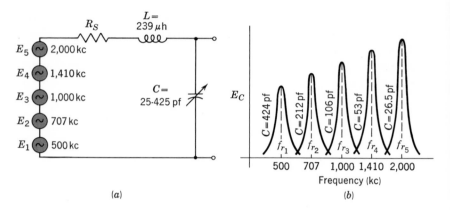

Fig. 22·12 *Tuning a series-resonant circuit with variable C. (a) Circuit with input voltage of different frequencies. (b) Resonant response at different frequencies when C is varied. Relative amplitudes not to scale.*

in Fig. 22·9 for measuring Z_T, but with a different circuit to determine its bandwidth and Q.

1. Tune the circuit to resonance and determine its maximum Z_T at f_r. In this example, assume that Z_T is 10,000 ohms at the resonant frequency of 200 kc.
2. Keep the same amount of input voltage but change its frequency slightly below f_r to determine the frequency f_1 which results in Z_1 equal to 70.7 per cent of Z_T. The required value here is $0.707 \times 10,000$, or 7,070 ohms, for Z_1 at f_1. Assume this frequency f_1 is determined to be 195 kc.
3. Similarly, find the frequency f_2 above f_r that results in the impedance Z_2 of 7,070 ohms. Assume f_2 is 205 kc.
4. The total bandwidth between the half-power frequencies then equals $f_2 - f_1$ or $205 - 195$, which is 10 kc for Δf.
5. Then $Q = f_r/\Delta f = 200 \text{ kc}/10 \text{ kc} = 20$.

22·7 Tuning

This means obtaining resonances at different frequencies by varying either L or C. As illustrated in Fig. 22·12, the variable capacitance C can

Table 22·4 *Tuning LC circuit by varying C*

L, μh	C, pf	f_r, kc
239	424	500
239	212	707
239	106	1,000
239	53	1,410
239	26.5	2,000

be adjusted to tune the series LC circuit to resonance at any one of the five different frequencies. Each of the voltages E_1 to E_5 indicates a-c input with a specific frequency. Which is selected for maximum output is determined by the resonant frequency of the LC circuit.

When C is set to 424 pf, for example, the resonant frequency of the LC circuit is 500 kc for f_{r_1}. The input voltage that has the frequency of 500 kc then produces a resonant rise of current which results in maximum output voltage across C. At other frequencies, such as 707 kc, the voltage output is less than the input. With C at 424 pf, therefore, the LC tuned to 500 kc selects this frequency by providing much more voltage output compared with other frequencies.

Suppose that we want maximum output for the a-c input voltage that has the frequency of 707 kc. Then C is set at 212 pf, to make the LC circuit resonant at 707 kc for f_{r_2}. Similarly, the tuned circuit can resonate at a different frequency for each input voltage. In this way, the LC circuit is tuned to select the desired frequency. The response curves in Fig. 22·12b are shown with increasing amplitude, but constant bandwidth, as Q increases for higher resonant frequencies when C is varied. If L is varied for tuning, the Q will decrease for higher resonant frequencies and the bandwidth varies as f_r^2.

The variable capacitance C can be set at the values listed in Table 22·4 to tune the LC circuit to different frequencies. Only five frequencies are listed here, but any one capacitance value between 26.5 and 424 pf can tune the 239-μh coil to resonance at any frequency in the range of 500 to 2,000 kc. It should be noted that a parallel-resonant circuit also can be tuned by varying C or L.

Tuning ratio. When an LC circuit is tuned, the change in resonant frequency is inversely proportional to the square root of the change in L or C. Referring to Table 22·4, notice that when C is decreased by one-fourth, from 424 to 106 pf, the resonant frequency doubles from 500 to 1,000 kc. Or, the frequency is increased by the factor $1/\sqrt{¼}$, which equals 2.

Suppose that we want to tune through the whole frequency range of 500 to 2,000 kc. This is a tuning ratio of 4:1 for the highest frequency to the lowest frequency. Then the capacitance must be varied from 424 to 26.5 pf, a 16:1 capacitance ratio.

Radio tuning dial. Figure 22·13 illustrates a common application of resonant circuits in tuning a receiver to the carrier frequency of a desired station in the band. The tuning is done by the air capacitor C, which can be varied from 360 pf with the plates completely in mesh to 40 pf out of mesh. Note that the lowest frequency F_L at 540 kc is tuned in with the highest C at 360 pf. Resonance at the highest frequency F_H results with the lowest C at 40 pf. The capacitance range of 40 to 360 pf tunes through the frequency range from 1,620 kc down to 540 kc. F_L is one-third F_H because the maximum C is nine times the minimum C. Note that the middle frequency of 1,080 kc is tuned in with 90-pf capacitance, as $f_r = 1/(2\pi\sqrt{LC})$. The middle capacitance of 200 pf tunes in approximately 726 kc.

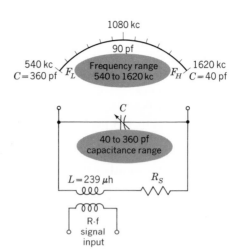

Fig. 22·13 Application of LC circuit tuning through the AM radio
broadcast band of 540 to 1,620 kc.

The same idea applies to tuning through the commercial FM broadcast band of 88 to 108 Mc, with smaller values of L and C. Also, television receivers are tuned to a specific broadcast channel by resonance at the desired frequencies.

22·8   Mistuning

For example, suppose that a series LC circuit is tuned to 1,000 kc but the frequency of the input voltage is 17 kc, completely off resonance. The circuit could provide a Q rise in output voltage for current having the frequency of 1,000 kc, but there is no input voltage and therefore no current at this frequency. The input voltage produces current that has the frequency of 17 kc. This frequency cannot produce a resonant rise in current, however, because the current is limited by the net reactance. When the frequency of the input voltage and the resonant frequency of the LC circuit are not the same, therefore, the mistuned circuit has very little output compared with the Q rise in voltage at resonance. Similarly, when a parallel circuit is mistuned, it does not have a high value of impedance. Furthermore, the net reactance off resonance makes the LC circuit either inductive or capacitive.

Series circuit off resonance. When the frequency of the input voltage is lower than the resonant frequency of a series LC circuit, the capacitive reactance is greater than the inductive reactance. As a result, there is more voltage across the capacitive reactance than across the inductive reactance. The series LC circuit is capacitive below resonance, therefore, with capacitive current leading the generator voltage. Above the resonant frequency, the inductive reactance is greater than the capacitive reactance. As a result, the circuit is inductive above resonance, with inductive current that lags the generator voltage. In both cases, there is much less output voltage than at resonance.

Parallel circuit off resonance. With a parallel LC circuit, the smaller amount of inductive reactance below resonance results in more inductive branch current than capacitive branch current. The net line current is inductive, therefore, making the parallel *LC* circuit inductive below resonance as the line current lags the generator voltage. Above the resonant frequency, the net line current is capacitive because of the higher value of capacitive branch current. Then the parallel *LC* circuit is capacitive with line current leading the generator voltage. In both cases the total impedance of the parallel circuit is much less than the maximum impedance at resonance.

22·9   Analysis of parallel-resonant circuits

Parallel resonance is more complex than series resonance because the reactive branch currents are not exactly equal when X_L equals X_C. The reason is that the coil has its series resistance R_s in the X_L branch, while the capacitor has only X_C in its branch. For high-Q circuits, we consider R_s to be negligible. In low-Q circuits, however, the inductive branch must be analyzed as a complex impedance with X_L and R_s in series. This impedance is in parallel with X_C, as shown in Fig. 22·14. The total impedance Z_T can then be calculated by using complex numbers, as explained in Chap. 21.

High-Q circuit. We can apply the general method in Fig. 22·14 to the parallel-resonant circuit in Fig. 22·6 to see if Z_T is 225,000 ohms. In this example, X_L and X_C are 1,500 ohms and R_s is 10 ohms. The calculations are

$$Z_T = \frac{Z_1 \times Z_2}{Z_1 + Z_2} = \frac{-j1,500 \times (j1,500 + 10)}{-j1,500 + j1,500 + 10}$$

$$= \frac{-j^2 2.25 \times 10^6 - j15,000}{10} = -j^2 2.25 \times 10^5 - j1,500$$

$$Z_T = 225,000 - j1,500 = 225,000\underline{/0^\circ} \text{ ohms} \quad \text{(approx)}$$

Note that $-j^2$ is $+1$. Also, the reactive $j1,500$ ohms is negligible compared with the resistive 225,000 ohms. This answer of 225,000 ohms for Z_T is the same as $Q \times X_L$, or $150 \times 15,000$, because of the high Q with negligibly small R_s.

Low-Q circuit. We can consider a Q less than 10 as low. For the same circuit in Fig. 22·6, if R_s is 300 ohms with X_L of 1,500 ohms, the Q will be 1,500/300, which equals 5. For this case of appreciable R_s, the branch cur-

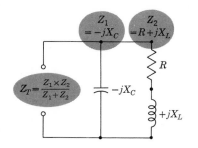

Fig. 22·14   *General method for calculating Z_T of a parallel-resonant circuit.*

rents cannot be equal when X_L and X_C are equal because then the inductive branch will have more impedance and less current. Also, Z_T must be calculated in terms of the branch impedances. For this example, the calculations are simpler with all impedances stated in kilohms:

$$Z_T = \frac{Z_1 \times Z_2}{Z_1 + Z_2} = \frac{-j1.5 \times (j1.5 + 0.3)}{-j1.5 + j1.5 + 0.3}$$

$$= \frac{-j^2 2.25 - j0.45}{0.3} = -j^2 7.5 - j1.5$$

$$Z_T = 7.5 - j1.5 = 7.65 \text{ K} \underline{/-11.3°} = 7,650\underline{/-11.3°} \text{ ohms}$$

The phase angle θ is not zero because the reactive branch currents are unequal, even though X_L and X_C are equal. The appreciable value of R_s in the X_L branch makes this branch current smaller than I_C in the X_C branch.

Criteria for parallel resonance. The frequency f_r that makes $X_L = X_C$ is always $1/(2\pi\sqrt{LC})$. However, for low-Q circuits f_r does not necessarily provide the desired resonance effect. The three main criteria for parallel resonance are

1. Zero phase angle and unity power factor.
2. Maximum impedance Z_T and minimum line current.
3. $X_L = X_C$. This is resonance at $f_r = 1/(2\pi\sqrt{LC})$.

These three effects do not occur at the same frequency in parallel circuits that have low Q. The condition for unity power factor is often called *antiresonance* in a parallel LC circuit to distinguish from the case of equal X_L and X_C.

It should be noted that when Q is 10 or higher for the parallel-resonant circuit all the variables are reduced to the definite statements that the branch currents are practically equal when $X_C = X_L$, $f_r = 1/(2\pi\sqrt{LC})$, the line current is minimum with zero phase angle and impedance is maximum at f_r. For a series-resonant circuit, the current is maximum at exactly f_r whether Q is high or low.

Parallel damping resistance. In Fig. 22·15b, R_P across the LC circuit is a damping resistance because it lowers the Q of the tuned circuit. R_P can

Fig. 22·15   Same Q for parallel-resonant circuit in terms of (a) coil resistance R_s and (b) parallel damping resistance R_P.

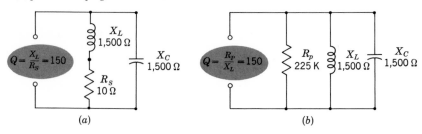

represent either the resistance of the source or an actual resistor added for lower Q and greater bandwidth.

The effect of varying the parallel resistance R_P is opposite from the series resistance R_s. A lower value of R_P lowers the Q and reduces the sharpness of resonance. Remember that less resistance in a parallel branch results in more current. This resistive branch current cannot be canceled at resonance by the reactive currents. Therefore, the resonant dip to minimum line current is less sharp with more resistive line current. Specifically, when Q is determined by parallel resistance,

$$Q = \frac{R_P}{X_L} \qquad (22 \cdot 10)$$

This is the reciprocal of the Q formula for series resistance. As shown in Fig. 22·15, R_s must be negligibly small to use the R_P formula, as the Q of the circuit cannot be more than the Q of the coil. Also, R_P is assumed infinitely high when calculating Q with R_s.

22·10   Choosing L and C for a resonant circuit

The following example illustrates how resonance is really just an application of X_L and X_C. Suppose that we have the problem of determining the inductance and capacitance for a circuit to be resonant at 159 kc. First, we need a known value for either L or C, in order to calculate the other. Which one to choose depends on the application. In some cases, particularly at very high frequencies, C must be the minimum possible value, which might be about 10 pf. At medium frequencies, though, we can choose L for the general case where an X_L of 1,000 ohms is desirable and can be obtained. Then the inductance of the required L, equal to $X_L/2\pi f$, is 0.001 h or 1 mh, for the inductive reactance of 1,000 ohms.

For resonance at 159 kc with 1-mh L the required C is 0.001 μf or 1,000 pf. This value of C can be calculated for an X_C of 1,000 ohms, equal to X_L at the f_r of 159 kc, or from Formula (22·3). In either case, if you substitute 1×10^{-9} farad for C and 1×10^{-3} henry for L in the resonant frequency formula, f_r will be 159 kc.

This combination is resonant at 159 kc whether L and C are in series or parallel. In series, the resonant effect is to produce maximum current and maximum voltage across L or C at 159 kc. In parallel, the resonant effect at 159 kc is minimum line current and maximum impedance across the generator.

If we assume the 1-mh coil used for L has an internal resistance of 20 ohms, the Q of the coil is 50. This value is also the Q of the series resonant circuit. If there is no shunt damping resistance across the parallel LC circuit, its Q is also 50. With a Q of 50 the bandwidth of the resonant circuit is 159 kc/50, which equals 3.18 kc for Δf.

SUMMARY

Series and parallel resonance are compared in Table 22·5. The main difference is that series resonance produces maximum current and very low impedance at f_r, but with parallel resonance the line current is minimum to provide a very high impedance. Remember that these formulas for parallel resonance are very close approximations that can be used for circuits with a Q higher than 10. For series resonance, the formulas apply whether the Q is high or low.

SELF-EXAMINATION (*Answers at back of book.*)

Here's a chance to find out how well you have learned the material in this chapter. These exercises are for your self-testing only.

1. For a series or parallel LC circuit, resonance occurs when (*a*) X_L is 10 times X_C or more; (*b*) X_C is 10 times X_L or more; (*c*) $X_L = X_C$; (*d*) the phase angle of the circuit is 90°.
2. When either L or C is increased, the resonant frequency of the LC circuit (*a*) increases; (*b*) decreases; (*c*) remains the same; (*d*) is determined by the shunt resistance.
3. The resonant frequency of an LC circuit is 1,000 kc. If L is doubled but C is reduced to one-eighth of its original value, the resonant frequency then is (*a*) 250 kc; (*b*) 500 kc; (*c*) 1,000 kc; (*d*) 2,000 kc.
4. A coil has 1,000-ohm X_L and 5-ohm internal resistance. Its Q equals (*a*) 0.005; (*b*) 5; (*c*) 200; (*d*) 1,000.
5. In a parallel LC circuit, at the resonant frequency, the (*a*) line current is maximum; (*b*) inductive branch current is minimum; (*c*) total impedance is minimum; (*d*) total impedance is maximum.
6. At resonance, the phase angle equals (*a*) 0°; (*b*) 90°; (*c*) 180°; (*d*) 270°.
7. In a series LC circuit, at the resonant frequency, the (*a*) current is minimum; (*b*) voltage across C is minimum; (*c*) impedance is maximum; (*d*) current is maximum.
8. A series LC circuit has a Q of 100 at resonance. When 5 mv is applied at the resonant frequency, the voltage across C equals (*a*) 5 mv; (*b*) 20 mv; (*c*) 100 mv; (*d*) 500 mv.
9. An LC circuit resonant at 1,000 kc has a Q of 100. The bandwidth between half-power points equals (*a*) 10 kc between 995 and 1,005 kc; (*b*) 10 kc between 1,000 and 1,010 kc; (*c*) 5 kc between 995 and 1,000 kc; (*d*) 200 kc between 900 and 1,100 kc.
10. In a low-Q parallel-resonant circuit, when $X_L = X_C$, (*a*) I_L equals I_C; (*b*) I_L is less than I_C; (*c*) I_L is more than I_C; (*d*) the phase angle is 0°.

Table 22·5 Comparison of series and parallel resonance

SERIES RESONANCE	PARALLEL RESONANCE (HIGH Q)
$f_r = 1/(2\pi \sqrt{LC})$	$f_r = 1/(2\pi \sqrt{LC})$
I maximum at f_r with 0° phase angle	I_T minimum at f_r with 0° phase angle
Impedance minimum at f_r	Impedance maximum at f_r
$Q = X_L/R_s$ or $Q = E_{out}/E_{in}$	$Q = X_L/R_s$, also $Q = R_P/X_L$
Q rise in voltage $= Q \times E_{gen}$	Q rise in impedance $= Q \times X_L$
Bandwidth $\Delta f = f_r/Q$	Bandwidth $\Delta f = f_r/Q$
Capacitive below f_r, inductive above f_r	Inductive below f_r, capacitive above f_r
Needs low-resistance generator for low R_s, high Q, and sharp tuning	Needs high-resistance generator for high R_P, high Q, and sharp tuning

ESSAY QUESTIONS

1. (*a*) State two characteristics of series resonance. (*b*) With a microammeter measuring current in the series *LC* circuit of Fig. 22·2, describe the meter readings for the different frequencies from 600 to 1,400 kc.
2. (*a*) State two characteristics of parallel resonance. (*b*) With a microammeter measuring current in the main line for the parallel *LC* circuit in Fig. 22·7*a*, describe the meter readings for the different frequencies from 600 to 1,400 kc.
3. State the *Q* formula for the following *LC* circuits: (*a*) series-resonant; (*b*) parallel-resonant, with series resistance R_s in the inductive branch; (*c*) parallel-resonant, with zero series resistance but shunt resistance R_P.
4. Explain briefly why a parallel *LC* circuit is inductive but a series *LC* circuit is capacitive below f_r.
5. What is the effect on *Q* and bandwidth of a parallel-resonant circuit if its shunt damping resistance is decreased from 50,000 to 10,000 ohms?
6. Describe briefly how you would use an a-c meter to measure the bandwidth of a series-resonant circuit for calculating its *Q*.
7. Why is a low-resistance generator good for high *Q* in series resonance, while a high-resistance generator is needed for high *Q* in parallel resonance?
8. Referring to Fig. 22·13, why is it that the middle frequency of 1,080 kc does not correspond to the middle capacitance value of 200 pf?
9. Give three criteria for parallel resonance. Why is the antiresonant frequency f_a different from f_r with a low-*Q* circuit? Why are they the same for a high-*Q* circuit?
10. Compare the two formulas for *Q* of a parallel-resonant circuit, in terms of the series resistance R_s and the parallel damping resistance R_P.
11. (*a*) Specify the edge frequencies f_1 and f_2 for each of the three response curves in Fig. 22·11. (*b*) Why does lower *Q* allow more bandwidth?
12. (*a*) Why does maximum Z_T for a parallel-resonant circuit correspond to minimum line current? (*b*) Why does zero phase angle for a resonant circuit correspond to unity power factor?

PROBLEMS (*Answers to selected problems at back of book.*)

1. Find f_r for a series-resonant circuit with 10-μf *C*, 16-henry *L*, and 5-ohm R_s.
2. Find f_r for a parallel-resonant circuit with 2-μf *C*, 2-henry *L*, and 5-ohm R_s.
3. In a series-resonant circuit, X_L is 1,500 ohms and the internal coil resistance is 15 ohms. At the resonant frequency, (*a*) How much is the *Q* of the circuit? (*b*) How much is X_C? (*c*) With a generator voltage of 15 mv, how much is the current? (*d*) How much is the voltage across X_C?
4. In a parallel-resonant circuit, X_L is 1,200 ohms, the resistance of the coil is practically zero, but there is a 36,000-ohm resistance across the *LC* circuit. At the resonant frequency, (*a*) How much is the *Q* of the circuit? (*b*) How much is X_C? (*c*) With a generator voltage of 12 mv and zero resistance in the main line, how much is the main-line current? (*d*) How much is the voltage across *L*, *C*, and *R*? (*e*) How much is the impedance across the main line?
5. What value of *L* is necessary with a *C* of 100 pf for series resonance at 1 Mc? At 4 Mc?
6. Calculate the *C* needed with 350-μh *L* for 200-kc f_r.
7. Calculate the lowest and highest values of *C* needed with 0.1-μh *L* to tune through the commercial FM broadcast band of 88 to 108 Mc.
8. (*a*) At what frequency will a 200-μh coil with 20-ohm R_s have 1,000 ohms X_L? (*b*) What size *C* is needed for 1,000 ohms X_C at this frequency? (*c*) What is f_r for this *LC* combination? (*d*) How much is the *Q* of the coil?
9. Draw the schematic diagram of a parallel-resonant circuit with the *L*, *C*, and R_s of Prob. 8. Let the applied voltage be 5 volts. Calculate the values of main-line current I_T, Z_T, and θ at the resonant frequency f_r, 0.1 Mc below f_r and 0.1 Mc above f_r.

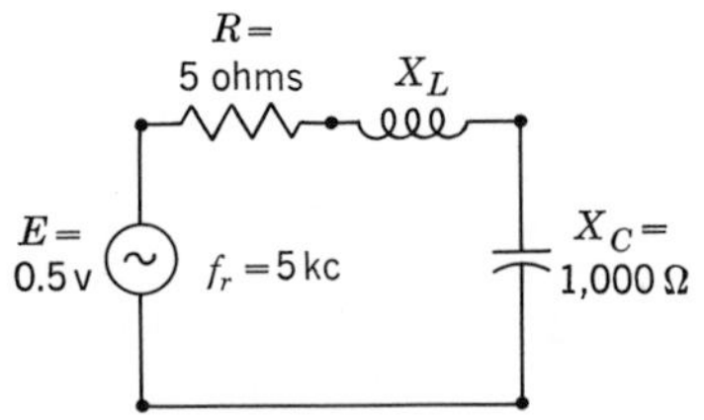

R=
5 ohms X_L

Fig. 22·16   See Prob. 10.   E=
0.5v (~) $f_r = 5$ kc $X_C =$
1,000 Ω

10. For the series-resonant circuit in Fig. 22·16, (a) How much is X_L? (b) Calculate L in mh and C in μf. (c) Calculate the Q and bandwidth. (d) Calculate E_C and E_L. (e) If L is doubled and C is one-half, what is f_r? Calculate Q and bandwidth for this case. (f) If the original values of both L and C are doubled, calculate f_r.

11. Redraw Fig. 22·16 as a parallel-resonant circuit with the original values and R_s in series with the coil. (a) What is the Q and bandwidth? (b) Calculate Z_T at f_r, f_1, and f_2.

12. For the same circuit as Prob. 11, let R_s increase to 500 ohms. (a) What is the Q now? (b) Calculate Z_T at f_r, one-half f_r, and twice f_r. (c) What value of R_P would be used for the same Q, if R_s were zero?

13. For the series circuit in Fig. 22·16: (a) Tabulate the I and θ values every kilocycle from 2 to 9 kc. (b) Draw the response curve showing I vs. frequency.

14. For the values in Fig. 22·16 connected for parallel resonance, (a) Calculate Z_T and θ every kilocycle from 2 to 9 kc. (b) Draw the response curve showing Z_T vs. frequency.

15. A series-resonant circuit produces 240 mv across L with 2 mv input. (a) How much is the Q of the coil? (b) Calculate R_s, if L is 5 mh and f_r is 0.3 Mc. (c) How much C is needed for f_r?

Chapter **23** Filters

This unit explains how capacitance and inductance can be used to eliminate undesired frequency variations. Such filtering is just another application of L and C components, including transformers, series or shunt capacitors, series or shunt chokes, and series- or parallel-resonant circuits. The topics are as follows:

23·1   Examples of filtering
23·2   Direct current combined with alternating current
23·3   Transformer coupling
23·4   Capacitive coupling
23·5   Bypass capacitors
23·6   Filter circuits
23·7   Low-pass filters
23·8   High-pass filters
23·9   Resonant filters
23·10 Interference filters

23·1   Examples of filtering

Electronic circuits often have currents of different frequencies corresponding to voltages of different frequencies. The reason is that a source produces current with the same frequency as the applied voltage. As examples, the a-c signal input to an audio circuit can have high and low audio frequencies; an r-f circuit can have a wide range of radio frequencies in its input; the audio detector in a radio has both radio frequencies and audio frequencies in the output. Finally, the rectifier in a power supply produces d-c output with an a-c ripple superimposed on the average d-c level.

In such applications where the current has different frequency components, it is usually necessary either to favor or to reject one frequency or a group of frequencies. Then an electrical filter is used to separate higher or lower frequencies. This action corresponds to a mechanical filter separating one component from the others. The electrical filter can pass the higher-frequency component to the load resistance, which is the case of a high-pass filter; or a low-pass filter can be used to favor the lower frequencies. In Fig. 23·1*a*, the high-pass filter allows 10 kc to produce output, while rejecting or attenuating the lower frequency of 100 cps. In *b*, the filtering action is reversed to pass the lower frequency of 100 cps, while attenuating 10 kc.

The electrical filtering is possible because of the opposite frequency characteristics of inductive and capacitive reactances. Since X_L increases with higher frequencies, but X_C increases for lower frequencies, combinations of L and C can be used for any required filtering. Furthermore, the L and C components can be connected in either series or parallel with the load resistance for opposite effects. In summary, then, filter circuits are just applications of inductance and capacitance to select or reject a particular frequency or band of frequencies. The most common filtering applications include separating radio frequencies from audio frequencies, or vice versa, and separating alternating current from direct current.

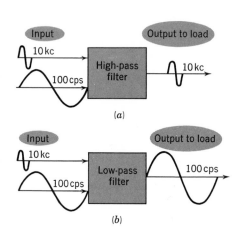

Fig. 23·1 *Function of electrical filters. (a) High-pass filter couples higher frequencies to the load. (b) Low-pass filter couples lower frequencies to the load.*

Fig. 23·2 *Pulsating direct current and voltage. (a) Circuit. (b) Graph of voltage across R_L is E_b plus E_a.*

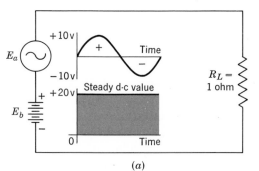

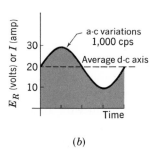

(a)

(b)

23·2 *Direct current combined with alternating current*

Current that varies in amplitude but does not reverse in polarity is considered *pulsating* or *fluctuating* direct current. It is not a steady direct current, because its value fluctuates. However, it is not alternating current because the polarity remains the same, either positive or negative. The same idea applies to voltages.

Figure 23·2 illustrates how a circuit can have pulsating direct current or voltage. Here, the steady d-c voltage of the battery E_b is in series with the a-c voltage E_a. Since the two series generators add, the voltage across R_L is the sum of the two applied voltages, as shown by the waveshape of E_R in *b*.

If values are taken at opposite peaks of the a-c variation, when E_a is at +10 volts, it adds to the +20 volts of the battery to provide +30 volts across R_L; when the a-c voltage is −10 volts, it bucks the battery voltage of +20 volts to provide +10 volts across R_L. When the a-c voltage is at zero, the voltage across R_L equals the battery voltage of +20 volts. The combined voltage E_R then consists of the a-c variations fluctuating above and below the battery voltage as the axis, instead of the zero axis for a-c voltage. The result is a pulsating d-c voltage, since it is fluctuating but always has positive polarity with respect to zero. The pulsating direct current I through R_L has the same waveform, fluctuating above and below the steady d-c level of 20 amp. The I and E values are the same because R is 1 ohm.

Another example is illustrated in Fig. 23·3. If the 100-ohm R_L is connected across the 120-volt 60-cycle a-c power line in *a*, the current in R_L will be E/R_L. This alternating current is a sine wave, with an RMS value of 1.2 amp. Also, if you connect the same R_L across the 200-volt d-c source in *b*, instead of using the a-c source, the steady direct current in R_L will be $^{200}/_{100}$ or 2 amp. The battery source voltage and its current are considered steady d-c values because there are no variations.

However, suppose that the a-c source E_a and d-c source E_b are connected in series with R_L, as in *c*. What will happen to the current and voltage

Fig. 23·3 *An example of providing fluctuating d-c voltage across R_L. (a) A-c source alone. (b) D-c source alone. (c) A-c source in series with d-c source.*

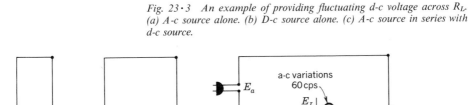

for R_L? Will E_a or E_b supply the current? The answer is that both sources will. Each voltage source produces current as though the other were not there, assuming the sources have negligibly small internal impedance. The result then is the fluctuating d-c voltage or current shown, with the a-c variations of E_a superimposed on the average d-c level of E_b.

D-c and a-c components. The pulsating d-c voltage E_R in Fig. $23 \cdot 2$ is just the original a-c voltage E_a with its axis shifted to a d-c level by the battery voltage E_b. In effect, a d-c component has been inserted into the a-c variations. If you measure across R_L with a d-c voltmeter, it will read the d-c level of 20 volts; if you measure with an a-c voltmeter, it will read the RMS value of the variations, which is 7.07 volts. It is convenient, therefore, to consider the pulsating or fluctuating voltage and current in two parts. One is the steady d-c component, which is the axis or average level of the variations; the other is the a-c component, consisting of the variations above and below the d-c axis. Here the d-c level for E_R is $+20$ volts, while the a-c component equals 10 volts peak or 7.07-volt RMS value.

It should be noted that with respect to the d-c level the fluctuations represent alternating voltage or current that actually reverses in polarity. For example, the change of E_R from $+20$ to $+10$ volts is just a decrease in positive voltage compared with zero, but compared with the d-c level of $+20$ volts, the value of $+10$ volts is 10 volts more negative than the axis.

Typical examples of d-c level with a-c component. As a common application, electron tubes and transistors always have fluctuating d-c voltage or current when used for amplifying an a-c signal. The tube or transistor amplifier needs steady d-c voltages to operate. The signal input is an a-c variation, usually with a d-c axis to establish the desired operating level.

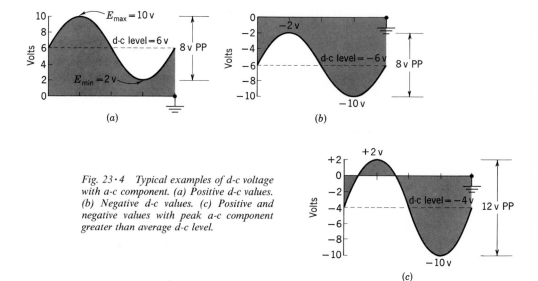

Fig. $23 \cdot 4$ *Typical examples of d-c voltage with a-c component. (a) Positive d-c values. (b) Negative d-c values. (c) Positive and negative values with peak a-c component greater than average d-c level.*

The amplified output is also an a-c variation superimposed on a d-c supply voltage that supplies the required power output. Therefore, the input and output circuits have fluctuating d-c voltage.

The examples in Fig. 23·4 illustrate three possibilities, in terms of polarities with respect to chassis ground. In *a*, the waveform is always positive, as in the previous examples. Note the specific values. The average d-c axis is the steady d-c level. The positive peak equals the d-c level plus the peak a-c value. The minimum point equals the d-c level minus the peak a-c value. The peak-to-peak value of the a-c component, or its RMS value, is the same as for the a-c signal alone. However, it is better to subtract the minimum from the maximum for the peak-to-peak value, in case the waveform is unsymmetrical. This is illustrated in Example 1 below.

All values in Fig. 23·4*a* are positive because the positive d-c level is higher than the peak of the a-c component. In *b* all the values are negative. Notice that here the positive peak of the a-c component subtracts from the d-c level because of the opposite polarities. Now the negative peak adds to the negative d-c level to provide a maximum point of negative voltage. Finally, in *c* the fluctuating d-c voltage with a negative d-c level goes positive at the positive peak of the a-c component. This condition of opposite polarity results because the peak a-c component is more than average d-c level.

Example 1. Specify the average, maximum, minimum, and peak-to-peak voltage for the fluctuating d-c waveform in Fig. 23·3*c*.

Answer. For 120 volts RMS the peak value is 170 volts. The average voltage is the d-c level of 200 volts.

Therefore,

$$E_{max} = E_{d-c} + E_{peak} = 200 + 170 = \textbf{370 volts}$$
$$E_{min} = E_{d-c} - E_{peak} = 200 - 170 = \textbf{30 volts}$$
$$E_{PP} = 370 - 30 = \textbf{340 volts}$$

Separating the a-c component. In many applications, the circuit has pulsating d-c voltage, but only the a-c component is desired. Then the a-c component can be passed to the load, while the steady d-c component is blocked, either with transformer coupling or with capacitive coupling. A transformer with a separate secondary winding isolates or blocks steady direct current in the primary. A capacitor isolates or blocks a steady d-c voltage.

23·3 *Transformer coupling*

Remember that a transformer produces induced secondary voltage just for variations in primary current. With pulsating direct current in the primary, the secondary has output voltage only for the a-c variations, therefore. The d-c component in the primary has no effect in the secondary. In Fig. 23·5, the pulsating d-c voltage in the primary produces pulsating primary current. The d-c axis corresponds to a steady direct primary cur-

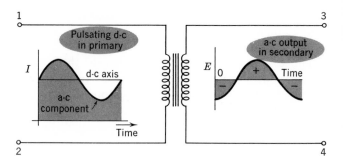

Fig. 23·5   Transformer coupling blocks d-c component. With pulsating direct current in primary, the output voltage in secondary has a-c component only.

rent that has a constant magnetic field, but only when the field changes can secondary voltage be induced. Therefore, only the fluctuations in the primary can produce output in the secondary. Since there is no output for the steady primary current, this d-c level corresponds to the zero level for the a-c output in the secondary.

When the primary current increases above the steady level, this increase produces one polarity for the secondary voltage as the field expands; when the primary current decreases below the steady level, the secondary voltage has reverse polarity as the field contracts. The result in the secondary is an a-c variation having opposite polarities with respect to the zero level. The phase of the a-c secondary voltage may be as shown or 180° opposite, depending on the connections and direction of the windings. Also, the a-c secondary output may be more or less than the a-c component in the primary, depending on the turns ratio. This ability to isolate the steady d-c component in the primary while providing a-c output in the secondary applies to all transformers with a separate secondary winding, whether iron-core or air-core.

23·4   Capacitive coupling

This method is probably the most common type of coupling in amplifier circuits. The coupling means connecting the output of one circuit to the input of the next. The requirements are to include all frequencies in the desired signal, while rejecting undesired components. Usually, the d-c component must be blocked from the input to a-c amplifiers. In Fig. 23·6, the pulsating d-c voltage across input terminals 1 and 2 is applied to the RC coupling circuit. C_c will charge to the steady d-c level, which is the average charging voltage. Thus the steady d-c component is blocked, since it cannot produce voltage across R. However, the a-c component is developed across R, between the output terminals 3 and 4. Note that the zero axis of the a-c voltage output corresponds to the average level of the pulsating d-c voltage input.

The d-c component across C_c. The voltage across C_c is the steady d-c component of the input voltage because the variations of the a-c component are symmetrical above and below the average level. Furthermore,

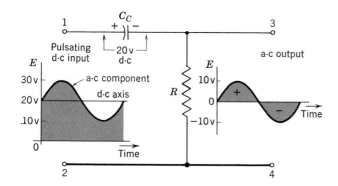

Fig. 23·6 RC coupling blocks d-c component. With pulsating d-c voltage applied, output voltage across R has a-c component only.

the series resistance is the same for charge and discharge. As a result, any increase in charging voltage above the average level is counteracted by an equal discharge below the average. In Fig. 23·6, for example, when E increases from 20 to 30 volts, this effect on charging C_c is nullified by the discharge when E decreases from 20 to 10 volts. At all times, however, E has a positive value that charges C_c in the polarity shown. The net result is that only the average voltage level is effective in charging C_c, since the variations from the axis neutralize each other. After a period of time equal to 5 RC time constants, C_c will charge to the average value of the pulsating d-c voltage applied, which is 20 volts here.

The a-c component across R. Although C_c is charged to the average d-c level, when the pulsating input voltage varies above and below this level, the charge and discharge current produces IR voltage corresponding to the fluctuations of the input. When E increases above the average level, C_c takes on charge, producing charging current through R. Even though the charging current may be too small to affect the voltage across C_c appreciably, the IR drop across a large value of resistance can be practically equal to the a-c component of the input voltage. In summary, a long RC time constant is needed for good coupling.

If the polarity is considered, in Fig. 23·6 the charging current produced when E increases produces electron flow from the low side of R to the top, adding electrons to the negative side of C_c. The voltage at the top of R is then positive with respect to the line below. When E decreases below the average level, C loses charge. The discharge current then is in the opposite direction through R, resulting in negative polarity for the a-c voltage coupled across R. When the input voltage is at its average level, there is no charge or discharge current, resulting in zero voltage across R. The zero level in the a-c voltage across R corresponds to the average level of the pulsating d-c voltage applied to the RC circuit. With positive pulsating d-c voltage applied, the values above the average produce the positive half-cycle of the a-c voltage across R; values below the average produce the negative half-cycle.

It is important to note that there is practically no phase shift. This rule

Table 23·1   *Typical a-f and r-f coupling capacitors**

Frequency	Values of C_c			Remarks
	R = 16 K	R = 160 K	R = 1.6 M	
100 cps	1 μf	0.1 μf	0.01 μf	Low audio frequencies
1,000 cps	0.1 μf	0.01 μf	0.001 μf	Medium frequencies
10 kc	0.01 μf	0.001 μf	100 pf	High audio frequencies
100 kc	1,000 pf	100 pf	10 pf	Radio frequencies
1 Mc	100 pf	10 pf	1.0 pf	Radio frequencies
100 Mc	1 pf	0.1 pf	0.01 pf	Very high frequencies

*For RC coupling circuit in Fig. 23·6, $X_{C_c} = \frac{1}{10}R$.

applies to all RC coupling circuits, since R must be 10 or more times X_C. Then the reactance is negligible compared with the series resistance, and the phase angle of less than 5.7° is practically zero.

Voltages around the RC coupling circuit. If you measure the pulsating d-c voltage input voltage across points 1 and 2 in Fig. 23·6 with a d-c voltmeter, it will read the average level of 20 volts. A voltmeter that reads only a-c values across these same points will read the fluctuating a-c component, equal to 7 volts RMS. Across points 1 and 3, a d-c voltmeter reads the steady d-c value of 20 volts across C_c. An a-c voltmeter across 1 and 3 reads zero. However, an a-c voltmeter across the output between points 3 and 4 will read the a-c voltage of 7 volts RMS; a d-c voltmeter across R reads zero.

Typical coupling capacitors. Common values of r-f and a-f coupling capacitors for different sizes of series R are listed in Table 23·1. In all cases the coupling capacitor blocks the steady d-c component of the input voltage, while the a-c component is passed to the resistance. The size of C_c required depends on the frequency of the a-c component. At each frequency, the values of capacitance in the horizontal row have X_C equal to $\frac{1}{10}$ the resistance value for each column. Typical audio coupling capacitors, then, are about 0.001 to 1.0 μf, depending on the lowest audio frequency to be coupled and the size of the series resistance. Similarly, typical r-f coupling capacitors are about 1 to 1,000 pf. These values are for vacuum-tube circuits. In transistor circuits larger values of C are used with smaller values of R.

23·5   Bypass capacitors

A bypass is a path around a component. In circuits, the bypass is a parallel or shunt path. Capacitors are often used in parallel with resistance, to bypass the a-c component of a pulsating d-c voltage. The result, then, is a steady d-c voltage across the RC parallel combination, if the bypass capacitance is large enough to have little reactance for the lowest frequency of the a-c variations.

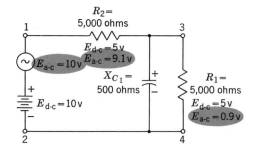

Fig. 23·7 Bypass capacitor C_1 shorts R_1 for a-c component of pulsating d-c input voltage.

As illustrated in Fig. 23·7, the capacitance C_1 in parallel with R_1 is an a-c bypass capacitor for R_1. For any frequency at which X_{C_1} is $\frac{1}{10} R_1$, or less, the a-c component is bypassed around R_1 through the low reactance in the shunt path. The result is practically zero a-c voltage across the bypass capacitor because of its low reactance. Since the voltage is the same across R_1 and C_1 because they are in parallel, there is also no a-c voltage across R_1 for the frequency at which C_1 is a bypass capacitor. We can say that R is bypassed for the frequency at which X_C is $\frac{1}{10} R$. The bypassing also applies to higher frequencies where X_C is less than $\frac{1}{10} R$. Then the a-c voltage across the bypass capacitor is even closer to zero because of its lower reactance.

Bypassing the a-c component of a pulsating d-c voltage. The voltages in Fig. 23·7 are calculated by considering the effect of C_1 separately for $E_{d\text{-}c}$ and for $E_{a\text{-}c}$. For direct current, C_1 is practically an open circuit. Then its reactance is so high compared with the 5,000-ohm R_1 that X_{C_1} can be ignored as a parallel branch. Therefore, R_1 can be considered as a voltage divider in series with R_2. Since R_1 and R_2 are equal, each has 5 volts, equal to one-half $E_{d\text{-}c}$. Although this d-c voltage division depends on R_1 and R_2, the d-c voltage across C_1 is the same 5 volts as across its parallel R_1.

For the a-c component of the applied voltage, however, the bypass capacitor has very low reactance. In fact, X_{C_1} must be $\frac{1}{10} R_1$, or less. Then the 5,000-ohm R_1 is so high compared with the low value of X_{C_1} that R_1 can be ignored as a parallel branch. Therefore, the 500-ohm X_{C_1} can be considered as a voltage divider in series with R_2. With X_{C_1} of 500 ohms, this value in series with the 5,000-ohm R_2 allows approximately one-eleventh of $E_{a\text{-}c}$ to be developed across C_1. This a-c voltage, equal to 0.9 volt here, is the same across R_1 and C_1 in parallel. The remainder of the a-c applied voltage, equal to approximately 9.1 volts, is across R_2. In summary, then, the bypass capacitor provides an a-c short circuit across its shunt resistance, so that little or no a-c voltage can be developed, without affecting the d-c voltages.

Measuring voltages around the circuit in Fig. 23·7, a d-c voltmeter reads 5 volts across R_1 and 5 volts across R_2. An a-c voltmeter across R_2 reads 9.1 volts, which is almost all the a-c input voltage. Across the bypass capacitor C_1 the a-c voltage is only 0.9 volt. In Table $23 \cdot 2$, typical sizes for r-f and a-f bypass capacitors are listed. The values of C have been calculated at different frequencies for X_C one-tenth the shunt resistance given in each column. Note that smaller values of R require larger values of C for bypassing. Also, when X_C equals $\frac{1}{10} R$ at one frequency, X_C will be even less for higher frequencies, improving the bypassing action. Therefore, the size of bypass capacitors should be considered on the basis of the lowest frequency to be bypassed.

Bypassing radio frequencies but not audio frequencies. See Fig. $23 \cdot 8$. At the audio frequency of 1,000 cps, C_1 has a reactance of 1,600,000 ohms. This reactance is so much higher than R_1 that the impedance of the parallel combination is essentially equal to the 16,000 ohms of R_1. Then R_1 and R_2 serve as a voltage divider for the applied a-f voltage of 10 volts. Each of the equal resistances has one-half the applied voltage, equal to 5 volts across R_2 and 5 volts across R_1. This 5 volts at 1,000 cps is also present across C_1, since it is in parallel with R_1.

For the r-f voltage at 1 Mc, however, the reactance of the bypass capacitor is only 1,600 ohms. This is $\frac{1}{10} R_1$. Then X_{C_1} and R_1 in parallel have a combined impedance equal to approximately 1,600 ohms. Now, with 1,600-ohm impedance for the $R_1 C_1$ bank in series with the 16,000 ohms of R_2, the voltage across R_1 and C_1 is one-eleventh the applied r-f voltage. Then there is 0.9 volt across the lower impedance of R_1 and C_1, with 9.1 volts across the larger resistance of R_2. As a result, the r-f component of the applied voltage can be considered bypassed. C_1 is the r-f bypass capacitor for R_1.

$23 \cdot 6$ Filter circuits

In terms of their function, filters can be classified as either low-pass or high-pass. A low-pass filter allows the lower-frequency components of the applied voltage to develop output voltage across the load resistance, while the higher frequency components are attenuated or reduced in the output. A high-pass filter does the opposite, allowing the higher-frequency com-

Table 23·2 Typical a-f and r-f bypass capacitors*

Fre-quency	Values of C				Remarks
	$R = 160,000$ ohms	$R = 16,000$ ohms	$R = 1,600$ ohms	$R = 160$ ohms	
100 cps	0.1 μf	1 μf	10 μf	100 μf	Low audio frequencies
1,000 cps	0.01 μf	0.1 μf	1 μf	10 μf	Medium audio frequencies
10 kc	0.001 μf	0.01 μf	0.1 μf	1 μf	High audio frequencies
1 Mc	10 pf	100 pf	0.001 μf	0.01 μf	Radio frequencies
100 Mc	0.1 μf	1 μf	10 pf	100 pf	Very high frequencies

* For RC bypass circuit in Fig. $23 \cdot 7$, $X_C = \frac{1}{10} R$.

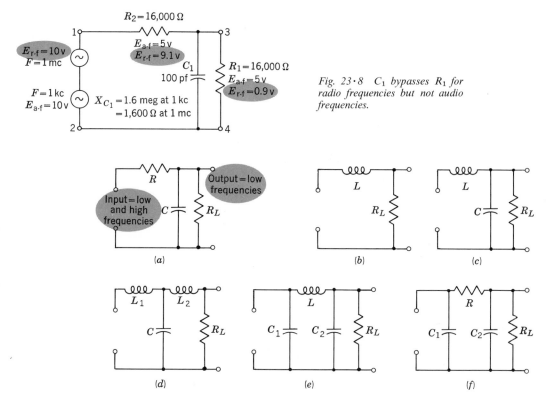

Fig. 23·8 C_1 bypasses R_1 for radio frequencies but not audio frequencies.

Fig. 23·9 Low-pass filter circuits. (a) Bypass capacitor in parallel with R_L. (b) Choke in series with R_L. (c) Inverted-L type with choke and bypass. (d) T type with two chokes and one bypass. (e) π type with one choke and two bypass capacitors. (f) π type with series resistor instead of choke.

ponents of the applied voltage to develop voltage across the output load resistance.

The case of an *RC* coupling circuit is an example of a high-pass filter because the a-c component of the input voltage is developed across *R* while the d-c voltage is blocked by the series capacitor. Furthermore, with higher frequencies in the a-c component, more a-c voltage is coupled. For the opposite case, a bypass capacitor is an example of a low-pass filter. The higher frequencies are bypassed, but the lower the frequency, the less the bypassing action. Then lower frequencies can develop output voltage across the shunt bypass capacitor.

In order to make the filtering more selective in terms of which frequencies are passed to produce output voltage across the load, filter circuits generally combine inductance and capacitance. Since inductive reactance increases with higher frequencies, while capacitive reactance decreases, the two opposite effects improve the filtering action. With combinations of *L* and *C*, filters are named to correspond to the circuit configuration. The most common type are the L, T, and π arrangements shown in Figs. 23·9 and $23 \cdot 11$. Any of the three types can function as either a low-pass or a high-pass filter.

For low-pass or high-pass filters with L and C the reactance X_L must increase with higher frequencies, while X_C decreases. However, the circuit connections are opposite to reverse the filtering action.

In general, high-pass filters use:

1. Coupling capacitance C in series with the load. Then X_C can be low for high frequencies to be passed to R_L, while low frequencies are blocked.
2. Choke inductance L in parallel across R_L. Then the shunt X_L can be high for high frequencies to prevent a short circuit across R_L, while low frequencies are bypassed.

The opposite characteristics for low-pass filters are:

1. Inductance L in series with the load. The high X_L for high frequencies can serve as a choke, while low frequencies can be passed to R_L.
2. Bypass capacitance C in parallel across R_L. Then high frequencies are bypassed by a small X_C, while low frequencies are not affected by the shunt path.

$23 \cdot 7$ Low-pass filters

Figure $23 \cdot 9$ illustrates low-pass circuits from the case of a single filter element with a shunt bypass capacitor in a or a series choke in b, to the more elaborate combinations of L-type filter in c, T-type in d, and π-type in e and f. With an applied input voltage having different frequency components, the low-pass filter action results in maximum low-frequency voltage across R_L, while most of the high-frequency voltage is developed across the series choke or resistance.

In a, the shunt capacitor C bypasses R_L for high frequencies. In b, the choke L acts as a voltage divider in series with R_L. Since L has maximum reactance for the highest frequencies, this component of the input voltage is developed across L, with little across R_L. For lower frequencies, L has low reactance and most of the input voltage can be developed across R_L. In c, the use of both the series choke and bypass capacitor improves the filtering by providing sharper cutoff between the low frequencies that can develop voltage across R_L and the higher frequencies stopped from the load by producing maximum voltage across L. Similarly, the T-type circuit in d and the π-type in e and f improve filtering. Using the series resistance in f, instead of a choke, provides an economical π filter needing less space.

The ability to reduce the amplitude of undesired frequencies is the *attenuation* of the filter. The frequency at which the attenuation reduces the output to 70.7 per cent response is the *cutoff frequency*.

As illustrated in Fig. $23 \cdot 10$, a low-pass filter attenuates frequencies above the cutoff frequency of 15 kc in this example. Any component of the input voltage having a frequency lower than 15 kc can produce ouput voltage across the load. These frequencies are in the *pass band*. Frequencies of

15 kc or more are in the *stop band*. The sharpness of filtering between the pass band and the stop band depends on the type of circuit. In general, the more L and C components, the sharper the response of the filter can be. In other words, π and T types are better filters than the L type and the bypass or choke alone.

The response curve in Fig. 23·10 is illustrated for the common application of a low-pass filter attenuating r-f voltages while passing audio frequencies to the load. This is necessary where the input voltage has r-f and a-f components but only the audio voltage is desired for the a-f circuits that follow the filter. A common example is filtering the audio output of the detector circuit in a radio receiver, after the r-f modulated carrier signal has been rectified. Another common application of low-pass filtering is where the steady d-c component of pulsating d-c input must be separated from the higher-frequency 60-cps a-c component, as in the pulsating d-c output of a power rectifier.

The choice between the T-type filter with a series input choke and the π-type with a shunt input capacitor depends upon the internal resistance of the generator supplying input voltage to the filter. A low-resistance generator needs the T filter so that the choke can provide a high series impedance for the bypass capacitor. Otherwise, the bypass must have extremely large values to short the low-resistance generator for high frequencies. The π filter is more suitable with a high-resistance generator where the input capacitor can be effective as a bypass. For the same reasons, the L filter can have the shunt bypass either in the input for a high-resistance generator or across the output for a low-resistance generator. For all the filter circuits, the series choke can be connected either in the high side of the line, as in Fig. 23·9, or in series in the opposite side of the line, without any effect on the filtering action. Also, the series components can be connected in both sides of the line for a *balanced filter* circuit.

23·8 High-pass filters

As illustrated in Fig. 23·11, the high-pass filter passes to the load all frequencies higher than the cutoff frequency, while lower frequencies cannot develop appreciable voltage across the load. The graph in *a* shows the

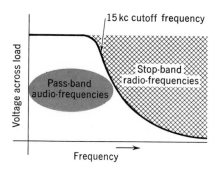

Fig. 23·10 Response of low-pass filter with cutoff at 15 kc, passing a-f voltage but attenuating radio frequencies.

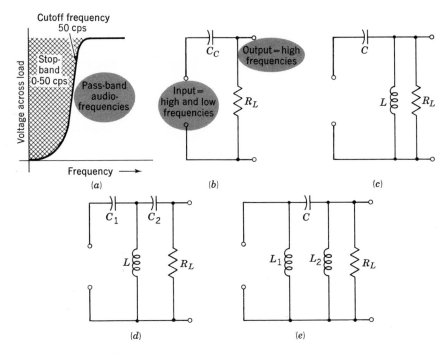

Fig. 23·11   High-pass filters. (a) Response curve for a-f filter cutting off at 50 cps. (b) RC coupling circuit. (c) Inverted-L type. (d) T type. (e) π type.

response of a high-pass filter with a stop band of 0 to 50 cps. Above the cutoff frequency of 50 cps, the higher audio frequencies in the pass band can produce a-f voltage across the output load resistance.

The high-pass filtering action results from using C as a coupling capacitor in series with the load, as in b. The L, T, and π types use the inductance for a high-reactance choke across the line. In this way the higher-frequency components of the input voltage can develop very little voltage across the series capacitance, allowing most of this voltage to be produced across R_L. The inductance across the line has higher reactance with increasing frequencies, allowing the shunt impedance to be no lower than the value of R_L. For low frequencies, however, R_L is effectively shorted by the low inductive reactance across the line. Also C_c has high reactance and develops most of the voltage at low frequencies, stopping these frequencies from developing voltage across the load.

Band-pass filtering. A high-pass filter can be combined with a low-pass filter. Then the net result is to pass the band of frequencies that are not stopped by either circuit. Such a band-pass response is shown in Fig. 23·12 for audio frequencies. In this example, the only frequencies passed by both filters are 50 to 15,000 cps. It should be noted, though, that filters for a specific band of frequencies are most often used at radio frequencies, as another application of resonant circuits.

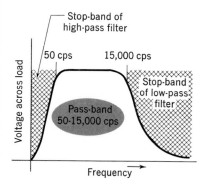

Fig. 23·12 Band-pass response curve for audio frequencies.

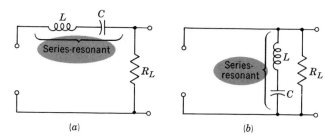

Fig. 23·13 Filtering action of series-resonant circuit. (a) Bandpass in series with R_L. (b) Band stop in shunt with R_L.

23·9 Resonant filters

Tuned circuits provide a convenient method of filtering a band of radio frequencies, because relatively small values of L and C are necessary for resonance. A tuned circuit provides filtering action by means of its maximum response at the resonant frequency. The width of the band of frequencies affected by resonance depends on the Q of the tuned circuit, higher Q providing narrower bandwidth. Because resonance is effective for a band of frequencies below and above f_r, resonant filters are called *band-stop* or *band-pass* filters. Series or parallel LC circuits can be used for either function, depending on the connections with respect to R_L.

Series-resonance filters. A series-resonant circuit has maximum current and minimum impedance at the resonant frequency. Connected in series with R_L, as in Fig. 23·13a, the series-tuned LC circuit allows frequencies at and near resonance to produce maximum output across R_L. Therefore, this is a case of band-pass filtering. When the series LC circuit is connected across R_L as in b, however, the resonant circuit provides a low-impedance shunt path that shorts R_L. Then there is minimum output. This action corresponds to a shunt bypass capacitor, but the resonant circuit is more selective, shorting R_L just for frequencies at and near resonance. For the bandwidth of the tuned circuit, therefore, the series-resonant circuit in shunt with R_L provides band-stop filtering.

Parallel-resonance filters. A parallel-resonant circuit has maximum impedance at the resonant frequency. Connected in series with R_L, as in Fig. 23·14a, the parallel-tuned LC circuit provides maximum impedance in series with R_L, at and near the resonant frequency. Then these frequencies produce maximum voltage across the LC circuit but minimum output voltage across R_L. This is a band-stop filter, therefore, for the bandwidth of the tuned circuit.

The parallel LC circuit connected across R_L, however, as in b, provides

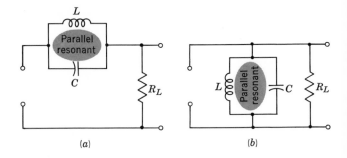

(a)   (b)

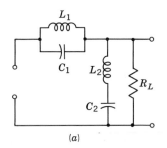

(a)

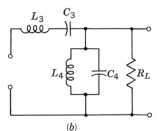

Fig. 23·15   Inverted-L filter with resonant circuits. (a) Band stop. (b) Band pass.

(b)

a band-pass filter. At resonance, the high impedance of the parallel LC circuit allows R_L to develop its output voltage. Below resonance, R_L is shorted by the low reactance of L; above resonance R_L is shorted by the low reactance of C. For frequencies at and near resonance, though, R_L is shunted by a high impedance, resulting in maximum output voltage.

L-type resonant filter. Series- and parallel-resonant circuits can be combined in L, T, or π sections to improve the filtering. Figure 23 · 15 illustrates the L-type filter, with band-stop filtering for the circuit arrangement in *a* but band-pass filtering in *b*. The circuit in *a* is a band-stop filter because the parallel-resonant circuit is in series with the load, while the series-resonant circuit is in shunt with the load. In *b* the band-pass filtering results from connecting the series-resonant circuit in series with the load, while the parallel-resonant circuit is across the load.

23·10   Interference filters

Voltage or current not at the desired frequency represents interference. Usually, such interference can be eliminated by a filter. Some typical applications are (1) low-pass filter to eliminate r-f interference from the 60-cps power-line input to a receiver, (2) high-pass filter to eliminate r-f interference from the signal picked up by a television receiving antenna, and (3) resonant filter to eliminate an interfering radio frequency from the desired r-f signal. The resonant band-stop filter is called a *wavetrap*.

Power-line filter. Although the power line is a source of 60-cps voltage, it is also a conductor for interfering r-f currents produced by motors, fluorescent-lighting circuits, and r-f equipment. When a receiver is connected to the power line, the r-f interference can produce noise and whistles in the receiver output. To minimize this interference, the filter shown in Fig. 23·16 can be used. The filter is plugged into the wall outlet for 60-cps power, while the receiver is plugged into the filter. An r-f bypass capacitor across the line with two series r-f chokes forms a low-pass balanced L-type filter. Using a choke in each side of the line makes the circuit balanced to ground.

The chokes provide high impedance for interfering r-f current but not for 60 cps, isolating the receiver input connections from r-f interference in the power line. Also, the bypass capacitor shorts the receiver input for radio frequencies but not for 60 cps. The unit then is a low-pass filter for 60-cps power applied to the receiver while rejecting higher frequencies. The current rating means the filter can be used for equipment that draws 3 amp or less from the power line, without excessive heat in the chokes.

Television antenna filter. When a television receiver has interference in the picture resulting from radio frequencies below the television broadcast band, picked up by the receiving antenna, this r-f interference can be reduced by the high-pass filter shown in Fig. 23·17. The filter attenuates

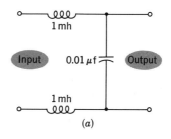

Fig. 23·16   Power-line filter to pass 60 cps but filter out radio frequencies. (a) Circuit of balanced-L low-pass filter. (b) Filter unit, rated at 3 amp, 120 volts. (P. R. Mallory and Co., Inc.)

Fig. 23·17   Television antenna filter to pass channel frequencies above 50 Mc but attenuate lower frequencies. (a) Filter unit. (b) Cover off, showing series capacitors and shunt chokes. (R. L. Drake Company.)

(a)   (b)

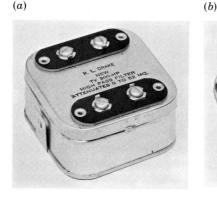

frequencies below 54 Mc, which is the lowest frequency for channel 2. At lower frequencies the series capacitances provide increasing reactance with a larger voltage drop, while the shunt inductances have less reactance and short the load. Higher frequencies are passed to the load as the series capacitive reactance decreases and the shunt inductive reactance increases. Connections to the filter unit are made at the receiver end of the line from the antenna. Either end of the filter is connected to the antenna terminals on the receiver with the opposite end to the antenna line.

SUMMARY

1. A filter separates high and low frequencies. With input of different frequencies, the high-pass filter allows the higher frequencies to produce output voltage across the load; a low-pass filter provides output voltage for the lower frequencies.
2. Pulsating or fluctuating direct current varies in amplitude but does not reverse its direction. Similarly, a pulsating or fluctuating d-c voltage varies in amplitude but maintains one polarity, either positive or negative. The pulsating direct current or voltage consists of a steady d-c level, equal to the average value, and an a-c component that reverses in polarity with respect to the average level. The d-c and a-c components can be separated by filters.
3. An RC coupling circuit is effectively a high-pass filter for pulsating direct current. C_c blocks the steady d-c voltage but passes the a-c component.
4. A transformer with an isolated secondary winding also is effectively a high-pass filter. With pulsating direct current in the primary, only the a-c component produces output voltage in the secondary.
5. A bypass capacitor in parallel with R provides a low-pass filter.
6. Combinations of L, C, and R can be arranged as L, T, or π filters for more selective filtering. All three arrangements can be used for either low-pass or high-pass action. In high-pass circuits, the capacitance must be in series with the load as a coupling capacitor, with shunt R or L across the line. For low-pass action, the capacitance is across the line as a bypass capacitor, while R or L then must be in series with the load.
7. A band-pass or band-stop filter has in effect two cutoff frequencies. The band-pass filter passes to the load those frequencies in the band between the cutoff frequencies, while attenuating all other frequencies higher and lower than the pass band. A band-stop filter does the opposite, attenuating the band between the cutoff frequencies, while passing to the load all other frequencies higher and lower than the stop band.
8. Resonant circuits are generally used for band-pass or band-stop filtering with radio frequencies. For band-pass filtering, the series-resonant LC circuit must be in series with the load, for minimum series opposition, while the high impedance of parallel resonance is across the load. For band-stop filtering, the circuit is reversed, with the parallel-resonant LC circuit in series with the load, while the series resonance is in shunt across the load. A wavetrap is an application of the resonant band-stop filter.

SELF-EXAMINATION (*Answers at back of book.*)

Here's a chance to find out how well you have learned the material in this chapter. These exercises are for your self-testing only.

1. With input frequencies from direct current up to 15 kc, a high-pass filter allows the most output voltage to be developed across the load resistance for which of the following frequencies? (*a*) Direct current; (*b*) 15 cps; (*c*) 150 cps; (*d*) 15,000 cps.
2. With input frequencies from direct current up to 15 kc, a low-pass filter allows the most output voltage to be developed across the load resistance for which of the following frequencies? (*a*) Direct current; (*b*) 15 cps; (*c*) 150 cps; (*d*) 15,000 cps.

3. An R_cC_c coupling circuit is a high-pass filter for pulsating d-c voltage because (a) C_c has high reactance for high frequencies; (b) C_c blocks d-c voltage; (c) C_c has low reactance for low frequencies; (d) R_c has minimum opposition for low frequencies.

4. A transformer with an isolated secondary winding is a high-pass filter for pulsating direct primary current because (a) the steady primary current has no magnetic field; (b) the a-c component of the primary current has the strongest field; (c) only variations in primary current can induce secondary voltage; (d) the secondary voltage is maximum for steady direct current in the primary.

5. Which of the following is a low-pass filter? (a) L-type with series C and shunt L; (b) π-type with series C and shunt L; (c) T-type with series C and shunt L; (d) L-type with series L and shunt C.

6. A bypass capacitor C_b across R_b provides low-pass filtering because (a) current in the C_b branch is maximum for low frequencies; (b) voltage across C_b is minimum for high frequencies; (c) voltage across C_b is minimum for low frequencies; (d) voltage across R_b is minimum for low frequencies.

7. An a-c voltmeter across C_c in Fig. $23 \cdot 6$ reads (a) practically zero; (b) 7.07 volts; (c) 10 volts; (d) 20 volts.

8. Which of the following L-type filters is the best band-stop filter? (a) Series-resonant LC circuit in series with the load and parallel-resonant LC circuit in shunt; (b) parallel-resonant LC circuit in series with the load and series-resonant LC circuit in shunt; (c) series-resonant LC circuits in series and in parallel with the load; (d) parallel-resonant LC circuits in series and in parallel with the load.

9. A 455-kc wavetrap is a resonant LC circuit tuned to 455 kc and connected as a (a) band-stop filter for frequencies at and near 455 kc; (b) band-pass filter for frequencies at and near 455 kc; (c) band-stop filter for frequencies from direct current up to 455 kc; (d) band-pass filter for frequencies from 455 kc up 300 Mc.

10. A power-line filter for rejecting r-f interference has (a) r-f coupling capacitors in series with the power line; (b) r-f chokes in shunt across the power line; (c) 60-cps chokes in series with the power line; (d) r-f bypass capacitors in shunt across the power line.

ESSAY QUESTIONS

1. What is the function of an electrical filter?

2. Give two examples where the voltage has different frequency components.

3. (a) What is meant by pulsating direct current or voltage? (b) What are the two components of a pulsating d-c voltage? (c) How can you measure the value of each of the two components?

4. Define the function of the following filters in terms of output voltage across the load resistance: (a) High-pass filter. Why is an R_cC_c coupling circuit an example? (b) Low-pass filter. Why is an R_bC_b bypass circuit an example? (c) Band-pass filter. How does it differ from a coupling circuit? (d) Band-stop filter. How does it differ from a band-pass filter?

5. Draw circuit diagrams for the following filter types. No values are necessary. (a) T-type high-pass and T-type low-pass; (b) π-type low-pass filter, balanced with a filter reactance in both sides of the line.

6. Draw the circuit diagrams for L-type band-pass and L-type band-stop filters. How do these two circuits differ from each other?

7. Draw the response curve for each of the following filters: (a) low-pass cutting off at 20,000 cps; (b) high-pass cutting off at 20 cps; (c) Band-pass for 20 to 20,000 cps; (d) band-pass for 450 to 460 kc.

8. Give one similarity and one difference in comparing a coupling capacitor and a bypass capacitor.

9. Give two differences between a low-pass filter and a high-pass filter.

10. Explain briefly why the power-line filter in Fig. $23 \cdot 16$ passes 60-cps alternating current but not 1-Mc r-f current.

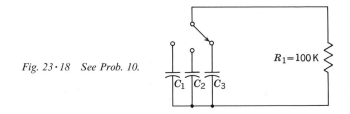

Fig. 23·18   See Prob. 10.

PROBLEMS (*Answers to selected problems at back of book.*)

1. Refer to the *RC* coupling circuit in Fig. 23·6, with *R* equal to 160,000 ohms. (*a*) Calculate the required value for C_c at 1,000 cps. (*b*) How much is the steady d-c voltage across C_c and across *R*? (*c*) How much is the a-c voltage across C_c and across *R*?
2. Refer to the R_1C_1 bypass circuit in Fig. 23·8. (*a*) Why is 1 Mc bypassed but not 1 kc? (*b*) If C_1 were doubled in capacitance, what is the lowest frequency that could be bypassed, maintaining 10:1 ratio of *R* to X_C?
3. Calculate the C_c needed to couple audio frequencies of 50 to 15,000 cps with 500-K *R*.
4. Show the fluctuating plate current i_b of a vacuum tube that has an average d-c axis of 24 ma and a square-wave a-c component with 10 ma peak value. Label the d-c axis, maximum and minimum positive values, and the peak-to-peak alternating current.
5. Show the fluctuating grid voltage e_C of a vacuum tube that has an average d-c axis of -8 volt and a sine-wave a-c component with 3 volts peak value. Label the d-c axis, maximum and minimum negative values, and peak-to-peak voltage.
6. Change the a-c component in Prob. 5 to 9 volts peak value. Label the d-c axis, maximum positive and negative values, and the peak-to-peak a-c voltage.
7. Draw an inverted-L-type band-stop filter used as a wavetrap for 455 kc. Give the inductance necessary with 80-pf *C*.
8. (*a*) Referring to Fig. 23·6, calculate the value of C_c necessary for coupling 50 cps when *R* is 500 K. (*b*) Referring to Fig. 23·7, calculate the value of C_1 necessary for bypassing R_1 at 50 cps.
9. Referring to the *RC* low-pass filter in Fig. 23·9a, draw the schematic diagram with values of 75 K for *R*, 0.001 µf for *C*, and 10 M for R_L. (*a*) For 10 volts input, calculate the values of V_C at 1 kc, 2 kc, 5 kc, 10 kc, and 15 kc. (*b*) Draw the response curve of the filter, plotting V_C vs. frequency.
10. Referring to the audio tone-control switch in Fig. 23·18, calculate the required capacitance values for the following: (*a*) C_1 to bypass R_1 at 10,000 cps; (*b*) C_2 to bypass R_1 at 5,000 cps; (*c*) C_3 to bypass R_1 at 2,000 cps.

Review of chapters ⬤20 to ⬤23

SUMMARY

1. X_C and X_L are opposite reactances. In series, the ohms of X_C and X_L cancel; in parallel, the capacitive and inductive branch currents cancel.

2. As a result, circuits with R, X_C, and X_L can be reduced to one net reactance and one equivalent resistance. In series circuits, the net reactance is added vectorially with the total resistance: $Z = \sqrt{R^2 + X^2}$; then $I = E/Z$. In parallel circuits, the net reactive branch current is added vectorially with the total resistive branch current: $I_T = \sqrt{I_R^2 + I_X^2}$; then $Z = E/I_T$.

3. The ohms of R, X_C, X_L, and Z in a-c circuits are compared in Table 20·1.

4. In a-c circuits with reactance, the real power in watts equals $I^2 R$, or $EI \cos \theta$, where θ is the phase angle of the circuit and $\cos \theta$ is the power factor.

5. A-c meter scales are generally calibrated in RMS values.

6. The wattmeter uses the dynamometer a-c meter movement to read E and I at the same time, measuring watts of real power.

7. Since X_L and X_C cancel in series, when they are equal, the net reactance is zero. In parallel, the net reactive branch current is zero. The frequency that makes $X_L = X_C$ is the resonant frequency $f_r = 1/(2\pi\sqrt{LC})$.

8. Larger values of L and C mean lower resonant frequencies, as f_r is inversely proportional to the square root of L or C. If L or C is quadrupled, for instance, f_r will decrease by one-half.

9. For a series-resonant LC circuit, the current is maximum, since the opposition is just the low resistance of the conductors; the voltage drop across each reactance is maximum, but they are equal and opposite; the phase angle is zero. The reactive voltage at resonance is Q times greater than the applied voltage.

10. For a parallel-resonant LC circuit, the impedance is maximum with minimum line current, since the reactive branch currents cancel. The impedance at resonance is Q times the X_L value, but it is resistive with a phase angle of zero.

11. The Q of the resonant circuit equals X_L/R_s for resistance in series with X_L, or R_P/X_L for resistance in parallel with X_L.

12. The bandwidth between half-power points is f_r/Q.

13. A filter uses inductance and capacitance to separate high or low frequencies. A low-pass filter allows low frequencies to develop output voltage across the load; a high-pass filter does the same for high frequencies. Series inductance or shunt capacitance provides low-pass filtering; series capacitance or shunt inductance provides high-pass filtering.

14. A fluctuating or pulsating direct current or voltage varies in amplitude but with one direction or polarity. It is equivalent to an a-c component varying in opposite directions around the average-value axis. The axis, which is just the arithmetical average of all the values in one cycle, is the steady d-c value.

15. An RC coupling circuit is effectively a high-pass filter for pulsating d-c voltage, passing the a-c component but blocking the d-c component.

16. A transformer with an isolated secondary is a high-pass filter for pulsating direct current, allowing a-c variations in the secondary but no output for the d-c level of primary current.

17. A bypass capacitor in parallel with R is effectively a low-pass filter, since its low reactance reduces the voltage across R for high frequencies.

18. The main types of filter circuits are π type, L type, and T type. These can be high-pass or low-pass, depending on how the L and C components are connected.
19. Resonant circuits can be used as band-pass or band-stop filters. For band-pass filtering, series-resonant circuits are in series with the load or parallel-resonant circuits are across the load. For band-stop filtering, parallel-resonant circuits are in series with the load or series-resonant circuits are across the load.
20. A wavetrap is an application of a resonant band-stop filter.

REFERENCES (*Additional references at back of book.*)

Annett, F. A., *Electrical Machinery*, 3d ed., McGraw-Hill Book Company, New York.

Dawes, C. L., *Industrial Electricity, Vol. 2, Alternating Currents*, 2d ed., McGraw-Hill Book Company, New York.

Gillie, A. C., *Electrical Principles of Electronics*, McGraw-Hill Book Company, New York.

Rider, J. F., and S. D. Uslan, *Understanding Vectors and Phase in Radio*, John F. Rider, Publisher, Inc., New York.

Sams, H. W., *Basic Radio Manual*, Howard W. Sams & Co., Inc., Indianapolis.

Siskind, C. S., *Electricity, Direct and Alternating Current*, 2d ed., McGraw-Hill Book Company, New York.

Stout, M. B., *Basic Electrical Measurements*, 2d ed., Prentice-Hall, Inc., Englewood Cliffs, N.J.

REVIEW SELF-EXAMINATION (*Answers at back of book.*)

Here's another chance to check your progress. Work the exercises just as you did those at the end of each chapter.

Fill in the numerical answer.

1. An a-c circuit with 100-ohm R_1 in series with 200-ohm R_2 has total resistance of _____ ohms.
2. With 100-ohm X_{C_1} in series with 200-ohm X_{C_2}, the total X_C equals _____ ohms.
3. With 100-ohm X_{L_1} in series with 200-ohm X_{L_2}, the total X_L equals _____ ohms.
4. Two X_C branches of 500 ohms each in parallel have a combined X_C value of _____ ohms.
5. Two X_L branches of 500 ohms each in parallel have a combined X_L value of _____ ohms.
6. With 500-ohm X_L in series with 300-ohm X_C, the net reactance equals _____ ohms.
7. With 500-ohm X_C in series with 300-ohm X_L, the net reactance equals _____ ohms.
8. With 10-ohm X_L in series with 10-ohm R, the total impedance equals _____ ohms.
9. With 10-ohm X_C in series with 10-ohm R, the total impedance equals _____ ohms.
10. With 14 volts applied across a total impedance of 14 ohms, the current equals _____ amp.
11. With 10-ohm X_L and 10-ohm R in series, the phase angle θ equals _____ degrees.
12. With 10-ohm X_C and 10-ohm R in series, the phase angle θ equals _____ degrees.
13. With 10-ohm X_L and 10-ohm R in parallel across 10 volts, each branch current equals _____ amp.
14. In question 13, the total line current equals _____ amp.
15. In questions 13 and 14, the combined impedance of the parallel branches equals _____ ohms.
16. An a-c circuit has 120 volts applied to produce 10 amp at a phase angle of 60°. A wattmeter will read the real power of _____ watts.
17. A 60-cycle a-c voltage with a peak value of 500 volts will be read by an iron-vane meter as _____ volts.
18. A circuit with L equal to 10 henrys and C of 40 μf will be resonant at approximately _____ cps.
19. A circuit with L of 100 μh and C of 400 pf will be resonant at approximately _____ Mc.
20. In question 19, if C is reduced to 100 pf, f_r will increase to _____ Mc.
21. In question 20, if L is increased to 400 μh, f_r will decrease to _____ Mc.
22. In a series-resonant circuit with 10 mv applied across 1-ohm R, 1,000-ohm X_L, and 1,000-ohm X_C, at resonance the current equals _____ ma.

23. In question 22, the voltage across X_C equals _____ volts.
24. In a parallel-resonant circuit with 1-ohm R in series with 1,000-ohm X_L in one branch and 1,000-ohm X_C in the other branch, with 10 mv applied the voltage across X_C equals _____ mv.
25. In question 24 the impedance of the parallel resonant circuit equals _____ M.
26. An LC circuit resonant at 500 kc has a Q of 100. Its total bandwidth between half-power points equals _____ kc.
27. In question 26, if the Q is reduced to 10 by a shunt damping resistor, the bandwidth becomes _____ kc.
28. A coupling capacitor for 40 to 15,000 cps in series with a 0.5-M resistor has the capacitance of _____ μf.
29. A bypass capacitor for 40 to 15,000 cps in shunt with a 1,000-ohm R has the capacitance of _____ μf.
30. A pulsating d-c voltage varying in a symmetrical sine wave between 100 and 200 volts has the average value of _____ volts.

   Answer true or false.
31. In an a-c circuit with X_C and R in series, if the frequency is increased, the current will increase.
32. In an a-c circuit with X_L and R in series, if the frequency is increased, the current will be reduced.
33. The volt-ampere is a unit of apparent power.
34. A circuit with a phase angle of $90°$ does not dissipate any real power.
35. Effective value and RMS value of a sine wave a-c voltage are the same.
36. In a capacitive voltage divider, the smallest C has the most voltage.
37. A steady direct current in the primary of a transformer cannot produce any a-c output voltage in the secondary.
38. A π-type filter with shunt capacitances is a low-pass filter.
39. An L-type filter with a parallel-resonant LC circuit in series with the load is a band-stop filter.
40. With pulsating d-c voltage applied across an RC coupling circuit, the average d-c level of the applied voltage is across the coupling capacitor.

Chapter

This unit describes the construction of electron tubes, the different types, and their applications as amplifiers to increase the amplitude of a desired signal or as rectifiers to change alternating current to direct current. Typical tube troubles are also given. The topics are:

24·1   Construction of tubes
24·2   Diodes
24·3   Plate current
24·4   Diode rectifier circuits
24·5   Triodes
24·6   How a triode amplifies the control-grid voltage
24·7   Triode characteristics
24·8   Tube constants
24·9   Tetrodes
24·10 Pentodes
24·11 Tube ratings
24·12 Tube types
24·13 Cathode-ray tubes
24·14 Phototubes
24·15 Gas tubes
24·16 Troubles in vacuum tubes

24·1   Construction of tubes

As illustrated in Fig. 24·1, a vacuum tube has a glass or metal envelope enclosing metal electrodes in a vacuum. The electrodes make it possible to have electrons flow through the evacuated space inside the tube. The electrode that emits electrons is the *cathode*. Generally, the cathode is heated by a wire filament, resulting in thermionic emission of electrons.

The electrode that collects the emitted electrons is the *anode,* or the *plate.*

The plate has a positive potential applied with respect to cathode, so that the emitted electrons are attracted to provide plate current. Between the cathode and plate the tube can also have a wire mesh serving as a control-grid electrode to increase or decrease electron flow to the plate. The current flow is almost instantaneous, a typical transit time being 0.001 μsec for electrons emitted from the cathode to reach the plate.

There are two advantages in using a vacuum tube to provide current. First, the emitted electrons can flow in only one direction from cathode to plate inside the tube. Thus the tube can serve as a rectifier, changing alternating current to direct current. Second, the amount of plate current can be controlled by the grid, so that in practice a small potential on the grid can control a much larger potential on the plate. Therefore, the tube can be used as an amplifier for electrical variations. For instance, an a-c signal variation of 1 volt RMS applied as input signal between control grid and cathode can be amplified 30 times, resulting in a similar variation but with an amplitude of 30 volts RMS for the output signal between plate and cathode.

The vacuum tube is fundamentally a low-current device, as the electron flow is limited by the amount of thermionic emission from the cathode. For conventional sizes, typical values of plate current are less than 1 ma to about 100 ma. Compared with transistors, most vacuum tubes have much higher internal resistance because of the relatively small plate current.

In their historical development, the first tubes were diodes, with a cathode and anode. Then triodes were invented, making use of the grid to control plate current. These were followed by tetrodes and pentodes. The tetrode has four electrodes, including two grids; the pentode has five elec-

Fig. 24·1   Typical vacuum tubes. (a) Eight-pin (octal) base. Height 3 in. (b) Seven-pin glass bulb. Height 1½ in. (c) Nine-pin (noval) glass bulb. Height 1½ in. (d) Miniature nuvistor. Height ½ in. (RCA.)

(a)   (b)   (c)   (d)

trodes with three grids. They all need the cathode to emit electrons and the plate to collect the emitted electrons. These are the main types of vacuum tubes.

In terms of their construction, the first receiver tubes had a relatively large envelope and base, like Fig. 24·2. In these tubes, the heater pins are thicker than the others. Then the octal type in Fig. 24·1a became almost a standard construction for receiver tubes, with either a metal shell or glass bulb. Now the smaller glass tubes with seven-pin base or nine-pin base are more common. The trend has been to smaller tubes for compact equipment and for use at higher frequencies. As a final example, the nuvistor in *d* is as small as many transistors.

24·2 Diodes

A diode has just two electrodes, cathode and plate, as shown in Fig. 24·2. Note the schematic symbol. The heater is not counted as an electrode because it is merely an incandescent filament to heat the cathode electrically. If any other method were convenient for heating the cathode to its emission temperature, it would serve just as well. The heater is insulated from the cathode so that there is no connection between the heater circuit and the current flow resulting from cathode emission.

Note that the plate surrounds the cathode. Therefore, electrons emitted from the surface of the cathode sleeve can be attracted to the metal anode to provide plate current. The plate is usually made of iron, nickel, or molybdenum. Larger plate area is used for tubes that conduct larger values of plate current.

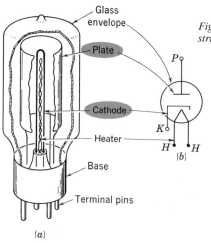

Fig. 24·2 Diode vacuum tube. (a) Construction. (b) Schematic symbol.

Fig. 24·3 (a) Filament cathode heated with direct current. (b) Indirectly heated cathode with a-c power for heater.

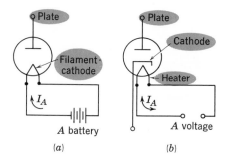

Thermionic emission. When a metal is heated, electrons in the atoms are accelerated in their random motion because of the added heat energy. With enough heat to make the metal glow as an incandescent filament, some internal electrons gain enough velocity to break away from the surface of the metal. In a sense, the electrons can be considered as "boiled off" the surface. Now the metal is a cathode that supplies electrons by thermionic emission.

Cathode construction. The two types are illustrated schematically in Fig. 24·3. In *a*, the filament-cathode is heated directly by electrical current, serving as an incandescent filament that produces thermionic emission. In *b*, the cathode is heated indirectly by a separate heater. The directly heated type is usually called a *filament,* while the filament for the indirectly heated cathode is called a *heater.*

An indirectly heated cathode consists of a heater wire inside a metal sleeve, which is the cathode (Fig. 24·2). The cathode sleeve is coated with a material very efficient in thermionic emission to release many electrons from the outer surface at relatively low temperatures. Generally, the alkaline earth elements such as barium, calcium, and strontium in oxide form are coated on a nickel-alloy base. The oxide coating requires a temperature of only about 725°C, glowing a dull red, for sufficient thermionic emission. In this construction, the heater is just a tungsten-alloy wire to heat the oxide-coated cathode. The metal sleeve and its coating are heated indirectly from the glowing heater wire by radiation and thermal conduction, since they are so close, but there is no electrical connection between the heater and cathode sleeve.

The directly heated filament-cathode (Fig. 24·4) is often made of tungsten. Pure tungsten produces thermionic emission when it glows white-hot at 2300°C. Thorium-coated tungsten provides thermionic emission at the lower temperature of 1700°C, glowing bright yellow. The directly heated filament-cathode is generally used in power tubes for large amounts of thermionic emission, or in small tubes operated from a battery, where efficiency and quick heating are important.

Filament current. Power for heating the filament is obtained by applying the rated filament voltage so that the correct amount of current can flow to heat the filament. The ratings are given in the manufacturer's tube manual. For instance, many tubes are rated at 6.3 volts, 0.3 amp for the heater; that is, 6.3 volts applied will produce the rated heater current of 0.3 amp. The hot resistance of the filament then is 6.3 volts/0.3 amp, which equals 21 ohms. The source for the heater is called the *A voltage,* corresponding to the A battery originally used for filament power.

Filament cathodes are usually heated with direct current, often from an A battery. For an indirectly heated cathode, the heater generally uses 60-cps alternating current from the power line with an RMS value equal to the d-c value. Most receiver tubes use an indirectly heated cathode, with 60-cps a-c heater current, because of its convenience.

The vacuum. After the tube is assembled, air is exhausted from the envelope. There are several reasons why the vacuum is necessary. First the heated filament would oxidize in air and burn. Also, the cathode emits more electrons in a vacuum. Finally, when it is desired that only the electrons emitted from the cathode travel to the plate, without ionizing air molecules, the electrodes must be in a vacuum.

When enough air has been pumped out, the envelope is sealed off. To improve the vacuum further, the entire assembly is then heated to force out any additional gas molecules in the metal electrodes. At this time, a magnesium *getter* compound, mounted on a small disk inside, vaporizes because of the heating. The resultant chemical action of the vaporized magnesium, with the gases released from the metal, removes the final traces of gas in the tube. After the tube cools off, the vaporized getter condenses on the inside of the envelope, forming the familiar silvery film usually seen in glass tubes.

A tube with a very good vacuum is often called a *hard tube;* a *soft tube* has more air. In a soft tube you may see a small amount of bluish glow, which is ionized air. Power tubes often have this glow in normal operation. If the vacuum tube is completely filled with the bluish glow, however, it is a gassy tube and must be replaced. It should be noted that some tube types are not vacuum tubes, however, but are purposely filled with mercury vapor or neon or argon gas for particular applications. These are gas tubes which glow with ionized gas in normal operation.

24·3 Plate current

Plate current flows in a vacuum tube because the plate is made positive with respect to the cathode in order to attract the emitted electrons. Furthermore, the plate circuit has a continuous path for the electron flow returning to the cathode. As illustrated in Fig. 24·4, thermionic emission results in a cloud of electrons near the cathode. Since electrons have a negative charge, they are attracted to the positive anode. The plate supply volt-

Fig. 24·4   Plate current flowing in cathode-plate circuit.

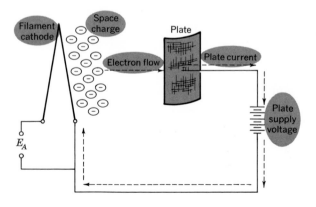

age is a d-c source that maintains the plate positive while the negative side returns to the cathode. Then electrons attracted to the plate inside the tube can flow through the plate circuit, with a continuous path for electron flow back to the cathode.

In Fig. 24·4, notice that the circuit for E_a to produce current to heat the filament is a complete path in itself, independent of the path for plate-cathode current shown by the dotted lines. As an indication of how the two circuits are separate, remember that the polarity of E_A does not matter in heating the filament; but the plate supply voltage must make the plate positive with respect to cathode, or there will be no plate current.

Space charge. As shown in Fig. 24·4, this charge is the cloud of electrons near the cathode, ejected by thermionic emission. The electrons cannot go to the anode, however, unless the plate is positive. Without the positive accelerating potential, some of the emitted electrons can fall back to the cathode, depending on their initial emission velocity. With the cathode heated to its normal operating temperature, equilibrium is established between the emitted electrons and returning electrons, resulting in the space charge near the cathode as a source of electrons that can be attracted to the plate.

When the positive plate attracts electrons from the space charge, additional electrons can be supplied by the thermionic cathode. The electrons in motion can be considered as the *space current* inside the tube.

Edison effect. The fact that electrons in the space charge can be attracted to the anode is called the *Edison effect*. In 1885, Thomas Edison observed that even in incandescent lamps, the heated filament could lose electrons that were attracted to a separate electrode.

Plate-current characteristics. If a milliammeter is connected in series in the plate circuit, as shown in Fig. 24·5a, the meter can read the values of plate current I produced by different amounts of plate voltage E. Remember that the plate voltage must be positive. The results are tabulated and

Fig. 24·5   *Measuring I for different plate voltages to obtain diode volt-ampere characteristic curve. (a) Schematic. (b) Graph.*

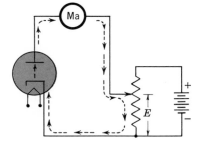

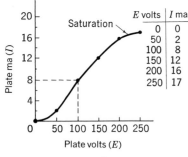

E volts	I ma
0	0
50	2
100	8
150	12
200	16
250	17

(a)

(b)

plotted on the graph in *b*. The procedure is simply to vary the potentiometer *R* to obtain the desired value of *E* and then read the corresponding *I*. A tube with an indirectly heated cathode is shown here, in order to concentrate on the plate current. The heater circuit is omitted as it operates at rated voltage and is not varied for this experiment. The resulting graph is a plate characteristic curve, plotting the amount of *I* for a corresponding *E* for this particular tube. For example, the curve shows that a plate voltage of 100 volts allows a plate current of 8 ma. Such a curve showing *I* plotted against *E* is called a volt-ampere *characteristic* of the diode.

Note the following important characteristics evident from the curve in Fig. 24·5*b*:

1. The plate current is practically zero without any plate voltage. Although the cathode supplies space charge, without the force of positive plate voltage the electrons cannot be attracted to the plate.

2. Only positive values of *E* are shown, since there is no plate current when the plate is negative with respect to cathode. Negative plate voltage only repels the space-charge electrons back toward the cathode. Also, the plate itself cannot produce thermionic emission because it is not heated. As a result, the electron current cannot flow in the reverse direction from plate to cathode inside the tube.

3. Increasing the amount of positive plate voltage increases the amount of plate current. The plate is close to the cathode in a diode, usually just about ⅛ in. or less. Then *E* produces an electrostatic field at the space charge with enough intensity to accelerate the electrons away from the cathode. Higher values of *E* produce a greater accelerating force to allow more electrons to be collected by the plate for higher values of *I*.

4. At a high enough value of positive plate voltage, however, *I* cannot increase with higher values of *E* because of saturation. The saturation value of *I* means that more electrons cannot be supplied by the space charge, unless the cathode temperature is increased for more emission.

The plate-current characteristic indicates that the tube is essentially a nonlinear device having comparatively high internal resistance from cathode to plate. For example, 8-ma *I* with 100-volt *E* means that the tube is a resistance equal to 100 volts/0.008 amp, or 12,500 ohms. The fact that the current flows through a vacuum does not change its nature as a resistance that allows 8 ma to flow with 100 volts applied across the plate-cathode circuit. It is a one-way conductor, however, since current can flow only from cathode to plate.

Also, the tube is a nonlinear resistance. Doubling the plate voltage does not always double the plate current. Particularly at low values of *E*, where the plate current is low, and for high values of *E*, where the plate current is limited by saturation, the tube characteristic is nonlinear. In addition, different tubes will have different plate characteristics, depending on their construction, especially the cathode emission. Where a small tube may provide 0.5-ma *I* with 50-volt *E*, a larger tube can supply over 100 ma with 400-volt *E*. For these reasons the plate-current characteristics of vacuum

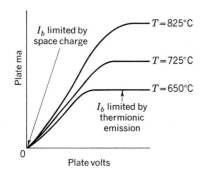

Fig. 24·6 Diode volt-ampere characteristics for different cathode temperatures.

tubes are described by curves such as the one in Fig. 24·5b. Characteristic curves for all tubes can be found in the manufacturer's tube manual.

Effect of cathode temperature. The three volt-ampere diode characteristics in Fig. 24·6 can be obtained experimentally by varying the filament voltage to see the effect of different cathode temperatures on saturation of the plate current. For the middle curve, the rated filament voltage is used for normal cathode temperature. The top curve shows the effect of a higher temperature with more filament voltage, while the bottom curve is for values lower than normal. Notice that all three curves are almost equal for low values of E. Then I is space-charge limited because of insufficient accelerating force. The amount of current is about the same, even with more thermionic emission, because of insufficient E to attract the electrons to the plate.

For higher values of E, though, more emission allows more plate current. Also, for any one curve, I increases with E, which is typical of normal operation. However, when E is high enough for the plate to collect all the emitted electrons, the plate current is saturated. Then more E does not increase the saturation plate current. It should be noted that these curves illustrate the factors that determine the amount of space current, but most tubes are generally operated at the rated filament voltage, which is not varied. In this case, a characteristic like the middle curve is typical of normal operation.

24·4   Diode rectifier circuits

The fact that the diode allows current to flow in only one direction means that it is useful as a rectifier to change alternating current to direct current. Such a diode rectifier circuit is shown in Fig. 24·7.

Load resistance. Plate current in a vacuum tube becomes useful when it is made to flow through an external load outside the tube. The purpose of using an external load resistance R_L is to have a load that can develop an IR_L voltage drop outside the tube that depends on the amount of plate current flowing within the tube. Then the IR_L drop is output voltage that can be coupled to another circuit. Since the value of the IR_L voltage depends on the amount of plate current, the tube can determine the output voltage. For the diode rectifier circuit in Fig. 24·7, therefore, R_L is connected in series with the diode V_1 and the a-c input voltage.

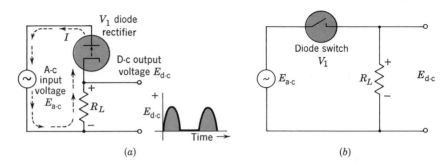

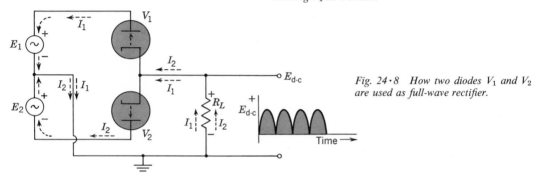

Fig. 24·7   *Diode half-wave rectifier circuit. (a) A-c input to V₁ rectified to pulsating d-c output. (b) Equivalent circuit showing V₁ as a switch.*

Fig. 24·8   *How two diodes V₁ and V₂ are used as full-wave rectifier.*

Half-wave rectifier. Referring to Fig. 24·7a, note that the voltage applied to the diode plate-cathode circuit through R_L is the a-c input voltage. There is no d-c supply voltage for the tube now, because the a-c input voltage drives the diode plate positive every half-cycle. When the plate is driven positive, plate current flows through the tube and the input voltage source, returning to the cathode through R_L. For the half-cycle when the input voltage makes the diode plate negative, there is no plate current and no output voltage across R_L. The result is half-cycles, or half-waves, of current through R_L in the direction shown. Current cannot flow in the opposite direction, because I flows only from cathode to plate in the tube. The output voltage across R_L equals IR_L. This output is a d-c voltage, therefore, because it has just one polarity.

Although not a steady d-c voltage, the pulsating d-c output has the fixed polarity shown, with a half-wave of rectified output for each cycle of the a-c input. The fluctuating component is the *ripple* in the d-c output, consisting of half-wave pulsations at the same frequency as the a-c input. Therefore, the ripple frequency of the half-wave rectifier for the 60-cycle a-c power-line voltage is 60 cps.

The rectified output has the polarity shown in Fig. 24·7a because the external load resistance R_L is connected in series between the cathode of the tube and one side of the a-c input voltage. Then I flowing in the plate circuit must return from the low side of R_L, through its resistance, and back to cathode. Since the electron flow is from minus to plus, the cathode side of R_L must be the positive side of the rectified output voltage. This polarity is just with respect to the opposite side of R_L. The cathode is still less positive than the plate voltage supplied by the a-c input when it drives the diode into conduction. Otherwise, there could be no plate current.

The diode as a one-way switch. In Fig. 24·7b, the rectifier circuit is redrawn to show the diode as a switch that lets current flow in only one direction. When the diode plate is positive, plate current flows. Then the tube is on, or the switch V_1 is closed. With the diode plate negative, the diode is an open circuit, as its resistance is practically infinite without plate current. Then the switch V_1 is open.

As a result, we can consider the rectification in terms of the switching action. Only when E_{a-c} is positive does the a-c input voltage become connected to R_L through V_1. Now we can also see why E_{d-c} across R_L must be positive at the cathode end. This terminal is connected to the positive side of E_{a-c} by the closed switch when V_1 conducts. Therefore, the only time output can be produced is when the cathode side of R_L is positive with respect to its opposite terminal.

Full-wave rectifier. As shown in Fig. 24·8, the full-wave rectifier uses both alternations of the a-c input voltage to produce rectified d-c output. Therefore, the full-wave circuit can supply more d-c power output than the equivalent half-wave circuit. Two diodes are necessary for the full-wave circuit. One diode conducts for one alternation while the other rests. On the next alternation, conditions reverse, and the other diode conducts. The a-c input supplies equal and opposite voltages for the two diodes.

In Fig. 24·8, the input voltage is shown with the polarity that makes the top diode plate positive. Therefore, V_1 conducts plate current I_1 through the a-c source E_1, to the center tap in the input circuit, to chassis ground returning current through R_L to the V_1 cathode. During this time, the V_2 plate is negative, and it cannot conduct. For the next half-cycle, however, the polarities shown for E_1 and E_2 reverse. Then V_1 cannot conduct, because its plate is negative while the V_2 plate is positive. The plate current I_2 for D_2 flows through the a-c source E_2, to the center tap in the input circuit, to chassis ground and returns through R_L to the V_2 cathode. Therefore, the diodes conduct on both half-cycles, utilizing the full cycle of the a-c input voltage.

Although the diodes conduct on opposite half-cycles, notice that for both cases the plate current for either tube flows in the same direction through R_L in returning to cathode. Therefore, the rectified output has one fixed polarity to provide d-c output voltage. This output is positive at the common cathode connection because R_L is in the cathode-to-ground circuit for both tubes.

The ripple frequency is double the frequency of the a-c input voltage, since each half-cycle produces a fluctuation of d-c output voltage. For 60-cps power-line voltage as a-c input, the ripple frequency in the d-c output is 120 cps. This is another advantage of the full-wave rectifier circuit, since the higher ripple frequency is easier to filter, requiring smaller capacitors for the same bypassing effect to produce steady d-c voltage output.

Power supply with full-wave rectifier. The rectifier circuit often has the function of providing d-c output voltage to be used as B+ voltage for the plate supply of additional amplifier tubes on the same chassis. In this application, the rectifier circuit is called a power supply. As illustrated in Fig. 24·9 for a full-wave rectifier, the power transformer T_1 steps up the a-c input voltage to provide the desired amount of B+ output voltage. The high-voltage secondary L_2 is center-tapped for equal and opposite a-c input voltages to the two diodes. For a half-wave rectifier, the high-voltage winding need not have the center tap. Note the low-voltage windings L_3 and L_4. A separate winding is necessary for the rectifier filament because it has the B+ voltage. L_4 provides a-c power to all the other heaters in parallel.

The rectifier tube changes the a-c input to d-c output. However, a filter is needed to provide a steady d-c voltage. This is the function of the π-type low-pass filter with C_1, L_5, and C_2 to filter out the 120-cycle a-c ripple. The result is a steady d-c voltage for the B+ output that supplies plate voltage to the amplifiers.

In power supplies, it is convenient to consider the B+ output voltage with respect to the metal chassis, which may or may not be connected to earth ground. In either case, any connection to the metal chassis is considered as chassis ground, with the symbol shown in Fig. 24·9. In this circuit, the chassis is also B minus because the center tap on the high-voltage winding is returned to chassis. We can consider that the center tap on L_2 for the input at the left is joined to the chassis ground connections for the output at the right in the schematic diagram.

Although there are usually additional circuits connected to a common chassis ground, the chassis does not change the return path of current flow for the rectifier. Any electrons leaving the cathode of the diode must return to the cathode, where they originated. The fact that the cathode emitted the

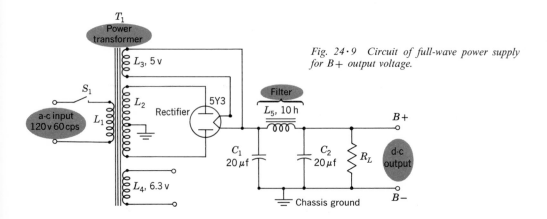

Fig. 24·9   Circuit of full-wave power supply for B+ output voltage.

electrons forming the plate current means the cathode has the potential needed to return to itself exactly the number of electrons in the space current of the diode.

Power-supply hum. In a receiver, insufficient filtering allows excessive ripple in the d-c output of the power supply, causing hum. This hum is often the result of an open or leaky filter capacitor. The hum frequency is 60 cps for a half-wave rectifier or 120 cps with a full-wave rectifier.

Diode applications. In addition to their use as power rectifiers, diodes are also used for detector circuits. A detector is a low-power rectifier circuit for a few volts of a-c signal voltage. For the audio detector in radio receivers, as an example, the a-c input is modulated r-f signal. This a-c signal input must be rectified to filter out the r-f variations and extract the audio modulation. Generally, the detector circuit has only one diode as a half-wave rectifier. Either a vacuum tube or semiconductor diode can be used.

For power supplies, which generally use 60-cps a-c input, the main types can be summarized as follows:

1. *Half-wave.* One diode rectifies the total a-c voltage input across the high-voltage winding of the power transformer. The ripple frequency to be filtered out is 60 cps.

2. *Inverted half-wave.* The a-c input is applied to the diode cathode, instead of the plate. The d-c output across R_L in the plate-to-ground circuit then is negative.

3. *Full-wave.* Two diodes are used to rectify one-half the total a-c voltage across the high-voltage winding of the power transformer. The ripple frequency is 120 cps. The advantages are more current output and better filtering.

4. *Transformerless or a-c/d-c.* No power transformer is used, for economy or to save weight and space. A half-wave rectifier is used for the 120-volt a-c input. For d-c operation, the diode is just a series resistance, when the input polarity makes the plate positive. The heaters of all the tubes are in series across the 120-volt power line.

5. *Full-wave bridge.* Four diodes are used in a full-wave circuit that can rectify the total a-c voltage across the high-voltage winding of the power transformer.

6. *Voltage doubler.* Two diodes are used, with or without a power transformer, to provide d-c output voltage almost double the peak of the a-c input voltage, depending on the load current. The circuit can be arranged as either a full-wave rectifier with 120-cps ripple, or half-wave rectifier with 60-cps ripple.

For all these power-supply rectifier circuits, vacuum tubes, gas tubes, or semiconductor diodes can be used.

24·5 Triodes

As illustrated in Fig. 24·10, a cathode and a plate are needed to provide plate current like a diode, but in addition the triode has the control-grid electrode. The grid is a fine metal wire, usually nickel, molybdenum, or iron, wrapped around two supports placed in the space between the cathode and the plate. All electrons attracted to the plate from the cathode go through the openings in the grid. The grid is connected to a base pin, however, so that it can have voltage applied to determine the amount of electrons that travel from cathode to plate and provide plate current. Now the plate current depends on two factors: the plate voltage and the control-grid voltage.

C— voltage. The potential applied to the control grid is usually a small negative voltage with respect to cathode, as shown in Fig. 24·11. This voltage completes the alphabet, with A voltage for the heater, B+ voltage for the plate, and C— for the control grid. The grid voltage is usually made negative so that it cannot attract electrons. Then there will be no grid current. The function of the control grid is not to provide current but to have its voltage control the plate current.

Effect of control grid on space charge. The reason the plate current depends on the grid voltage is that the grid is close to the cathode. As a result, the grid voltage is much more effective in controlling the cloud of electrons near the cathode, which is the space charge. The plate has a positive potential providing a field with a force tending to attract electrons out of the space charge to the plate. The plate is relatively far away, however, reducing its field strength at the cathode. The grid is at the space charge, and the field of the grid potential exists in the spaces between grid wires.

Whether plate current can flow and how much depends on both the plate and grid potentials. For example, with a small negative grid potential such as −3 volts, and a strong positive plate potential of several hundred volts, the attracting force of the plate can be strong enough to attract electrons to provide plate current. If, however, the grid is made just 1 volt more negative, for example, its repelling force on the space charge may nullify 100 volts of plate potential and the plate current is reduced. Or making the grid voltage slightly less negative has a great effect on increasing the plate current.

How much effect the grid has on the plate current depends on the spacing of the turns of grid wire, how close the grid structure is to the cathode, and how much the control-grid voltage is. The effect of the grid voltage on plate current can be summarized as follows:

1. Less negative grid voltage increases the plate current.
2. More negative grid voltage decreases the plate current.
3. If the grid voltage is made negative enough, there will be no plate current even with the plate positive.

Grid-cutoff voltage. The amount of negative grid voltage required to cut off the plate current with a specified amount of positive voltage on the plate is called the *grid-cutoff* voltage. For some tubes, the grid-cutoff voltage may be as little as −1 volt; for others, the grid-cutoff voltage may be −60 volts, as typical examples. The grid-cutoff voltage is a characteristic of the tube construction, but also depends on the amount of plate voltage.

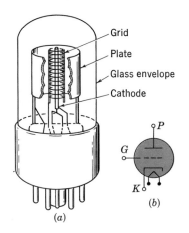

(a)

Grid
Plate
Glass envelope
Cathode

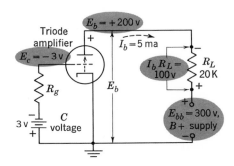

(b)

Fig. 24·10 Triode vacuum tube. (a) Construction. (b) Schematic symbol.

Fig. 24·11 Triode circuit with C— voltage E_c for grid and E_b for plate voltage.

Closer spacing of the wires in the grid allows more control of the plate current. Then a small voltage on the grid has a strong field in the space between the grid wires and a great effect on the space charge. Similarly, placing the grid structure closer to the cathode allows more control of plate current by the grid. These combinations of close spacing make the tube have a sharp cutoff characteristic; that is, a small negative voltage of 1 to 6 volts can cut off the plate current.

Triode circuit. Current flows in the triode plate circuit in Fig. 24·11 because the plate has its positive voltage and the control-grid potential is less than the grid-cutoff voltage. The electron flow inside the tube is from the cathode through the spaces between the grid wire to the anode. In the external plate circuit, the electrons flow through the plate-load resistor R_L and the B supply, returning to the cathode through the chassis. Assuming 5-ma plate current, the $I_b R_L$ drop equals $0.005 \times 20,000$, which is 100 volts.

The plate-to-cathode circuit of the tube and R_L are in series as a voltage divider across the 300-volt B supply E_{bb}. Therefore, the plate-to-cathode voltage E_b equals 300 volts minus the 100-volt drop across R_L, or 200 volts. As a formula,

$$E_b = E_{bb} - I_b R_L \qquad (24·1)$$

This formula is often used in order to determine the actual plate-cathode voltage.

E_b is important because this voltage moves the space charge in the tube. The B+ supply is the source for the plate voltage, but E_b is always less than E_{bb} because of the voltage drop across the external plate load resistance R_L. Although it may seem a disadvantage, the external R_L is needed to provide voltage output that can be coupled to another circuit. Remember that all references to plate voltage mean E_b, not the supply voltage E_{bb}.

Example 1. Calculate E_b for 20-ma I_b with 2,000-ohm R_L and 250-volt B+.

Answer. $\quad E_b = E_{bb} - I_b R_L = 250 - (20 \times 10^{-3} \times 2 \times 10^3)$
$\qquad\qquad E_b = 250 - 40 = \textbf{210 volts}$

Example 2. For the same B+, calculate E_b with 2-ma I_b and 100-K R_L.

Answer. $\qquad\qquad\qquad E_b = 250 - 200 = \textbf{50 volts}$

Control-grid bias. In the control-grid circuit, the C voltage is connected with the negative side toward the grid and the positive side to chassis ground. The cathode is connected to chassis. As a result, the positive side of the C voltage is connected to the cathode. The C voltage makes the grid negative, therefore, with respect to the cathode. The grid resistor R_g is inserted to provide a d-c path for the C voltage to the control grid. If the C voltage illustrated by the 3-volt battery in Fig. 24·11 is the only control-grid voltage, it can be connected directly to the grid and R_g will not be needed. When another voltage is connected to the grid, however, R_g is necessary as a *grid load resistance* to prevent the grid from being shorted to cathode by the low resistance of the C battery, while still providing a d-c path for the C voltage. In this case the C battery voltage is the negative d-c bias voltage of the control grid. Its function is to maintain the average grid voltage negative with respect to the cathode, even if additional voltage at the grid should be positive.

Symbols for tube voltages. In analyzing vacuum-tube amplifier circuits, we must distinguish between plate or grid voltages and between plate-cathode voltage or the B+ supply. Furthermore, when a-c signal is amplified the grid and plate voltages have fluctuating d-c waveforms with an

Table 24·1   Vacuum-tube letter symbols

E_{bb} = d-c plate supply voltage, equal to B+

E_b = average d-c plate-cathode voltage

e_b = instantaneous value of the fluctuating d-c plate voltage with signal variations

e_p = a-c component of the fluctuating d-c plate voltage. This is the amplified a-c signal output

E_{cc} = control-grid d-c bias supply voltage

E_c = average control-grid d-c voltage. This equals E_{cc} when there is no control-grid current

e_c = instantaneous value of the fluctuating d-c grid voltage with signal variations

e_g = a-c signal input to the control grid

---

*Table 24·2   Amplification**

	e_c, volts	i_b, ma	i_bR_L, volts	$e_b = 300 - i_bR_L$, volts
	−2	6	120	180
Average level ⟶	−3	5	100	200
	−4	4	80	220

* R_L = 20 K and B+ = 300 volts.

average d-c value and an a-c component. The symbols in Table 24·1 are generally used.

The same system of nomenclature also applies to the plate current, with I_b for average d-c, i_b for instantaneous d-c, and i_p for a-c values. These symbols are used for diodes, triodes, tetrodes, or pentodes.

24·6   How a triode amplifies the control-grid voltage

The main advantage in having the control grid is the fact that it enables the vacuum tube to amplify a small voltage at the grid to provide much more voltage at the plate. The amplification results from the ability of the control-grid voltage to vary the plate current.

Consider the numerical examples listed in Table 24·2. For the circuit in Fig. 24·11, let the plate current i_b be 5 ma with −3 volts for the control-grid bias voltage e_c. These values are listed in the middle row of Table 24·2. With 5-ma i_b, the plate voltage equals 200 volts. The 300-volt B+ voltage drops to 200 volts for the plate because of the 100-volt IR drop across the 20,000-ohm R_L.

Now suppose the grid voltage e_c is reduced from −3 to −2 volts. The grid, being less negative, allows more plate current. For the case of i_b increasing to 6 ma, then, the voltage drop across R_L increases to 120 volts. The voltage for e_b is less, however, falling to 180 volts as the remainder of the 300-volt B supply minus the i_bR_L drop.

For the third case, in the bottom row, when e_c is made more negative, from −3 volts to −4, less plate current flows. Then i_b is reduced to 4 ma. This change results in a smaller i_bR_L drop of 80 volts. The resulting plate voltage, equal to 300 volts minus 80 volts, rises to 220 volts.

Note the effect of the changes as the grid voltage e_c varies ±1 volt, above and below the −3-volt middle value. Similarly, i_b varies ±1 ma around the 5-ma middle value. So far, all that the control-grid voltage has done is vary the plate current. In terms of plate voltage, however, e_b varies ±20 volts above and below the middle value of 200 volts. Here is where the amplification is accomplished. The changes in plate current through the plate-load resistance allow the plate voltage to vary by a much larger amount than the grid-voltage variation. In this example, the grid-voltage variation of ±1 volt has been multiplied by the factor of 20 to produce a corresponding plate voltage variation of ±20 volts. For amplication, the requirements are that (1) the grid voltage must vary the plate current and (2) the plate circuit must have a plate-load resistance that can vary the plate voltage as the plate current varies.

It is important to realize that the variation in plate voltage is an amplified duplicate of the variation in grid voltage. For the example here of a $\pm$20-volt change in e_b, there is no problem in having a d-c voltage vary by 20 volts. This change could be made without a triode. The feature of the triode amplification, though, is the fact that the relatively large plate voltage variations are the same as the grid variations but larger. In other words, tubes can amplify very small grid voltage variations up to almost any value. For instance, a 100-μv a-c signal can be increased by several amplifiers to provide more than 100-volt amplitude of the same variations.

The symbol for the voltage gain of an amplifier is A_v. Its value can be calculated as $A_v = e_{out}/e_{in}$. These are a-c signal voltages, in RMS, peak or peak-to-peak values, as long as the same measure is used for both. As examples, for 200 μvolts output signal with 20 μvolts input signal, A_v is 200/20 or 10; also, if we know A_v is 30, with an input signal of 2 volts, the output signal equals 30×2 or 60 volts.

24·7   Triode characteristics

The plate current is not linear for all values of electrode voltages. Therefore, it is necessary to show tube characteristics by curves. The way that plate current i_b is affected by both plate voltage e_b and control-grid voltage e_c is shown by the characteristic curves in Fig. 24·12. The plate characteristics in *a* are shown for a 6J5 triode with 2 volts for e_c. With this grid voltage, the curve shows that 80 volts on the plate allows slightly less than 4-ma i_b; or 120-volt e_b produces 8-ma i_b, as examples. The e_b values are plate-to-cathode voltages, not the B supply voltage. With current through

Fig. 24·12   *Triode characteristic curves. (a) Graph of e_b and i_b values for one value of e_c. (b) Family of plate characteristics with e_b and i_b values for different e_c values.*

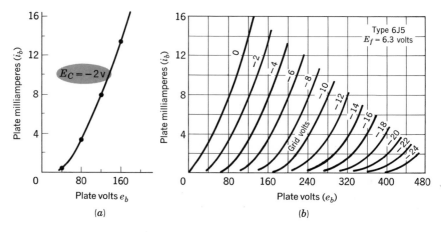

R_L, the plate-to-cathode voltage e_b is less than the B supply voltage E_{bb} by the amount of $i_b R_L$ voltage drop across the plate load.

The manufacturer's tube manual shows a family of plate characteristics for different values of e_c. Typical curves are shown in Fig. 24·12b. Note that the curve marked -2 volts for e_c in b is the same characteristic shown in a. The family of characteristics, however, shows more information for typical values of negative grid voltage. From left to right, the individual curves show plate characteristics for e_c values of 0, -2, -4, -6, and more negative voltage up to -24 volts. The family of curves shows all the plate-current characteristics of the tube.

For any fixed value of e_c, just read the one curve to determine i_b for a specified e_b. For instance, with -4 volts for e_c, this curve intersects the vertical line for 160-volt e_b at the horizontal line for 8-ma i_b. Therefore, the grid potential of -4 volts allows 8-ma i_b with 160-volt e_b. As another example, -8 volts for e_c with the same 160-volt e_b allows only 1 ma plate current. The cutoff grid voltage resulting in zero plate current is approximately -10 volts, for 160 volts on the plate.

24·8   Tube constants

The characteristics of the tube can be specified by factors which are relatively constant when operation is over the linear part of the characteristic curves. These include the amplification factor μ, or mu, the internal plate-cathode resistance r_p, and the grid-plate mutual transconductance g_m. These tube characteristics apply to triodes, tetrodes, and pentodes.

Amplification factor. This factor compares the effectiveness of the control-grid voltage e_c to the plate voltage e_b in changing the plate current i_b:

$$\mu = \frac{\Delta e_b}{\Delta e_c} \qquad \text{for the same } i_b \qquad (24\cdot2)$$

For example, in Fig. 24·12, with e_b fixed at 160 volts when e_c is changed from -4 to -2 volts, i_b changes from 8 to 13 ma. Therefore, Δe_c of 2 volts produces Δi_b of 5 ma. For the same Δi_b of 5 ma, with e_c fixed at -2 volts, the e_b value must be decreased from 160 to 120 volts to decrease i_b from 13 to 8 ma. As a result, e_b must be changed 40 volts to have the same 5-ma change in i_b. Therefore,

$$\mu = \frac{\Delta e_b}{\Delta e_c} = \frac{40 \text{ volts}}{2 \text{ volts}} = 20$$

The μ of this tube, therefore, is 20. There are no units, since μ is a ratio of two voltages and the volt units cancel.

It should be noted that the μ of the tube is definitely not the same as the A_v of the amplifier stage. The μ is a characteristic of the tube construction, while the voltage amplification depends on the tube and the amplifier circuit. Actually, the voltage gain of the amplifier circuit must be less than the tube amplification factor, as μ represents a maximum value that A_v can only approach.

Plate resistance. This factor is the equivalent resistance of the plate-to-cathode circuit of the tube. Since plate voltage is applied across the tube and plate current is flowing through it, the tube has a resistance equal to its e/i ratio:

$$r_p = \frac{\Delta e_b}{\Delta i_b} \qquad \text{for the same } e_c \qquad (24 \cdot 3)$$

Considering the grid voltage constant at -2 volts in Fig. $24 \cdot 12$, remember that for this example i_b changed by 5 ma when e_b changed by 40 volts. Therefore,

$$r_p = \frac{\Delta e_b}{\Delta i_b} = \frac{40 \text{ volts}}{0.005 \text{ amp}} = 8,000 \text{ ohms}$$

This value is considered the a-c or small-signal r_p, since it is calculated from small changes. The d-c or large-signal values, indicated R_P, can be calculated simply as E_b/I_b. For the same example of -2 volts E_C, the E_b/I_b ratio is $160/0.013$, which equals 12,300 ohms for R_P.

Transconductance. This factor states how effective the grid is in changing the plate current:

$$g_m = \frac{\Delta i_b}{\Delta e_c} \qquad \text{for the same } e_b \qquad (24 \cdot 4)$$

In Fig. $24 \cdot 12$, Δe_c of 2 volts changed i_b by 5 ma, with e_b at 160 volts. Therefore,

$$g_m = \frac{\Delta i_b}{\Delta e_c} = \frac{0.005 \text{ amp}}{2 \text{ volts}} = 0.0025 \text{ mho} = 2,500 \times 10^{-6} \text{ mho}$$

$$= 2,500 \text{ } \mu\text{mhos}$$

The unit for g_m is mhos for conductance, since an i/e ratio is the reciprocal of ohms. Since vacuum tubes are low-current devices, the transconductance will be a fraction of 1 mho. It is more convenient, therefore, to specify g_m in micromhos. Typical values for receiver tubes are 2,000 to 14,000 μmhos.

24·9   Tetrodes

This construction is similar to the triode, with cathode, control grid, and plate, but there is an additional electrode called the *screen grid* between the control grid and the plate. See Fig. $24 \cdot 13$. The control grid is grid No. 1, placed close to the cathode so that it still functions to control the space charge. The screen grid is grid No. 2, closer to the plate. It is not used to

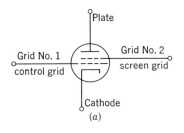

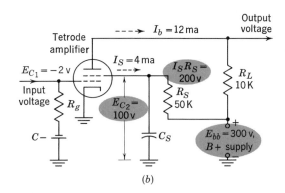

Fig. 24·13   The tetrode. (a) Schematic symbol.
(b) Circuit with positive d-c voltage for screen
grid in addition to plate.

control the plate current but has steady positive d-c voltage to help accelerate electrons to be collected by the plate. The path for plate current
inside the tube is from the cathode, through the control grid, and through
the spaces in the screen grid to be collected by the plate. Since the screen
grid is positive, it will collect some electrons. These provide screen-grid
current that returns to the cathode through the screen-grid circuit. The
screen-grid current is *waste current,* however, since it is not used in the
output circuit. The plate current is the desired current that flows across
the plate-load resistor. Although the screen grid has some waste current,
it is only a small part of the total electrons flowing through the tube. Most
of the electrons can go through the spaces in the screen grid, attracted by
the higher positive potential of the plate. As a typical example, the desired
plate current may be 12 ma, while the screen-grid waste current is 4 ma.

Screen-grid voltage. The screen grid must have a positive accelerating
potential, or there will be no electrons attracted toward the plate. With no
screen-grid voltage, there will be no plate current. Usually the screen grid
is made less positive than the plate to reduce the screen current. The positive screen-grid potential E_{C_2} can be obtained from the same B supply that
provides plate voltage. As shown in Fig. 24·13b, the resistor R_S, called the
screen-dropping resistor, is in series with the screen-grid-to-B+ circuit.
Then the screen current returning through the B supply to the cathode
flows through R_S. The $I_S R_S$ voltage drop allows the screen-grid voltage to
be less than the B+ voltage by the amount of voltage across the screen-
dropping resistor. For this example, the $I_S R_S$ voltage drop of 4 ma through
50,000 ohms equals 200 volts across R_S. The remainder for the screen-grid–
cathode circuit then is the 300 volts of the B supply minus the 200-volt
IR drop across R_S, which is equal to 100 volts for the screen-grid voltage.
As a formula, we can say that

$$E_{C_2} = E_{bb} - I_s R_s \qquad (24·5)$$

Example 3. Calculate E_{C_2} with 20-K R_s, 8-ma I_s, and 250-volt B+.

Answer. $E_{C_2} = E_{bb} - I_s R_s = 250 - 0.008 \times 20,000$
$E_{C_2} = 250 - 160 = $ **90 volts**

Example 4. What size R_s is needed for 125-volt E_{C_2} with 3-ma I_s and 275-volt E_{bb}?

Answer. $I_sR_s = E_{bb} - E_{C_2} = 275 - 125 = 150$ volts

$$R_s = \frac{150}{0.003} = \textbf{50,000 ohms}$$

In order to make sure that the voltage remains fixed at its steady d-c value, the screen-grid resistor is bypassed to the cathode by the screen-bypass capacitor C_S. As a bypass, its capacitance value must be large enough to have reactance low enough to be one-tenth or less of R_s. The reactance is figured at the lowest frequency of the a-c signal being amplified by the control-grid and plate circuits of the tube.

Characteristics of a screen-grid tube. The effect of the screen grid with its positive voltage is to reduce the effectiveness of plate voltage in determining plate current. Although the screen-grid voltage is usually lower than the plate voltage, the screen grid is closer to the cathode than the plate is. The control grid is still effective, however, in controlling the space charge near the cathode. As a result, screen-grid tubes can have much higher values of amplification factor, compared with triodes, higher r_p, and sharper cutoff.

Interelectrode capacitances. The screen grid also reduces the capacitance between control grid and plate inside the tube. This capacitance is noted as C_{gp} in Fig. 24·14. The reason for the capacitance is simply the fact that the control grid and plate are two metal conductors separated by an insulator, which is the vacuum in the tube. As Fig. 24·14b shows, the typical value of 4 pf for a triode is reduced by a factor of ¹⁄₁,₀₀₀ to the low

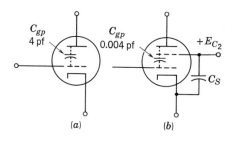

(a)   (b)

Fig. 24·14   *Interelectrode capacitance between plate and control grid. (a) In triode. (b) In screen-grid tube.*

Fig. 24·15   *Volt-ampere characteristic of negative resistance illustrated for a tetrode tube.*

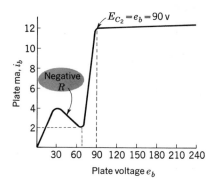

value of 0.004 pf for C_{gp} in the equivalent tube with a screen grid. The reason for the reduced value of C_{gp} is that the screen grid acts as a shield between plate and control grid for a-c signal.

Additional electrode capacitances to be considered are the input and output capacitances of the tube. The input capacitance is from control grid to cathode. The output capacitance is from plate to cathode. As listed in the manufacturer's tube manual, typical values of input capacitance are 3 to 10 pf; output capacitance values are 3 to 6 pf. Triodes generally have less input capacitance than pentodes. Lower values of all interelectrode capacitances are obtained with smaller electrodes in miniature glass tubes. Small capacitances are necessary in amplifying high frequencies.

Secondary emission. Metals have the property of releasing electrons when the surface is bombarded by incident electrons. No heat is necessary. The requirement is high positive voltage to provide a strong accelerating field so that the incident electrons can strike at high velocity. The electrons released are then called *secondary electrons,* and the process is *secondary emission.* In a vacuum tube, the metal plate is bombarded by the electrons attracted from the cathode. Therefore, the plate has secondary emission. In a diode or triode, though, the secondary electrons are no problem, because any secondary electrons near the plate are promptly collected by the positive anode. In a tetrode, however, the screen grid can attract secondary electrons emitted from the plate when e_b drops below E_{C_2}. This effect reduces the plate current, as shown in Fig. 24·15. For this reason, tetrodes are not commonly used in amplifier circuits. One older tetrode tube is the type 24A. Generally, when a screen-grid tube is desired for an amplifier, a pentode is used.

Volt-ampere characteristic of negative resistance in a tetrode. A special feature of a tetrode characteristic curve is that for a range of values less than E_{C_2}, the plate current i_b is reduced when e_b is increased as shown in Fig. 24·15. This characteristic of less current for more voltage is called *negative resistance.* The curve in Fig. 24·15 indicates that the tetrode plate-cathode circuit acts like a negative resistance for values of e_b from 30 to 70 volts. Specifically, when e_b increases from 30 to 70 volts, i_b decreases from 4 to 2 ma. This negative slope in the characteristic curve results from the ability of the screen grid to collect secondary electrons from the plate. Below 30 volts e_b, there is little secondary emission. Above 70 volts e_b, the secondary electrons are attracted back to the plate.

The importance of a negative resistance or a negative slope in the volt-ampere characteristic is the fact that any device like this, including some semiconductors, can be used in an oscillator circuit. An *oscillator* is a circuit that can generate a-c output, from its d-c power input, without the need for any a-c signal input.

24·10   Pentodes

As shown in Fig. 24·16, the pentode has the same kind of construction as a tetrode but with the addition of a suppressor grid in the space between

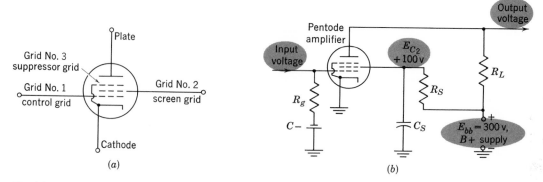

Fig. 24·16 (a) Pentode schematic symbol, showing suppressor tied internally to cathode. (b) Pentode amplifier circuit.

the screen grid and the plate. Since it is a screen-grid tube, the pentode has the advantages of little grid-to-plate capacitance and operating characteristics like a tetrode, but negligible secondary emission from the plate because of the suppressor grid. In the schematic in Fig. 24·16a, note that the first grid is the control grid, grid No. 2 is the screen grid, and grid No. 3 is the *suppressor grid.* The suppressor grid is not used for input or output signal but has a fixed potential, usually equal to the cathode voltage. In most pentodes, the suppressor is connected internally to the cathode. When the suppressor has its own external pin connection, it is connected to either the cathode pin or chassis ground.

Since the suppressor is close to the plate but has the cathode potential that is negative with respect to the plate, any secondary electrons emitted are repelled back to the plate. The plate can still attract electrons from the cathode, however, to provide plate current. Inside the tube, the electrons released by thermionic emission from the cathode flow through the spaces between wires in the control grid, screen grid, and suppressor grid. The positive potential on the plate provides an accelerating field that is able to accelerate electrons from the space charge and through the grids to be collected by the plate.

Referring to the pentode circuit in Fig. 24· 16b, note that the screen-grid voltage is operated at a fixed positive d-c voltage, as for a tetrode. Just as in triodes, the input voltage to be amplified is connected to the control-grid circuit, which has its required negative C-bias voltage. The amplified output signal voltage in the plate circuit results from plate current flowing through the plate-load resistor R_L.

Current paths. In a circuit like Fig. 24·16b, it is important to keep in mind the different currents for each electrode. Let us assume I_b is 12 ma and I_{c_2} is 3 ma. This means 12-ma I_b flows in the plate circuit through R_L. Also, 3-ma I_{c_2} flows in the screen-grid circuit through R_S. In the B supply, both I_b and I_{c_2} add to result in 15 ma. This 15 ma is actually the space cur-

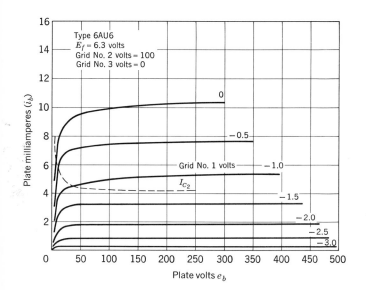

Fig. 24·17 Plate characteristic curves for miniature glass pentode 6AU6.

rent in the tube, which must return to the cathode. If you insert a milliammeter in the cathode circuit, it will read 15 ma. Furthermore, if the control grid goes positive, it can attract electrons to produce grid current I_{c_1}. Assume an I_{c_1} of 1 ma. Then 1-ma I_{c_1} flows through R_g and the C supply back to cathode.

In summary, the cathode current is the space current, equal to the sum of all the individual electrode currents. As a formula, $I_k = I_b + I_{c_2} + I_{c_1}$. If we assume 40 ma, 8 ma and 1 ma for these values, as an example, $I_k = 40 + 8 + 1 = 49$ ma.

Pentode characteristics. As for triodes, the manufacturer's tube manual shows plate characteristic curves of pentodes for different values of control-grid voltage. For the e_{c_1} value of -1 volt in Fig. 24·17 as an example, the curve shows that plate current increases from approximately 5 ma with 100-volt e_b to 5.5 ma with 400-volt e_b. The very slow rise of the curve means that the plate current increases very little with increased plate voltage in a pentode. This characteristic is a result of the screen-grid voltage, which is constant. In terms of the plate resistance of the tube, its r_p is very high because i_b changes very little with a change in e_b.

However, the control grid still has its effect on plate current. For example, with e_b at 100 volts, when e_{c_1} is made more negative from -1 volt to -2 volts, the plate current decreases from 5 to 1.8 ma. Zero plate current results with e_{c_1} at approximately -4 volts, which is the grid-cutoff voltage for this sharp-cutoff tube. Since changes in grid voltage e_{c_1} are more effective in varying the plate current than changes in plate voltage e_b, this effect corresponds to very high values of amplification factor for pentodes.

Note that the pentode characteristics in Fig. 24·17 are nonlinear below the knee of the curve at about 25-volt e_b. Therefore, operation should be limited to plate-voltage values above the knee.

The dashed curve in Fig. 24·17 shows how much screen-grid current (I_{c_2}) flows for different values of E_b, with the control-grid voltage at zero. Note, though, that the screen-grid voltage is steady at 100 volts, as listed at the top left of the graph. With typical operating values of e_b above 25 volts, the screen-grid current is fairly constant at about 4.2 ma. This value can be used for this tube in calculating the screen resistor needed for the desired screen-grid voltage.

Remote-cutoff pentodes. Because pentodes tend to have sharp cutoff, some tubes are constructed with a control grid that has different spacing between turns. The grid turns are closely spaced at both ends but have wider spacing in the center. With small negative values of e_{c_1} electrons can flow through all the spaces in the grid. When the negative grid voltage is increased, the close-spaced part of the grid cuts off electron flow, but the wider spaces allow plate current. Much higher negative values of e_{c_1} are required for the wider spaces of the grid to cut off electron flow. For example, a pentode with a sharp cutoff of −6 volts may correspond to a similar remote-cutoff tube that cuts off plate current at −30 volts for e_{c_1}. The remote-cutoff pentodes are also called *supercontrol* or *variable-μ* tubes.

24·11   Tube ratings

It is important not to exceed the maximum ratings specified by the manufacturer, or the tube will be damaged, by either excessive heat or arcing in the tube.

Plate dissipation. This is the power dissipated in the form of heat by the plate as a result of electron bombardment. For instance, the 6AU6 miniature glass pentode has a maximum rating of 3-watt plate dissipation. In general, the larger the tube and its plate, the greater is the permissible plate dissipation. The power dissipated in the plate can be calculated approximately for linear operation as the product of the average direct plate voltage and current. For example, with 150-volt E_b and 3-ma I_b, as typical values, the plate dissipation equals 150×0.003, or 0.45 watt. This answer is the average d-c power dissipated by the plate, without any a-c signal.

Grid No. 2 input. This rating states the maximum power dissipation permitted for the screen grid. For the 6AU6, for example, the maximum permissible value is 0.65 watt. Typical operation, with 100 volts E_{c_2} and 4-ma I_{c_2} produces 100×0.004, or 0.4 watt.

Peak heater-cathode voltage. For indirectly heated tubes, this rating states the highest instantaneous voltage the tube can withstand without internal arcing between cathode and heater.

Maximum peak-inverse plate voltage. For power-supply rectifier tubes, this rating states the highest inverse voltage, making the plate negative, that the tube can withstand without internal arcing between cathode and plate.

Maximum peak plate current. For power-supply rectifier tubes, this rating states the highest instantaneous value of plate current the tube can conduct without damage to the tube.

Maximum output current. For rectifier tubes, this rating states the highest amount of load current the rectifier can conduct without damage to the tube.

23·12 Tube types

There are many types of diode, triode, and pentode tubes to meet specific needs in different applications. For instance, some types are called *power tubes*. They have the function of providing appreciable plate current for power output. This type would be necessary where the load resistance is relatively low. For example, a power rectifier is a diode to supply 100 ma load current, compared with less than 1 ma for a small diode detector. Or a pentode power amplifier tube could supply 50-ma plate current compared with a voltage amplifier tube for appreciable output voltage with a high R_L and plate current of 3 ma. In general, power tubes are comparatively large.

Tube numbers. The first digits in a tube type number usually indicate the filament or heater voltage. For example, the 6SK7 heater voltage is 6.3 volts, the 12SK7 needs 12.6 volts, and the 50L6 uses 50 volts. Many power rectifiers require 5-volt filament voltage, such as the 5Y3 and 5U4. Some noval base tubes, such as the 12AX7, have a center-tapped heater that can be wired for either 12.6 or 6.3 volts. The 6.3-volt tubes are intended for wiring of heaters in parallel. Other heater voltages such as 3, 5, 19, 25, 35, and 50 are usually for series circuits, where the heater voltages add to equal the a-c line voltage of 120 volts.

The last digit in the tube-type number generally gives the number of pins used. The middle letters often indicate the type of tube. Letters at the end of the alphabet are for power rectifiers, such as the 6X5, 5Y3, and 35Z5-GT; letters at the start of the alphabet are for amplifiers, such as the 6AU6 pentode. There are so many different tubes, though, that this rule does not always apply.

Pin connections. The octal base is shown in Fig. 24·18a. This base is made of Bakelite, with eight pins equally spaced. The black mark between pins 1 and 8 indicates the keyway to line up with a notch in the socket so that corresponding pin numbers are connected on the socket and base. The octal-socket pins are numbered clockwise from 1 to 8, when you look at it from the bottom, as in Fig. 24·18. The top view is opposite. The seven- and nine-pin miniature glass tubes in *b* and *c* are also numbered clockwise, bottom view, starting from the wider space between pins 1 and 7 or between pins 1 and 9. These tubes do not have a base or a keyway.

When there are base pins not connected internally, these are dummy pins. The corresponding socket terminals are often used as tie points for wiring.

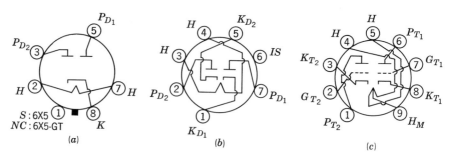

Fig. 24·18 *Sockets with pin connections. Bottom view. (a) Octal.
(b) Seven-pin. (c) Nine-pin.*

Tube shields. Metal tubes have an internal shield usually connected to pin 1, which should be tied to chassis ground. Glass tubes often have an external metal shield, as shown in Fig. 24·19. The shield slips over the tube and contacts spring clips connected to the chassis. Tubes that have two or more sections in one envelope usually have an internal shield between sections. A shield minimizes interaction between tubes amplifying high frequencies.

Multipurpose tubes. To save space, one envelope often includes two or more tube functions. As examples, the 6SN7 is a twin triode, with each section the same as one 6J5; the 6AV6 and 6AT6 are miniature glass tubes with duodiode and triode in one envelope, all with a common cathode; the 6AN8 is a triode-pentode. The *compactron* type in Fig. 24·20 combines two diodes and two triodes.

Beam-power tubes. These tubes operate as pentodes, but instead of a suppressor grid the tube has internal beam-forming plates tied to the cathode. The feature of this construction is low screen current, which is important for power tubes. In this application, the screen grid can be at approximately the same potential as the plate because of the small waste current in the screen-grid circuit. Typical tubes are the 6DQ6, 6V6, 35L6, and 50C5.

Fig. 24·19 *Typical tube sockets and shield cans.*

Fig. 24·20 Compactron multifunc-
tion tube 6B10, combining two diodes
and two triodes. Height 1½ in. Base
has twelve pins, with 1 and 12 for
the heater. (GE.)

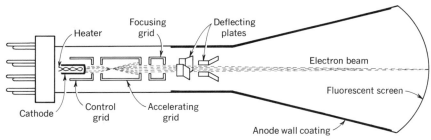

Fig. 24·21 Cathode-ray tube using electrostatic deflection and focusing.
Screen diameter is generally 3 in. or 5 in. for oscilloscopes.

High-power tubes. In transmitters, larger tubes are generally used to produce the required amount of output power. Typical ratings are several hundred watts up to kilowatts. The larger tubes may have a water-cooled anode.

24·13 Cathode-ray tubes

As illustrated in Fig. 24·21, the cathode-ray tube, or CRT, consists of an electron gun, deflection plates, and a fluorescent screen inside the evacuated glass envelope. Although the cathode, control-grid, and anode electrodes are constructed as cylinders, their function is the same as in conventional vacuum tubes. The cathode is heated to emit electrons, and the control grid controls the flow of electrons attracted by the positive potential of the anodes. High voltages are used on the order of 2 to 80 kv for the last anode. The entire cylinder assembly can be considered an *electron gun*, producing electrons formed into a narrow beam attracted to the screen. The inside surface of the front glass faceplate is coated with a fluorescent material that emits light when bombarded by electrons. Green and white are two common colors of illumination that can be produced by the screen, depending on its chemical composition.

When the electron beam hits the screen, it produces a spot of light visible through the glass. In order to deflect the electron beam and move the position of the light spot on the screen, deflection voltage can be applied to the

Fig. 24·22 Phototube. Wide curved electrode is the photocathode; narrow rod at the center is the anode connected to top cap. Height is 2 in.

deflection plates. A pair of horizontal deflection plates provides the potential difference needed to move the electron beam left or right. Similarly, the pair of vertical deflection plates can move the beam up or down. This type of CRT is used in the *oscilloscope*, which is a test instrument that shows the waveform of voltage applied to its input terminals. An example is the sine-wave photograph shown in Fig. 13·1. Similarly, the picture reproduced on the screen of the picture tube in a television receiver is another application of the CRT, but picture tubes use magnetic deflection because of the larger screen.

24·14   Phototubes

Some elements are photosensitive, being able to change their characteristics when illuminated. Selenium, for instance, changes its resistance with light, and cesium emits electrons when illuminated. Such electrons emitted by photoelectric materials are *photoelectrons.* The emitter then is a *photocathode.* When an anode with a positive potential is placed close by, the electrons can be collected to provide photoelectric current. The anode and photocathode in a vacuum glass envelope provide a photoelectric tube, or PE cell. An example is shown in Fig. 24·22.

24·15   Gas tubes

Although not vacuum tubes, gas-filled tubes are often used in similar applications especially for power supplies, where appreciable load current must be supplied. Gas tubes can conduct much more current than the equivalent vacuum tube. The reason is that when current flows, the gas is ionized to provide ionization current much greater than the electron flow from the cathode. An example of a gas tube is the 866 mercury-vapor rectifier shown in Fig. 24·23a. Note the dot symbol to indicate a gas tube. With this type of rectifier, it is important that the filament be heated sufficiently to produce space charge before positive plate voltage is applied. Otherwise, ionized gas particles can destroy the cathode-emitting material.

The VR-150 in Fig. 24·24 is a voltage-regulator gas diode rated at 150 volts. This is a cold-cathode gas tube, without any heater. The gas is a helium-argon mixture.

There are gas triodes also, but they generally do not have the same applications as vacuum-tube amplifiers. A gas tube with a control grid is called a *thyratron.*

24·16 Troubles in vacuum tubes

The most common troubles in vacuum tubes are an open heater or weak emission from the cathode. Sometimes there may be an internal short between electrodes, or the tube may be microphonic. Also, tubes may have excessive cathode-to-heater leakage, which causes hum. In all cases, the defective tube must be replaced.

Open filament. There is no current and the tube is cold. In glass tubes usually you can see that the filament is not lit. The possibility of an open can be checked by the ohmmeter, with power off. Just place the ohmmeter leads across the two filament pins and check continuity. In many octal tubes, the heater pins are 2 and 7; for a seven-pin tube, the heater is usually pins 3 and 4; for noval tubes, the heater is usually pins 4 and 5.

Typical resistance for the cold heater is 1 to 50 ohms, depending on the tube. A low resistance reading indicates that there is no open and that the filament is normal. Note that the cold resistance of the filament is much less than the hot resistance, by a factor of about one-tenth. For example, a tube rated for 0.3-amp heater current at 6.3 volts has a hot resistance in normal operation of 6.3 volts/0.3 amp, which equals 21 ohms. The normal resistance of the cold heater, however, as checked by an ohmmeter, is only about 2 ohms.

Microphonics. A tube with electrodes that are not perfectly rigid is called *microphonic* because the electrodes can act like a microphone if the tube vibrates. In a receiver, when a microphonic tube is tapped, it produces a hollow ringing noise that dies out slowly. At loud volume settings, the sound can make the microphonic tube vibrate, and it causes a sustained howl.

Cathode-to-heater leakage. If the insulation resistance between cathode and heater is not high enough, this leakage resistance can cause hum in the

Fig. 24·23 Gas tubes. (a) Type 866 mercury-vapor power rectifier tube. (b) Schematic symbol with dot to indicate gas tube.

Fig. 24·24 (a) Cold-cathode glow tube. (b) Symbol.

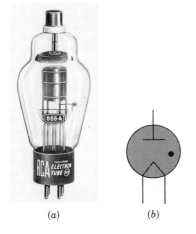

(a)   (b)

(a)   (b)

receiver. With 60-cycle alternating current for the heater, the hum frequency is 60 cps.

Tube noise. Although it is not necessarily a defect, tubes do produce a small amount of noise. In a receiver the tube noise produces a continuous hissing or "frying" sound. This noise can often be heard between stations with the volume all the way up. Much of the tube noise results from the random flow of electrons forming the plate current and is called *shot effect.* The resultant noise voltage is in the order of microvolts, but for tubes with a small amount of signal voltage input that will be amplified to a great extent, the noise generated in the first stages of amplification may be significant.

In general, the more grids there are, the more noise the tube will generate because of the partition effect of the grids on the space current, causing a more random electron flow to the plate. Triodes are therefore less noisy than equivalent multigrid types. As a result, where low tube noise is important, triodes may be used in preference to pentodes.

Tube checkers. As shown in Fig. 24·25, this instrument provides operating voltages for a tube inserted in its proper socket, and conduction is indicated by a meter on the panel that reads "good" or "bad." There are two types. In the emission tester only static plate current is indicated. In the mutual-conductance type, a small a-c voltage is applied to the grid, and the change in plate current indicates whether the tube is good or bad. This type, which is preferable, can have the meter scale calibrated in micromhos in addition to the good/bad scale. The LINE-ADJUST control must be set to provide equal line voltage for tubes that draw different amounts of heater power from the 60-cycle a-c power-line input.

The scale of a tube checker has a question mark at the center range to indicate a tube of doubtful quality. For power tubes, it is usually better to replace questionable tubes.

Fig. 24·25 Tube checker. (Hickok Electrical Instrument Co.)

SUMMARY

1. Diodes have a heated cathode and anode. The cathode emits electrons by thermionic emission; the cloud of emitted electrons near the cathode is the space charge. The anode attracts the electrons when it is positive with respect to cathode. The plate current can flow in only one direction from cathode to plate. The more positive the plate voltage e_b, the more plate current i_b, up to saturation.
2. In a filament cathode, the heated filament emits electrons and serves as the cathode. With an indirectly heated cathode, a separate heater makes the insulated cathode emit electrons.
3. The diode is useful as a rectifier to change alternating to direct current. One diode is used as a half-wave rectifier; two diodes can be used in a full-wave rectifier circuit.
4. In a triode, the control grid determines how many electrons from the space charge are attracted by the positive plate to provide plate current. The more negative the control grid voltage e_c is, the less the plate current. The negative e_c value that results in zero i_b is the grid-cutoff voltage. The fixed negative d-c voltage for E_c is the grid bias.
5. The function of the triode is to amplify a grid-voltage variation. Amplification requires a steady positive d-c plate voltage, to allow plate current and an external plate load resistance R_L in series between the plate and B+. Plate current flowing through R_L can produce changes in plate voltage much greater than the changes in grid voltage.
6. The three main characteristics for triode, tetrode, and pentode amplifier tubes are the amplification factor μ equal to $\Delta e_b/\Delta e_c$, plate resistance r_p equal to $\Delta e_b/\Delta i_b$, and transconductance g_m equal to $\Delta i_b/\Delta e_c$.
7. Tetrodes have the cathode, control-grid, and plate structure of a triode, plus the screen grid between the control grid and plate. The screen grid must have a positive d-c voltage, bypassed to the cathode at the a-c signal frequency.
8. Because of secondary emission, the plate circuit of a tetrode can have a negative resistance characteristic, meaning that the current decreases with more applied voltage.
9. Pentodes have the cathode, control grid, screen grid, and plate plus the suppressor grid between the plate and screen grid. The suppressor grid eliminates the effect of secondary emission from the plate. The screen grid reduces C_{gp}.
10. Table 24·3 summarizes the main points about pentodes, tetrodes, triodes, and diodes. The nomenclature for electrode voltages is given in Table 24·1.
11. In tube-type numbers, the first digit indicates the filament voltage, the letters indicate the type, and the final digits give the number of pins actually used. The main types are the octal eight-pin base and seven- and nine-pin miniature glass tubes.
12. The most common tube troubles are low emission or an open heater.

SELF-EXAMINATION (*Answers at back of book.*)

Here's a chance to find out how well you have learned the material in this chapter. These exercises are for your self-testing only.
1. In a diode the plate current increases when the (*a*) plate voltage is made more positive; (*b*) plate voltage is made less positive; (*c*) control-grid voltage is made less negative; (*d*) saturation plate current is reached.
2. With an indirectly heated cathode, the heater voltage (*a*) is applied to the cathode; (*b*) is separate from the cathode circuit; (*c*) must be a steady d-c voltage; (*d*) is equal to the C bias voltage.
3. In a triode, tetrode, or pentode, the plate current increases when the (*a*) control-grid voltage is made more negative; (*b*) control-grid voltage is made less negative; (*c*) plate voltage is made less positive; (*d*) screen-grid voltage is made less positive.
4. The screen grid in a pentode (*a*) makes the plate current more dependent on plate voltage; (*b*) has the same potential as the cathode; (*c*) decreases the grid-plate capacitance, as compared with a triode; (*d*) eliminates the problem of secondary emission from the plate.
5. The suppressor grid in a pentode (*a*) reduces the grid-plate capacitance, as compared with a triode; (*b*) eliminates the problem of secondary emission from the plate; (*c*) usually has a positive d-c potential less than the plate voltage; (*d*) is usually connected internally to the control grid.

Table 24·3 Types of vacuum tubes

Tube	Symbol*	Electrodes	Characteristics	Applications
Diode		Plate Cathode	When plate is positive, conducts current only from cathode to plate	One diode for half-wave rectifier, two diodes for full-wave rectifier
Triode		Plate Control grid Cathode	Negative grid controls plate current; has large C_{gp}	Triode amplifier with external R_L, for a-f amplifiers; low tube noise
Tetrode		Plate Screen grid Control grid Cathode	Screen grid reduces C_{gp}, screen must have $+$d-c voltage and by-pass to cathode for a-c signal	Tetrode little used because of secondary emission from plate
Pentode		Plate Suppressor grid Screen grid Control grid Cathode	Suppressor grid eliminates secondary emission; screen grid provides high μ and high r_p	For a-f or r-f amplifiers; sharp cutoff except variable-μ tubes

* Tubes shown with indirectly heated cathode.

6. With 250-volt E_{bb} and 10-ma I_b through 20-K R_L, the plate-cathode voltage E_b equals (a) 10; (b) 20; (c) 50; (d) 250.
7. In a half-wave rectifier circuit, the diode conducts when the (a) plate is made positive by the positive alternation of the a-c input voltage; (b) plate is made negative by the negative alternation of the a-c input voltage; (c) cathode is made positive by the positive alternation of the a-c input voltage; (d) a-c input voltage is at its average value of zero.
8. In a pentode, when e_c varies ± 2 volts, the plate current varies ± 10 ma. The grid-plate transconductance g_m equals (a) 500 μmhos; (b) 1,000 μmhos; (c) 2,000 μmhos; (d) 5,000 μmhos.
9. The heater power required for the 12BA6 remote-cutoff pentode is (a) 7 volts at 0.15 amp; (b) 12.6 volts at 0.15 amp; (c) 6.3 volts at 0.3 amp; (d) 12.6 volts at 0.3 amp.
10. With 8-ma I_b, 2-ma I_{c_2}, and 500 μa I_{c_1}, the total cathode current I_K equals (a) 2 ma; (b) 8 ma; (c) 10.5 ma; (d) 500 ma.

ESSAY QUESTIONS

1. Draw the schematic symbols for diode, triode, and pentode vacuum tubes, labeling all electrodes.
2. Show the schematic symbols for a filament cathode and an indirectly heated cathode. Give one advantage of each.
3. Define the following in terms of vacuum-tube operation: (a) saturation plate current; (b) space charge; (c) grid-plate capacitance; (d) input capacitance; (e) output capacitance.
4. (a) Redraw Fig. 24·9 as a half-wave rectifier, using one diode of the 5Y3 and one-half the L_2 winding. (b) What is the ripple frequency now? (c) Why would larger values of L and C be used for the filter?
5. Draw the schematic diagram of a triode amplifier circuit with a plate-load R_L. Give the function of (a) A voltage; (b) B voltage; (c) C voltage; (d) R_L.

6. Draw the schematic diagram of a pentode amplifier with a plate load resistance R_L. (*a*) What is the function of the screen-grid resistor R_s? (*b*) What is the function of the screen bypass capacitor C_s? (*c*) What is the path of plate current? (*d*) What is the path of screen current? (*e*) Why is there no control-grid current?

7. Define μ, r_p, and g_m for a triode or pentode amplifier tube.

8. Define the following symbols: E_{bb}, E_b, e_b, E_{c_2}, E_{c_1}.

9. (*a*) Define negative resistance. (*b*) How does the graph in Fig. 24·15 illustrate this? (*c*) For what operating conditions does a tetrode have negative resistance?

10. Referring to the full-wave power supply in Fig. 24·9, give the function of S_1, T_1, the 5Y3, C_1, L_5, and C_2.

11. Explain briefly why in a rectifier circuit the d-c output voltage at the cathode of the rectifier is positive with respect to chassis ground. Why is the chassis then B minus?

12. What is the advantage of gas tubes as rectifiers, compared with vacuum tubes?

13. Describe briefly four types of power-supply circuits.

14. Give eight different types of electron tubes.

15. Give two possible causes of hum in a radio receiver.

16. Referring to Fig. 24·16, why is a bypass capacitor used for R_S in the screen-grid circuit but not for R_L in the plate circuit?

17. How would you test for an open heater with an ohmmeter?

18. Give three kinds of tube troubles.

PROBLEMS (*Answers to selected problems at back of book.*)

1. (*a*) Calculate E_{c2}, with 4-ma I_{c2}, 25-K R_s, and 250-volt E_{bb}. (*b*) Calculate E_b, with 12-ma I_b, 5-K R_L, and 250-volt E_{bb}. (*c*) For these values, calculate the d-c power dissipated at the screen grid and at the plate.

2. Referring to the triode plate characteristic curves in Fig. 24·12, how much is the plate current i_b for the following? (*a*) e_b is 120 volts, e_c is 0 volts; (*b*) same e_b but e_c is −2 volts; (*c*) same e_b but e_c is −6 volts; (*d*) e_c is −6 volts but e_b is 200 volts; (*e*) e_b is 400 volts and e_c is −18 volts. (*f*) How much negative grid voltage e_c is required for zero i_b with 400 volts e_b?

3. Referring to the pentode plate characteristic curves in Fig. 24·17, how much is i_b with −2.5 volts e_c when e_b has values of 100, 200, 250, and 300 volts? Why do these values indicate that plate current is relatively independent of plate voltage in a screen-grid tube?

4. Referring to the family of plate characteristics for the pentode in Fig. 24·17: (*a*) Tabulate the values of i_b, with a constant e_b at 250 volts, for e_c values in 0.5-volt steps from 0 to −3.5 volts. (*b*) Draw a graph showing i_b on the vertical axis vs. e_c on the horizontal axis.

5. Referring to Fig. 24·17, with e_b constant at 200 volts calculate g_m for an e_c change of 0.5 volt from an average E_C of −1 volt.

6. (*a*) Calculate R_s to drop E_{bb} of 300 volts to 90 volts for E_{C_2}, with I_{C_2} of 4 ma. (*b*) Calculate C_s needed to bypass R_s at 50 cps.

7. (*a*) Calculate R_L for 40-volt E_b with 300 volts for E_{bb} and 2-ma I_b. (*b*) Calculate the d-c plate power dissipation. (*c*) Calculate the d-c power dissipated in R_L.

8. In Fig. 24·9, with a turns ratio of 8:1 between the entire winding of L_2 to L_1: (*a*) How much a-c voltage is applied to each diode of the 5Y3 full-wave rectifier? (*b*) How much a-c voltage would be applied to a half-wave diode using all the turns of L_2?

9. In Fig. 24·9, calculate the reactance of the filter choke L_5 and the filter capacitors C_1 and C_2 at 60 cps and at 120 cps.

10. In Fig. 24·9, assume 120 ma d-c load current, 480 volts d-c output at the rectifier cathode, and d-c resistance of 200 ohms for the filter choke L_1. How much is the B+ voltage output?

11. In Fig. 24·16: (*a*) Calculate the total cathode current I_K if $I_b = 12$ ma, $I_{c_2} = 4$ ma, and $I_{c_1} = 0$. (*b*) Calculate I_b if $I_k = 18$ ma, $I_{c_1} = 1$ ma, and $I_{c_2} = 4$ ma.

12. (*a*) An amplifier has 50 μv a-c input signal and 600 μv output. How much is the voltage gain A_v? (*b*) If the gain were 24, how much would the a-c output voltage be?

Chapter 25 Transistors

This unit describes semiconductors such as germanium and silicon and how they are used as transistor amplifiers and diode rectifiers. These semiconductor devices are rapidly replacing vacuum tubes in many applications because of their small size and efficient operation. The nature of current flow in the solid semiconductor is analyzed in detail to show how the transistor can serve as an amplifier. The topics are as follows:

25·1   Advantages of transistors
25·2   Semiconductors
25·3   Atomic structure of germanium
25·4   N-type germanium
25·5   P-type germanium
25·6   The PN junction
25·7   Forward bias
25·8   Reverse bias
25·9   Transistor action
25·10 Transistor circuit arrangements
25·11 Transistor amplifier circuit
25·12 Collector characteristic curves
25·13 Transistor types
25·14 Semiconductor diodes
25·15 Troubles in transistors

25·1 Advantages of transistors

Invented in 1948 by J. Bardeen and W. H. Brattain of the Bell Telephone Laboratories, the transistor is an application of current flow in solid semiconductor materials such as germanium and silicon to provide amplification. Typical transistors are shown in Fig. 25·1. Inside the hermetically sealed metal case is a tiny piece of solid semiconductor. Control of the current through the solid provides transistor action. The three leads in *a* are connections for the input and output circuits, with one lead common to both. In the integrated circuit of *f*, the transistor amplifiers and *R*, *L* and *C* components are all made as integral parts of one unit, combining printed wiring with semiconductor techniques for extreme miniaturization of complete circuit modules.

One advantage of the transistor is its extremely small size, which allows miniature circuits for transistor amplifiers. The transistor has a long service life of many years in normal operation because there is no heated filament. Operation is instantaneous without any warm-up time, starting when the required d-c electrode voltages are applied. Since transistors operate with low d-c voltages of 1 to 25 volts and with no heater current, the power drain is much less than for vacuum tubes. For this reason, transistors are often operated with miniature B batteries. A common application is the transistor portable radio receiver. Finally, the transistor is nonmicrophonic because it is mechanically rugged. A disadvantage is the fact that temperature extremes, particularly overheating in power amplifiers, can damage the transistor. Typical power ratings are 1 mw to 50 watts, at temperatures from 20 to 200°C. The higher temperature ratings are for silicon transistors.

25·2 Semiconductors

Some semiconductor elements are carbon (C), selenium (Se), silicon (Si), and germanium (Ge). They have more resistance than metal conduc-

Fig. 25·1 Typical semiconductors. Height about ½ in. without leads. (a) PNP, Ge transistor 2N398, rated at 200 ma, 105 volts, 150 mw. (b) PNP, Si 3-amp power transistor 2N3021. (c) Dual transistors in one case. (d) 50-watt zener diode. (e) Silicon controlled rectifier rated at 18 amp. (f) Integrated flip-flop pulse generator circuit in one package. (Motorola Semiconductor Products Inc.)

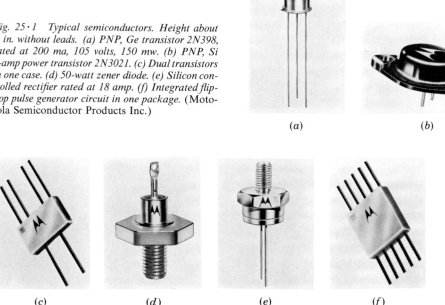

(a) (b)

(c) (d) (e) (f)

tors but still can be considered conductors compared with insulators like glass or quartz. Also, the semiconductors have a negative temperature coefficient of resistivity, their resistance decreasing with higher temperatures. At very low temperatures, germanium is actually an insulator; at high temperatures, it becomes a good conductor. Of the four semiconductors, germanium has the lowest resistivity of 0.5 to 80 ohm-cm at a temperature of 25° C, depending on purity. In addition, germanium and silicon have an atomic structure that is most suitable for allowing control of the current flowing through the solid. It is the control of the semiconductor current that enables it to serve as an amplifier. For these reasons, germanium and silicon are the most common semiconductor materials for transistors.

Germanium is an earth element discovered in 1886. Pure germanium is recovered from the ash of certain coals or from the flue dust of zinc smelters. For electronic applications, the recovered germanium is in the form of germanium dioxide powder, which is then reduced to pure germanium in solid form, with only one foreign atom to each billion germanium atoms.

Silicon is an element in most common rocks. Sand is actually silicon dioxide. The silicon compounds can be reduced chemically to elementary silicon that is almost 100 per cent pure for use as a semiconductor.

Doping. The extreme purification is necessary so that the semiconductor can have a controlled amount of impurities added. Often arsenic, indium, antimony, or gallium is used for doping germanium. This is necessary to give the semiconductor the characteristics needed for transistors. In one method of preparing germanium, a small single crystal called the *seed* is dipped into molten germanium and slowly raised. The seed has a molecular arrangement which provides the required crystalline structure. As the seed is raised, with correct temperature conditions, the molten germanium freezes to the seed in the same crystal orientation. After several hours of slow withdrawal, a long slender crystal is formed with enough germanium for several thousand transistors. The required doping is done while the crystal is growing, by means of impurities added to the molten germanium. Although an extremely small amount of the doping element is added, it gives the semiconductor its required characteristics. For example, to produce germanium with a resistance of 1 ohm-cm, 6.7×10^{-5} gram of antimony is added to 100 grams of germanium.

N and P types. Depending on the type of impurity added, doping can make germanium conduct either positive or negative charges. Doping with arsenic or antimony results in an excess of electrons in the germanium, making it a carrier of negative charges that can be made to flow in the semiconductor. This is *N-type,* or *negative,* germanium.

For the opposite case, doping with gallium or indium results in a deficiency of electrons. Then the germanium can serve as a conductor of positive charges. This is *P-type,* or *positive,* germanium.

Transistor combinations. To make a transistor, the N and P types of germanium are combined as illustrated in Fig. 25·2. One type, either N

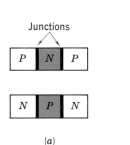

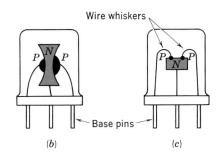

Junctions

(a)

(b)

(c)

Fig. 25·2   Transistor construction illustrating PN and NP junctions. (a) Equivalent circuit with two junctions. (b) Alloy-junction construction. (c) Point-contact type.

or P, is sandwiched between a pair of the opposite type. As shown in *a*, the result is either a PNP or NPN transistor. The germanium in the middle is the *base*. Where the base contacts the opposite germanium type is a *junction*. Therefore, the sandwich arrangement is a junction transistor, which may be either PNP or NPN type. The equivalent results are shown in *a*, but the physical structure may be as shown in *b*, or *c*.

Many other types of construction have been developed to improve the transistor characteristics but the net effect is the same as illustrated in *a*. The two junctions at the base control the input current and output current through the solid semiconductor. Germanium and silicon are generally used, with silicon having the advantage of being able to operate at higher temperatures.

25·3   Atomic structure of germanium

As described in Chap. 1, every element has its own atomic structure that determines its electrical, physical, and chemical characteristics. Electrically, the atom can be considered as a positively charged nucleus with negative electrons in orbits around the nucleus, as shown in Fig. 25·3. The net positive charge in the nucleus is equal to the atomic number of the element. The atomic numbers of the semiconductor elements are 32 for germanium, 14 for silicon, 6 for carbon, and 34 for selenium.

Germanium, with an atomic number of 32, has a net positive charge of 32 protons in its nucleus. To balance this positive charge, outside the nucleus are 32 electrons in successive orbits or rings. The electrons are in four rings, with 2 electrons in the first ring followed by 8 and 18 in the next two rings, accounting for 28 electrons. The remaining 4 electrons are in the fourth ring. Since the last outside ring must have 8 electrons for stability, germanium has 4 electrons in an incomplete 8-ring.

Valence electrons. These are the electrons in the outermost ring equal to the valence number of the element. The valence of an element determines how well its atoms can combine with other atoms. Germanium has a valence of 4. Silicon also has a valence of 4.

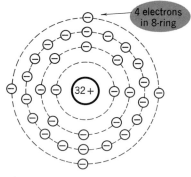

Fig. 25·3   Atomic structure of germanium atom with 4 valence electrons.

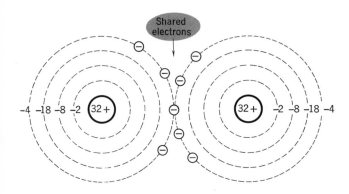

Fig. 25·4   Two germanium atoms sharing their valence electrons to form covalent bond.

Covalent bonds. Atoms with a valence of 4 often form covalent bonds, as illustrated in Fig. 25·4 for two germanium atoms. Note that the 4 valence electrons in one atom can just as well be considered part of the other atom. The attracting force of each nucleus is the same because both atoms have an equal number of outside rings. The location of the valence electrons in the outside ring has no significance in the two-dimensional drawing here. Actually, each valence electron is spinning in its own orbit around the nucleus, in addition to its level in the outside ring. As a result, with many germanium atoms close together, the 4 valence electrons of each atom can be shared, tending to form stable rings with 8 electrons.

Each atom tends to share 4 valence electrons from another atom, but the germanium atom cannot easily lose its valence electrons. If these 4 electrons were lost, then the next ring would have 18 electrons when it should have 8 for stability as an outside ring. Therefore, the germanium atoms neither gain nor lose their valence electrons but share them, forming *covalent bonds*. A covalent bond is a union of 2 atoms, each sharing an equal number of valence electrons. The bond is held together by the attracting force of one atom's nucleus on the other atom's valence electrons, but without any change in chemical or electrical characteristics.

In solid materials covalent bonds can be formed between atoms of the same element or with two different elements having similar characteristics. There are two requirements:

1. A valence of 3, 4, or 5 so that the atoms do not easily lose or gain valence electrons.
2. Atomic numbers that are nearly equal, so that the atoms have the same number of electron rings outside the nucleus.

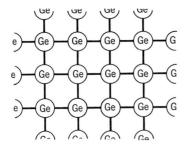

Fig. 25·5 Crystal lattice structure of pure germanium illustrating covalent bonds between atoms.

Crystalline solids. In addition to its covalent bonds, germanium in the solid state has a crystalline structure. A *crystal* has a definite geometrical form with plane faces that meet to form straight-line edges at a characteristic angle. A diamond is a perfect example of the crystalline structure of carbon. When a crystalline solid is broken into parts, the smaller pieces have the same characteristic angle between faces. If we imagine the individual atoms in a crystal to be connected as in Fig. 25·5, the result is a lattice that illustrates the crystalline structure. One feature of the crystalline structure is that it has no molecules but just the atoms held together in covalent bonds. Therefore, a doping element can be added to alter the electrical charges in the crystalline semiconductor without changing its physical structure. The most common doping elements are summarized in Table 25·1.

It should be noted that the doped semiconductors are still electrically neutral, although they are labeled N-type and P-type. After all, the doping only adds neutral impurity atoms to neutral covalent bonds. However, the added impurity atoms in the doped semiconductor do produce electrons or hole charges that are loosely bound and can be made to move to produce

Table 25·1 Doping elements and semiconductors

Element	Symbol	Atomic number	Valence electrons	Applications
Antimony	Sb	51	5	*Donor* impurity elements. Give electrons to Ge or Si atoms to form N-type semiconductor. As and Sb used for Ge; phosphorus for Si
Arsenic	As	33	5	
Phosphorus	P	15	5	
Germanium	Ge	32	4	*Intrinsic* semiconductors used in pure crystal form to be doped with impurity elements
Silicon	Si	14	4	
Aluminum	Al	13	3	*Acceptor* impurity elements. Take electrons from Ge or Si atoms to form P-type semiconductor. Ga and In used for Ge; Al and B for Si
Boron	B	5	3	
Gallium	Ga	31	3	
Indium	In	49	3	

current. We can compare this with free electrons as charge carriers in a copper wire. The wire as a whole has no net electrical charge but a potential difference can easily produce a current of free electrons because they are loosely bound to the copper atoms. Similarly, a current of electrons or hole charges can easily be produced in N-type or P-type semiconductors.

25·4   N-type germanium

Since germanium has 4 valence electrons, when it is doped with an element having 5 valence electrons, 4 of these can form covalent bonds with the germanium atoms, allowing 1 extra electron per atom to make the germanium negative. Two elements suitable for such negative doping are arsenic (As), with an atomic number of 33, or antimony (Sb), with an atomic number of 51. Both have 5 valence electrons. These elements are called *donor* impurities, since they give electrons to the germanium.

The atomic structure for arsenic is illustrated in Fig. 25·6. With an atomic number of 33, compared with 32 for germanium, the arsenic atom has the same number of electron rings but 5 valence electrons in the last ring. As a result, covalent bonds can be formed between arsenic and germanium atoms. Four valence electrons of each arsenic atom can be shared by a germanium atom. The extra electron is free to drift from atom to atom as a negative charge that can provide electron current through the N-type germanium. The idea of the free negative charges in the crystalline solid is illustrated by the lattice structure in Fig. 25·7. Each arsenic atom provides 1 free electron, but doping germanium with just a trace of arsenic provides enough atoms to supply billions of free electrons, since the atoms of arsenic are distributed throughout the atoms of germanium.

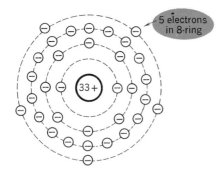

Fig. 25·6 *Atomic structure of arsenic with 5 valence electrons.*

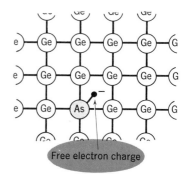

Fig. 25·7 *Crystal lattice structure of germanium doped with arsenic. Covalent bonds have a free negative electron charge because of the arsenic atom.*

25·5   P-type germanium

The opposite case of doping to make the germanium positive can be done with elements having 3 valence electrons. Two suitable elements are gallium (Ga), with an atomic number of 31, or indium (In), with an atomic number of 49. Both have 3 valence electrons. These elements are called *acceptor* impurities because they take on the valence electrons of germanium to form covalent bonds.

The atomic structure of gallium is illustrated in Fig. 25·8. With an atomic number of 31, compared with 32 for germanium, the gallium atom has the same number of electron rings but 3 valence electrons in the last ring. The gallium atom cannot lose its valence electrons easily because the next ring has 18 electrons, which is not a stable form of outside ring. The germanium atom also cannot lose its 4 valence electrons easily. The result is that the gallium and germanium atoms form covalent bonds, sharing the 7 valence electrons.

Positive hole charges. The one missing electron in the covalent bond having 7 valence electrons instead of 8 is a positive charge called a *hole.* Bear in mind that without the gallium impurity, germanium atoms could form covalent bonds having complete outside rings of 8 electrons. Doping with the gallium changed the germanium, therefore, from a crystalline structure with neutral covalent bonds to bonds where each is missing 1 electron for each union of the gallium atom with a germanium atom.

A positive hole charge is illustrated in the crystal lattice structure in Fig. 25·9 for P-type germanium, doped with gallium. Each atom of gallium provides one hole charge in a covalent bond with a germanium atom. Doping with a slight trace of gallium, however, supplies enough atoms for billions of hole charges, since the impurity atoms are distributed throughout the atoms of germanium.

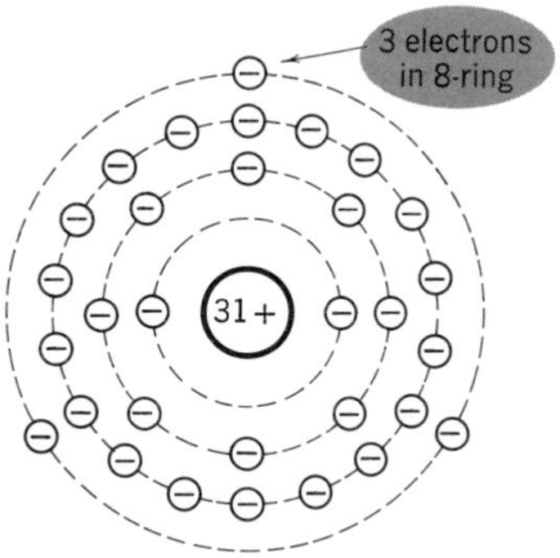

Fig. 25·8   Atomic structure of gallium with 3 valence electrons.

3 electrons in 8-ring

31 +

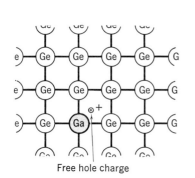

Free hole charge

Fig. 25·9   Crystal lattice structure of germanium doped with gallium. Covalent bonds have a free positive hole charge because of the gallium.

Table 25·2   Comparison of electrons and hole charges

Carrier	Charge	Polarity	Mobility
Electron	0.16×10^{-18} coul	Negative	3,800 cm per sec
Hole	0.16×10^{-18} coul	Positive	1,900 cm per sec

The hole is a positive charge, equal to a 1-electron charge but with opposite polarity. Note that the hole is a physical charge just as much as is an electron. It is a new source of electrical charge that can be produced in P-type semiconductors because of the unfilled covalent bond structure.

The hole and electron are compared in Table 25·2. Both are called *charge carriers,* as either electrons or holes in motion provide current. However, the direction of positive charges in the hole current is opposite from electron current. Also, electrons have greater mobility, meaning that these charges can be moved more easily than holes by the force of an electric field. The reason why is that an electron is alone by itself outside a filled 8-electron ring, but moving a hole involves redistributing the charges in a 7-electron ring. The mobilities in Table 25 · 2 are specified for a unit electric field strength of 1 volt per cm.

Example 1. Calculate the current I for 1×10^{18} electron charges per second.

Answer.
$$I = \frac{Q}{t} = \frac{1 \times 10^{18} \times 0.16 \times 10^{-18} \text{ coul}}{1 \text{ sec}}$$
$$I = 0.16 \text{ coul per sec} = \textbf{0.16 amp}$$

Note that Q is found by multiplying the charge of one electron by the number of electrons.

Example 2. Calculate I for 2×10^{18} hole charges in 2 sec.

Answer.
$$I = \frac{Q}{t} = \frac{2 \times 10^{18} \times 0.16 \times 10^{-18} \text{ coul}}{2 \text{ sec}}$$
$$I = 0.16 \text{ coul per sec} = \textbf{0.16 amp}$$

Note that hole charges are just as effective as electrons in producing current.

25·6   The PN junction

Two opposite types of germanium in contact form a PN or NP junction where the two faces meet, as shown in Fig. 25 · 10. Some electrons in the N germanium can move through the junction to the P germanium, while at the same time some hole charges move in the opposite direction. Very little charge is redistributed, however, before a potential barrier forms at the junction to prevent any more current. The amount of this barrier voltage (V_b) is approximately 0.3 volt for germanium or 0.6 volt for silicon, at room temperature. It should be noted that the junction is not necessarily

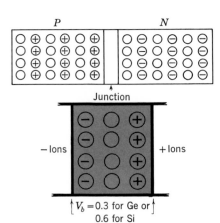

Fig. 25·10 PN junction with depletion zone magnified to show ion charges that produce barrier voltage V_b.

an abrupt line but just represents the *transition area* between opposite impurities in a single crystal.

The internal barrier voltage at the junction. The reason for V_b is illustrated by the charge distribution in Fig. 25·10. Where the P and N types touch at the junction, they exchange charges. Electrons in the N type move toward the P type, while holes in the P type move to the N type. This diffusion of charges results in some neutral bonds, as indicated in the middle column of the drawing. Notice, though, that three columns are illustrated with the junction magnified to show the charges at the two opposite faces. On the N side, the face at the junction has a positive charge; on the P side, the face at the junction has a negative charge. These two opposite charges provide the potential difference equal to V_b.

The barrier voltage is a steady d-c potential difference across the junction because V_b is a result of ion charges that do not move. Remember that when an electron moves across the junction from the N zone to the P zone, each of these electrons leaves behind an unbalanced impurity atom with a positive charge of $+1$, corresponding to the missing electron. Such charged atoms are the positive ions that remain at the N side of the junction. Similarly, hole charges that move from the P zone to the N zone leave negative ions at the P side of the junction. This process continues until the potential difference of V_b is enough to prevent any more charge carriers from moving across the junction.

The net result of the redistributed charges, then, is to produce the potential difference V_b across the junction. The thickness of this charged barrier may be only a few atoms wide, but V_b opposes any further current through the junction. Electrons from the N type cannot cross the barrier to the P type, because its negative face repels electrons. Similarly, hole charges from the P type cannot cross the barrier to the N type, because its positive face repels holes. Typical values of V_b are 0.3 volt for Ge and 0.6 volt for Si, at normal room temperature of $300°$K[1] or $27°$C. For either

[1] See Appendix D, Physics Units, for explanation of different temperature scales.

Ge or Si, the value of V_b decreases 2 mv per degree rise in temperature.

The junction area is often called the *depletion zone,* as there are no mobile charge carriers here. Ions of the impurity atoms, which produce V_b at the junction, are not charge carriers because they are anchored in position in the solid crystal. Any electrons and holes in this area are recombined to become neutral.

Applying an external voltage. It is important to realize that the barrier voltage makes the junction useful, since its effect can be controlled by an external applied voltage. Without the internal potential difference of V_b, two pure semiconductors would serve only as an ordinary resistance. With separated charges at the junction, though, its potential difference can be varied by an external voltage to determine the volt-ampere characteristics of the junction.

Basically, there are only two possibilities. An external voltage of opposite polarity from the internal V_b neutralizes the barrier voltage to allow more current through the junction. This polarity of external voltage is *forward voltage,* producing *forward current* or *easy current.* The opposite polarity of external voltage has the same polarity as the internal V_b. This polarity that prevents forward current is *reverse voltage.* The externally applied voltage is generally called *bias* when it has a steady d-c value. In summary, then, forward bias on the junction allows forward current, while reverse bias prevents current.

25·7   Forward bias

Figure 25·11 shows how an external voltage (E_F) can be applied across the junction to neutralize V_b and produce forward current. E_F is applied by wire conductors connected to the two ends of the Ge crystals. Then the potential difference of E_F is applied across the junction. Forward current is produced because E_F has the required polarity. Two examples are illustrated for PN and NP junctions, but in both cases the polarity of E_F fits the following requirements of forward bias:

1. The P side of the junction is connected to $+E_F$ and N to $-E_F$. In other words, the polarity of E_F corresponds to the semiconductor types.
2. Then E_F repels charge carriers in the semiconductor toward the junction. In the N type, electrons move, while hole charges move in the P type.

Fig. 25·11   Forward bias repelling charge carriers toward junction. (a) NP junction. (b) PN junction.

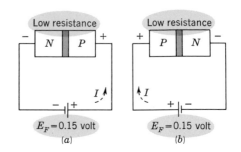

Low resistance   Low resistance

$E_F = 0.15$ volt $E_F = 0.15$ volt

(a)   (b)

Applying an external voltage to move the internal charge carriers toward the junction is a requirement of forward bias because this action neutralizes V_b. Electrons in the N type that are repelled to the junction neutralize the positive ions at the positive side of V_b. Also, hole charges in the P type that are repelled to the junction neutralize the negative ions at the negative side of V_b. With the barrier voltage neutralized, the external forward bias allows charge carriers to flow through the junction in the forward direction. Either all or part of V_b may be canceled, depending on the amount of forward voltage.

Drift current and diffusion current. Charge carriers that are forced to move by the electric field of a potential difference are considered to form a *drift current.* This type of current corresponds to electron flow in a wire, produced by an applied voltage. The amount of drift current increases with a higher potential difference.

A *diffusion current* results from a difference in concentration of charge carriers in adjacent areas of the crystal. They have a random motion of their own, from heat energy that depends on temperature. Even at room temperature, the charge carriers will diffuse from areas of higher concentration to areas of lower concentration. This process is similar to osmosis between liquids of different densities. The diffusion current increases with higher temperatures.

It should be noted, however, that the forward current through the junction is primarily a drift current resulting from the forward voltage. The current inside the semiconductor can be a drift of either electrons from N to P as in Fig. 25·11a, or hole charges from P to N, as in b. The current in the external wire conductors, though, must still be electrons in motion. For the case of hole current in the semiconductor, each hole charge moving to an external terminal is exchanged for an electron moving in the opposite direction.

25·8 Reverse bias

Figure 25·12 shows how the junction can be biased to prevent any forward drift current. The reverse bias voltage E_R has the polarity needed to attract charge carriers away from the junction. This polarity means E_R is reversed from the semiconductor types, with $+E_R$ to N and $-E_R$ to P.

In Fig. 25·12a, the P type has a negative potential applied by E_R attracting the hole charges, while the positive potential on the N type attracts

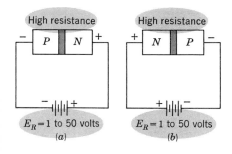

Fig. 25·12 Reverse bias attracting charge carriers away from junction. (a) PN junction. (b) NP junction.

electrons. For both cases, the charge carriers are attracted away from the junction. Then the ion charges remain intact at the junction to maintain V_b and prevent charge carriers from drifting across. In *b*, the opposite connections to the battery still keep the junction biased in the reverse direction because the charge carriers are forced away from the junction. With reverse bias, therefore, the junction has high resistance as no forward current can flow. Note the higher values of 1 to 50 volts that can be used with reverse bias, compared with a fraction of a volt for forward bias. Actually, transistors are continually being developed for even higher values of reverse voltage.

Reverse leakage current. There is a small amount of current with reverse bias, as a result of the diffusion of minority charge carriers. This diffusion current is considered leakage because the ideal condition would be zero current with reverse bias. Also, this current flows in the opposite direction from the forward drift current. Typical values of this reverse leakage current are 7.5 μa for Ge and 2.8 μa for Si, at room temperature of 300°K. However, these values are very sensitive to temperature as they result from diffusion current.

Majority and minority charge carriers. The reason why there is any reverse current at all is the diffusion of minority charge carriers. The minority charges have opposite polarity and are fewer in number, compared with the majority charges of the P or N doping. Even at room temperature, the valence bonds of pure Ge or Si atoms are not static but continuously move through the semiconductor. Thermal energy accounts for these random changes in the covalent bonds. As a result, although the N type has excess electrons equal to the number of impurity atoms, there are also a few hole charges in random motion. Therefore, an N-type semiconductor has some minority hole charges, in addition to the majority electron charges. Similarly, in a P-type semiconductor the holes are majority charges but there are some minority electron charges.

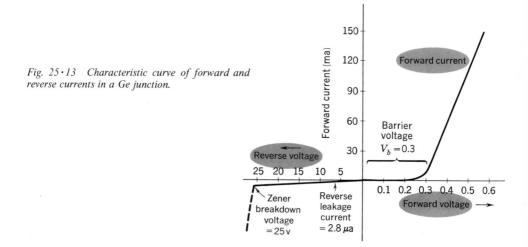

Fig. 25·13   Characteristic curve of forward and reverse currents in a Ge junction.

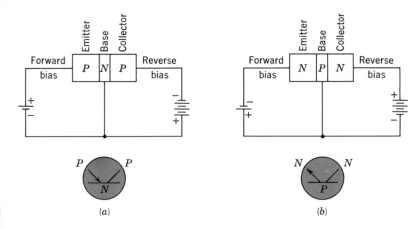

Fig. 25·14   Transistors with emitter, base, and collector. (a) PNP transistor and symbol. (b) NPN transistor and symbol.

The minority charges provide the reverse leakage current by diffusion, with reverse bias. Since the minority carriers have opposite polarity, this current is in the reverse direction, compared with the forward drift of majority carriers with forward bias. The number of minority charges available for the reverse diffusion current depends on temperature.

Volt-ampere characteristic of the junction.   The curve in Fig. 25·13 summarizes the characteristics of forward and reverse currents. In the forward direction, when the applied voltage exceeds the barrier voltage V_b, appreciable forward current flows. In the reverse direction, very little current flows, even with relatively high values of applied voltage. This reverse leakage current is also called *saturation reverse current* as it increases only slightly with more reverse voltage.

We can compare the resistance of the junction in the forward and reverse directions, for the same value of 0.3 volt applied. In the forward or easy direction the d-c resistance is very low, equal to 0.3/0.06, which is 5 ohms. In the reverse direction, the d-c resistance of 0.3 volt/7.5 μa is equal to 40,000 ohms. This value is also considered the *leakage resistance,* corresponding to the reverse leakage current.

The reverse current is constant at a very small value until the reverse bias reaches the breakdown voltage. This value, called the *zener voltage,* is 25 volts here. Then a large amount of current can flow in the reverse direction. This *avalanche current* in the reverse direction is useful for voltage-regulator diodes. However, for transistor action the forward current and the small reverse leakage current are more important, as they can be controlled in order to provide amplification.

25·9   Transistor action

As shown in Fig. 25·14, the transistor consists of a PN junction and an NP junction formed by placing either a P-type or N-type semiconductor between a pair of opposite types. The idea is to have the first section supply charges, either holes or electrons, to be collected by the third section through the middle section. The electrode that supplies charges is the *emitter;* the electrode on the opposite side to collect the charges is the *collector.* The *base* is in the middle to form two junctions between the emitter and collector.

Emitter. The emitter is always biased in the forward direction so that it can supply a large number of majority charges. As shown in Fig. 25·14a, the P-type emitter supplies hole charges to its junction with the base, as indicated by the arrow at the emitter. This movement of positive charges is the conventional direction of current.

For the NPN transistor shown in Fig. 25·14b, the emitter supplies electron charges. Therefore, the symbol for the N emitter shows the arrow out from the base. The N emitter, however, is supplying electron charges to its junction. Since the direction of the arrow always indicates which way positive hole charges would move, the arrow is outward for the emitter providing electrons. In schematic symbols, only the emitter has an arrow to indicate which electrode is the emitter. An arrow pointing in means a PNP transistor; an arrow pointing out indicates an NPN transistor.

Collector. The collector is always biased in the reverse direction. Its function is to remove charges from its junction with the base. In Fig. 25·14a, the PNP transistor has a P collector receiving hole charges that flow in its output circuit. For the NPN transistor in Fig. 25·14b, the N collector receives electrons.

Base. The base in the middle separates the input circuit of the emitter from the output circuit of the collector. This results because of the two junctions formed, each with its barrier voltage. The base-emitter junction is forward-biased, allowing low resistance for the emitter circuit. The base-collector junction is reverse-biased, however, providing high resistance in the collector circuit. The final requirement in producing transistor action is to allow the emitter current in the base to control the collector current.

Base injection. The base is much thinner than the emitter, while the collector is wider than both. This difference is illustrated in Fig. 25·15 with a beaded-type of transistor construction shown to emphasize the relative widths. The emitter also has more doping. In addition, the reverse-bias voltage on the collector is much higher than the forward bias on the emitter. Because of these factors, practically all the charges supplied by the emitter to the base are made to flow in the collector circuit. The charges then are considered to be injected from the base into the collector.

The base has a PN junction at one side but an opposite NP junction at the other side. Therefore, the polarities are reversed for the barrier voltages at opposite ends of the base. If we consider the PNP transistor in Fig. 25·15, the P emitter supplies hole charges as majority carriers to the base through the PN junction. Forward bias enables the emitter to overcome the junction barrier voltage. At the collector junction, however, the barrier voltage has reversed polarity because it is an NP junction. Here the barrier voltage aids the flow of hole charges through the junction. Note also

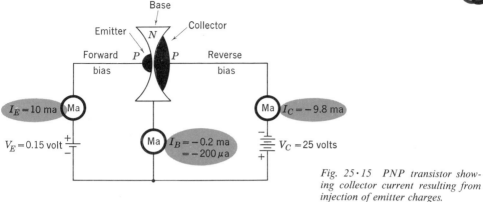

Fig. 25·15 PNP transistor showing collector current resulting from injection of emitter charges.

that the reverse leakage current in the NP junction of the collector is a movement of hole charges as minority carriers. This combination means that hole charges supplied by the emitter can easily become part of the collector reverse bias current. Instead of returning through the base, the charges injected by the emitter are attracted into the collector to increase its output current.

Injection of charges into the collector is increased by making the base very thin. Then the resistance is very low through the thin base to the collector. The path across the width of the base to its electrode has much higher resistance. Furthermore, the fact that the reverse-bias voltage is high means that its electric field can have a great effect on charges at the collector junction. The result, therefore, is that practically all the forward current supplied by the emitter circuit becomes reverse current in the collector circuit. As an example, in Fig. 25·15, the emitter supplies 10 ma forward current. Approximately 9.8 ma is injected into the collector circuit. Only 0.2 ma, or 200 μa, flows through the base terminal in returning to the emitter. As a formula,

$$I_E = I_C + I_B \qquad (25 \cdot 1)$$

This formula states that the collector and base currents must add to equal the emitter current, which is the source. The idea is the same as saying that all the electrode currents must add to equal the cathode current for vacuum tubes. Note that similar nomenclature is used for currents and voltages, with capital letters for average d-c values and small letters for instantaneous or a-c values. However, V is used instead of E for voltages, in order to avoid confusion with symbols for the emitter.

Example 3. How much is the emitter current with 960 μa collector current and 40 μa base current?

Answer. $I_E = I_C + I_B = 960 + 40 = $ **1,000 μa**

Example 4. With 800 μa emitter current and 770 μa collector current, how much is the base current?

Answer. $$I_B = I_E - I_B = 800 - 770 = \mathbf{30 \ \mu a}$$

25·10 Transistor circuit arrangements

The transistor circuits considered so far are called *common-base* circuits, since the emitter input and collector output circuits both return to the common-base connection, but this circuit is just one of the three main arrangements for transistors. In addition, there are the *common-emitter* and *common-collector* circuits as illustrated in Fig. 25·16. For each arrangement both PNP and NPN transistors are shown in identical circuits except that the emitter and collector bias voltages are reversed. These circuits are also called *grounded-base, grounded-emitter,* and *grounded-collector* circuits because the common electrode is often connected to chassis ground. The common-emitter circuit is the one most often used in transistor amplifiers because it provides the highest gain.

The characteristics of all three circuit arrangements are summarized in Table 25·3. It should be noted that even with the different circuit arrangements, in all cases the emitter circuit has forward bias to provide low resistance, while the collector circuit has reverse bias with high resistance.

Common-base circuit. See Fig. 25·16a. In this circuit the input voltage is applied in series with the emitter-base circuit. Since the base is grounded, it is also the return for the collector output circuit. The batteries shown for the bias voltages V_E and V_C can be considered practically direct returns to

Fig. 25·16 *Transistor circuit arrangements for PNP and NPN types. (a) Common base. (b) Common emitter. (c) Common collector.*

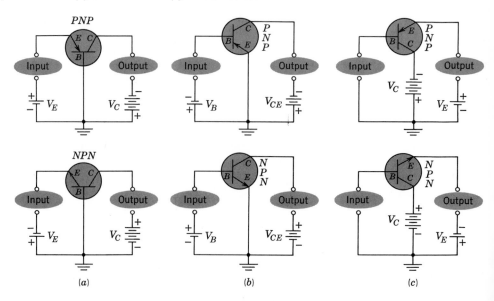

(a)   (b)   (c)

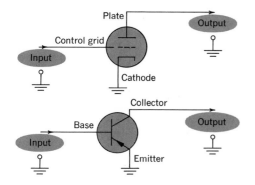

Fig. 25·17 How grounded-emitter transistor circuit with base input corresponds to grounded-cathode triode vacuum-tube circuit with grid input.

chassis ground for a-c signal voltage input and output. As listed in Table 25·3, the input emitter circuit has very low resistance r_i of about 50 ohms while the collector's output circuit has very high resistance r_o of about 1 M. These values are for the internal resistance of the biased semiconductor electrodes to the common base.

Common-emitter circuit. See Fig. 25·16b. In this circuit the input voltage is applied to the base, while the emitter returns directly to chassis ground. The output voltage again is taken from the collector with respect to chassis ground. However, there are two important differences compared with the common-base circuit.

1. Now the collector output circuit returns to the grounded emitter instead of the base. This connection is indicated by the symbol V_{CE} for the reverse bias applied to the collector.
2. In the input circuit, the forward bias V_B is applied to the base, instead of the emitter. As a result, the effect of voltage polarity for base input with respect to the emitter is opposite from emitter input with respect to the base.

Note that when the emitter is biased by V_B in the base-to-ground circuit, as in Fig. 25·16b, its polarity for forward bias on the emitter is the same with respect to chassis ground as the polarity of the reverse-bias voltage V_{CE} for the collector. This arrangement allows the convenience of using one battery for both bias voltages. A voltage-dropping resistor can be used for the lower voltage needed for forward bias, as in Fig. 25·18.

The common-emitter circuit is similar to the conventional vacuum-tube amplifier circuit using a triode with the cathode grounded, as shown in Fig. 25·17. Notice how the emitter corresponds to the cathode as a source of charge carriers. Also, the collector and plate collect the charges for the output circuit, while the base or grid controls the output current. The input signal is applied to the base, with respect to emitter, to control collector current in the transistor; or the input signal is applied to the grid to control plate current in the tube. The same comparison applies whether the transistor is PNP or NPN.

The main advantage of the common-emitter circuit is its high gain. The reason is that a small part of V_{CE} in the output circuit is across the base-emitter junction to aid the forward bias in the input circuit. Another feature is that the common-emitter circuit inverts the polarity of its amplified

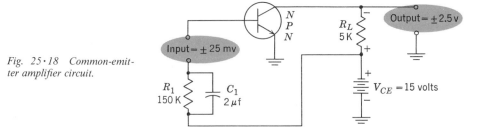

Fig. 25·18   Common-emitter amplifier circuit.

signal, while the other two circuits do not. The phase inversion means that, with sine-wave signal, the amplified output voltage is 180° out of phase with the input voltage. This phase inversion is neither an advantage nor a disadvantage but just a characteristic of the amplifier circuit. Similarly, the grounded-cathode vacuum-tube amplifier circuit also inverts the signal polarity.

Common collector. As shown in Fig. 25·16c, this circuit is the reverse of the common-emitter circuit. With the collector grounded, input voltage is applied to the base-collector circuit. In this case, the input circuit has high resistance, and the output is taken from the low-resistance emitter circuit. This feature can be used for impedance matching, between a low-impedance load and a high-impedance source.

Remember that all the circuits need forward bias in the input and reverse bias in the output. However, the required polarities depend on the circuit. Two helpful rules are:

1. $+V$ to a P electrode or $-V$ to an N electrode results in forward bias. Or, for forward bias the electrode is connected to a V terminal of the same polarity.
2. $+V$ to an N electrode or $-V$ to a P electrode results in reverse bias. Or, for reverse bias the electrode is connected to a V terminal of the opposite polarity.

If you check these rules against the diagrams in Fig. 25·16, you will see that they apply to the three circuits using either PNP or NPN transistors.

25·11   Transistor amplifier circuit

The fact that the amount of collector current in the output circuit can be controlled by the current of the input circuit means that the transistor can amplify a small voltage applied to the input, providing a much greater voltage output. This is accomplished by having an external load resistance R_L in the collector circuit, so that the collector current can produce output voltage across R_L. Either the common-base or the common-emitter circuit can provide amplification, but the common-emitter arrangement is generally used because it has the most gain. For example, with a common-emitter circuit, an input voltage of ± 25 mv in the base-emitter circuit can be amplified to provide $\pm 2,500$ mv, or ± 2.5 volts, in the collector output circuit. The voltage gain then is 100.

Table 25·3   Comparison of transistor circuits

Characteristic*	Common base	Common emitter	Common collector
Input resistance, r_i, ohms	50	1,000	250,000
Output resistance, r_o, ohms	1 M	50,000	500
Power gain (with external R_L)	1,000	10,000	Less than 1
Phase inversion of signal voltage	No	Yes	No
Advantage	High r_o	High gain	High r_i

* Values vary with transistor type, bias, and R_L.

A typical NPN common-emitter voltage amplifier circuit is shown in Fig. 25·18. Reverse bias is applied by the 15-volt supply V_{CE}. R_L is a 5,000-ohm collector load resistor to produce varying output voltage when the collector current varies. Note that one bias supply is used for both collector and base in the common-emitter circuit. The polarity required to bias the base emitter in the forward direction is the same as the reverse-bias polarity for the collector.

The collector voltage would be much too high for forward bias, however. R_1 is connected in series with the base, therefore, as a voltage-dropping resistor. Its value of 150,000 ohms limits the base current to 100 μa with the 15-volt supply. The internal forward resistance of the transistor can be considered negligible compared with R_1.

The bypass capacitor C_1 allows the input signal voltage to vary the forward current without the series resistance of R_1. This way, a very small change of input voltage can produce an appreciable change in base current. The low side of C_1 can be returned to chassis ground with the same results.

Summarizing the transistor action in providing gain, we can consider the amplification in the following steps:

1. The input voltage varies the input current, which is base current for the common-emitter circuit.
2. Varying the input current varies the collector current.
3. An external load resistance in the collector circuit provides varying IR voltages corresponding to the varying collector current.
4. The collector output voltage across R_L is much larger than the input voltage.
5. The voltage gain results from the fact that varying the current in the low-resistance emitter circuit produces corresponding current variations in the high-resistance collector circuit.

Notice that V_{CE} in Fig. 25 · 18 is a positive supply voltage for the collector circuit, like B+ voltage for the plate circuit of a vacuum tube. This similarity results because the collector current is electron flow in the NPN transistor. With the PNP type, however, negative collector supply voltage would be used. The negative polarity V_{CE} is necessary for the hole charges that provide the collector current. In either case, the circuit functions the same way to amplify the input signal voltage.

25·12 *Collector characteristic curves*

The manufacturer's data give the characteristic curves for each transistor type. Typical curves are shown in Figs. 25·19 and 25·20. Both are characteristic curves of collector current for values of collector voltage. The family of curves in Fig. 25·19, however, gives values of collector current for different emitter currents, which is important for a common-base circuit, while Fig. 25·20 gives collector currents for different base currents, which is the important characteristic in a common-emitter circuit.

Characteristic curves for common-base circuit. In Fig. 25·19, a common-base circuit is illustrated in *a* for a PNP transistor, while the graph in *b* gives the characteristic curves of the transistor. In the circuit, the emitter voltage V_E can be varied to change the emitter current I_E from 1 to 15 ma. More forward-bias voltage produces more emitter current. However, the maximum permissible emitter current for this transistor is 15 ma.

In the collector circuit, the collector voltage V_C can also be varied. Within the normal reverse-bias values, however, the collector current is independent of V_C, depending only on the amount of injected emitter current, as shown by the characteristic curves in *b*. Here the graph gives values of collector voltage V_C on the horizontal axis, while collector current values I_C are on the vertical axis. Note that the reverse-bias voltages for the P collector are negative, but the graph shows these values to the right because reverse bias is the important operating characteristic.

As an example of reading values, consider that the emitter current is

Fig. 25·19 α characteristic of common base circuit, for PNP transistor.
(a) Circuit. (b) Family of curves plotting collector current vs. collector voltage for different values of emitter current.

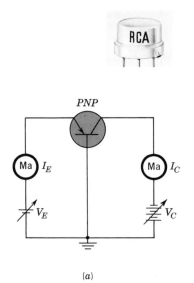

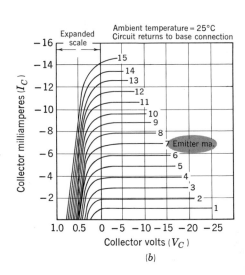

(a)

(b)

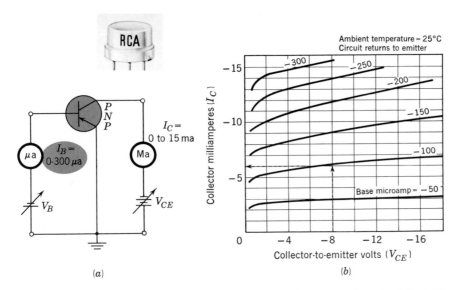

Fig. 25·20 β *characteristic of common-emitter circuit for PNP transistor.*
(a) Circuit. (b) Family of curves plotting collector current vs. collector voltage
for different values of base current.

10 ma, as determined by the emitter voltage. The effect on the collector
circuit is shown by the tenth curve up from the bottom. If the straight part
over to the I_C values at the left is taken, the curve is practically horizontal
at approximately 9.6 ma. This value of collector current is essentially constant with reverse-bias voltages greater than 2.5 volts. When the emitter
current I_E is varied, though, the collector current varies. The group of
curves for different values of I_E is the family of collector characteristics for
a common-base circuit.

Characteristic curves for common-emitter circuit. Figure 25·20 shows a
common-emitter circuit in *a,* with the characteristic curves in *b.* These
curves show the changes in collector current for different values of base
current. Note that the base-current values are in microamperes.

As an example of reading the graph, assume $I_B = 100$ μa, with -8 volts
for V_{CE}. The corresponding value of collector current I_C is 6 ma, as shown
by the arrows on the graph. If I_B swings ± 50 μa around the average level
of 100 μa, I_C will swing ± 3 ma around the average level of 6 ma. Then the
peak I_C is 9 ma and the minimum I_C is 3 ma. Notice how the variations of
I_C in the collector output circuit correspond to the variations of I_B in the
base input circuit.

Alpha characteristic. The ratio of collector current to total emitter current is the α (alpha) characteristic of the transistor. For example, if 98 per
cent of the emitter current is injected into the collector circuit, α equals
0.98. The remaining 2 per cent is base current. Typical values of α are 0.96
to 0.99. As a formula,

$$\alpha = \frac{I_C}{I_E} \qquad\qquad (25 \cdot 2)$$

There are no units for α, as it is a ratio of two currents. This ratio is always less than 1 because I_c must be less than I_E by the amount of I_B. Therefore, the current gain between the output collector circuit and the input emitter must be less than 1. However, voltage gain is obtained as I_c produces output voltage across R_L that is much greater than the input voltage.

Example 5. Calculate α for 8-ma I_E, 7.87-ma I_c, and 130-μa I_B, at a steady V_c of 10 volts.

Answer.
$$\alpha = \frac{I_c}{I_E} = \frac{7.87 \text{ ma}}{8 \text{ ma}} = \mathbf{0.984}$$

The base current I_B is not used for calculating α in this example.

Beta characteristic. The ratio of collector current to base current is the β (beta) characteristic of the transistor. When the ratio is taken as a small-signal change in collector current caused by a change in base current, the β characteristic can be considered as the current transfer ratio, or current gain, in a common-emitter circuit. As a formula,

$$\beta = \frac{\Delta i_c}{\Delta i_B} \tag{25$\cdot$3}$$

Again there are no units for the ratio of two currents. Typical values of β are 20 to 200.

Example 6. Calculate β from Fig. 25$\cdot$20b, where Δi_B of 50 μa produces Δi_c of 3 ma, with V_{CE} at 8 volts.

Answer.
$$\beta = \frac{\Delta i_c}{\Delta i_B} = \frac{3,000 \text{ } \mu\text{a}}{50 \text{ } \mu\text{a}} = \mathbf{60}$$

Since I_B is the difference between I_E and I_c, the factors α and β are related as follows:

$$\beta = \frac{\alpha}{1 - \alpha} \tag{25$\cdot$4}$$

As an example, for $\alpha = 0.984$,

$$\beta = \frac{0.984}{1 - 0.984} = \frac{0.984}{0.016} = \mathbf{61.5}$$

Power dissipation. The power dissipated in the collector is the product of $I_c \times V_c$. For example, with 10-ma I_c and 10 volts for V_c, the dissipated power is 0.01×10, which equals 0.01 watt, or 100 mw. The maximum d-c power dissipation of the type 2N104 is approximately 150 mw at the temperature of 25°C. Power transistors have ratings up to 50 watts.

25·13 Transistor types

Germanium and silicon are commonly used. Silicon transistors can operate at higher temperatures and have higher leakage resistance. For both germanium and silicon, there are several different transistor types according to their construction.

Two-junction transistors. This is the conventional PNP or NPN type, with two junctions at opposite sides of the single base. In one method of preparation, the junction between opposite conductors is produced in the crystal itself while it is grown from the melted semiconductor. This *grown-junction* technique generally applies to NPN germanium transistors. Another method alloys the doping material on opposite surfaces of the grown crystal. This is an *alloy-junction transistor.* A third method is diffusing the impurities in vapor form onto the surface of the semiconductor wafer. Then plane-parallel junctions can be formed with a base that has different resistivity values from one end to the next. This type is called a *drift* transistor. A similar diffusion technique applies to *epitaxial transistors,* in which layers of semiconductor are deposited on each other. This method provides control of the doping level, or the type of doping, for the base, with either abrupt or continuous junctions. The *mesa transistor* is another type where the base region is diffused into the collector pellet, for better control of the base width. Finally, silicon *planar transistors* are made by diffusing the emitter as well as the base. All these techniques of transistor construction have been developed for greater reliability and power dissipation, with less leakage current and smaller interelectrode capacitances.

Encapsulation. The transistor unit is generally sealed in a metal case with a gas or inert-liquid filler. Encapsulation is necessary for mechanical ruggedness and to prevent moisture from contaminating the semiconductor. In addition, the method of encapsulation affects the thermal rating and stability of the electrical characteristics.

Voltage and power amplifiers. For voltage amplifier stages, the transistors are very small, usually less than ½ in. wide, since the required power dissipation is in the order of milliwatts. For higher power applications, larger transistors of 1 in. diameter or more can provide a power-dissipation rating up to 50 watts. Power transistors often have metal fins to help radiate heat. In addition, they may be constructed for a mounting to the metal chassis that conducts heat. This arrangement is called a *heat sink* for the transistor.

Transistor sockets. Small transistors often have thin flexible wire leads soldered directly into the circuit without a socket. Others use the socket types shown in Fig. 25·21 with pin connections. Notice that the base pin is at the center in *a* and *b*. The collector has a tab or red dot or is spaced farther away than the emitter. In *c* the collector is internally connected to the metal case to dissipate heat. Instead of the locating pins, this type of power transistor often has holes at opposite ends for mounting screws. A thin spacer can be used to insulate the collector case from chassis ground.

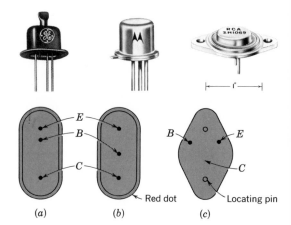

Fig. 25·21　Typical transistor sockets and pin connections.

(a)　　　(b)　　　(c)

Red dot　　Locating pin

Transistor type numbers. The only standard numbering system is the use of the prefix 1 for diodes, as in 1N248 and the prefix 2 for triodes as in 2N3118. More details are in the manufacturer's transistor manual for different types, such as the GE and RCA manuals.

25·14　Semiconductor diodes

The types of solid-state diodes include germanium, silicon, selenium, and copper oxide. Selenium and copper oxide are also called metallic rectifiers. However, most common are the point-contact germanium diodes for signal detectors (Fig. 25·22) and silicon junction diodes, for power supplies. Typical ratings for small silicon rectifiers (Fig. 25·23) are 300 ma forward current with a maximum peak inverse rating of 600 volts, at 25°C.

Fig. 25·22　Germanium diode detector. Length ½ in. without leads. (Sylvania Electric Products Inc.)

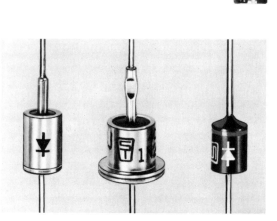

Fig. 25·23　Silicon diode power rectifiers. Length is ½ in. (Sarkes-Tarzian Inc.)

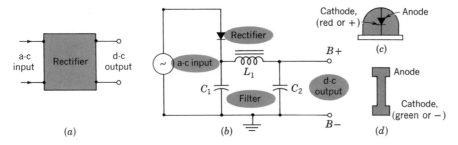

Fig. 25·24 *Semiconductor rectifier circuits. (a) General form for any rectifier circuit. (b) Power supply with half-wave rectifier. Note symbol for diode. (c) Coding for power diode rectifier. (d) Coding for signal diode detector.*

Larger units are rated in terms of amperes for the load current in the forward direction. Stacking diode units in series can provide higher peak-inverse ratings up to thousands of volts. Also, the diodes are available in matched pairs for use as a full-wave rectifier.

Semiconductor diode rectifiers. A diode rectifier is a one-way conductor, whether a tube or semiconductor is used. As a result, a-c voltage applied to the input is converted to d-c voltage in the output, as illustrated in Fig. 25·24a. The circuit in *b* shows a half-wave power supply using a silicon diode. Note the schematic symbol and coding shown in *c*. The arrow always indicates the direction of conventional current, or hole current, which is opposite from electron flow. Therefore, the arrow is at the more positive terminal, which is the *anode*, corresponding to the plate in a vacuum tube; the opposite side is the cathode.

Fig. 25·25 *Special-purpose semiconductors. (a) Tunnel diode. (b) Zener or avalanche diode. (c) Silicon controlled rectifier.*

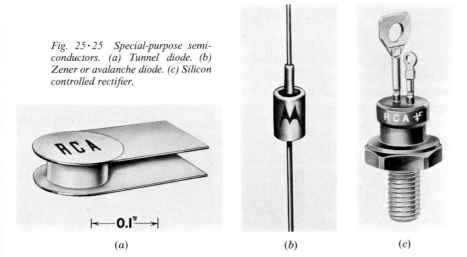

It should be noted, though, that the B+ voltage output of a power diode must be taken from the cathode. Therefore, the cathode terminal is coded red or + on power rectifiers, as shown in Fig. 25·25c. This means you can take +d-c output from the cathode by applying a-c input to the anode. For signal diodes, though, the cathode terminal is coded green or with a − sign. This means you can apply a-c signal to the cathode terminal to take negative d-c output from the anode.

In either case, the semiconductor diode is a rectifier that allows maximum current in the forward direction but only the reverse leakage current in the opposite direction. The ratio of reverse to forward resistance is usually more than 100:1, as measured on one scale of an ohmmeter.

Special-purpose semiconductors. In addition to their uses as diode rectifiers and triode transistor amplifiers, important developments are continually being made as the state of the art in solid-state devices advances to new materials and new applications. Some of these special-purpose devices are shown in Fig. 25·25. These include the following types.

Zener or avalanche diodes. These are silicon diodes designed for a specific breakdown voltage with reverse bias. As shown in Fig. 25·13, the reverse current increases sharply with an avalanche of minority charge carriers when the zener voltage is reached. Furthermore, the voltage across the diode remains constant. This characteristic makes the diode useful as a voltage regulator, connected in parallel with a load resistance. Multiple diodes in series can be used for increasing the voltage rating.

Silicon controlled rectifier. This is a three-junction device, usually with a silicon PNPN structure. One electrode serves as a *gate* to control the amount of forward bias needed to start conduction in the forward direction. The applications are similar to the thyratron gas tube with a control grid. There are many uses in power control.

Varactor diode. It is useful to note that the barrier voltage at the junction allows it to serve as a capacitance because of the separated charges. Therefore, the amount of junction capacitance can be controlled by the reverse voltage. Diodes designed for this effect of a voltage-sensitive capacitance are varactors.

Tunnel diodes. These are also called *Esaki diodes,* for the man who discovered that very heavy doping can provide a negative resistance characteristic at low values of forward voltage. Apparently what happens is that the extra doping allows minority charge carriers to tunnel through the junction to reduce the forward current. Because of its negative resistance the tunnel diode can be used as an amplifier. Essentially, this is a low-power device that features very high frequency response and freedom from temperature and radiation effects.

Photo diodes. A junction diode with reverse bias is photosensitive, as the amount of reverse leakage current varies with the light intensity. This photoconductive effect has many applications in light control. Compared with phototubes, which are most sensitive to blue light, semiconductor photodiodes can be used for the longer wavelengths of yellow, red and infrared.

25·15   Troubles in transistors

Excessive heat can damage a transistor. The heat may result from excessive current, ambient temperature, or soldering the transistor leads. Use long-nose pliers to hold the transistor leads, to provide a heat sink. When soldering leads to the transistor socket, remove the transistor first. Solder connections should be made quickly, with a small iron. A 25- to 50-watt pencil iron is generally used for the small solder connections in miniaturized transistor circuits.

Transistors are generally used on printed-circuit boards. To remove a defective resistor or capacitor, the best procedure is to clip the old component from the board but leave its pigtail leads. Then solder the new component to the old leads. This way the printed wiring is not disturbed. Figure 25·26 illustrates this technique.

Transistors can be damaged by even small transient voltage surges, which can produce excessive forward bias. For this reason, the power switch should be off when a transistor or the supply battery is replaced.

When checking resistances in transistor circuits with an ohmmeter, remove the transistors if convenient. If not, use a high ohms range, as the internal battery can produce excessive forward bias. It is preferable to make current and voltage tests. Note that the voltmeter must be capable of accurate readings within 0.1 volt for testing forward bias voltages.

A rough test of whether the transistor junctions are good or bad can be made with the ohmmeter. Remove the transistor from its socket, to eliminate parallel paths, and use the $R \times 100$ or $R \times 10,000$ range to prevent excessive current. Effectively, there are two diode junctions between base and emitter and from base to collector. For each junction, check the low resistance with forward bias and reverse the ohmmeter leads to read the high value of reverse resistance. With small transistors, the reverse resistance should be about 1,000 times higher than the forward resistance.

Fig. 25·26 Removing defective component from printed-circuit board. (Admiral Corp.)

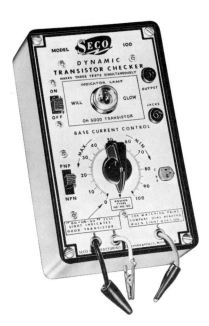

Fig. 25·27 Transistor checker.
(Seco Electronics Inc.)

Typical values are less than 500 ohms in the forward direction. The reverse resistance is about 150,000 ohms for Ge, with 10 μa leakage current and 1.5-volt ohmmeter battery, or 3 M for Si with 0.5 μa. Power transistors have lower resistances, with about ten times more leakage current. To make the ohmmeter check more useful, the resistances can be compared with the values for a transistor of the same type, known to be in good operating condition. When the junctions have their normal resistance values, the transistor is likely to operate normally.

For more exact tests, a transistor checker (Fig. 25·27) can be used. This tester measures α, β, and leakage current.

SUMMARY

1. The transistor is an amplifier that makes use of current flow in solid semiconductor materials, usually silicon and germanium.
2. Doping the semiconductor with controlled impurities makes it positive or negative. N type is negative because it has excess electrons; P type is positive because it has excess hole charges. The hole is a positive charge equal to the negative charge of an electron.
3. N- and P-type semiconductors form a PN or NP junction where they meet. A barrier voltage V_b forms at the junction to oppose current through the junction. V_b is 0.3 volt for Ge or 0.6 volt for Si.
4. Forward bias applied externally to a PN or NP combination can overcome the barrier voltage and force current to flow across the junction. The forward current is a drift of hole charges in P-type semiconductor or a drift of electron charges in N-type.
5. Reverse-bias voltage applied externally to a PN or NP combination has the polarity needed to prevent any forward current. However, a small amount of reverse leakage current flows in the opposite direction from forward current.
6. A transistor consists of a PNP or NPN combination with one type between two opposite types to form two opposite junctions. Of the three electrodes, one end is the emitter to

Table 25·4   SEMICONDUCTOR SYMBOLS

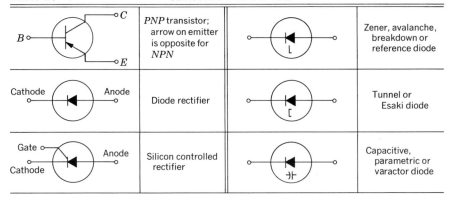

PNP transistor; arrow on emitter is opposite for NPN		Zener, avalanche, breakdown or reference diode
Diode rectifier		Tunnel or Esaki diode
Silicon controlled rectifier		Capacitive, parametric or varactor diode

supply electrons or hole charges to the base in the middle; the collector at the opposite end receives the emitter charges by injection from the base.

7. The emitter always has forward bias for low resistance in the base-emitter circuit.
8. The collector always has reverse bias for high resistance in the base-collector circuit.
9. The schematic symbols for semiconductors are summarized in Table 25·4.
10. The three main types of transistor circuit arrangements are the common-base, common-emitter, and common-collector circuits. These circuits are shown in Fig. 25·16. The common-emitter arrangement is the most common because it has the most gain. Table 25·3 compares the features of these three types of circuits.
11. For common-base circuits the main characteristic of the transistor is its α (alpha), which equals I_c/I_e. Typical values are 0.96 or more but less than 1.
12. For common-emitter circuits, the main characteristic of the transistor is its β (beta), which equals $\Delta i_c/\Delta i_b$, where β is the current-amplification factor of the transistor. Typical values of β are 50 to 100.
13. Silicon diodes are often used in power-supply rectifier circuits. In the diode symbol, the arrow indicates the direction of conventional current.
14. The main problem with semiconductors is to prevent overheating, especially with power transistors and diodes. They are often mounted with a heat sink, which is a metal path to conduct heat away from the semiconductor. When soldering transistor leads, do not apply too much heat. In checking circuits, do not allow excessive current to flow through the transistor.

SELF-EXAMINATION (*Answers at back of book.*)

Here's a chance to find out how well you have learned the material in this chapter. These exercises are for your self-testing only.

1. Because the transistor has no heater, it features (*a*) long warm-up time in amplifier circuits; (*b*) high power ratings up to 10 kw; (*c*) no hum from heater-cathode leakage; (*d*) short service life because of its solid construction.
2. In doping germanium with a controlled amount of impurity, (*a*) N type with excess electrons is produced by doping with arsenic; (*b*) N type with excess electrons is produced by doping with indium; (*c*) N type with excess holes is produced by doping with arsenic; (*d*) P type with excess holes is produced by doping with arsenic.
3. Hole current is the movement of (*a*) positive charges in the opposite direction from electron current; (*b*) positive charges in the same direction as electron current; (*c*) negative

charges in the opposite direction from electron current; (d) neutral charges in the opposite direction from electron current.

4. The barrier voltage at a PN or NP junction for Ge is (a) 2 volts, aiding forward current; (b) 0.3 volt, opposing forward current; (c) 25 volts, opposing forward current; (d) 25 volts, aiding forward current.

5. The collector circuit in a transistor amplifier circuit has (a) forward bias at all times; (b) reverse bias at all times; (c) reverse bias for NPN but forward bias for PNP; (d) reverse bias for PNP but forward bias for NPN.

6. The battery connections required for forward bias on a PN junction (a) are + battery terminal to P and − terminal to N; (b) are + battery terminal to N and − terminal to P; (c) depend on whether the transistor is PNP or NPN type; (d) are needed to move charges away from the junction.

7. Of the three types of transistor circuit the (a) common-base circuit is used most because it has the most gain; (b) common-emitter circuit is used most because it has the most gain; (c) common-collector circuit is used most because the collector then has forward bias; (d) common-emitter circuit is little used because of its extremely low input resistance.

8. The arrow in the symbol for a transistor indicates the direction of (a) electron current in the emitter; (b) hole current in the emitter; (c) hole current in the collector; (d) electron current in the collector.

9. When a change in base current from 30 to 40 ma changes the collector current from 500 to 900 ma, the β factor for this power transistor equals (a) 900; (b) 500; (c) 3; (d) 40.

10. A heat sink is often used with transistors and semiconductor diodes to (a) increase the forward current; (b) increase the reverse current; (c) prevent excessive temperature rise; (d) compensate for excessive doping.

ESSAY QUESTIONS

1. Name three semiconductor materials. Give one characteristic of all semiconductors that differs from metal conductors and one characteristic that differs from insulators.

2. Given that the atomic number of silicon is 14, show the arrangement of nucleus and orbital electrons, indicating the four valence electrons.

3. Define the following terms: (a) doping; (b) N-type silicon or germanium; (c) P-type silicon or germanium; (d) PN junction; (e) barrier voltage.

4. Describe briefly what is meant by (a) forward current; (b) reverse leakage current; (c) zener breakdown voltage.

5. For both PN and NP junctions show a battery applying (a) forward-bias voltage; (b) reverse-bias voltage.

6. Show the schematic symbol for a PNP transistor and for a NPN transistor, indicating the emitter, base, and collector.

7. Draw the complete schematic diagram of a common-base amplifier circuit using an NPN transistor with an external load resistor R_L. Indicate where input voltage is applied and amplified output voltage is obtained, and give typical values for the bias voltages.

8. Draw the schematic diagram of a full-wave rectifier circuit using silicon diodes to rectify the 60-cps a-c power-line voltage to produce B^+ voltage output with respect to chassis ground.

9. (a) Compare two types of transistors, giving one feature of each. (b) Compare two types of transistor amplifier circuits giving one feature of each.

10. Give three precautions that are important when you are working on transistor circuits.

PROBLEMS (Answers to selected problems at back of book.)

1. Refer to the alpha characteristic curves for the transistor in Fig. 25·19. (a) Give the values of collector current I_C, for the different emitter currents of 3 ma, 6 ma, 9 ma, and 12 ma, with a constant collector voltage V_C of − 10 volts. (b) How much is the collector current I_C for collector voltage V_C of − 5 volts and − 10 volts with a constant emitter current of 8 ma? (c) If

the input resistance between emitter and base is 100 ohms for this transistor, how much emitter-base voltage is necessary for an emitter current of 8 ma?

2. Refer to the beta characteristic curves for the transistor in Fig. 25·20: (*a*) Give the values of collector current I_C for the different base currents of -100 μa, -150 μa, and -200 μa with a constant collector-emitter voltage V_{CE} of -12 volts. (*b*) Give the values of collector current I_C for different collector-emitter voltages V_{CE} of -4 volts, -8 volts, and -12 volts with a constant base current of -150 μa.

3. Refer to Fig. 25·18, (*a*) If the average $I_C = 1$ ma, calculate the average V_C. (*b*) Calculate the d-c power dissipated by the collector, without a-c signal. (*c*) If I_C varies ± 500 μa, calculate the corresponding values of V_C. (*d*) Calculate the peak-to-peak a-c output voltage for the i_C variations in *c*.

4. Given that $I_C = 9$ ma and $I_B = 150$ μa, how much is I_E? Calculate α and β for this transistor.

5. Prove that $\beta = \alpha/1 - \alpha$.

6. (*a*) Given that $I_E = 20$ ma and α is 0.98, calculate I_C. (*b*) Calculate β for this transistor. (*c*) How much is the base current I_B?

7. Determine the forward bias and reverse bias for the following electrode voltages to chassis ground in a PNP grounded-emitter circuit: (*a*) $V_C = 40$ volts, $V_E = 8$ volts, $V_B = 8.2$ volts. Show a circuit with these voltages. (*b*) $V_C = 0$ volt, $V_E = -32$ volts, $V_B = -31.8$ volts. Show a circuit with these voltages.

8. In a common-emitter circuit, i_b variations of ± 100 μa swing i_c by ± 5 ma, with an R_L of 2,000 ohms: (*a*) How much is the current gain? (*b*) Calculate the peak-to-peak a-c output voltage across R_L. (*c*) If the input voltage is ± 40 mv, how much is the voltage gain?

Review of chapters ●24 and ●25

SUMMARY

1. In vacuum tubes the cathode is heated to emit electrons while the anode or plate collects these electrons to provide plate current. The main tube types are diodes, triodes, tetrodes, and pentodes. The diode has a cathode and a plate, the triode has a control grid also, in the tetrode the screen grid is added, while the pentode has all these plus the suppressor grid.
2. Diodes are used as rectifiers to change alternating to direct current.
3. Triodes, tetrodes, and pentodes are used for amplifiers, since the control-grid voltage controls the plate current. Making the control-grid voltage more negative decreases the plate current; making it less negative increases the plate current.
4. In addition to the a-c signal voltage, the operating voltages for a vacuum tube include filament voltage or heater voltage for an indirectly heated cathode, negative C bias for the control grid, and positive B^+ voltage for the plate supply and for the screen-grid voltage.
5. The three main characteristics for amplifier tubes are the amplification factor μ equal to $\Delta e_b/\Delta e_c$, internal plate resistance r_p equal to $\Delta e_b/\Delta i_b$, and transconductance g_m, which is equal to $\Delta i_b/\Delta e_c$.
6. Transistors are amplifiers making use of controlled current flow in solid semiconductors such as germanium and silicon. No heater is necessary. The transistor is smaller and more rugged and uses less power as compared with vacuum tubes.
7. N-type germanium or silicon is doped with an impurity that makes it negative with a surplus of electrons; P type has a surplus of positive hole charges.
8. A PNP transistor has a wafer of N-type semiconductor forming two junctions with two P-type wafers. An NPN transistor is the reverse. Both types are used as amplifiers. The semiconductor in the center is the base. The emitter at one end has forward bias to supply charges to its junction with the base; the collector at the other end has reverse bias and receives charges from its junction with the base. Forward bias has the polarity needed to make charges move to the junction; reverse bias makes charges move away from the junction.
9. In the schematic symbol the arrowhead on the emitter indicates the direction of hole current into the base for a P emitter or out from the base for an N emitter.
10. The main types of transistor circuits are common-base, common-emitter, and common collector. The common-emitter circuit is generally used for amplifiers because it has the most gain.
11. The two main characteristics of a transistor are its α (alpha), which is the ratio of collector current to emitter current, and β (beta), which is the ratio of collector current to base current.
12. Silicon and germanium diodes are often used in rectifier circuits. Germanium is for low-power detector circuits and silicon for power rectifiers.

REFERENCES (*Additional references at back of book.*)

Books

American Radio Relay League, Newington, Conn., "Radio Amateur's Handbook."

Cutler, P., *Semiconductor Circuit Analysis,* McGraw-Hill Book Company, New York.

Eastman, A. V., *Fundamentals of Vacuum Tubes,* McGraw-Hill Book Company, New York.

Fitchen, F. C., *Transistor Circuit Analysis and Design,* D. Van Nostrand Company, Inc., Princeton, N.J.

Kiver, M., *Transistors,* 3d ed., McGraw-Hill Book Company, New York.

Langford-Smith, *Radiotron Designer's Handbook,* published by Amalgamated Wireless Valve Co. PTY, Ltd., Australia, distributed by RCA Tube Division, Harrison, N.J.

Millman, J., *Vacuum-tube and Semiconductor Electronics,* McGraw-Hill Book Company, New York.

Rider, J. F., and H. Jacobowitz, *Basic Vacuum Tubes and Their Uses,* John F. Rider, Publisher, Inc., New York.

Turner, R. P., *Oscilloscope Handbook,* John F. Rider, Publisher, Inc., New York.

Pamphlets and catalogues

Eitel-McCullough, Inc., San Bruno, Calif., "Eimac Catalogue of Transmitting Tubes."

General Electric Co., Semiconductor Products, Syracuse, N.Y., "GE Transistor Manual."

RCA Tube Division, Harrison, N.J., "Photubes, Cathode-ray and Special Tubes."

RCA Tube Division, Harrison, N.J., "RCA Receiving Tube Manual."

RCA Semiconductor Products, Somerville, N.J., "RCA Transistor Manual."

Raytheon Mfg. Co., Waltham, Mass., "Raytheon Catologue of Microwave Tube Characteristics."

Sylvania Electric Products, Inc., Emporium, Pa., "Sylvania Tube Manual."

REVIEW SELF-EXAMINATION

Here's another chance to check your progress. Work the exercises just as you did those at the end of each chapter. (Answers at back of book.)

Answer true or false.

1. A thermionic cathode is heated to emit electrons.
2. The anode has a positive potential with respect to cathode to attract electrons.
3. Plate current can flow in only one direction.
4. A potential more negative than the grid-cutoff voltage results in zero plate current.
5. If the control-grid voltage changes from -2 volts to -1 volt, the plate current will increase.
6. The current through an external plate-load resistor is the same as the internal electron flow in the tube to the plate.
7. The cathode is often returned to chassis ground when the chassis is B minus.
8. The screen grid reduces the control grid-to-plate capacitance.
9. The suppressor grid reduces secondary emission from the plate.
10. The suppressor grid is usually grid No. 2.
11. The screen-grid voltage is a steady positive d-c potential.
12. If the plate current of a tube increases by 5 ma when the control-grid voltage is made 2 volts less negative, its g_m equals 5,000 μmhos.
13. Pentodes have higher μ than triodes because the screen-grid voltage makes the plate current less dependent on plate voltage.
14. An indirectly heated cathode can use a-c voltage for the heater.
15. The hot resistance of the heater is much higher than its cold resistance measured by an ohmmeter.
16. An open heater results in zero plate current.
17. Zero screen-grid voltage results in no plate current.
18. Zero control-grid voltage results in a high value of plate current.
19. Germanium and silicon are semiconductors commonly used for transistors.
20. An N-type semiconductor has excess electrons, while P type has excess hole charges.
21. The emitter is always forward-biased, while the collector has reverse bias.
22. The schematic symbol with an arrowhead into the base indicates a PNP transistor.
23. Forward bias is applied to a PNP transistor by $+$ to emitter and $-$ to the base.
24. Transistors are efficient amplifiers because they do not depend on thermionic emission of electrons.
25. The α characteristic of transistors is the ratio of collector current to base current.
26. Typical values of β for transistors are 0.98 to 0.99.
27. In a PNP transistor circuit the collector current consists of hole charges supplied by the emitter.
28. Typical values of collector voltage are 200 to 300 volts.
29. Reverse bias is applied to an NPN transistor by $+$ to collector and $-$ to the base.
30. The $+$ mark on silicon diode power rectifiers indicates where positive d-c output voltage is obtained.

Appendix A

Electronic frequency spectrum

Frequency or wavelength*	Name	Applications
0 cps	Steady direct current or voltage	D-c motors, solenoids, relays, electrode voltages for tubes and transistors
16–16,000 cps	Audio frequencies	60-cps power, a-c motors, audio amplifiers, microphones, loudspeakers, phonographs, tape recorders, high-fidelity equipment, public address systems, and intercoms
16 kc–30 kc	Ultrasonic frequencies or very low radio frequencies	Sound waves for ultrasonic cleaning, vibration testing, thickness gaging, flow detection, and sonar; electromagnetic waves for induction heating
30 kc–30,000 Mc	Radio frequencies (see Appendix B)	Radio communications and broadcasting, including television, radio navigation, radio astronomy, industrial, medical, and scientific radio, and military fire control
30,000–300,000 Mc or 1–0.1 cm	Especially high frequencies	Experimental, weather radar, amateur, government
300,000–7,600 A	Infrared light rays	Heating, infrared photography
7,600–3,900 A	Visible light rays	Color, illumination, photography
3,900–320 A	Ultraviolet rays	Sterilizing, deodorizing, medical
320–0.1 A	X rays	Thickness gages, inspection, absorption analysis, medical
0.1–0.006 A	Gamma rays	Radiation detection; more penetrating than hardest X rays
Shortest of all electromagnetic waves	Cosmic rays	Exist in outer space; can penetrate 70 m of water or 1 m of lead

* Frequency and wavelength are inversely proportional to each other. The higher the frequency, the shorter the wavelength, and vice versa. A-f and r-f waves are generally considered in terms of frequency because the wavelength is so long. The exception is microwaves, which are often designated by wavelength because their frequencies are so high. Light waves, X rays, and gamma rays are also generally considered in wavelength because their frequencies are so high. The units of wavelength are the angstrom (abbreviated A), which is 10^{-10} m, or the micron (abbreviated μ) equal to 10^{-6} m.

Appendix B

FCC frequency allocations from 30 kc to 300,000 Mc

Band	Allocation	Remarks
30–535 kc	Includes maritime communications and navigation, international fixed public band, aeronautical radio navigation	Very low, low, and medium radio frequencies
535–1,605 kc	Standard radio broadcast band	AM broadcasting
1,605 kc–30 Mc	Includes amateur radio, loran, government radio, international short-wave broadcast, fixed and mobile communications, radio navigation, industrial, scientific, and medical	Amateur bands 3.5–4.0 Mc and 28–29.7 Mc; industrial, scientific, and medical band 26.95–27.54 Mc; Citizen's band class D for voice is 26.965–27.225 Mc and 27.255 Mc
30–50 Mc	Government and nongovernment, fixed and mobile	Includes police, fire, forestry, highway, and railroad services; VHF band starts at 30 Mc
50–54 Mc	Amateur	6-meter band
54–72 Mc	Television broadcast channels 2–4	Also fixed and mobile services
72–76	Government and nongovernment services	Aeronautical marker beacon on 75 Mc
76–88	Television broadcast channels 5 and 6	Also fixed and mobile services
88–108 Mc	FM broadcast	Also available for facsimile broadcast; 88–92-Mc educational FM broadcast
108–122 Mc	Aeronautical navigation	Localizers, radio range, and airport control
122–174 Mc	Government and nongovernment, fixed and mobile, amateur broadcast	144–148-Mc amateur band

FCC frequency allocations from 30 kc to 300,000 Mc (continued)

Band	Allocation	Remarks
174–216 Mc	Television broadcast channels 7–13	Also fixed and mobile services
216–470 Mc	Amateur broadcast, government and nongovernment, fixed and mobile, aeronautical navigation, citizens' radio	Radio, altimeter, glide path and meteorological equipment; citizens' radio band 462.5–465 Mc; civil aviation 225–400 Mc; UHF band starts at 300 Mc
470–890 Mc	Television broadcasting	UHF television broadcast channels 14–83
890–3,000 Mc	Aeronautical radionavigation, amateur broadcast, studio-transmitter relay, government and nongovernment, fixed and mobile	Radar bands 1,300–1,600 Mc
3,000–30,000 Mc	Government and nongovernment, fixed and mobile, amateur broadcast, radio navigation	Super-high frequencies (SHF); 8,400 to 8,500 Mc satellite communications
30,000–300,000 Mc	Experimental, government, amateur	Extra-high frequencies (EHF)

Appendix C

Alphabetical listing of the chemical elements

Element	Symbol	Atomic number	Year of discovery	Remarks*
Actinium	Ac	89	1899	
Aluminum	Al	13	1825	Metal conductor
Antimony	Sb	51	Ancient	
Argon	Ar	18	1894	Inert gas
Arsenic	As	33	1649	
Barium	Ba	56	1808	End of 8-electron 0 shell
Beryllium	Be	4	1798	
Bismuth	Bi	83	1753	
Boron	B	5	1808	
Bromine	Br	35	1826	
Cadmium	Cd	48	1817	
Calcium	Ca	20	1808	End of 8-electron M shell
Carbon	C	6	Ancient	Semiconductor
Cerium	Ce	58	1803	Starts rare-earth series 58–71
Cesium	Cs	55	1860	Photosensitive
Chlorine	Cl	17	1774	Active gas
Chromium	Cr	24	1798	
Cobalt	Co	27	1735	
Copper	Cu	29	Ancient	Metal conductor
Fluorine	F	9	1771	Active gas
Gallium	Ga	31	1875	
Germanium	Ge	32	1886	Semiconductor
Gold	Au	79	Ancient	Metal conductor
Hafnium	Hf	72	1923	Start of 32-electron N shell
Helium	He	2	1895	Inert gas
Hydrogen	H	1	1766	Active gas
Indium	In	49	1863	
Iodine	I	53	1811	
Iridium	Ir	77	1804	
Iron	Fe	26	Ancient	Magnetic

Alphabetical listing of the chemical elements (continued)

Element	Symbol	Atomic number	Year of discovery	Remarks*
Krypton	Kr	36	1898	Inert gas
Lanthanum	La	57	1839	
Lead	Pb	82	Ancient	
Lithium	Li	3	1817	
Magnesium	Mg	12	1755	
Manganese	Mn	25	1774	
Mercury	Hg	80	Ancient	
Molybdenum	Mo	42	1781	
Neon	Ne	10	1898	Inert gas
Nickel	Ni	28	1751	
Niobium	Nb	41	1801	
Nitrogen	N	7	1772	
Osmium	Os	76	1804	
Oxygen	O	8	1774	
Palladium	Pd	46	1803	N shell has 18 electrons
Phosphorus	P	15	1669	
Platinum	Pt	78	1735	
Polonium	Po	84	1898	
Potassium	K	19	1807	
Radium	Ra	88	1898	
Radon	Rn	86	1900	Inert gas
Rhenium	Re	75	1925	
Rhodium	Rh	45	1803	
Rubidium	Rb	37	1861	
Ruthenium	Ru	44	1844	
Scandium	Sc	21	1879	
Selenium	Se	34	1818	Photosensitive
Silicon	Si	14	1823	Semiconductor
Silver	Ag	47	Ancient	Metal conductor
Sodium	Na	11	1807	
Strontium	Sr	38	1790	End of 8-electron N shell
Sulfur	S	16	Ancient	
Tantalum	Ta	73	1802	
Technetium	Tc	43	1937	
Tellurium	Te	52	1783	
Thallium	Tl	81	1861	
Thorium	Th	90	1829	Starts rare-earth series 90–103
Tin	Sn	50	Ancient	
Titanium	Ti	22	1791	
Tungsten	W	74	1783	
Uranium	U	92	1789	
Vanadium	V	23	1831	
Xenon	Xe	54	1898	Inert gas
Yttrium	Y	39	1843	
Zinc	Zn	30	1746	
Zirconium	Zr	40	1789	

* Rare-earth elements, with atomic numbers 58 to 71 and 90 to 103, are omitted.

Appendix D

PHYSICS UNITS

All the units are based on the fundamental dimensions of length, mass, and time. These are considered basic quantities, compared with derived quantities such as area, force, velocity, and acceleration, which are only different combinations of length, mass, and time. Each of the basic dimensions has units in the English system and in the decimal or metric system, as listed in Table D·1.

Systems of units

The cgs system is an abbreviation for its basic units of centimeters, grams, and seconds. The mks system based on meters, kilograms, and seconds provides larger units which are closer to practical values, since the kilogram is 1,000 grams and the meter is 100 cm.

In many cases, it is necessary to convert between English and metric units. Then the following conversions can be used:

LENGTH	MASS
1 meter = 39.37 in.	1 kilogram = 2.2 lb
1 in. = 2.54 cm	1 gram = 0.03527 ounce

The basic unit of time is the second in all systems.

Mass

The dimension of mass is often considered similar to the weight of an object. However, weight is actually the force due to the acceleration of gravity. To define mass more specifically,

Table D·1   Units for basic dimensions

Dimension	English unit	Metric unit	
		cgs	mks
Length (L)	foot	cm	meter
Mass (M)	slug*	gram	kilogram
Time (T)	sec	sec	sec

* 1 slug is the mass of a 1-lb weight.

it is necessary to use Newton's second law of motion: $F = Ma$. This can be transposed to $M = F/a$, which states that the mass is defined by how much force is necessary for a given amount of acceleration.

Derived quantities

A simple example is velocity, as a combination of the basic dimensions of length and time. The units can be feet per second, meters per second, or centimeters per second. Still, basically velocity is just L/T, meaning it is the time rate of change of length. Sometimes speed and velocity are used interchangeably. However, velocity is a vector quantity that has direction, while speed is a scalar quantity without direction. Another derived quantity is acceleration, the time rate of change of velocity. In the mks system the unit is meters per second per second, or m per sec². The basic dimensions are L/T^2, which results from L/T for velocity, divided by T. Additional derived quantities are force, work or energy, and power.

Force

Newton's law of acceleration is used to derive the units of force. For the formula $F = Ma$ in the cgs system, 1 *dyne* is the force needed for an acceleration of 1 cm per sec² with a mass of 1 gram. In the mks system, one *newton* is the force needed for an acceleration of 1 m per sec² with a mass of 1 k. One newton equals 10^5 dynes.

Work and energy

Work W is the product of force F times the distance s through which the force acts. As a formula, $W = Fs$. For example, if you lift a 20-lb weight through a distance of 2 ft, the work equals 40 ft-lb.

In the cgs system, F is in dyne-cm, which is an *erg*. A larger cgs unit is the *joule*, equal to 10^7 ergs.

In the mks system, F is in newton-meters. This unit is the same as 10^7 ergs. Or, 1 newton-meter equals 1 joule. The joule unit of work is named after James P. Joule (1818–1889), an important English physicist.

Energy is the ability to do work. Kinetic energy is due to the motion of a mass, as when you throw a ball. Potential energy is stored energy, as in a coiled spring. The units for both kinetic and potential energy are the same as for work.

Power

This is the time rate of doing work, or $P = W/T$. The practical unit in the metric system is the joule per sec, equal to 1 *watt*. In the English system the unit is ft-lb per sec. For a larger unit, 550 ft-lb per sec equal 1 horsepower.

Temperature scales

The centigrade scale, invented by A. Celsius, has 100 divisions between 0° for the freezing point of water and 100° for the boiling point. The Fahrenheit scale, invented by G. D. Fahrenheit, is used for weather observations and general purposes. On this scale, the freezing point is 32°F while the boiling point is 212°, with 180° divisions between. To convert from one scale to the other,

$$T_C = \frac{5}{9}(T_F - 32°) \qquad \text{and} \qquad T_F = \frac{9}{5}T_C + 32°$$

The Kelvin or absolute temperature scale was devised by Lord Kelvin. On this scale, the zero point is absolute zero, 273° below 0°C. At this temperature, any material loses all its thermal energy and the temperature cannot go any lower. The study of materials at these extremely low temperatures near absolute zero is called *cryogenics*.

The divisions of the °C scale and °K scale are the same. Therefore, to convert from °C to °K, just add 273°. Thus, 0°C equals 273°K. To convert from °K to °C, subtract 273°. Then 0°K equals -273°C.

Table D·2   Summary of physics units

Quantity	English (fps) units	Cgs units	mks units	Dimensions
Length	foot	centimeter	meter	L
Mass	slug	gram	kilogram	M
Time	second	second	second	T
Velocity	ft per sec	cm per sec	m per sec	L/T
Acceleration	ft per sec²	cm per sec²	m per sec²	L/T^2
Force	pound (lb)	dyne	newton	$Ma = ML/T^2$
Work and energy	ft-lb*	erg = dyne-cm; 10^7 ergs = 1 joule	joule = newton-meter	Force $\times L$
Power	ft-lb per sec; 1 hp = 550 ft-lb per sec	erg per sec; 10^7 ergs per sec = 1 watt	watt = joules per sec	Work/T
Heat	Btu	calorie	kilocalorie	1 cal = 4.19 joules

* ft-lb is a unit of work, while lb-ft is used for angular torque.

Average room temperature is generally considered about 20 to 25°C. This equals 68 to 77°F. On the absolute scale, the corresponding temperatures are 293 to 298°K.

Units of heat energy

In the cgs system, one *calorie* is the amount of heat needed to raise the temperature of 1 gram of water by 1°C. In mks units, the amount of heat to raise the temperature of 1 kilogram of water by 1°C is equal to 1 kilocalorie. In English units, the *British thermal unit (Btu)* is the amount of heat needed to raise the temperature of 1 pound of water by 1°F. The Btu is the larger unit, as 1 Btu equals 252 calories. The fact that heat is a form of energy can be seen from the fact that 1 calorie is equivalent to 4.19 joules of energy or work. These units are listed in Table D·2, which summarizes the main derived units and their dimensions.

For more details on physics, chemistry, the periodic table, and atomic structure the following references can be helpful:

Chemical Education Material Study, *Chemistry, an Experimental Science,* W. H. Freeman and Company, San Francisco, Calif.
Dull, Metcalfe, and Williams, *Modern Physics,* Holt, Rinehart and Winston, Inc., New York.
Ewing-Meyer, *Chemistry: A Survey of Principles,* John Wiley & Sons, Inc., New York.
Holton and Roller, *Foundations of Modern Physical Science,* Addison-Wesley Publishing Company, Inc., Reading, Mass.
Key to Welch Periodic Chart of the Atoms, W. M. Welch Scientific Co., Chicago, Ill.
Semat, H., *Fundamentals of Physics,* Holt, Rinehart and Winston, Inc., New York.
White, Manning, and Weber, *Practical Physics,* McGraw-Hill Book Company, New York.

Appendix E

MATHEMATICS

The ability to work with exponents certainly can save time in examples with very large or very small numbers, particularly when you are working with microfarads or picofarads of capacitance. Also, many problems require transposing equations and finding the square or square root of a number. These operations are explained here. Finally, there are some fundamentals of trigonometry, which is the study of angles. Trigonometry is necessary to analyze the characteristics of sine-wave alternating current or voltage.

Exponents

The number of times a number is multiplied by itself is called the *exponent* of the number:

$$10^3 = 10 \times 10 \times 10 = 1,000$$

The number taken as an example here is 10. Its exponent is 3, meaning it is multiplied by itself three times. The exponent is written as a small digit above the number itself, which is the *base*. The number 10 is the *common base* for exponents. This can also be stated as "10 to the third power." As examples:

$$10^1 = 10$$
$$10^2 = 10 \times 10 = 100$$
$$10^3 = 10 \times 10 \times 10 = 1,000$$
$$10^4 = 10 \times 10 \times 10 \times 10 = 10,000$$
$$10^5 = 10 \times 10 \times 10 \times 10 \times 10 = 100,000$$
$$10^6 = 10 \times 10 \times 10 \times 10 \times 10 \times 10 = 1,000,000$$

A number written without an exponent actually has the exponent 1. For instance, 10 and 10^1 are the same. Also, in a number without a decimal point, it is assumed to be after the last digit. For instance, in the number 103, the decimal point is after the last digit 3.

For the opposite case of decimal fractions smaller than 1, the exponent then is negative. As examples:

$$10^{-1} = 0.1 = \tfrac{1}{10}$$
$$10^{-2} = 0.01 = \tfrac{1}{100}$$
$$10^{-3} = 0.001 = \tfrac{1}{1,000}$$
$$10^{-4} = 0.0001 = \tfrac{1}{10,000}$$
$$10^{-5} = 0.00001 = \tfrac{1}{100,000}$$
$$10^{-6} = 0.000001 = \tfrac{1}{1,000,000}$$

These examples of positive powers of 10 up to a million and negative powers down to a millionth should be memorized, as they help simplify calculations in our decimal system of numbers.

Converting to powers of 10

When a number is not exactly in tens, hundreds, or thousands, etc., it can be converted into two factors so that the base 10 can be used with an exponent. This is illustrated here:

$$10 = 1 \times 10 = 1 \times 10^1$$
$$20 = 2 \times 10 = 2 \times 10^1$$
$$75 = 7.5 \times 10 = 7.5 \times 10^1$$
$$98 = 9.8 \times 10 = 9.8 \times 10^1$$
$$100 = 1 \times 100 = 1 \times 10^2$$
$$750 = 7.5 \times 100 = 7.5 \times 10^2$$
$$980 = 9.8 \times 100 = 9.8 \times 10^2$$
$$1,000 = 1 \times 1,000 = 1 \times 10^3$$
$$7,500 = 7.5 \times 1,000 = 7.5 \times 10^3$$
$$9,000 = 9 \times 1,000 = 9 \times 10^3$$
$$9,830 = 9.83 \times 1,000 = 9.83 \times 10^3$$

Notice that the exponent is the number of places the decimal point moves to the left. For instance, in $980 = 9.8 \times 10^2$, the exponent is 2 because the decimal point was moved two places in changing 980 to 9.8 as a factor or coefficient of 10^2.

The same idea applies to fractions smaller than 1, but now the negative exponent is the number of places the decimal point is moved to the right. Some examples are

$$0.01 = 1 \times 0.01 = 1 \times 10^{-2}$$
$$0.02 = 2 \times 0.01 = 2 \times 10^{-2}$$
$$0.05 = 5 \times 0.01 = 5 \times 10^{-2}$$
$$0.09 = 9 \times 0.01 = 9 \times 10^{-2}$$
$$0.093 = 9.3 \times 0.01 = 9.3 \times 10^{-2}$$

It should be noted that in a number like 9×10^3, the 9 is a factor or *coefficient* to be multiplied by the base with its power. In this case 9 is multiplied by 10^3 or 1,000, for a product equal to 9,000. When there is no coefficient it is assumed to be 1. Thus 1,000 can be written as 1×10^3 or simply 10^3.

Numbers greater than 1 always have a positive exponent for the power of 10. Decimal fractions less than 1 always have a negative exponent. Furthermore, the exponent is the number of places you move the decimal point, when converting to a power of 10. Moving the decimal point to the left lowers the numerical value, corresponding to division. Therefore, you must raise the positive exponent to keep the number the same. Thus 123 and 1.23×10^2 are the same. For the opposite case, moving the decimal point to the right raises the numerical value, corresponding to multiplication. Then you must decrease a positive exponent or increase a negative exponent, to keep the same value. Thus 0.002, 0.2×10^{-2} and 2×10^{-3} are all the same. Also, 9.83×10^3 is the same as 98.3×10^2, as both are equal to 9,830.

The question of how many places to move the decimal point can be answered by using the following procedures. When you convert to powers of 10, to set up the calculations for a problem, make the coefficient a number between 1 and 10. For instance, convert 9,830 to 9.83×10^3. This is called the *slide-rule form.* Its advantage is that the decimal point in the final answer can be determined more readily, when all the numbers are in this form with one decimal place. Another feature of this form is that the power of 10 is then the characteristic in the common logarithm of the number. However, for the final answer to a problem, it may be preferable to have the power of 10 as a multiple of 3 or 6 in order to use multiple and sub-multiple units. For instance, 42×10^{-3} amp for an answer shows it equals 42 ma, better than 4.2×10^{-2} amp. Note that both these values equal 0.042 amp.

Operations with exponents

Powers of 10 are convenient for multiplying or dividing numbers that are very large or small because the process is reduced to adding or subtracting exponents.

Rule *1*. To multiply factors with base 10, just add their exponents. For example,

$$(1 \times 10^4) \times (1 \times 10^2) = 1 \times 10^6$$

or
$$10,000 \times 100 = 1,000,000$$

Note, though, that only the exponents of base 10 are added. The coefficients are still multiplied. Here 1×1 still equals 1. As an example of other coefficients,

$$(2 \times 10^4) \times (3 \times 10^2) = 6 \times 10^6$$

or
$$20,000 \times 300 = 6,000,000$$

When there are negative exponents they add to produce a larger negative number:

$$(1 \times 10^{-2}) \times (1 \times 10^{-1}) = 1 \times 10^{-3}$$
$$0.01 \times 0.1 = 0.001$$

For the case of negative and positive exponents, take the difference between the two and give it the sign of the larger exponent:

$$(1 \times 10^5) \times (1 \times 10^{-3}) = 1 \times 10^2$$
$$(1 \times 10^{-5}) \times (1 \times 10^3) = 1 \times 10^{-2}$$

Rule *2*. To divide factors with the base 10, just subtract their exponents. For example,

$$(1 \times 10^6) \div (1 \times 10^3) = 1 \times 10^3$$

or
$$1,000,000 \div 1,000 = 1,000$$

Only the powers of 10 are subtracted. The coefficients are still divided:

$$6 \times 10^6 \div 3 \times 10^3 = 2 \times 10^3$$

or
$$6,000,000 \div 3,000 = 2,000$$

For the case of a divisor with a negative exponent, change its sign and add. For example,

$$(1 \times 10^5) \div (1 \times 10^{-3}) = 1 \times 10^8$$
$$(1 \times 10^{-5}) \div (1 \times 10^{-3}) = 1 \times 10^{-2}$$

An interesting case of division occurs when numerator and denominator are equal. Then the quotient must be 1. As an example,

$$1 \times 10^4 \div 1 \times 10^4 = 1 \times 10^0 = 1 \times 1 = 1$$

This example shows that for any base to the zero power the number is 1, as the 0 power indicates a fraction with the same numerator and denominator.

Rule *3*. To add or subtract numbers expressed in powers of 10, they must have the same exponent. Then add or subtract the coefficients but keep the same exponent. For example,

$$(6 \times 10^3) + (2 \times 10^3) = 8 \times 10^3$$
$$(6 \times 10^3) - (2 \times 10^3) = 4 \times 10^3$$

If the numbers do not have the same exponent, they must be changed to this form before you can add or subtract. Any exponent can be used but they must all be the same.

Decimal Fractions

It is often necessary in calculations to convert a fraction to a decimal equivalent, particularly in working with the slide rule. For this reason, the following conversions should be memorized

$$
\begin{array}{ll}
\tfrac{1}{2} = 0.5 & \tfrac{1}{6} = 0.167 \\
\tfrac{1}{3} = 0.333 & \tfrac{1}{7} = 0.143 \\
\tfrac{1}{4} = 0.25 & \tfrac{1}{8} = 0.125 \\
\tfrac{1}{5} = 0.2 & \tfrac{1}{9} = 0.111
\end{array}
$$

Squares and square roots

The exponent 2 for a number means it is squared. For instance, 10^2 equals 100, or 100 is the square of 10. Therefore, the square is just the number multiplied by itself. For example, 6^2 equals 6×6, or 36. For the reverse operation, the square root of a number is the factor which multiplied by itself equals the number. The square root of 36 equals 6, for example. This can be written as $\sqrt{36}$, or $(36)^{1/2} = 6$. The radical sign $\sqrt{}$ means square root. Squares and square roots are given in Table E·1. Any number in the N column has its square in the N^2 column and its square root in the $\sqrt{N}$ column.

This table is for numbers up to 120. For larger numbers, divide into smaller factors. For instance, $\sqrt{300} = \sqrt{3} \times \sqrt{100} = 1.732 \times 10 = 17.32$. Or, the slide rule can be used to find the square or square root of any number.

Transposing equations

In many cases a simple algebraic equation must have its factors transposed before you can do the problem. The three forms of Ohm's law are just transposed versions of $E = IR$, $I = E/R$, or $R = E/I$. One method of transposing can be accomplished by using the following system. A rule of equations is that multiplying or dividing both sides by the same factor does not change the equality. Therefore, if the correct factor is used, there can be a cancellation on one side that provides the desired equation. For example, suppose that, in the equation $E = IR$, it is desired to transpose to the form where I is by itself. Then the idea is to divide both sides by R so that it cancels in the IR term:

$$
E = IR
$$

dividing by R, we have

$$
\frac{E}{R} = \frac{I\cancel{R}}{\cancel{R}} = I
$$

or

$$
I = \frac{E}{R}
$$

It does not matter which side of the equation has the I, because the equality extends both ways. As another example, suppose we have the formula $X_L = 2\pi f L$ and want it in the form of L by itself on one side. Then divide both sides by $2\pi f$. The procedure is illustrated here:

$$
X_L = 2\pi f L
$$

dividing by $2\pi f$ gives

$$
\frac{X_L}{2\pi f} = \frac{2\pi f L}{2\pi f} = L
$$

or

$$
L = \frac{X_L}{2\pi f}
$$

This procedure of multiplying both sides by a factor that cancels can be applied to all equations.

Table E·1   Squares and square roots

N	N²	$\sqrt{N}$	N	N²	$\sqrt{N}$	N	N²	$\sqrt{N}$
1	1	1.000	41	1681	6.4031	81	6561	9.0000
2	4	1.414	42	1764	6.4807	82	6724	9.0554
3	9	1.732	43	1849	6.5574	83	6889	9.1104
4	16	2.000	44	1936	6.6332	84	7056	9.1652
5	25	2.236	45	2025	6.7082	85	7225	9.2195
6	36	2.449	46	2116	6.7823	86	7396	9.2736
7	49	2.646	47	2209	6.8557	87	7569	9.3274
8	64	2.828	48	2304	6.9282	88	7744	9.3808
9	81	3.000	49	2401	7.0000	89	7921	9.4340
10	100	3.162	50	2500	7.0711	90	8100	9.4868
11	121	3.3166	51	2601	7.1414	91	8281	9.5394
12	144	3.4641	52	2704	7.2111	92	8464	9.5917
13	169	3.6056	53	2809	7.2801	93	8649	9.6437
14	196	3.7417	54	2916	7.3485	94	8836	9.6954
15	225	3.8730	55	3025	7.4162	95	9025	9.7468
16	256	4.0000	56	3136	7.4833	96	9216	9.7980
17	289	4.1231	57	3249	7.5498	97	9409	9.8489
18	324	4.2426	58	3364	7.6158	98	9604	9.8995
19	361	4.3589	59	3481	7.6811	99	9801	9.9499
20	400	4.4721	60	3600	7.7460	100	10000	10.0000
21	441	4.5826	61	3721	7.8102	101	10201	10.0499
22	484	4.6904	62	3844	7.8740	102	10404	10.0995
23	529	4.7958	63	3969	7.9373	103	10609	10.1489
24	576	4.8990	64	4096	8.0000	104	10816	10.1980
25	625	5.0000	65	4225	8.0623	105	11025	10.2470
26	676	5.0990	66	4356	8.1240	106	11236	10.2956
27	729	5.1962	67	4489	8.1854	107	11449	10.3441
28	784	5.2915	68	4624	8.2462	108	11664	10.3923
29	841	5.3852	69	4761	8.3066	109	11881	10.4403
30	900	5.4772	70	4900	8.3666	110	12100	10.4881
31	961	5.5678	71	5041	8.4261	111	12321	10.5357
32	1024	5.6569	72	5184	8.4853	112	12544	10.5830
33	1089	5.7446	73	5329	8.5440	113	12769	10.6301
34	1156	5.8310	74	5476	8.6023	114	12996	10.6771
35	1225	5.9161	75	5625	8.6603	115	13225	10.7238
36	1296	6.0000	76	5776	8.7178	116	13456	10.7703
37	1369	6.0828	77	5929	8.7750	117	13689	10.8167
38	1444	6.1644	78	6084	8.8318	118	13924	10.8628
39	1521	6.2450	79	6241	8.8882	119	14161	10.9087
40	1600	6.3246	80	6400	8.9443	120	14400	10.9545

Trigonometry

This is the study of angles, so necessary in working with alternating current or voltage. As shown in Fig. E·1, if the line OA is hinged at point O and moves to the position OB, the line sweeps out or generates the angle AOB. The lines OA and OB are the sides of the angle, while point O is the origin. The symbol for the angle included between the two sides is gen-

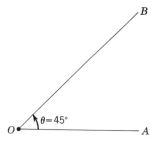

Fig. E·1

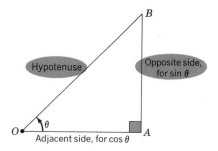

Fig. E·2

erally θ. By convention, θ is positive when produced by counterclockwise motion or negative for clockwise rotation. Complete rotation through a circle produces an angle of 360°. Angles are *acute* if less than 90° and *obtuse* if more than 90°.

Trigonometric functions are used to define the characteristics of an angle. These functions are sine, cosine, tangent, cotangent, secant, and cosecant. Only sin θ, cos θ, and tan θ are defined here, however, because they are commonly used in a-c circuits. The definitions are in terms of the sides of the right triangle OAB illustrated in Fig. E·2, with perpendicular sides OA and AB forming a right angle. The side opposite the right angle is the hypotenuse OB:

$$\sin \theta = \frac{\text{opposite side}}{\text{hypotenuse}} = \frac{AB}{OB}$$

$$\cos \theta = \frac{\text{adjacent side}}{\text{hypotenuse}} = \frac{OA}{OB}$$

$$\tan \theta = \frac{\text{opposite side}}{\text{adjacent side}} = \frac{AB}{OA}$$

By means of the trigonometric functions, when any two of the three factors are known, the third can be found from the table of trigonometric functions given here.

Note that the value of the sine is 0 for 0° and increases to a maximum of 1 for 90°. The cosine is just the opposite, with a maximum value of 1 for 0° and decreasing to 0 for 90°. The tangent value increases for greater angles, from 0 for 0° to a tangent of 1 for an angle of 45° with equal sides. Tangent values larger than 1 are for angles greater than 45°.

To use the table, just look for the angle in the left column, and find the corresponding value in the column for either sine, cosine, or tangent. For instance, sin 30° equals 0.5; cos 30° equals 0.866; tan 30° equals 0.5774. The reverse can also be done to find the angle that has a given value for the function. As an example, if sin θ = 0.7071, then the angle is 45°.

The angles considered so far are just up to 90°. For larger angles up to 360°, the full circle is divided into four quadrants, as shown in Fig. E·3. To use the table of trigonometric functions for obtuse angles in quadrants II, III, and IV, convert to the equivalent acute angles in quadrant I by the following rules: In quadrant II, use 180° − θ; in quadrant III, use θ − 180°; in quadrant IV, use 360° − θ. Also, use the appropriate sign or polarity for the trigonometric functions in different quadrants, as in Fig. E·3. As examples,

In quadrant II: tan 120° = −tan (180° − 120°) = −tan 60° = −1.7321
In quadrant III: tan 210° = tan (210° − 180°) = tan 30° = 0.5774
In quadrant IV: tan 300° = −tan (360° − 300°) = −tan 60° = −1.7321

All the functions are positive in quadrant I. Notice that the tangent alternates in polarity

Table E · 2   Trigonometric functions

Angle	sin	cos	tan	Angle	sin	cos	tan
0°	0.0000	1.000	0.0000	**45°**	0.7071	0.7071	1.0000
1	.0175	.9998	.0175	**46**	.7193	.6947	1.0355
2	.0349	.9994	.0349	**47**	.7314	.6820	1.0724
3	.0523	.9986	.0524	**48**	.7431	.6691	1.1106
4	.0698	.9976	.0699	**49**	.7547	.6561	1.1504
5	.0872	.9962	.0875	**50**	.7660	.6428	1.1918
6	.1045	.9945	.1051	**51**	.7771	.6293	1.2349
7	.1219	.9925	.1228	**52**	.7880	.6157	1.2799
8	.1392	.9903	.1405	**53**	.7986	.6018	1.3270
9	.1564	.9877	.1584	**54**	.8090	.5878	1.3764
10	.1736	.9848	.1763	**55**	.8192	.5736	1.4281
11	.1908	.9816	.1944	**56**	.8290	.5592	1.4826
12	.2079	.9781	.2126	**57**	.8387	.5446	1.5399
13	.2250	.9744	.2309	**58**	.8480	.5299	1.6003
14	.2419	.9703	.2493	**59**	.8572	.5150	1.6643
15	.2588	.9659	.2679	**60**	.8660	.5000	1.7321
16	.2756	.9613	.2867	**61**	.8746	.4848	1.8040
17	.2924	.9563	.3057	**62**	.8829	.4695	1.8807
18	.3090	.9511	.3249	**63**	.8910	.4540	1.9626
19	.3256	.9455	.3443	**64**	.8988	.4384	2.0503
20	.3420	.9397	.3640	**65**	.9063	.4226	2.1445
21	.3584	.9336	.3839	**66**	.9135	.4067	2.2460
22	.3746	.9272	.4040	**67**	.9205	.3907	2.3559
23	.3907	.9205	.4245	**68**	.9272	.3746	2.4751
24	.4067	.9135	.4452	**69**	.9336	.3584	2.6051
25	.4226	.9063	.4663	**70**	.9397	.3420	2.7475
26	.4384	.8988	.4877	**71**	.9455	.3256	2.9042
27	.4540	.8910	.5095	**72**	.9511	.3090	3.0777
28	.4695	.8829	.5317	**73**	.9563	.2924	3.2709
29	.4848	.8746	.5543	**74**	.9613	.2756	3.4874
30	.5000	.8660	.5774	**75**	.9659	.2588	3.7321
31	.5150	.8572	.6009	**76**	.9703	.2419	4.0108
32	.5299	.8480	.6249	**77**	.9744	.2250	4.3315
33	.5446	.8387	.6494	**78**	.9781	.2079	4.7046
34	.5592	.8290	.6745	**79**	.9816	.1908	5.1446
35	.5736	.8192	.7002	**80**	.9848	.1736	5.6713
36	.5878	.8090	.7265	**81**	.9877	.1564	6.3138
37	.6018	.7986	.7536	**82**	.9903	.1392	7.1154
38	.6157	.7880	.7813	**83**	.9925	.1219	8.1443
39	.6293	.7771	.8098	**84**	.9945	.1045	9.5144
40	.6428	.7660	.8391	**85**	.9962	.0872	11.43
41	.6561	.7547	.8693	**86**	.9976	.0698	14.30
42	.6691	.7431	.9004	**87**	.9986	.0523	19.08
43	.6820	.7314	.9325	**88**	.9994	.0349	28.64
44	.6947	.7193	.9657	**89**	.9998	.0175	57.29
				90	1.0000	.0000	

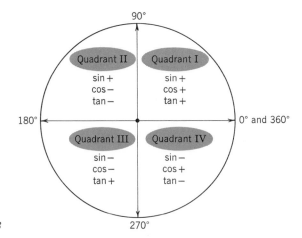

Fig. E·3

through quadrants I, II, III, and IV. In all the quadrants, the sine is + when the vertical ordinate is up or − when the ordinate is down. Similarly, the cosine is + when the horizontal abscissa is to the right or − to the left. The hypotenuse has no polarity. Finally, the tangent is + when the sine and cosine have the same polarity, either both + in quadrant I or both − in quadrant III. For more details on trigonometry and mathematics in general, applied to electronics, selected books are listed in the bibliography on page 567.

Appendix F

UNIVERSAL TIME-CONSTANT GRAPH FOR RC OR RL CIRCUITS

With the curves in Fig. F·1 you can determine voltage and current values for any amount of time. The rising curve *a* shows how the voltage builds up across *C* as it charges in an *RC* circuit; the same curve applies to the current increasing in the inductance for an *RL* circuit. The decreasing curve *b* shows how the capacitor voltage declines as *C* discharges in an *RC* circuit or the decay of current in an inductance.

Note that the horizontal axis is in units of time constants, rather than absolute time. The time constant is the *RC* product for capacitive circuits but equals *L/R* for inductive circuits. For example, suppose that the time constant of a capacitive circuit is 5 μsec. Therefore, one *RC* unit corresponds to 5 μsec, two *RC* units equals 10 μsec, three *RC* units equals 15 μsec, etc. To find how much voltage is across the capacitor after 10 μsec of charging, take the value

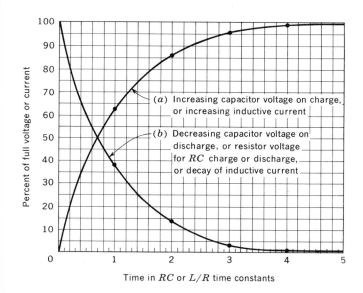

(a) Increasing capacitor voltage on charge, or increasing inductive current

(b) Decreasing capacitor voltage on discharge, or resistor voltage for *RC* charge or discharge, or decay of inductive current

Time in *RC* or *L/R* time constants

Fig. F·1

Table F · 1

FACTOR	CHANGE, PER CENT
0.5 time constant	40
0.7 time constant	50
1 time constant	63
2 time constants	86
3 time constants	96
4 time constants	98
5 time constants	99

on graph *a* corresponding to two time constants, or approximately 86 per cent of the applied charging voltage. The point where curves *a* and *b* intersect shows that a 50 per cent change is accomplished in 0.7 time constant. The curves can be considered linear within the first 40 per cent of change, or within 0.5 time constant.

In Fig. F · 1 the entire *RC* charge curve actually adds 63 per cent of the net charging voltage for each increment of 1 time constant, although it may not appear so. In the second interval of *RC* time, for instance, e_c adds 63 per cent of the net charging voltage, which is $0.37E$. Then 0.63×0.37 equals 0.23, which is added to 0.63 to give 0.86 or 86 per cent. This value of 86 per cent is the change from the start, at zero time, as are all the values listed in Table F · 1.

Appendix G

COLOR CODES

Included here are color codes for chassis wiring, carbon resistors, and small fixed capacitors with mica or ceramic dielectric. Most of these codes are standardized by the Electronic Industries Association (EIA). Members are not required to follow the codes but it is industry practice to do so where practical.

Chassis wiring

Colors for the wires in electronic circuits generally follow the system in Table G·1. By noting the wiring color code, you can often save time in tracing the connections.

Table G·1   Chassis wiring color code

COLOR	CONNECTED TO
Red	B+ voltage supply
Blue	Plate of amplifier tube or collector of transistor
Green	Control grid of amplifier tube or base of transistor (also for input to diode detector)
Yellow	Cathode of amplifier tube or emitter of transistor
Orange	Screen grid
Brown	Heaters or filaments
Black	Chassis ground return
White	Return for control grid (AVC bias)

Carbon resistors

For ratings of 2 watts or less, carbon resistors are color-coded with either bands or the body-end-dot system as summarized in Table G·2.

The color values summarized in Table G·3 apply to both resistors and capacitors. However, the colors for voltage ratings apply only to capacitors. Also, only gold or silver is used for carbon-composition resistor tolerance, but all the colors apply to tolerances for capacitors or film resistors.

Similarly, the preferred values in Table G·4 are for resistance values in ohms or capacitor values in picofarads. Only the basic value is listed, from which multiple values are derived. As an example, a 1,500-ohm R or 1,500-pf C is a standard component value, with a tolerance of either 20, 10, or 5 per cent. However, 2,000 is only in 5 per cent tolerance.

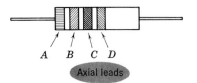

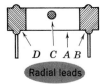

Axial leads   Radial leads

Table G·2   Color codes for carbon resistors

Axial leads	Color	Radial leads
B and A	First significant figure	Body A
B and B	Second significant figure	End B
B and C	Decimal multiplier	Dot C
B and D	Tolerance	End D

Notes: Band *A* is double width for wirewound resistors with axial leads. Body-end-dot system is a discontinued standard but may still be found on some old resistors. For resistors with color stripes and axial leads, body color is not used for color-coded value. Film resistors have five stripes; fourth stripe is multiplier and fifth is tolerance.

Mica capacitors

White, EIA
Black, MIL
White, AWS paper

1st) significant
2nd) figure

Multiplier
Tolerance
Classification

Present six-dot code

1st) significant
2nd) figure
3rd)

Multiplier
Tolerance
Working voltage

Old six-dot code

Table G·3   Color values for resistor and capacitor codes

Color	Significant figure	Decimal multiplier	Tolerance,* %	Voltage rating*
Black	0	1	20	
Brown	1	10	1	100
Red	2	10^2	2	200
Orange	3	10^3	3	300
Yellow	4	10^4	4	400
Green	5	10^5	5	500
Blue	6	10^6	6	600
Violet	7	10^7	7	700
Gray	8	10^8	8	800
White	9	10^9	9	900
Gold		0.1	5	1,000
Silver		0.01	10	2,000
No color			20	500

* Tolerance colors other than gold and silver and voltage-rating colors for capacitors only.

Mica capacitors

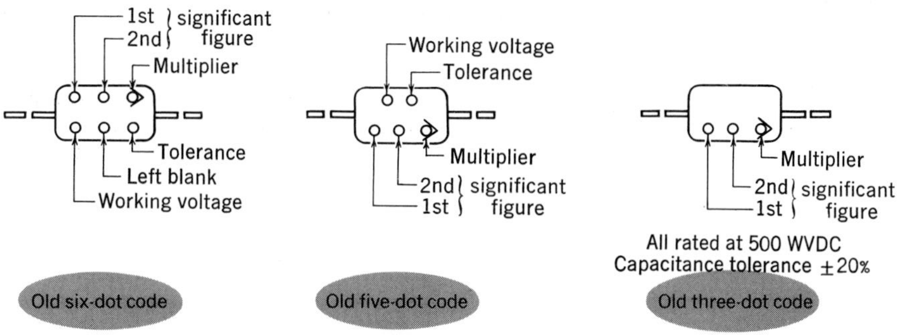

All rated at 500 WVDC
Capacitance tolerance ±20%

Table G·4   Preferred values for resistors and capacitors

20% tolerance	10% tolerance	5% tolerance
10*	10	10
		11
	12	12
		13
15	15	15
		16
	18	18
		20
22	22	22
		24
	27	27
		30
33	33	33
		36
	39	39
		43
47	47	47
		51
	56	56
		62
68	68	68
		75
	82	82
		91
100	100	100

* Numbers and decimal multiples for ohms or pf.

Mica capacitors

These may be coded with old RMA or new EIA methods, military (MIL), Joint Army Navy (JAN) specifications, or American War Standards (AWS). Actually, for both mica and ceramic capacitors the trend has been for manufacturers to print the values on the capacitor, to avoid confusion with different color codes.

The new EIA six-dot code starts with a white dot. If this dot is black it indicates the MIL six-dot code. Or, if this dot is silver, it indicates a paper capacitor in the AWS code. In all three cases, though, the capacitance in pf units is read from the next three color dots. However, if the first dot has a color, this indicates the old EIA six-dot code, where the first four dots are used for the capacitor value.

The characteristics indicated by the last dot in the new EIA six-dot code specify five classes from A to E, according to leakage resistance, temperature coefficient, and other factors.

Ceramic capacitors

These have stripes or dots with three colors or five colors. With five stripes or dots, the first and last colors indicate temperature coefficient and tolerance, as listed in Table G·5. The middle three colors give the capacitance in picofarads, with the same color values as for resistors and mica capacitors. The fourth color is for tolerance, in per cent for sizes larger than 10 pf but in pf units for smaller capacitors.

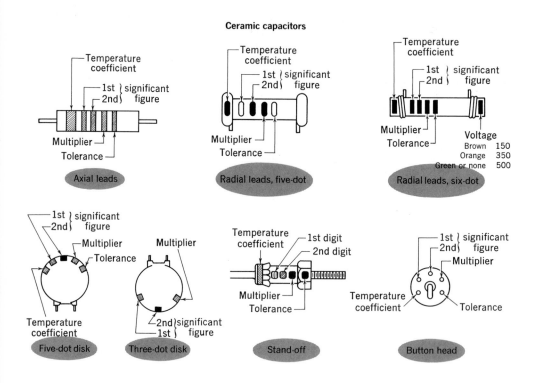

Ceramic capacitors

Table G·5   Color code for ceramic capacitors

Color	Decimal multiplier	Tolerance Above 10 pf, %	Tolerance Below 10 pf, in pf	Temp. coeff. ppm per °C
Black	1	20	2.0	0
Brown	10	1		−30
Red	100	2		−80
Orange	1,000			−150
Yellow				−220
Green		5	0.5	−330
Blue				−470
Violet				−750
Gray	0.01		0.25	30
White	0.1	10	1.0	500

Appendix H

ABBREVIATIONS AND SCHEMATIC SYMBOLS

Table H·1   Greek letters

Letter	Meaning	Letter	Meaning
α (alpha)	Ratio of collector current to emitter current in transistors	Ω (omega)	Ohm unit of resistance
β (beta)	Ratio of collector current to base current in transistors	ϕ (phi) π (pi)	Magnetic flux Constant of 3.14, generally used as 2π or 6.28
Δ (delta) or d	A small change in value	ρ (rho)	Resistivity
λ (lambda)	Wavelength	θ (theta)	Angle, often the phase angle in a-c circuits
μ (mu)	Amplification factor of tube, or permeability of magnetic material, or prefix meaning one-millionth		

Table H·2   Electrical units

Quantity	Symbol	Basic unit
Current	I or i *	ampere
Charge	Q or q	coulomb
Voltage	V or v	volt
(electromotive force, potential difference)	emf, E or e PD	
Power	P	watt
Resistance	R†	ohm
Reactance	X	ohm
Impedance	Z	ohm
Conductance	G	mho
Admittance	Y	mho
Susceptance	B	mho
Capacitance	C	farad
Inductance	L	henry
Frequency	F or f	cps
Period	T	second

* Capital letter for I, Q, V, and E generally used for peak, RMS, or d-c value; small letter for instantaneous values.

† Small r and g usually for internal values, as r_p and g_m of a tube.

Table H·3   Multiples and submultiples of units

Value	Prefix	Symbol	Example
$1\ 000\ 000\ 000\ 000 = 10^{12}$	tera	T	Tc $= 10^{12}$ cps
$1\ 000\ 000\ 000 = 10^9$	giga	G	Gc $= 10^9$ cps
$1\ 000\ 000 = 10^6$	mega	M	Mc $= 10^6$ cps
$1\ 000 = 10^3$	kilo	K or k	kv $= 10^3$ volts
$100 = 10^2$	hecto	h	hm $= 10^2$ meters
$10 = 10$	deka	dk	dkm $= 10$ meters
$0.1 = 10^{-1}$	deci	d	dm $= 10^{-1}$ meter
$0.01 = 10^{-2}$	centi	c	cm $= 10^{-2}$ meter
$0.001 = 10^{-3}$	milli	m	ma $= 10^{-3}$ amp
$0.000\ 001 = 10^{-6}$	micro	μ	μv $= 10^{-6}$ volt
$0.000\ 000\ 001 = 10^{-9}$	nano	n	nsec $= 10^{-9}$ second
$0.000\ 000\ 000\ 001 = 10^{-12}$	pico	p	pf $= 10^{-12}$ farad

SCHEMATIC SYMBOLS

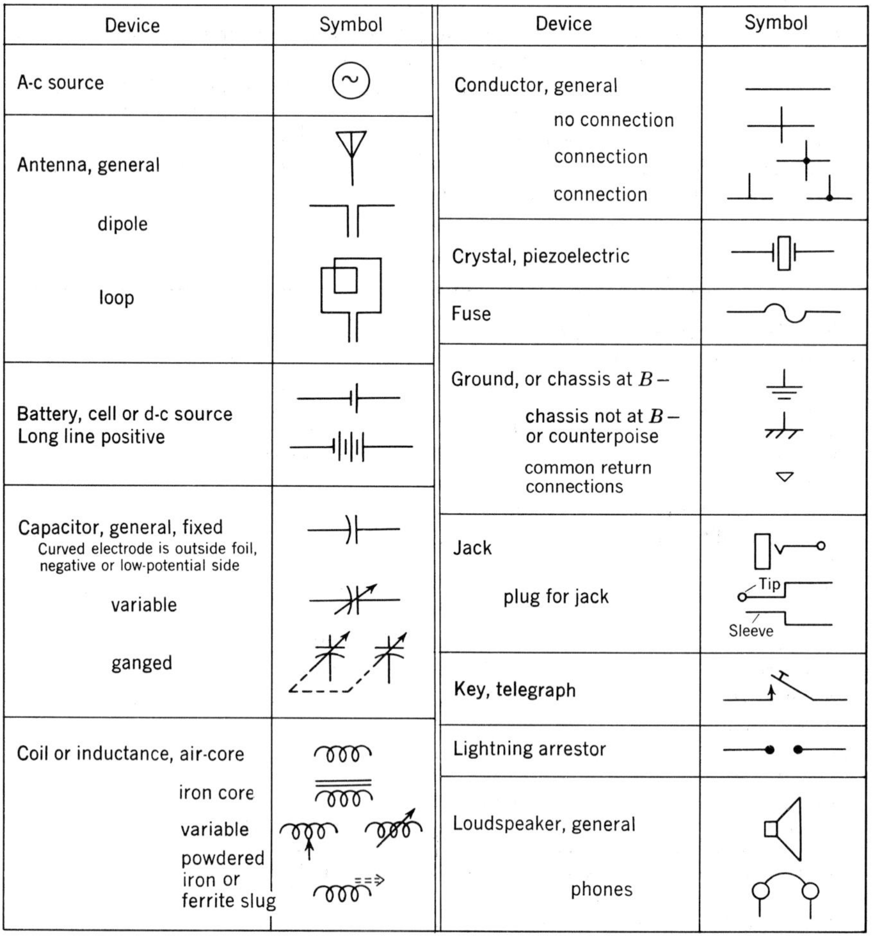

Device	Symbol	Device	Symbol
A-c source		Conductor, general	
		no connection	
Antenna, general		connection	
		connection	
dipole		Crystal, piezoelectric	
loop		Fuse	
Battery, cell or d-c source Long line positive		Ground, or chassis at $B-$	
		chassis not at $B-$ or counterpoise	
		common return connections	
Capacitor, general, fixed Curved electrode is outside foil, negative or low-potential side		Jack	
variable		plug for jack	Tip Sleeve
ganged		Key, telegraph	
Coil or inductance, air-core		Lightning arrestor	
iron core			
variable		Loudspeaker, general	
powdered iron or ferrite slug		phones	

SCHEMATIC SYMBOLS

Device	Symbol	Device	Symbol
Magnet, permanent	PM	Relay, coil	
electromagnet		contacts	
Meters, letter or symbol to indicate range or function	 (A) (MA) (V)		
Resistor, fixed		Transistors and semiconductors *PNP* triode transistor	e c b
tapped			
variable		*NPN* triode transistor	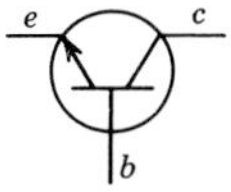 e c b
Switch, general			
toggle		Rectifier (arrow shows hole current)	
2-pole, double throw			
3-pole, 3-circuit wafer		Gate-controlled rectifier	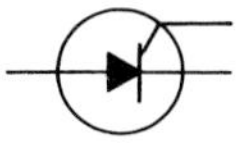
		Zener, avalanche, breakdown or voltage reference diode	
Shielding			
shielded conductor		Tunnel diode or Esaki diode	
Thermistor, general		Varactor, varicap, reactance diode or parametric diode	
Thermocouple		Photodiode or solar cell	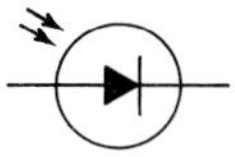
Transformer, air core		Tubes, envelope	
iron-core		gas-filled	
autotransformer		directly heated cathode	
link coupling		indirectly heated cathode	
		grid	 - - -

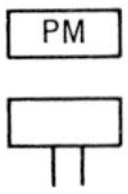

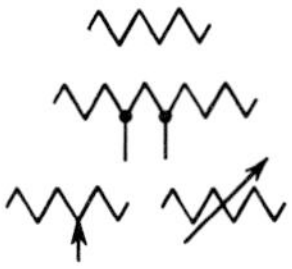

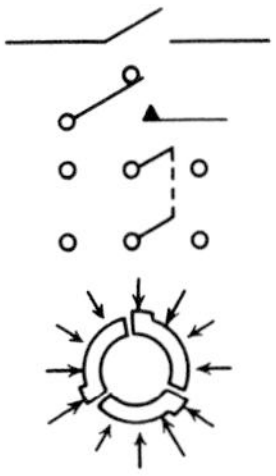

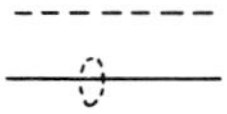

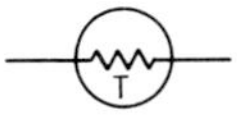

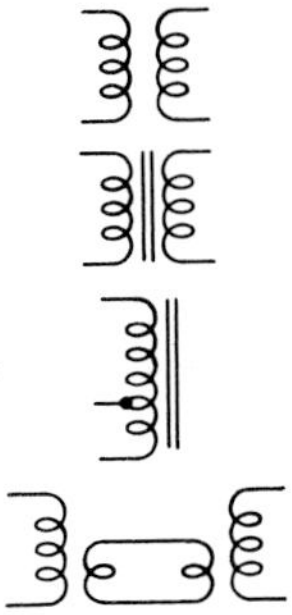

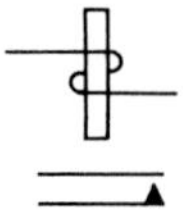

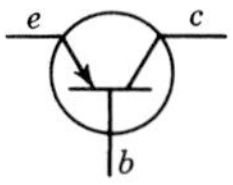

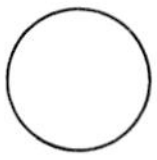

SCHEMATIC SYMBOLS

Device	Symbol	Device	Symbol
Tubes, contd.		Tubes, contd.	
diode		cold-cathode gas diode	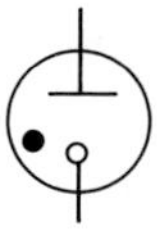
triode	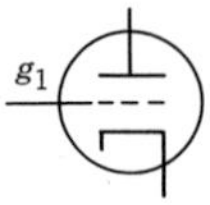	phototube	
tetrode	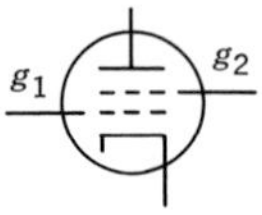		
pentode	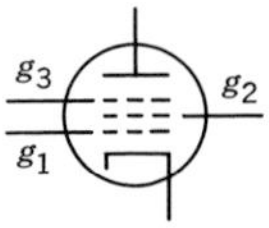	cathode-ray tube with electrostatic deflection plates	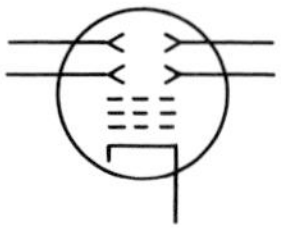

Appendix I

SOLDERING AND TOOLS

In addition to the usual workshop tools, working on electronic equipment often requires long-nose or needle-nose pliers to bend the end of a wire, diagonal cutting pliers to cut wire, ¼-in. socket wrench for machine screws with ¼-in. hexagonal head, and a Phillips screwdriver. These tools are shown in Fig. I·1.

The cutting pliers can be used when you want to strip about an inch or less of the insulation from the end of stranded wire that is not the push-back type. First crush the insulation by squeezing below the cutting edges of the pliers; then notch the crushed insulation with the cutting edge down to the wire, being careful not to cut the wire; finally pull off the crushed insulation with the cutting edges of the pliers in the notch. A wire stripper is a special tool for this, but you can do a professional job with the diagonal cutting pliers.

Soldering

Solder is an alloy of tin and lead used for fusing metals at relatively low temperatures of about 500 to 600° F. First, the joint where two metal conductors are to be fused is heated and

Fig. I·1 From left to right: cutting pliers, long-nose pliers, straight-edge screwdriver, Phillips-head screwdriver, hexagonal socket wrench, straight-edge plastic alignment tool and hexagonal plastic alignment tool.

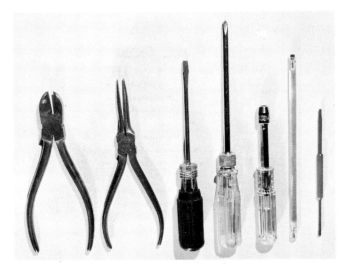

Fig. I·2   (a) Soldering iron. (b) Soldering pencil. (c) Soldering gun.

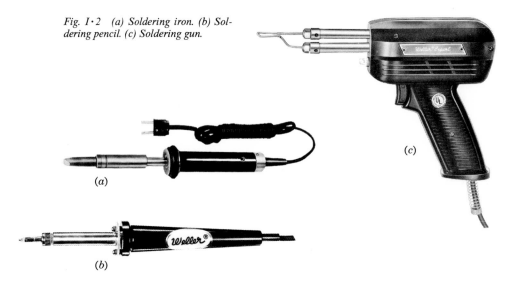

(a)

(b)

(c)

then solder is applied so that it can melt and cover the connection. The reason for soldering connections is that it makes a good bond between the joined metal, covering the joint completely to prevent oxidation. The coating of solder provides protection for practically an indefinite period of time.

The trick in soldering is to heat the joint, not the solder. When the joint is hot enough to melt the solder, it flows smoothly to fill all the cracks forming a shiny cover without any air spaces. Do not move the joint until the solder has set, which takes only a few seconds.

Either a soldering iron or soldering gun can be used, rated at 75 to 100 watts. See Fig. I·2. The gun is convenient for intermittent operation, since it heats almost instantaneously when you press the trigger. The small pencil iron of 25 to 40 watts is helpful for soldering small connections where excessive heat can cause damage. This precaution is particularly important when working on printed circuits, where too much heat can soften the plastic form and loosen the metal eyelet connections.

The three grades of solder generally used for electronics work are 40–60, 50–50, and 60–40 solder. The first figure is the percentage of tin, while the other is the percentage of lead. The 60–40 solder costs more, but it flows more freely, takes less time to harden, and generally makes it easier to do a good soldering job. In addition to the solder, there must be flux to remove any oxide film on the metals being joined. Otherwise they cannot fuse. The flux enables the molten solder to wet the metals so that the solder can stick. The two types are acid flux and rosin flux. Acid flux is more active in cleaning metals but is corrosive. Rosin flux is always used for the light soldering work in making wire connections. Generally, the rosin is in the hollow core of solder intended for electronics work, so that a separate flux is unnecessary. Such rosin-core solder is the type generally used. It should be noted, though, that the flux is not a substitute for cleaning the metals to be fused. They must be shiny clean for the solder to stick.

For more details on soldering, tools, and machines, the following references can be helpful:

Ford Trade School, *Shop Theory,* McGraw-Hill Book Company, New York.
Kester Solder Co., *Solder,* Kester Solder Co., Chicago, Ill.
Manko, H. M., *Solders and Soldering,* McGraw-Hill Book Company, New York.
Radio Amateur's Handbook, American Radio Relay League, Newington, Conn., (chapter on Construction Practices).

Bibliography

Mathematics

Cooke, N. M., *Basic Mathematics for Electronics,* 2d ed., McGraw-Hill Book Company, New York.
Fischer, B., and H. V. Jacobs, *Elements of Mathematics for Radio, Television and Electronics,* The Macmillan Company, New York.
Machovina, P. E., *A Manual for the Slide Rule,* McGraw-Hill Book Company, New York.
Maedel, G. F., *Basic Mathematics for Radio and Television,* Prentice-Hall, Inc., Englewood Cliffs, N.J.
Rice, H. S., and R. M. Knight, *Technical Mathematics,* McGraw-Hill Book Company, New York.
Roberts and Stockton, *Elements of Mathematics,* Addison-Wesley Publishing Company, Inc., Reading, Mass.
Stein, P., *Graphical Analysis,* Hayden Publishing Company, New York.

Radio communications and electronics

Carson, R. S., *Principles of Applied Electronics,* McGraw-Hill Book Company, New York.
Chute, G. M., *Electronics in Industry,* 2d ed., McGraw-Hill Book Company, New York.
DeFrance, J. J., *General Electronic Circuits,* Holt, Rhinehart and Winston, Inc., New York.
Everitt, W. L., and G. E. Anner, *Communication Engineering,* 3d ed., McGraw-Hill Book Company, New York.
Gray, T. S., *Applied Electronics,* John Wiley & Sons, Inc., New York.
Grob, B., *Basic Television,* 3d ed., McGraw-Hill Book Company, New York.
Grob, B., and M. S. Kiver, *Applications of Electronics,* McGraw-Hill Book Company, New York.
Kaufman, M., *Radio Operator's License Q and A Manual,* John F. Rider, Publisher, Inc., New York.
Kiver, M. S., *FM Simplified,* D. Van Nostrand Company, Inc., Princeton, N.J.
Lurch, E. N., *Fundamentals of Electronics,* John Wiley & Sons, Inc., New York.
Mueller, G. V., *Introduction to Electrical Engineering,* McGraw-Hill Book Company, New York.
Radio Amateur's Handbook, American Radio Relay League, Newington, Conn.
Richter, H., *Practical Electrical Wiring,* 6th ed., McGraw-Hill Book Company, New York.
Sams, H. W., *Basic Radio Manual,* Howard W. Sams & Co., Inc., Indianapolis, Ind.
Shrader, R. L., *Electronic Communication,* McGraw-Hill Book Company, New York.
Slurzberg, M., and W. Osterheld, *Essentials of Radio-Electronics,* 2d ed., McGraw-Hill Book Company, New York.
Swiggett, R. L., *Introduction to Printed Circuits,* John F. Rider, Publisher, Inc., New York.

Terman, F. E., *Electronic and Radio Engineering,* McGraw Hill Book Company, New York.

Zbar, P., and S. Schildkraut, *Basic Electronics—Laboratory Manual,* 2d ed., McGraw-Hill Book Company, New York.

Tubes and transistors

Cutler, P., *Semiconductor Circuit Analysis,* McGraw-Hill Book Company, New York.

Eastman, A. V., *Fundamentals of Vacuum Tubes,* 3d ed., McGraw-Hill Book Company, New York.

Fitchen, F. C., *Transistor Circuit Analysis and Design,* D. Van Nostrand Company, Inc., Princeton, N.J.

GE Transistor Manual, General Electric Company, Semiconductor Products, Syracuse, N.Y.

Hunter, L. P., *Handbook of Semiconductor Electronics,* McGraw-Hill Book Company, New York.

Kiver, M. S., *Transistors,* 3d ed., McGraw-Hill Book Company, New York.

Kiver, M. S., and B. Van Emden, *Transistor Laboratory Manual,* McGraw-Hill Book Company, New York.

Langford-Smith, *Radiotron Designer's Handbook,* Amalgamated Wireless Valve Co., PTY Ltd., Australia, distributed by RCA Tube Division, Harrison, N.J.

RCA Transistor Manual, Radio Corporation of America, Semiconductor Division, Somerville, N.J.

RCA Tube Manual, Radio Corporation of America, Electron Tube Division, Harrison, N.J.

Seidman, A. H., and S. L. Marshall, *Semiconductor Fundamentals,* John Wiley & Sons, Inc., New York.

Sylvania Tube Manual, Sylvania Electric Products, Emporium, Pa.

Manufacturers' periodical publications

Aerovox Research Worker, Aerovox Corp., New Bedford, Mass., and Monrovia, Calif.

Amphenol Engineering News, Amphenol Electronics Corp., Chicago.

Capacitor, Cornell-Dubilier Electric Corp., South Plainfield, N.J.

International Rectifier News, International Rectifier Corp., El Segundo, Calif.

RCA Service News, RCA Service Co., Camden, N.J.

Sylvania News, Sylvania Electric Products, Emporium, Pa.

Magazines

Electronics, McGraw-Hill Publications, New York.

Electronic Servicing, Cowan Publishing Corp., New York.

Electronic Technician, Ojibway Press Inc., Duluth, Minn.

PF Reporter, Howard W. Sams & Co., Inc., Indianapolis, Ind.

QST, American Radio Relay League, West Hartford, Conn.

Radio-Electronics, Gernsback Publications, Inc., New York.

Radio & TV News, Ziff-Davis Publishing Co., New York.

Service, Bryan Davis Publishing Co., Inc., New York.

Answers to self-examinations

Chapter 1

1. T	2. T	3. T	4. T	5. T
6. T	7. T	8. T	9. T	10. T
11. T	12. T	13. T	14. T	15. T
16. T	17. F	18. T	19. F	20. F

Chapter 2

1. 2	2. 4	3. 16	4. 0.5	5. 2
6. 25	7. 25	8. 10	9. 0.4	10. 72
11. 8	12. 2	13. 2	14. 4.17	15. 28.8
16. 2	17. 500	18. 3	19. 0.2	20. 0.12

Chapter 3

1. (d)	2. (c)	3. (d)	4. (b)	5. (c)
6. (d)	7. (c)	8. (b)	9. (b)	10. (d)

Chapter 4

1. (b)	2. (a)	3. (a)	4. (d)	5. (a)
6. (c)	7. (c)	8. (b)	9. (c)	10. (b)

Chapter 5

1. (c)	2. (c)	3. (c)	4. (c)	5. (d)
6. (c)	7. (b)	8. (d)	9. (d)	10. (d)

Chapter 6

1. (b)	2. (a)	3. (c)	4. (b)	5. (b)	6. (b)
7. (b)	8. (a)	9. (c)	10. (a)	11. (c)	12. (b)

Review of chapters 1 to 6

1. (c)	2. (c)	3. (c)	4. (b)	5. (c)	6. (b)
7. (d)	8. (b)	9. (a)	10. (b)	11. (c)	12. (a)

Chapter 7

1. (a)	2. (c)	3. (a)	4. (a)	5. (c)
6. (c)	7. (a)	8. (c)	9. (d)	10. (c)

Chapter 8

1. (a)	2. (d)	3. (d)	4. (b)	5. (b)
6. (a)	7. (b)	8. (c)	9. (c)	10. (c)

Chapter 9

1. (*d*)	2. (*a*)	3. (*d*)	4. (*c*)	5. (*a*)
6. (*b*)	7. (*d*)	8. (*a*)	9. (*b*)	10. (*c*)

Chapter 10

1. (*d*)	2. (*c*)	3. (*b*)	4. (*a*)	5. (*d*)
6. (*d*)	7. (*a*)	8. (*c*)	9. (*a*)	10. (*d*)

Review of chapters 7 to 10

1. (*d*)	2. (*b*)	3. (*b*)	4. (*c*)	5. (*d*)
6. (*c*)	7. (*b*)	8. (*c*)	9. (*c*)	10. (*b*)

Chapter 11

1. to 25. True

Chapter 12

1. to 20. True

Chapter 13

1. to 10. True

11. 28	12. 1.2	13. 70.7	14. 3×10^4	15. 0.001
16. 60	17. 0.01	18. 0.25	19. 7.07	20. 30
21. 30	22. 6⅔	23. 30	24. 1,000	25. ⅟₆₀

Review of chapters 11 to 13

1. (*b*)	2. (*a*)	3. (*c*)	4. (*d*)	5. (*b*)
6. (*d*)	7. (*a*)	8. (*d*)	9. (*c*)	10. (*a*)

Chapter 14

1. (*b*)	2. (*c*)	3. (*c*)	4. (*d*)	5. (*c*)
6. (*d*)	7. (*b*)	8. (*d*)	9. (*b*)	10. (*a*)

Chapter 15

1. (*a*)	2. (*c*)	3. (*c*)	4. (*d*)	5. (*a*)
6. (*c*)	7. (*c*)	8. (*b*)	9. (*d*)	10. (*c*)

Chapter 16

1. (*c*)	2. (*c*)	3. (*c*)	4. (*c*)	5. (*b*)
6. (*b*)	7. (*c*)	8. (*b*)	9. (*b*)	10. (*b*)

Review of chapters 14 to 16

1. (*a*)	2. (*b*)	3. (*d*)	4. (*d*)	5. (*d*)
6. (*d*)	7. (*c*)	8. (*a*)	9. (*b*)	10. (*c*)

Chapter 17

1. (*a*)	2. (*b*)	3. (*b*)	4. (*c*)	5. (*c*)
6. (*c*)	7. (*c*)	8. (*b*)	9. (*c*)	10. (*b*)

Chapter 18

1. *b*	2. *c*	3. *c*	4. *b*	5. *d*
6. *a*	7. *a*	8. *d*	9. *b*	10. *a*

Chapter 19

1. *d*	2. *b*	3. *a*	4. *b*	5. *b*
6. *b*	7. *c*	8. *c*	9. *b*	10. *b*

Review of chapters 17 to 19

1. T	2. T	3. T	4. T	5. T
6. T	7. T	8. T	9. F	10. T
11. T	12. T	13. F	14. T	15. T
16. T	17. F	18. T	19. T	20. T
21. T	22. T	23. T	24. T	25. T
26. T	27. T	28. T	29. T	30. T
31. F	32. T	33. T	34. T	35. T
36. T	37. F	38. F	39. T	40. T

Chapter 20

1. (b)	2. (c)	3. (a)	4. (c)	5. (c)
6. (a)	7. (b)	8. (c)	9. (c)	10. (a)

Chapter 21

1. (d)	2. (m)	3. (n)	4. (j)
5. (h)	6. (l)	7. (o)	8. (k)
9. (e)	10. (a)	11. (b)	12. (f)
13. (g)	14. (i)	15. (c)	16. (p)

Chapter 22

1. (c)	2. (b)	3. (d)	4. (c)	5. (d)
6. (a)	7. (d)	8. (d)	9. (a)	10. (b)

Chapter 23

1. (d)	2. (a)	3. (b)	4. (c)	5. (d)
6. (b)	7. (a)	8. (b)	9. (a)	10. (d)

Review of chapters 20 to 23

1. 300	2. 300	3. 300	4. 250	5. 250
6. 200	7. 200	8. 14.1	9. 14.1	10. 1
11. 45	12. −45	13. 1	14. 1.41	15. 7.07
16. 600	17. 353.5	18. 8	19. 0.8	20. 1.6
21. 0.8	22. 10	23. 10	24. 10	25. 1
26. 5	27. 50	28. 0.08	29. 40	30. 150
31. T	32. T	33. T	34. T	35. T
36. T	37. T	38. T	39. T	40. T

Chapter 24

1. (a)	2. (b)	3. (b)	4. (c)	5. (b)
6. (c)	7. (a)	8. (d)	9. (b)	10. (c)

Chapter 25

1. (c)	2. (a)	3. (a)	4. (b)	5. (b)
6. (a)	7. (b)	8. (b)	9. (d)	10. (c)

Review of chapters 24 to 25

1. T	2. T	3. T	4. T	5. T
6. T	7. T	8. T	9. T	10. F
11. T	12. F	13. T	14. T	15. T
16. T	17. T	18. T	19. T	20. T
21. T	22. T	23. T	24. T	25. F
26. F	27. T	28. F	29. T	30. T

Answers to selected problems

Chapter 1

1. −4 coul
2. +8 coul
4. 8 coul
6. (a) 1,000 ohms
   (b) 0.5 ohm
   (c) 0.01 ohm
7. 0.2 amp
8. 1 amp

Chapter 2

2. (b) 18 watts
   (c) 18 watts
   (d) 9 watts
4. (b) 21 ohms
6. 10,000 volts
8. (b) 208×10^{-6} amp
10. (b) 18 ohms

Chapter 3

2. $I = 1$ amp
   $R_2 = 10$ ohms
4. $V_2 = 0.3$ volt
6. $E_T = 30$ volts
   $I = 1$ amp
8. 2,552,470 ohms
9. Each R is 15K

Chapter 4

2. 180 watts
4. (b) $E = 20$ volts
   (c) 2 amp and 4 amp
6. (b) 2,000 ohms
   (d) 54.6 ohms
   (f) 5,000 ohms
8. (b) 33.3K ohms
10. 0.038 mho
12. $R_T = 3.82$ ohms

Chapter 5

2. 400 watts
4. (a) 6 ohms
   (b) 24 ohms
6. (a) 100 watts
   (b) 25 watts
8. (a) $I_1 = 1.33$ amp
     $I_2 = 4$ amp
     $I_3 = 0.444$ amp
     $I_4 = 0.133$ amp
   (b) $P_1 = 42.6$ watts
     $P_2 = 128$ watts
     $P_3 = 14.2$ watts
     $P_4 = 4.26$ watts
10. (a) $P_3 = 4.8$ watts
     $P_2 = 1.76$ watts
     $P_1 = 1$ watt
   (b) $R_c = 8,330$ ohms
     $R_s = 10,000$ ohms
     $R_P = 5,000$ ohms
12. (a) $R_x = 600$ ohms
   (b) E_x and $E_1 = 0.5$ volt
     E_s and $E_2 = 1.0$ volt

Chapter 6

1. $V_{Th} = 15$ volts
   $R_{Th} = 3$ ohms (Fig. 6·33)

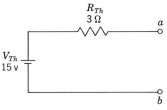

Fig. 6·33

2. $I_N = 5$ amp
   $R_N = 3$ ohms (Fig. 6·34)

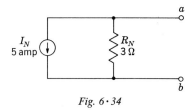

Fig. 6·34

3. $E_o = +58$ volts
5. $I_L = 0.0292$ amp

4. $E_L = 35$ volts
6. $V_{Th} = 24$ volts
   $R_{Th} = 3$ ohms (Fig. 6·35)

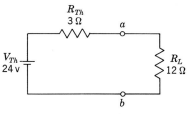

Fig. 6·35

7. $I_N = 8$ amp
   $R_N = 3$ ohms (Fig. 6·36)

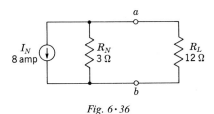

Fig. 6·36

8. $V_1 = 0.8$ volt
   $V_2 = 19.2$ volts
   $V_3 = 16.8$ volts
   $I_1 = 0.2$ amp
   $I_2 = 1.6$ amp
   $I_3 = 1.4$ amp

9. $I_1 = 0.3$ amp
   $I_2 = 1.35$ amp
   $I_3 = 1.06$ amp

10. See Fig. 6·37

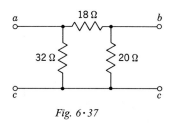

Fig. 6·37

11. See Fig. 6·38

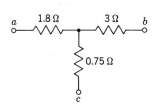

Fig. 6·38

12. $I_1 = 1.6$ amp

Chapter 7
1. (a) 50 ohms
   (b) 5.55 ohms
   (c) 0.505 ohm
4. 50K
   0.5M
   5M
   5M
6. $R_S = 5.025$ ohms for 10-ma range

2. (c) 99,950 ohms or 100K

5. $R_M = 199,000$ ohms for 10-volt range

8. 48.8 volts

Chapter 8
1. (a) 1,024 circular mils
   (b) No. 20
   (c) 1 ohm, approx
8. 5,000 ft

4. 100 ft of No. 10 = 0.1018 ohm
   200 ft of No. 7 = 0.1016 ohm

10. No. 20 wire = 10 ohms
    No. 30 wire = 105 ohms

6. 5,500 ohms

12. No. 16 wire

Chapter 9
2. (a) 10,000 ohms
   (b) 0.01 watt
6. (b) 0.15 watt

4. (a) 10,000 ohms
   (b) 2,200 ohms
8. 50 ohms
   1 watt

Chapter 10
1. 1.5 ma
6. (a) 600 ohms
   (b) 1,200 ohms
   (c) 600 ohms

3. 600 amp
8. 20,000 ohms

Chapter 11
2. 1,000 gauss = 0.1 weber

6. (a) 125.6 gilberts
   (b) 6.28 oersteds
   (c) 1,256 gauss
   (d) 6.28 gauss

4. 100
   75

10. (b) 40 volts
    (c) 12.6 oersteds
    (d) 3,780 gauss
    (e) 30,240 lines
    (f) 8.33×10^{-3} gilberts/maxwell

Chapter 12
1. 9,000 volts

3. (d) 2 webers/sec

5. (a) 0.2 amp
   (b) 80 amp-turns
   (c) 100.8 gilberts
   (d) 5.04 oersteds
   (e) 2,520 gauss
   (f) 15,120 maxwells

Chapter 13
2. (b) 10 cps
   (d) 100 cps

8. $V_1 = 133.3$ volts
   $V_2 = 66.6$ volts
   $P_1 = 177.5$ μwatts
   $P_2 = 88.5$ μwatts

4. (b) 0.2 μsec

10. $V_1 = V_3 = 40$ volts
    $V_2 = V_4 = 80$ volts

6. $P_1 = 180$ watts
   $P_2 = 45$ watts
   $P_3 = 45$ watts

Chapter 14

2. (b) 10,000 amp/sec
   (d) 10,000 amp/sec
6. 24 amp

4. 2 mh

10. (c) 20 mv

Chapter 15

2. for 1,000 cps, $L = 0.1$ henry
8. 6,280 ohms

4. (b) 7,540 ohms
9. $L_1 = 2.65$ henrys
   $L_2 = 10.6$ henrys

5. 3.2 henry
12. (b) 3,520 ohms

Chapter 16

2. (c) $I_R = 2$ amp,
   $I_L = 2$ amp,
   $I_T = 2.8$ amp,
   $Z = 35.4$ ohms,
   $\theta = 45°$
8. 94 ohms
14. $I_R = 0.25$ amp
    $I_L = 0.25$ amp
    $I_T = 0.354$ amp
    $Z = 283$ ohms
    $\theta = -45°$

4. (b) 0.63 amp
   (c) 1 amp

10. 0.5×10^{-3} sec

6. 400 ohms

12. 12,560 ohms

Chapter 17

2. 100 volts
   50 volts

6. 40 μf
   37.50×10^{15} electrons
   electrolytic

4. $Q = 10 \times 10^{-3}$ coul
   $V_1 = 10,000$ volts
   $V_2 = 1,000$ volts
8. $Q_1 = Q_2 = 500$ μcoul
   $Q_t = 1,000$ μcoul
   $C_t = 2$ μf

Chapter 18

2. 0.0159 μf

8. (b) $X_{C_T} = 1,000$ ohms
   (c) $I = 40$ ma
   (d) $E_1 = 4$ volts
       $E_2 = 8$ volts
       $E_3 = 12$ volts
       $E_4 = 16$ volts
   (e) $C_1 = 1,000$ pf
       $C_2 = 500$ pf
       $C_3 = 333$ pf
       $C_4 = 250$ pf

4. 2.2 μf

10. (a) $C_T = 1.33$ μf
    (b) $X_{C_T} = 23.9$ ohms

6. (b) $I_1 = 0.01$ amp
   (c) $I_2 = 0.0025$ amp
   (d) $I_L = 0.0125$ amp
14. 422 pf

Chapter 19

2. (b) $I_R = 2.5$ amp
       $I_C = 3.33$ amp
   (c) 4.17 amp
   (d) 23.9 ohms
   (e) 53.2°
   (f) 90°

4. (a) $E_2 = 1,000$ volts
   (b) $C_2 = 8,100$ pf

8. 8.6 volts

6. (a) 0.001 sec
   (d) 1 μsec

10. 2.5×10^{-2} joules
    12.5 joules
    320×10^{-2} joules

Chapter 20

2. (b) $V_R = 40$ volts
   $V_L = 80$ volts
   $V_c = 120$ volts
   (c) $E_a = 56$ volts
   (d) 0.707
   (e) $\theta_z = -45°$
5. $I = 0.8$ amp
   $\theta_z = 53°$
12. $R = 960$ ohms

3. (b) 10 ohms
   (c) $0°$
   (d) 10 amp

6. $I = 4.05$ amp
   $\theta_I = 9.1°$
14. 300 pf

4. $X_L = 120$ ohms
   $X_C = 45$ ohms
   $Z = 85$ ohms
   $I = 1.18$ amp
   $\theta_I = -61.9°$

8. $I = 0.144$ amp
   $\theta_I = -46.3°$

Chapter 21

1. (a) $4 - j3$ ohms
   (d) $3 - j3$ ohms
9. $12.65/18.5°$ ohms

4. (a) $4.45 - j2.27$ ohms
   (d) $3 - j3$ ohms
12. $5.25/-13.6°$ ohms

6. (a) $450/78°$
   (d) $72/-78°$
14. $Z = 50/-37°$ ohms
   $I = 2/37°$ amp
   $E_R = 80/37°$ volts
   $E_L = 120/127°$ volts
   $E_C = 180/-53°$ volts

16. $X_L = 2,510$ ohms
   $X_C = 1,990$ ohms
   $Z = 2,060$ ohms $/14.6°$

Chapter 22

1. 12.6 cps

5. 254 μh at 1 Mc
   127 μh at 4 Mc
8. (a) 795 Kc
   (b) 200 pf
   (c) 795 Kc
   (d) $Q = 50$

2. 79.5 cps

6. 1,810 pf

10. (a) $X_L = 1,000$ ohms
   (b) $L = 31.8$ millihenrys
   $C = 0.032$ μf
   (c) $Q = 200$
   $BW = 25$ cps
   (d) 100 volts

4. (a) $Q = 30$
   (b) $X_C = 1,200$ ohms
   (c) 0.33 μamp
   (d) 12 millivolts
   (e) 36,000 ohms

Chapter 23

2. (b) 0.5 Mc
8. (a) 0.064 μf
   (b) 6.4 μf

3. 0.064 μf
10. (b) 0.0032 μf

7. 1.53 millihenrys

Chapter 24

1. (a) 150 volts
   (b) 190 volts
   (c) 0.6 watt
   2.28 watts
7. (a) 130,000 ohms
   (b) 0.08 watt
   (c) 0.52 watt
12. (a) 12
   (b) 1,200 μvolts

5. $g_m = 4,800$ micromhos

10. 456 volts

6. (a) 52,500 ohms
   (b) 0.6 μf

11. (a) 16 ma
   (b) 13 ma

Chapter 25

1. (*b*) 7.9 ma
   (*c*) 0.8 volt

6. (*a*) 19.6 ma
   (*b*) 49
   (*c*) 0.4 ma

3. (*a*) 10 volts
   (*b*) 0.01 watt
   (*c*) 10 volts $\pm$ 2.5 volts
   (*d*) 5 volts

7. reverse bias = 32 volts
   forward bias = 0.2 volt

4. $I_E = 9.15$ ma
   $\alpha = 0.984$
   $\beta = 61.5$

8. (*a*) 50
   (*b*) 20 volts *PP*
   (*c*) 250

Index

A batteries, 175–176
Acceptor impurities, 511
Admittance, 415
Air gap, 203–205
α (alpha) characteristic, 525–526
Alternating current, 26–27, 237–263
  average value, 244
  circuits, 255–257, 383–397
  effective value, 244–246
  frequency, 246–248
  generator, 238–241, 258–259
  impedance, 306–307, 388–392
  peak value, 244–246, 260
  period, 249
  phase angle, 251–255
  resistance, 313–314
  RMS value, 244–246
  sine-wave, 241–242
  three-phase, 259
Alternating-current circuits, analysis, 255–257, 383–397
  impedance, 388–392
  ohms, types of, 396–397
  parallel, 256, 383–397
  power factor, 393–394
  series, 256
  vectors, types of, 397–398
Alternating-current meters, 394–396
Alternating voltage, 237–263

Alternation, defined, 240
Amateur radio, 5
Ambient temperature, 167
American Wire Gage, 143–144
Ammeters, 117–124
Ampere, 21, 36–37
Ampere-turns, 208, 218–219
Amplification factor, 487
Anode, 28, 471, 529
Apparent power, 394
Armature, 258–259
Atomic number, 14, 542–543
Atomic structure, 10–16, 152–156
  semiconductors, 507–511
Attenuation, 458
Audio frequencies, 247
Autotransformer, 279–280
Avalanche current, 517
Average value, 244
Ayrton shunt, 122–124

B batteries, 175–176
B-plus voltage, 480–481
Back-off ohmmeter, 131–132
Ballistic galvanometer, 117
Band-pass filters, 460–462, 466
Bandwidth, 435–438
  measurement, 437
Bank, parallel, 64

Barrier voltage, 513–517
Base, transistor, 518
Bass tone, 248
Batteries, 175–195
    charging, 185–188
    dry cells, 179–181
    Edison cell, 185–188
    lead-acid, 182–188
    mercury cell, 185–188
    nickel-cadmium, 186–188
    parallel, 181–182
    polarization, 179–180
    primary, 178–181
    secondary, 178, 182–188
    series, 181–182
    solar, 188
    specific gravity, 184–185
    types of, 186–187
    voltaic cell, 176–179
Bayonet base, 149
Beam-power tubes, 496
β (beta) characteristic, 526
Bezel, 149
Bias, grid, 482, 484
Bleeder current, 80
Blocking capacitor, 452–454
Bobbin resistors, 170
Bohr atom, 13–16
Branch currents, 59–63
Broadcasting, radio, 3–5
Brown and Sharpe gage, 143–144
Brushes, motor or generator, 259
Btu, heat unit, 546
Bypass capacitors, 454–456

C batteries, 175–176, 482
C-bias, 482, 484
Calorie, 546
Capacitance, 327–334
    charge and discharge, 349–351, 356–357
    farad unit, 331–333
    interelectrode, 490–491
    stray, 342–343

Capacitive circuits, 363–382
    bypassing, 454–456
    coupling, 375–376, 452–454
    phase angle, 363–364
    time constant, 371–374, 555–556
    voltage dividers, 369–371
Capacitive reactance, 349–361
    applications, 355–356
    calculations, 351–354
    parallel, 354–355
    series, 354–355
Capacitors, ceramic, 337–338
    color code, 339–340, 558–560
    dielectric, 157, 333–334
    electrolytic, 337–339
    mica, 335
    paper, 335–336
    parallel, 340–341
    power factor, 343
    series, 340–341
    tantalum, 338
    tolerance, 338
    troubles in, 344–346
    variable, 337
    voltage rating, 333–334
Carbon resistors, 163–168
    color code, 164–166, 557–558
Carrier wave, 3–4
Cathode, 28, 473–474
Cathode-ray tubes, 497–498
Cgs units, 544
Charge, coulomb unit, 16–18
    electrostatic field, 328–329
    stored, 330–332
Charger, battery, 185–188
Chokes, 319–320
Circular mils, 144
Coils, inductance, 269–270
    Q, 313–314
    troubles in, 286–287
Collector, transistor, 518
Color codes, capacitor, 339–340, 558–560
    resistors, 164–166, 557–558
    wiring, 557

Common-base circuit, 520–521
Common-collector circuit, 522
Common-emitter circuit, 522
Commutator, 259
Compactron tubes, 496
Complex numbers, 401–419
  in a-c circuits, 404–406, 413–418
  j operator, 402–403
  operations with, 406–408
  polar form, 408–412
  rectangular form, 408–412
Compound, 155
Condensers (*see* Capacitors)
Conductance, 24, 415
  in parallel, 67–68
Conductors, 12, 142–146
  gage sizes, 143–144
  printed wiring, 146, 531
  resistance wire, 151–152
Constant-current generator, 191
Constant-voltage generator, 191
Continuity testing, 138–139
Conventional current, 23
Corona effect, 158
Cosine of angle, 552
Coulomb, 16–18, 329
Coupling capacitors, 375–376, 452–
  454
Coupling coefficient, 273–274
Covalent bonds, 156, 508–509
Cps unit, 246
CRT, 497–498
Cryogenics, 545
Crystalline solids, 509
Current, alternating, 26–27, 237–263
  ampere unit, 21
  conventional, 23
  direct, 26–27, 31–110
  electron, 23
  hole charge, 515
  ion, 153–155
Current dividers, 69–70
Cutoff frequency, 458–459
Cutoff voltage, grid, 452–453
Cycle, defined, 239–240

Damping resistance, 442–443
D'Arsonval movement, 117
Decade resistance box, 164
Delta networks, 107–110
Demagnetization, 214
Depolarizer, dry cell, 179–180
Derating, resistor, 167–168
Diamagnetic materials, 207
Dielectric, 12
Dielectric constant, 333–334
Dielectric field, 328–329
Dielectric materials, 156–158
Dielectric strength, 157, 333–334
Diodes, semiconductor, 528–531
  tubes, 472–481
Direct current, 31–110
  defined, 26–27
Direct-current circuits, 31–110
  networks, 88–110
  Ohm's law, 31–45
  parallel, 59–73
  series, 46–58
Direct-current meters (*see* Meters,
  d-c)
Dissipation, power, 40–43
Donor impurities, 510
Doping, semiconductor, 28, 156,
  506, 509
Dry cells, 179–181
Dynamometer, 394–395

Easy current, 514
Eddy currents, 280–281
Edison battery, 185–188
Edison effect, 475
EDP, defined, 5
Effective value, 244–246
Efficiency, transformer, 280
EIA color codes, 557–560
Electricity, 9–30
  alternating current, 26–27, 237–
    263
  charge, 16–18
  current, 20–23

Electricity, direct current, 26–27, 31–110
  polarity, 9–10
  sources of, 28
  static, 16, 28
  units, 29, 561
  voltage, 18–19
Electrolytes, 154
Electrolytic capacitors, 337–339
Electromagnetism, 198–219
  units, 218–219
Electromagnets, 198–199, 205–207
Electromotive force, 19
Electromotive series, 178–179
Electron gun, 497
Electron tubes, 470–503
Electron-volt, 40
Electronics, components, 6–7
  defined, 1–2
Electrons, 9
  in atom, 10–16
  charge of, 15
Electrostatic field, 328–329
Elements, chemical, 13, 542–543
Emf, 19
Emitter, 518
Encapsulation, 527
Energy, in capacitance 374–375
  in inductance, 319
Esaki diode, 530
Exponential curve, 371, 374, 555
Exponents, use of, 547–549

Farad unit, 331–333
Faraday screen, 344
Federal Communications Commission, 3
  frequency allocations, 540–551
Ferrites, 208, 282
Ferromagnetism, defined, 207
Filament, tube, 472–474
Filters, analysis of, 447–469
  bandpass, 460–462, 466
  high-pass, 447–448, 459–460

Filters, interference, 462–463
  low-pass, 447–448, 458–459
  resonant, 461–462
  types of, 456–464
Fluctuating direct current, 449–456
Flux, dielectric, 328–330
  magnetic, 200–202, 218–219
  soldering, 565–566
FM broadcast band, 4, 540
Forward bias, 514–515
Forward current, 514
Frequency, allocations, 540–541
  audio, 247
  radio, 246–247
  sonic, 248
  spectrum, 539
  units, 246–247
Full-wave rectifier, 479–481
Fuses, 147–149
Fusible resistors, 170

Galvanometer, 117
Gas tubes, 498–499
Gauss unit, 200–202, 218–219
Generators, a-c, 238–241
  types of, 258–259
Germanium, semiconductor, 507–512
Getter, 474
Gigacycle, 247
Gilbert unit, 215–219
G_m of tube, 488
Grid, control, 481–483
Ground, chassis, 480

Half-wave rectifier, 478–479
Heat sink, 531
Heaters, construction, 473–474
  parallel, 69
  series, 79–80
Henry unit, 268
High-pass filters, 447–448, 459–460
Hole charges, 155–156, 511–512

Hot resistance, 152–153
Hot-wire meter, 394–395
Hum, 481
Hydrometer, 185
Hysteresis, 212–214, 281
Hz unit, 246

Impedance, calculations, 383–392
  complex form, 405–406
  defined, 306–307
  matching, 192–193
Induced voltage, 230–234, 271–272, 297–300
  nonsinusoidal, 317–319
Inductance, 266–289
  autotransformers, 279–280
  coils, 269–270
  defined, 268–270
  energy in, 319
  henry unit, 268
  mutual, 272–275
  parallel, 283–285
  self-, 268–270
  series, 283–285
  stray, 285–286
  time constant, 315–316, 555–556
  transformers, 275–283
  variable, 282–283
Inductive reactance, 290–302
  applications, 296–297
  calculations, 292–295
  chokes, 319–320
  phase angle, 303, 304
  with resistance, 304–312
Insulators, 12, 156–158
Interelectrode capacitances, 490–491
Interference filters, 462–463
Internal resistance, generator, 189–193
  matching to load, 192–193
  measurement of, 191–192
Inverted power supply, 481
Ionization current, 154
Ions, 153–155

IR drop, 50–54
Iron-vane meter, 394–395

j operator, 402–403
Joule unit, 39, 545
Junction, PN or NP, 512–517
  barrier voltage, 513–517
  forward bias, 514–515
  reverse bias, 515–517

Keeper, magnet, 205
Kelvin scale, 545
Kilocycles, defined, 247
Kilowatthours, 40
Kirchhoff's laws, 82–83, 88–94

L, inductance, 266–289
L-type filter, 457–458, 462
Laminations, core, 281–282
Lead-acid batteries, 182–188
Leclanché cell, 186
Lenz's law, 229–230, 271–272
Light, velocity of, 250
Litz wire, 314
Load current, 26
Load resistance, 26
Loading effect, voltmeter, 129–130
Local action, cell, 181
Loose coupling, 274
Low-pass filters, 447–449
L/R time constant, 315–316, 555–556

Magnetic field, flux, 200–202
Magnetic lines, 198–202
Magnetic units, 200–202, 218–219
Magnetism, 198–220
  air gap, 203–205
  electromagnets, 198–199, 205–207
  field lines, 199–202
  hysteresis, 212–214
  induction, 202, 203

Magnetism, Ohm's law for, 214–217
  permanent magnets, 198–199,
    206–207
  poles, 199–200
  shielding, 217
  units, 218–219
Magnetomotive force, 214–217
Magnetostriction, 207–208
Main line, 61–62
Maxwell unit, 200, 218–219
Megacycle, defined, 247
Mercury batteries, 185–188
Mesh currents, 93–94
Meters, a-c, 394–396
  d-c, 116–141
    ammeter, 117–124
    applications, 137–139
    continuity checking, 138–139
    loading, voltmeter, 129–130
    multimeters, 135–137
    ohmmeters, 130–135
    shunts, 121–124
  voltmeters, 125–130
  VOM, 135–137
  VTVM, 135–137
Metric units, 544
Mho, defined, 24
Mica capacitors, 335
Microphonics, 499
Microwaves, 248
Millman's theorem, 103–104
Mks units, 544
Molecules, 13, 155
Motor action, 225–227
Motors and generators, 258–259
Mu of tube, 487
Multimeters, 135–137
Multipliers, voltmeter, 125–127
Mutual inductance, 272–275
  coupling coefficient, 273–274
  transformers, 275–283

Nanosecond, 249
Negative resistance, 491

Network theorems, 88–103
  delta-wye, 107–108
  Kirchhoff, 88–94
  Millman, 103–104
  Norton, 98–104, 256–257
  superposition, 104–107
  Thévenin, 94–98, 101–103
Neutron, 15
Newton, unit, 545
Nickel-cadmium battery, 186–188
Nonsinusoidal waveforms, 259–261,
  317–319
Norton's theorem, 98–104, 256–257
Nucleus in atom, 11–16

Oersted unit, 209–210, 218–219
Ohm unit, 23, 37
Ohmmeters, 130–135
  back-off type, 131–132
  continuity measurements, 138–139
  series circuit, 129–132
  shunt circuit, 132–133
  testing, capacitors, 344–346
    coils, 286–287
    resistors, 171–172
    transistors, 532
Ohms, types of, 396–397
OHMS ADJUST control, 137
Ohm's law, analysis, 31–45
  a-c circuits, 383–397
  d-c circuits, 31–45
  magnetic circuits, 214–217
Ohms-per-volt rating, 128–130
Open circuit, 56–57, 71

Paper capacitors, 335–336
Parallax error, 118
Parallel circuits, 59–73
  a-c source, 256, 383–397
  branch currents, 59–63
  capacitances, 340–341
  compared with series, 85
  conductances, 67–68

Parallel circuits, current dividers, 69–70
  d-c source, 59–73
  heaters, 69
  inductances, 283–285
  open in, 71
  power in, 68
  resistances, 63–67
  resonant, 425–428
Parallel resonance, analysis, 425–428, 441–443
  bandwidth, 435–438
  compared with series, 441, 444
  damping, 442–443
  Q, 433–434
  Z, measurement of, 434
Paramagnetic materials, 207
Peak value, 244–246, 260
Pentodes, characteristics, 493–494
  construction, 491–492
  remote cutoff, 494
  suppressor grid, 492
Period, defined, 249
Permanent magnets, 198–199, 206–207
Permeability, 203, 218–219
Phase angle, 251–255, 303, 304, 363–364
Phasor, defined, 252–254
Photodiodes, 530
Photoelectricity, 28
Phototubes, 498
Physics units, 544–546
π networks, 107–110
π-type filter, 457–458
Picofarad unit, 332
Plate resistance, 488
Plate of tube, 471
Polarization, cell, 178–180
Poles, magnetic, 199–200
Potential, defined, 18
Potential difference, 18–19
Potentiometers, 163–164
Power, apparent, 394
  parallel, 68

Power, real, 392–394
  series, 54
  wattmeter, 395–396
  watts, 38–43
Power factor, 393–394
  of capacitor, 343
Power rating, resistor, 166–169
Power supplies, 480–481
Powers of 10, 547–549
Preferred values, 166, 559
Primary cell, 178–181
Primary winding, 272–273
Printed wiring, 146, 531
Proton in atom, 9–16
Pulsating direct current, 449–456

Q, charge, 16–18
  of coil, 313–314
Q factor, 431–444
  bandwidth, 435–438
  low, 441–443
  measurement, 437–438

Radian, 241
Radio, defined, 1
Radio broadcasting, 3–5
Radio frequencies, 246–247
Ramp voltage, 260
RC time constant, 371–374, 555–556
Reactance, capacitive, 349–361
  inductive, 290–302
Real power, 392–394
Reciprocal formula, 65
Rectifiers, full-wave, 479–481
  half-wave, 478–479
  hum in, 481
  semiconductor, 528–529
Reluctance, 215–219
Remote-cutoff tubes, 494
Resistance, 23–35
  a-c, 313–314
  decade box, 164
Resistance wire, 151–152

Resistors, carbon, 163–168
  color code, 164–166, 557–558
  controls, 163–164
  derating, 167
  parallel, 63–67
  power rating, 166–169
  preferred values, 166, 559
  series, 48
  special types, 169–170
  troubles, 170–172
  wirewound, 162–163
Resonance, 420–446
  bandwidth, 435–438
  calculations, 428–431
  parallel, 425–428, 441–443
  Q, 431–434
    low Q, 441–443
  series, 421–425
  tuning, 438–440
Resonant filters, 461–462
Response curve, resonant, 435–438
Reverse bias, 515–517
Rheostats, 163–164
Ring magnet, 204–205
Rms value, 244–246
Rosin-core solder, 566
Rotor, capacitor, 337
  motor, 258

Saturation, magnetic, 210–212
  plate current, 475
Sawtooth waveform, 261
Schematic symbols, 562–564
Scientific notation, 547–549
Screen-grid voltage, 488–490
Secondary cell, 178, 182–188
Secondary emission, 491
Secondary winding, 272–273
Self-inductance, 268–270
Semiconductors, 12, 28, 155–156,
    504–535
  barrier voltage, 513–517
  diodes, 528–531
  doping, 28, 156, 506, 509

Semiconductors, elements, 505–506
  junction, 512–517
  N-type, 510–511
  P-type, 511–512
  symbols, 533
  transistors, 517–520
Series circuits, 46–58
  a-c source, 256
  capacitances, 341–342
  cells, 181–182
  compared with parallel, 85
  d-c source, 46–58
  heaters, 50–51, 57
  inductances, 283–285
  open in, 56–57
  power in, 54
  resistances, 48–49
  resonant, 421–425
  voltage dividers, 52, 80–83
Series-parallel circuits, 74–87, 256–
    257
Series resonance, 421–425
  compared with parallel, 444
Shelf life, capacitors, 346
  dry cells, 180
Shielding, 217, 281
Shock, electric, 43–44
Short circuit, 84–85
Shunts, meter, 121–124
Silicon, 155–157, 505–507
Silicon-controlled rectifier, 530
Sine of angle, 552
Sine wave, average value, 244
  defined, 241–242
  peak value, 244–245
  rms value, 244–246
Sinusoid, 241–242
Skin effect, 313
Sockets, transistor, 527–528
  tube, 495
Solar battery, 188
Soldering, 565–566
Solenoid, 220–221
Sonic frequencies, 248
Sound, velocity, 251

Space charge, 475, 482
Spaghetti, 145
Specific gravity, 184–185
Specific resistance, 150
Square roots, 550–551
Square wave, 261
Static electricity, 16, 28
Stator, capacitor, 337
    motor, 258
Steady-state value, 315
Storage cell, 178, 182–188
Stray capacitance, 342–344
Stray inductance, 343–344
String, series, 48–49
Supercontrol tubes, 494
Superposition theorem, 104–107
Supersonic frequencies, 5, 248
Suppressor grid, 492
Susceptance, 415
Switches, 146–147
Symbols, 561–564

T networks, 107–110
T-type filter, 457–458
Tangent of angle, 552
Tantalum capacitors, 338
Temperature coefficient, capacitors,
    340
    conductors, 152
Temperature scales, 545
Tetrodes, construction, 488–489
    negative resistance, 491
    screen grid, 488–490
    secondary emission, 491
Thermionic emission, 28, 473
Thermistors, 170
Thermocouple meter, 394–395
Thévenin's theorem, 94–98, 101–103,
    256–257
Thyratron, 498
Tight coupling, 274
Time constant, *RC*, 371–374, 555–
    556
    RL, 315–316, 555–556

Tolerance, capacitors, 338
    resistors, 165
Tools, 565–566
Toroid magnet, 204–205
Torque, 227
Transconductance, 488
Transformers, 275–283
    autotransformer, 279–280
    core losses, 280–282
    coupling, 275–283, 451–452
    efficiency, 280
    troubles in, 287
    turns ratio, 276–280
Transient response, capacitance,
    371–374, 555–556
    inductance, 315–316, 555–556
Transistors, 504–535
    advantages, 504–505
    (α) alpha, 525–526
    amplification, 517–520, 522–524
    barrier voltage, 513–517
    base, 518
    (β) beta, 526
    characteristic curves, 524–526
    checker, 532
    circuits, 520–523
    collector, 518
    doping, 506, 509–512
    electron charges, 510–511
    emitter, 518
    forward bias, 514–515
    hole charges, 511–512
    reverse bias, 515–517
    sockets, 527–528
    troubles, 531–532
    types of, 527–528
Treble tone, 248
Trickle charge, 187
Trigonometry, 551–554
Triodes, 481–487
Troubles, capacitors, 344–346
    coils, 286–287
    resistors, 170–172
    transistors, 531–532
    tubes, 499–500

Tubes, 3, 7, 470–503
  bias, grid, 482, 484
  capacitances, 490–491
  cathode, 472–474
  cathode-ray, 497–498
  checker, 500
  constants, 487–488
  construction, 470–472
  diodes, 472–481
  Edison effect, 475
  gas-filled, 498–499
  heater, 472–474
  pentodes, 491–494
  photo, 498
  plate current, 474–477
  ratings, 494–495
  sockets, 495
  space charge, 475
  tetrodes, 488–491
  thermionic emission, 473
  triodes, 481–487
  troubles, 499–500
  types, 495–497, 502
  vacuum, 474
Tuning, 420–446
  applications, 438–440
Tunnel diodes, 530
Turns ratio, 276–280
Twin-lead, 145

Ultrasonics, 5
Units, electrical, 29, 561
  frequency, 247
  magnetic, 218–219
Universal shunt, 122–124

Vacuum tubes, 470–503
Valence, electron, 15, 507–508
Varactor diode, 530
Variable-mu tubes, 494

Vector, defined, 252–254
  types of, 397–398
Volt-ampere, 394
Volt unit, 18–19, 37
Voltage dividers, 52, 80–83
  capacitive, 369–371
Voltage doubler, 481
Voltage drops, 50–54
Voltaic cell, 176–179
Voltmeters, 125–130
  loading effect, 129–130
  sensitivity, 128–130
VOM, 116, 135–136
VTVM, 136–137
  adjustments, 137

Waste current, 489
Watt, 38–39
Wattmeter, 395–396
Wavelength, 249–251
Weber unit, 200, 218–219
Weston movement, 117
Wheatstone bridge, 83
Wire, circular mils, 144
  color code, 557
  resistance, 150–151
  sizes, 143–144
  types, 145–146
Wirewound resistors, 162–163
Work units, 39–40, 544–545
Wye networks, 107–110

X_C, capacitive reactance, 349–361
X_L, inductive reactance, 290–302

Y networks, 107–110

Zener voltage, 517, 530
Zero-ohms adjustment, 135